PHYSIOLOGY OF
THE NERVOUS
SYSTEM

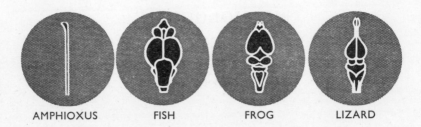

AMPHIOXUS   FISH   FROG   LIZARD

BIRD   DOG   MAN

The great development of the cerebral cortex in man is illustrated by this figure. Vertebrate evolution has involved a strange experiment. In the large amphibious dinosaurs there is evidence of a second 'brain' at the lower end of the spinal cord four times as large as that within the cranium. The excessive length and massive proportions of the tail and hind-limbs contributed, no doubt, to this development. (From Frolov, 1937, after a scientific film by Galkin)

PHYSIOLOGY OF THE NERVOUS SYSTEM

BY

E. GEOFFREY WALSH

M.A. (Oxon.), M.D. (Harvard), M.R.C.P. (London)

With chapters on Somatic Sensibility
and the Applied Physiology of Pain
by
JOHN MARSHALL
M.D. (Manchester), M.R.C.P., D.P.M. (London)

LONGMANS, GREEN AND CO
LONDON · NEW YORK · TORONTO

LONGMANS, GREEN AND CO LTD
6 & 7 CLIFFORD STREET LONDON W I
BOSTON HOUSE STRAND STREET CAPE TOWN
605-611 LONSDALE STREET MELBOURNE C I

LONGMANS, GREEN AND CO INC
55 FIFTH AVENUE NEW YORK 3

LONGMANS, GREEN AND CO
20 CRANFIELD ROAD TORONTO 16

ORIENT LONGMANS PRIVATE LTD
CALCUTTA BOMBAY MADRAS
DELHI HYDERABAD DACCA

First published 1957

PREFACE

'. . . The antithesis sometimes made between the science and practice of medicine is false and mischievous.'

G. W. PICKERING

ONE purpose of this book is to place before those interested in clinical neurology an account of the physiology of the nervous system. In the text will be found numerous examples in which it is clear that a profound understanding of common clinical problems can be achieved only by thinking in neurophysiological terms. The opportunity has also been taken of offering to the psychologist a description, in some detail, of the physiology of the sense organs and of the cerebral cortex. The advanced student of physiology may find it useful to have a summary of neurophysiology in one volume and should use the book as a guide to the original literature. It is not to be expected that the medical student will, at first, find all of the sections easy to comprehend but much will become clearer as his years of training proceed, and the volume will afford a link between the preclinical and clinical years.

E. G. W.

DEPARTMENT OF PHYSIOLOGY
EDINBURGH UNIVERSITY
January 1956

149

ACKNOWLEDGEMENTS

THE author is indebted to Professor D. Whitteridge for stimulating his interest in neurophysiology some fifteen years ago and for encouragement and assistance that has extended over the subsequent period. A number of friends and colleagues have assisted greatly by reading the manuscript: Dr. M. H. Draper, Dr. A. Iggo, J. Irvine, Esq., Dr. S. R. Mukherjee, Dr. R. Passmore, Dr. C. G. Phillips, Dr. Mary Pickford and Dr. A. Swan. The author is fortunate in having been able to turn for advice to Dr. J. Marshall who has also contributed two chapters that deal with subjects of which he has first-hand knowledge. These sections were read, in manuscript form, by Professor G. J. Romanes and Dr. P. Nathan. The manuscript was typed by Mrs. D. Boyd and Miss D. Taylor; certain quotations were verified by Miss E. J. Walsh. The book would not have been completed without the tolerance and active assistance of the author's wife.

We are indebted to the following for permission to quote copyright material:

The Managing Editor of the American Medical Association for an extract from 'A Comparative Sensory Analysis of Helen Keller and Laura Bridgman, II : Its Bearing on the Further Development of the Human Brain', by Dr. F. Tilney, from *The Archives of Neurology and Psychiatry*, June 1929; the Editor for an extract from Walker's 'The Somatic Functions of the Central Nervous System' from volume 8 of the *Annual Review of Physiology*; the Editor of *The Annals of Otology, Rhinology and Laryngology* for an extract from Tait's 'Is All Hearing Cochlea?'; the Secretary of the Association for Research in Nervous and Mental Disease for extracts from Brickner's *Telencephalisation of Survival Characteristics* and Walker & Johnson's *Normal and Pathological After-discharge from the Frontal Cortex*; Messrs. Baillière, Tindall & Cox, Ltd., for an extract from *The Principles of Anatomy as Seen in the Hand*, by Wood Jones; Messrs. Blackwell Scientific Publications, Ltd., for an extract from Walker's *Post-Traumatic Epilepsy*; the Editor of the *British Medical Journal* for an extract from 'The Basis of Sensation', by Lord Adrian; the Editor of the *British Journal of Psychology* for material from Coppen's

'The Differential Threshold for the Subjective Judgement of the Elastic and Plastic Properties of Soft Bodies'; Cambridge University Press for an extract from *Man on His Nature*, by Sir Charles Sherrington; Messrs. Chapman & Hall, Ltd., for extracts from Ashby's *Design for a Brain*; Messrs. J. & A. Churchill, Ltd., for an extract from Guttman's *Peripheral Circulation in Man*; The Clarendon Press for an extract from *Neurophysiological Basis of Mind*, by J. C. Eccles; Dr. Robert S. Dow and the American Medical Association for material from 'Effect of Lesions in the Vestibular Part of the Cerebellum in Primates' from *The Archives of Neurology and Psychiatry*, September 1938; the Editor of the *Daily Telegraph* for an extract from the December 23, 1952, issue; Sir Ronald Fisher for an extract from *The Design of Experiments*, published by Messrs. Oliver & Boyd, Ltd.; Dr. Gesell, Messrs. Hamish Hamilton, Ltd., and Messrs. Harper & Brothers for an extract from Gesell and Amatruda's *The Embryology of Behaviour*; the Controller of Her Majesty's Stationery Office for extracts from *History of the Second World War: Surgery*; the authors and Messrs. Paul B. Hoeber, Inc., for material from *Diseases of the Muscle*, by Adams, Denny-Brown & Pearson; the *Journal of Comparative Neurology* for an extract from 'The Functional Significance of the Inferior Olive in the Cat', by Wilson & Magoun; the *Journal of Electroencephalography and Clinical Neurophysiology* for an extract from 'Homeostasis of Cerebral Excitability', E.E.G.C.N.2 (1950); the *Bulletin of the Johns Hopkins Hospital* for extracts from 'Clinical Observations upon the Importance of the Vestibular Reflexes', by Ford & Walsh, 'Studies in Neurology II : On Cerebellar Function', by Ingvar, and 'A study of four cats deprived of neocortex and additional portions of the forebrain', by Bard & Rioch; the Managing Editor of the *Journal of Nervous and Mental Disease* for an extract from Lashley's 'Factors Limiting Recovery after Central Nervous Lesions'; the Editor of the *Journal of the Optical Society of America* for an extract from Helmholtz's 'Physiological Optics', translated by J. P. C. Southall (1924); Professor B. Katz and the Company of Biologists, Ltd., for an extract from 'The Properties of the Nerve Membrane' from *The Symposia of the Society for Experimental Biology*; Dr. K. S. Lashley and the American Medical Association for extracts from 'Patterns of Cerebral Integration indicated by the Scotomas of Migraine' from *The Archives of Neurology and Psychiatry*, 1941; Messrs. Macmillan & Co., Ltd., for various extracts from articles which appeared in *Brain*; Oxford University Press, Inc., for an extract from Southall's *Introduction to Physiological Optics*; Penguin Books Ltd. for material from *Science News*, No. 33; the Royal Society for an extract from the *Proceedings of the Royal Society*, Series B; Messrs. Martin Secker & Warburg, Ltd., and Messrs. Abelard-Schuman, Inc., for material from *Victory Over Pain*, by Victor Robinson (copyright, 1946); the University of Chicago Press for an extract from Lashley's *Brain Mechanisms and Intelligence* (copyright, 1929); Dr. A. Earl Walker and the Editor of the *Journal of Anatomy* for an extract from 'The projection of the medial geniculate body to the cerebral cortex in the macaque monkey' from the *Journal of Anatomy*, 1937 ; Messrs. C. A. Watts & Co., Ltd., for an extract from the Thinker's Library edition of *First Principles*, by Herbert Spencer ; Messrs. John Wiley & Sons, Inc., for material from *Handbook of Experimental Psychology*, edited by Stevens (copyright, 1951), and *Cybernetics*, by Wiener (copyright, 1948) ; and the Williams and Wilkins Company for an extract from Sperry's 'The problem of central nervous reorganisation after nerve regeneration and muscle transposition' from the *Quarterly Review of Biology*.

For permission either to reproduce or to redraw diagrams we are indebted to the following :

The Editors, *Acta Physiologica Scandinavica*, *Journal of the Royal Aeronautical Society*, *American Journal of Psychology*, *British Medical Journal*, *Clinical Science*, *Electroencephalography and Clinical Neurophysiology*, *Journal of Laryngology and Otology*, *Quarterly Journal of Microscopical Science*, *Journal of Neurophysiology*, *Annual Review of Physiology*, *Wireless World*, *Bell System Technical Journal* ; the authors concerned and the Editors, *Journal of the American Medical Association*, *Journal of Anatomy*, *The Biological Bulletin*, *Brain*, *Journal of Clinical Investigation*, *Archives of Disease in Childhood*, *The Lancet*, *Journal of Neurology, Neurosurgery and Psychiatry*, *Proceedings of the Royal Society of Medicine* ; the authors and the American Medical Association for figures from *Archives of Neurology and Psychiatry*; the American Physiological Society for figures from the *American Journal of Physiology*; the Association for Research in Nervous and Mental Diseases for figures from various volumes in the Association Series ; the author and the Mayo Clinic for a figure from *Proceedings of the Mayo Clinic* ; the Editorial Board, *Journal of Physiology* ; Council of the Royal Society for figures from *Proceedings of the Royal Society* ; the Wistar Institute of Anatomy and Biology for figures from the *Journal of Comparative Neurology* ; The Johns Hopkins Press and the Editors, *Bulletin of the Johns Hopkins Hospital* ; and for figures from the following publications by permission of the publishers and authors stated : Hilgard & Marquis, *Conditioning and Learning*, Appleton-Century Crofts, Inc. ; Purves-Stewart, *The Diagnosis of Nervous Diseases*, Messrs. Edward Arnold (Publishers), Ltd. ; Bremer, *Some Problems in Neurophysiology*, The Athlone Press, University of London ; Beatty, *Hearing in Man and Animals*, Messrs. George Bell & Sons, Ltd.; *Brain Mechanisms and Consciousness*, ed. J. F. Delafresnaye, Blackwell Scientific Publications Ltd. ; Coghill, *Anatomy and the Problem of Behaviour*, and Head, *Aphasia and Kindred Disorders of Speech*, Cambridge University Press ; Murchison, *The Foundation of Experimental Psychology*, Clark University Press, Worcester, Mass. ; Adrian, *The Basis of Sensation*, Messrs. Christophers (Publishers), Ltd. ; Starling, *Principles of Human Physiology*, and Davson, *Physiology of the Eye* ; Messrs. J. & A.

Churchill, Ltd. ; Merton, *Ciba Foundation Symposium on the Spinal Cord*, Ciba Foundation and Messrs. J. & A. Churchill, Ltd. ; Walls, *The Vertebrate Eye and its Adaptive Radiation*, author and Cranbrook Institute of Science, Michigan ; *Archiv für anatomische Physiologie*, Walter de Gruyter & Co., Berlin ; Gesell & Amatruda, *The Embryology of Behaviour*, Dr. Gesell & Messrs. Hamish Hamilton, Ltd. ; Cobb, *Borderlands of Psychiatry*, Harvard University Press ; *Harvey Lectures*, The Harvey Society, Inc., New York ; Moncrieff, *The Chemical Senses*, Messrs. Leonard Hill (Books), Ltd. ; Gesell & Amatruda, *Developmental Diagnosis*, Dr. Gesell & Paul B. Hoeber, Inc. ; *Proceedings IVth International Congress of Otolaryngology*, the General Secretary of the Congress ; Traquair, *Introduction to Clinical Perimetry*, Messrs. Henry Kimpton ; Bell, Davidson & Scarborough, *Textbook of Physiology and Biochemistry*, Messrs. E. & S. Livingstone, Ltd. ; White & Benson, *The Physics and Medicine of the Upper Atmosphere*, the Lovelace Foundation and the University of New Mexico Press ; Penfield & Rasmussen, *The Cerebral Cortex of Man*, The Macmillan Company, New York ; André-Thomas, *Équilibre et équilibration*, author and Masson et Cie, Paris ; Cobb, *Emotions and Clinical Medicine*, W. W. Norton & Company, Inc. ; *Edinburgh Medical Journal*, Messrs. Oliver & Boyd, Ltd. ; Young, *Doubt and Certainty in Science*, Brodal, *Neurological Anatomy*, Eccles, *The Neurophysiological Basis of Mind*, Creed *et al.*, *Reflex Activity of the Spinal Cord*, Adrian, *The Physical Background of Perception*, Fulton, *Functional Localisation in the Frontal Lobe and Cerebellum* and the authors concerned and the Oxford University Press ; Fulton, *The Physiology of the Nervous System*, Oxford University Press, Inc., New York ; Mann & Pirie, *The Science of Seeing*, Penguin Books Ltd. ; Brazier, *The Electrical Activity of the Nervous System*, Pitman Medical Publishing Co., Ltd. ; Frolov, *Pavlov and his School*, Messrs. Routledge & Kegan Paul, Ltd. ; Dorland, *The American Illustrated Medical Dictionary*, W. B. Saunders Company, New York ; Ogle, *Binocular Vision*, Fulton, *Textbook of Physiology*, Prosser, *Comparative Animal Physiology*, Herrick, *An Introduction to Neurology* and Ranson & Clark, *Anatomy of the Nervous System*, the authors concerned and W. B. Saunders Company, Philadelphia ; Bell, Davidson & Scarborough, *Electrical Signs of Nervous Activity*, the authors and the University of Pennsylvania Press ; *Philosophical Magazine*, 6th Series, Messrs. Taylor & Francis, Ltd. ; *The Journal of Neurophysiology*, Messrs. Charles C. Thomas, Publishers, Ill. ; Tasaki, *Nervous Transmission*, and Gastaut, *The Epilepsies*, the authors concerned and Messrs. Charles C. Thomas, Publishers, Ill. ; Geldard, *The Human Senses*, and Stevens & Davis, *Hearing*, John Wiley & Sons, Inc. ; Best & Taylor, *The Physiological Basis of Medical Practice*, and Cobb, *Foundations of Neuropsychiatry*, The Williams & Wilkins Company, Baltimore ; Wright, *Applied Physiology*, Oxford University Press ; Lashley, *Brain Mechanisms and Intelligence*, Copyright (1929) by the University of Chicago Press, and Walker, *The Primate Thalmus*, Copyright (1938) by the University of Chicago Press.

CONTENTS

CHAPTER 1
NERVE AND MUSCLE

CHAPTER 2
SOMATIC SENSIBILITY

CHAPTER 3
THE APPLIED PHYSIOLOGY OF PAIN

CHAPTER 4

THE SPINAL CORD

CHAPTER 5

POSTURE : THE LABYRINTH

CHAPTER 6

THE CEREBELLUM

CONTENTS   xi

CHAPTER 10

THE CORTICAL CONTROL OF MOVEMENT : CORTICO-SPINAL AND EXTRA-PYRAMIDAL PATHWAYS

CHAPTER 11

THE SENSORY PATHWAY, THALAMUS AND PARIETAL LOBE, SPEECH

CHAPTER 12

HYPOTHALAMUS, RHINENCEPHALON
AND FRONTAL LOBES

PLATES

In the following account the ordinary common-sense distinction of *structure* and *function* will be used. The distinction rests upon abstractions but it is convenient for exposition. The notion of structure arises by considering the organism at an instant, abstracted from time. The abstraction is valuable because within the history of the organism there are relatively stable events which do not change much and these are called *structure*. In contrast there are unstable events and these are *function*. In the end the distinction is quantitative and rests upon the time scale we are using.

A. D. RITCHIE, *The Natural History of Mind*

CHAPTER I

NERVE AND MUSCLE

Who, when Galvani touched the muscles of a frog with different metals, and noticed their contraction, could have dreamt that eighty years afterwards, in virtue of the self-same process, whose earliest manifestations attracted his attention in his anatomical researches, all Europe would be traversed with wires, flashing intelligence from Madrid to St. Petersburg with the speed of lightning ? In the hands of Galvani, and at first even in Volta's, electrical currents were phenomena capable of exerting only the feeblest forces, and could not be detected except by the most delicate apparatus. Had they been neglected, on the ground that the investigation of them promised no immediate practical result, we should now be ignorant of the most important and most interesting of the links between the various forces of nature.—HELMHOLTZ (1893).

THE ACTION POTENTIAL

THE brain can be regarded as a signalling system ; to understand the ways in which information may flow within it, and in the periphery, it is necessary to know something of the messages that can be transmitted along individual nerve fibres. A knowledge of the properties of individual nerve fibres allows a number of aspects of the form and function of the nervous system to be understood that otherwise would be unintelligible. The brain has been likened to a telephone exchange and the nerve fibres to telegraph wires ; one function of this first chapter is to examine the extent to which this 'telegraph wire' analogy is valid, another is to demonstrate that certain pathological processes affecting nerve and muscle can only be evaluated intelligently by a knowledge of the processes of excitation in single fibres.

It is over a hundred years since the *action potential* was discovered. By this term neurophysiologists refer to the electrical disturbance which signifies that a message is being transmitted through nerve fibres and the corresponding disturbance that is

B

normally found in muscles preceding contraction. A related type [1] of disturbance in the plates of the *electric organ* of a fish is responsible for the shocks that these structures can deliver. In the electric eel potentials of several hundred volts may be developed by the summation, in series, of the small currents produced by the numerous plates.

'The essential component of an electrical organ is a disc, upon one surface of which a nerve twig ramifies, while the other surface is vascular. The electrical organ consists of piles of such discs, surface to surface, like

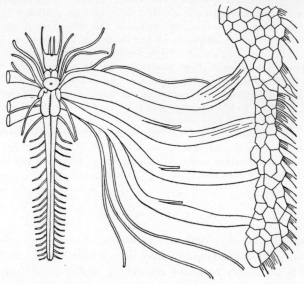

FIG. 1.1.—Diagram of an electric organ in the torpedo with its large extrinsic nerves. (After Feldberg, 1951)

the elements of an old-fashioned voltaic pile ; its structure, as well as the great electro-motive force of the discharge, suggests that it is actually a battery of which the elements (discs) are disposed in series' (Waller, 1903).

John Walsh (1773) was able to demonstrate the electrical nature of the shock produced by the torpedo and he interested John Hunter in its anatomy (Fig. 1.1). These electric discharges have since that time attracted a good deal of attention (*vide* Fessard, 1952) ; one interesting problem concerns the ways by which the component

---

[1] The electric organs of different animals show a good deal of diversity in their reactions. In some cases the electric potentials produced by the plates may be of the nature of an end-plate potential (p. 28) rather than homologous with a propagated action potential.

plates, situated at considerable distances from one another, are brought into play at the same moment in order to allow their short-lasting voltages to summate effectively.

Mammalian nerve fibres are of small diameter, rarely being larger than 20μ in diameter, whilst the majority are much smaller. It is a matter of considerable technical difficulty to approach directly the problems of excitation in such filamentous structures. Much of our information about the details of nervous action have for this reason been obtained by studying the much larger nerve fibres that are found in some invertebrates. There is reason to believe that the processes are fundamentally rather similar throughout the nerve fibres that are found in the animal kingdom.

Nerve fibres may be obtained from the squid that are nearly 1 mm. in diameter. When a fine electrode is inserted into the interior of the cell it is found to be some 60 mV negative with respect to the outside. This potential difference is a reflection of the chemical differences between the inside and the outside of the fibre and of the properties of the *cell membrane*. In introducing this term we are accepting the view that the chemical differences that distinguish the axoplasm from the extra-cellular fluid are found on either side of a fine boundary. It is on the properties of this membrane that the processes of excitation largely depend.

In exciting a nerve, mechanical or perhaps thermal stimuli (Laget & Lundberg, 1949) could be used, but for ease of control electrical shocks are preferable. On excitation of the squid axone a disturbance travels down the fibre at a velocity of some 25 m./sec. By inserting a fine electrode into the core of the axone it can be shown that this disturbance is associated with a reversal of the direction of polarisation of the cell membrane. The internal electrode becomes momentarily positive with respect to the outside of the fibre. The disturbance is abrupt and of short duration (1 msec.) at any given point. Each wave of excitation is similar; indeed if the stimuli are not repeated too rapidly, the size of the electrical disturbances is constant. Nerve fibres are therefore said to obey the 'All-or-None' law. Excitation is an explosive process, and a second stimulus arriving at the moment of excitation is in-effective; the nerve fibre is said to be in an *absolutely refractory state*. As the action potential declines the nerve is found to respond to strong stimuli by discharging an action potential that is smaller than normal; it is in the *relative refractory state*. The 'All-or-None' law is of the greatest importance in understanding the nervous system ; information may be transmitted only by varying the time at which impulses are discharged or by bringing into play different fibres. The physical intensity of a stimulus cannot be transmitted by a change in the intensity of signal.

If two nerve impulses travel towards the central region of an axone from opposite ends of the fibre they will extinguish one another, for each will run into the refractory state of the other. To avoid collisions the signals in the nervous system usually follow routes of the 'one-way-traffic' type.[1] A clear and well-known example of this segregation of pathways is in the anterior and posterior roots of the spinal cord. That the anterior roots serve motor functions and the posterior roots sensory functions is known as the 'Bell-Magendie Law'. This name gives credit both to Sir Charles Bell (1774–1842) and to François Magendie (1783–1855). Bell studied medicine in Edinburgh but later moved to London. When he married in 1811 the young bride found that research into nerve function 'was the important object of his life' and she did her best to understand what he talked about. The Bell-Magendie law has stood the test of time, but there are those who believe that the posterior roots contain some efferent fibres (*e.g.* Kahr & Sheehan, 1933). The evidence on this point, reviewed in Mitchell's book (1953), appears to be inconclusive at present. The anterior roots may contain a few afferent fibres but their importance is problematical (White & Sweet, 1955). Finally it may be noted that sensory nerve fibres frequently supply more than one end-organ and some interference between the trains of impulses discharged by the various receptors is to be expected.

The discontinuous nature and invariable polarity of the nerve signals suggests that one further feature will be found—*spontaneous activity*. It will often be necessary to signal the increase or decrease of some variable, and it may be advantageous therefore to have a 'resting discharge' that can be modified appropriately. The sensitivity of such a mechanism can be high, and such activity is common both in afferent fibres and in neurones within the C.N.S.

The action potential has been likened to the 'tick' of a clock; both signify that an event is taking place but by themselves they do not reveal the nature of the changes involved. Present-day

---

[1] This appears always to be the case in vertebrates and is dependent upon the properties of the synaptic junctions. Examples are known in invertebrates of 'two-way transmission', synaptic junctions being found that conduct in both directions (Bullock in Wolstenholme, 1953).

theories of excitation were foreshadowed in the beginning of this century by the work of Overton. He showed that excitation is impossible if the excitable tissue is bathed in a solution lacking in sodium. Under certain circumstances excitability may be restored by the replacement of sodium or by supplying lithium. The difference that exists between the chemical composition of the axoplasm and the extra-cellular fluid explains the production of the resting potential difference between the inside and the outside of the fibre ; it is assumed that at rest the membrane is freely permeable to potassium and chloride ions but almost impenetrable by those of sodium. At the start of excitation the movement of sodium ions suddenly becomes much more free and these particles, accordingly, flow inwards. It follows that as the fibre passes back into the resting state sodium must be pumped out again against a concentration gradient. As there is normally a small inward leak of this substance, there must be some baling out the whole time (Hodgkin, 1951).

It is at first sight surprising that a membrane should be almost impermeable to sodium ions whilst potassium ions should pass moderately freely, for potassium is a larger atom than sodium. Measurements of the conductivity of solutions of sodium and potassium salts have suggested, however, that there is a greater shell of water molecules surrounding the sodium ion, and this may account for the paradox. Making certain assumptions (vide Steinbach in Merritt, 1951), it has been calculated that the effective radius of the hydrated ions are as follows :

Table 1

Ion	Atomic Weight	Radius of Hydrated Ion (Ångström Units)
K	39·1	1·98
Na	23·0	2·56
Li	6·9	3·09
Ca	40·1	4·8
Mg	24·3	5·2
Cl	35·5	1·93

Excitation involves a self-propagating chain reaction. If the potential across the cell membrane is lowered sufficiently the resistance suddenly falls and accentuates this lowering ; finally the potential gradient is reversed in sign. For excitation to ensue it is necessary that a certain minimal length of the fibre should be brought into action (*i.e.* depolarised). With the use of electrical stimuli just below threshold it is possible to detect the occurrence of an active change in the membrane that does not lead to an action potential. This abortive impulse, or *local response*, is indicative of the fact that a sufficiently extensive length of the nerve fibre has not been activated for the chain reaction to occur.

The local response varies in size according to the strength of the stimulus that is used; unlike the propagated impulse, it does not obey the All-or-None law. The local response is of short duration (*e.g.* $1\frac{1}{2}$ msec.). Whilst it lasts the fibre is in a state of enhanced excitability; a stimulus which is normally too weak may now successfully excite the fibre. The existence of a local response accordingly affords a satisfactory explanation of 'latent addition': two stimuli delivered in rapid succession may be effective whilst either by itself is not. The longer the duration of the changes of excitability associated with the local response the longer will the effects of weak depolarisations summate; accordingly, changes in the strength-duration curve (p. 19) will be expected if the characteristics of the local response alter.

When an impulse is being propagated the inactive regions ahead of the discharge are depolarised by discharging their membrane potential into the active area. There is good evidence that local currents carried by ions in the surrounding medium are responsible for the spread of activity in this way; thus, if the external resistance of the medium is high, the impulse is propagated relatively slowly. In addition to these effects it has been supposed that chemical reactions involving acetylcholine play a rôle in excitation (Nachmansonn, 1953; cf. von Muralt, 1947). The evidence for this view is not entirely conclusive (*vide* Merritt, 1952) and the rôle of acetylcholine in the metabolism of axones must be regarded as still unknown. One difficulty in accepting the view that this substance is essential for excitation lies in the fact that it is absent from the dorsal roots. During normal conduction, impulses are passed with a high safety factor. This means that the energy in the active region is substantially in excess of that needed to fire off the inactive regions ahead. It is not easy to estimate the safety factor quantitatively, but there are grounds for believing that in axones the amount of energy available may be ten times or more the minimal needed for excitation to proceed.

The safety factor is not everywhere high, however. Transmission is performed precariously in T-pieces such as occur on the posterior root fibres as they enter the spinal cord (Fig. 1.2) and in the dorsal root ganglia themselves (Dun, 1955). At such sites it is uncertain whether an impulse will or will not pass, for the initial axone has to excite both branches. It is probable that wherever fibres branch, as, for example, towards the ends of the motor and sensory nerves, there will be doubt as to whether impulses will be propagated throughout the system.

It is the active participation of the fibre that enables signals to be propagated. Katz (1952) has made the following remarks about the cable-like properties of nerve fibres :

'We have seen that nerve fibres are provided with an electro-chemical accumulator which keeps the cell charged at $\frac{1}{20}-\frac{1}{10}$ V. negative to its surroundings and maintains large differences of ion concentrations. The

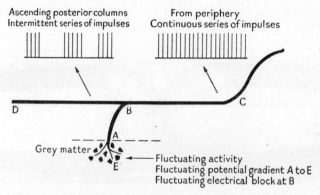

FIG. 1.2.—T-piece effect. At the branching of a nerve fibre the 'safety factor' is low and impulse transmission is subject to certain vagaries. Above is shown a posterior root fibre. Transmission upwards to D appears to depend upon the electrical field generated by the adjacent grey matter, for this influences the excitability at the junctional region B. (From Barron & Matthews, 1935)

potential energy stored in this system is utilised during the passage of an impulse so as to ensure its forward conduction over long distances without loss of speed or signal strength. It was considered at one stage that, even in the absence of such local energy resources, an electric signal started at one end might be propagated along a nerve fibre owing to its "core-conductor" or cable properties. It is true that the presence of an insulating surface membrane endows the axon with cable-like properties, but this is a resemblance only on a miniature scale. If we compare the electric constants . . . with those of ordinary communication cables, we find that the leakage of the axon membrane, per cm.², is about a hundred million times and its capacity about a million times higher, while the conductivity of the axon core is about a hundred million times lower than that in an ordinary commercial cable. Needless to say, these defects arise because nature uses quite different materials and very different gauges to those employed by the electrical engineer.'

Owing to the losses in the neuronal cable, energy has to be expended to boost the signal as it passes on its way. Excitation can be regarded as a membrane reaction that amplifies the passive lowering of the surface potential.

THE MYELIN SHEATH

A squid axone of diameter 500μ may conduct at 30 m./sec., whilst a mammalian nerve of diameter 20μ may conduct at 100 m./sec. (Plate 1). Upon what does this difference depend? The mammalian nerve operates at a higher temperature, but this factor alone is inadequate to account for the discrepancy.

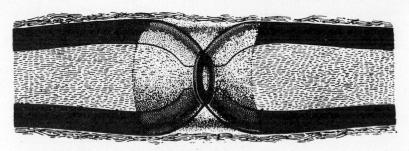

FIG. 1.3.—Node of Ranvier. Experiments upon fibres that have been cut or constricted suggest that there is a continual flow of material from the nerve cell body along the axone, fluid being lost from the surface. The submicroscopic structure of nerve fibres has been reviewed by Fernández-Morán (1954). (Figure reproduced from Hess & Young, 1952)

Prominent in any discussion of this problem is a consideration of the functions of the myelin sheath. This fatty envelope is interrupted every few millimetres in peripheral nerve by the nodes of Ranvier (Fig. 1.3). The internodal distance is greater the larger the fibre. Similar nodes are found in the central nervous system (Hess & Young, 1952).

Lillie (1925) pointed out that 'in the most rapidly conducting protoplasmic tracts known, the medullated nerves of vertebrates, the conducting element (axone) is enclosed by a tubular sheath (myelin) of apparently high electrical resistance, the medullary sheath

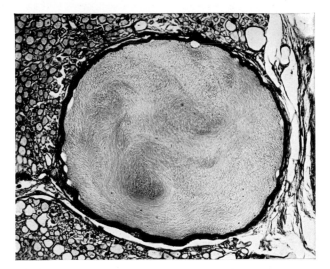

Single nerve fibre of the squid. This axone controls the muscles that produce the 'jet propulsion'. Smaller nerve fibres are also seen. The large fibre conducts at about 22 m./sec. (50 miles per hour)

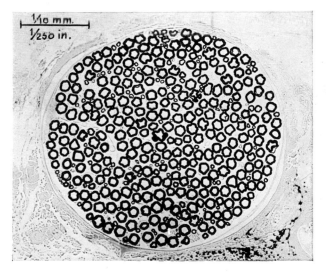

Nerve supplying the calf muscle of a rabbit shown at the same magnification as the squid fibre shown above. The myelin sheath found around many of the mammalian nerve fibres enables the filaments, though fine, to conduct rapidly. In the section two groups of fibre can be distinguished—large and small. The large fibres conduct at some 90 m./sec. (200 m.p.h.). The small fibres run to receptors, known as muscle spindles and adjust the range of muscle lengths over which effective signalling may occur (vide p. 54 and Fig. 2.9, p. 48). Reproduced from J. Z. Young (1951b)

Plate 1

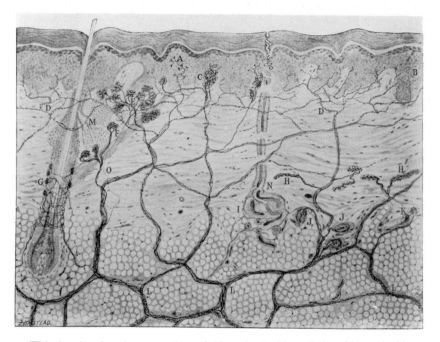

This drawing, based upon sections of skin stained with methylene blue and with silver may be compared with the line drawings of Fig. 2.2 (p. 37). Line drawings are a necessary simplification for some purposes but may mislead those who do not themselves handle histological preparations into believing that some of the distinctions between different types of receptor are made more readily than is in fact so.

A. Merkel's discs; *B.* Free endings; *C.* Meissner's corpuscles; *D.* Nerve fibres; *E.* Krause's end bulbs; *F.* Ruffini's endings; *G.* Nerve fibres and endings on hair follicle subserving touch; *H.* Ruffini's endings *I.* Sympathetic nerve fibres innervating a sweat gland; *J.* Pacinian corpuscles subserving pressure; *K.* Golgi-Mazzoni endings; *L.* Nerve trunks containing thick and thin fibres; *M.* Sebaceous gland; *N.* Sweat gland. *O.* Sympathetic nerve fibres supplying arrector pili muscle. (From Woollard, Weddell, Harpman, J. A. 1940)

Plate 2

which is constricted or interrupted at regular intervals'. He stated that 'the electrical resistance between the surface of the axone and the surrounding medium may be assumed to be relatively low at the constrictions ; diffusing substances (dyes) enter most rapidly at those regions, and the same is presumably true of ions'.

This view appears to have now been established. The threshold of a single myelinated nerve fibre varies, rising at the internodes and falling in between (Fig. 1.4). The delay in the passage of an impulse down a fibre at the nodes supports the view that conduction is 'saltatory' (Fig. 1.5). The time taken to travel along an internode is scarcely measurable ; it is at the nodes that delay occurs.

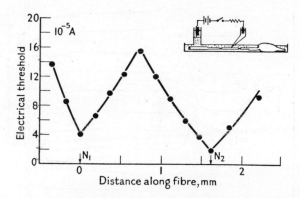

Fig. 1.4.—Variation of threshold of myelinated fibre. Greatest excitability is at nodes of Ranvier. (From Tasaki, 1953)

It thus appears that the cable-like properties of the internodes is the clue to understanding the high velocites reached by messages travelling in myelinated fibres.

Such filaments may be regarded as a string of active nodes separated by passive conductor elements. Accordingly transmission should not now be compared with that along a telegraph wire ; the performance of a submarine cable would be a more appropriate analogy. Such cables may be dropped onto the floor of an ocean ; they are equipped with repeater relays at intervals along their length. These relays reshape the electrical pulses before they lose their identity, owing to losses in the cable and electrical interference. In the nerve fibre the losses are much greater, and the interference also is probably substantial ; accordingly the action potential is 'reshaped' every few millimetres at the nodes of Ranvier.

Saltatory conduction is a specialisation that enables impulses to be transmitted economically. 'The mechanism of saltatory conduction reduces the amount of sodium which is necessary to conduct an impulse to 1/300 of that exchanged in a non-medullated fibre of the same diameter. The heat production per impulse is reduced to an even higher proportion' (Stämpfli, 1954).

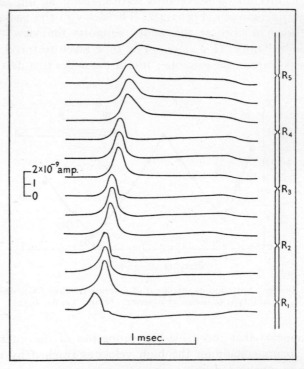

FIG. 1.5.—Saltatory conduction. An action potential is shown recorded from a number of points along a myelinated nerve fibre (*right*). Note the delay at the nodes of Ranvier (R_1, R_2, R_3, R_4 and R_5). (From Huxley & Stämpfli, 1949)

Many mammalian nerve fibres are, however, *unmyelinated* and little is known of the mode of propagation of impulses in these fine strands. The distinction between myelinated and unmyelinated is less clear-cut than might appear, for examination of unmyelinated fibres with polarised light indicates that they do in fact possess a very fine fatty membrane (Schmidt & Bear, 1939). A wealth of new structure has been revealed by the electron microscope. It is sobering to realise that nerve fibres, or branches of nerve fibres, may be so small that they cannot be seen in ordinary histological preparations (*vide* Fernández-Morán, 1954).

The development of the myelin sheath opened the way for the evolution of animals with highly developed sense organs, for it became practicable to use many fibres having rapid velocities of conduction. The ability to depend upon such fine filaments enabled a great multiplicity of pathways to develop. Schmitt [in Merritt (1952)] remarked that : 'In designing gadgets, we are not familiar with having inexpensive, low performance elements available in abundance. . . . In a system which can afford multiplicity, where redundancy is everywhere, where a hundred different channels are all concerned with approximately the same thing, where there are the equivalent of a dozen different basic combinations of servo-mechanisms, each directed at some slightly different effect, all computing simultaneously, overall properties quite different from those of familiar engineering devices will be found.'

The 'All-or-None' nature of the propagated nerve impulses implies that continuous changes in the environment must be transmitted as a series of discontinuous alterations in the neurones. It is evident, therefore, that much transformation of the sensory signals must occur at the level of the sense organs. Nerve fibres cannot normally discharge at rates above about 300/sec., and it is found that sense organs are selective : certain features only of environmental conditions are signalled to the sensorium. The loss of information is mitigated to some extent by the multiplicity of nerve fibres that often are available. Engineers have recently developed ways of measuring *information* (*vide* Andrew, 1953). They have been interested in developing such quantitative relationships in order to ascertain the most economical ways of transmitting data by means of wireless and cable. It is interesting that the engineers find it desirable to transmit rather more information than is strictly needed ; they introduce 'redundancy' to offset interference that might arise due to background noise. In the nervous system also the same information is often transmitted along different routes (p. 214).

A multiplicity of alternative pathways is found in the peripheral as well as in the central nervous system. The rectus abdominis muscle, for instance, is at each of its segments supplied by at least three intercostal nerves. Communications between intercostal nerves whilst they are in the thorax, and when they are lying on the transversus abdominis muscle, ensure that each segment of the rectus abdominis is supplied by at least three parent trunks. Surgeons are frequently forced to sacrifice some of the branches supplying this muscle, but the resulting paralysis is usually trivial or undetectable by usual methods of clinical examination. When a cutaneous nerve is divided the area in which sensation is lost is very much smaller than the area to which the nerve can be seen to be distributed by anatomical means, or to which sensations are referred when the nerve trunk is stimulated. The extent to which different modalities of sensation overlap varies; thus it may appear, after a nerve injury, that there is a region from which pain but no other sensation can be elicited. On the other hand, with a sensory loss due to section of posterior roots the overlap may be least for pain. It must be pointed out, however, that in comparing the overlap of different modalities serious difficulties are encountered of a logical nature, for who can equate the intensities of different forms of stimulation such as those of heat and contact? The boundaries of the areas of sensory loss that are revealed depend to an important degree on the intensity of the stimulus that is employed (Cobb, 1919).

The myelin sheath is of great interest to the pathologist. Of the various *demyelinating diseases* disseminated sclerosis is by far the most common. According to the usual interpretation of the histological findings the axis cylinders in this condition persist but the myelin sheath degenerates. Much interest has been taken in demyelination induced by interference with oxidative mechanisms. It is usually supposed that grey matter is more susceptible to anoxia than is white, and indeed it has long been known that the grey matter is much more richly vascularised: 'Willis, looking at the facts for himself, had been struck by the greater richness of blood supply to the grey nervous matter than to the white' (Sherrington, 1951). It does not necessarily follow, however, that white matter is always less susceptible than grey to anoxia; the reverse may be the case with small, repeated episodes, as may be caused by injections of cyanide.

Many other agents are known to give rise to demyelinisation and there is at the present time much interest in the possibility that demyelinisation may be the result of interference with 'non-specific' cholinesterase (*vide* Cavanagh & Thompson, 1954). This enzyme is widely distributed in the nervous system and is often seen histochemically to be associated with the myelin sheath; it is also present in the plasma. Biochemical studies may thus prove to lead to a much better understanding of certain clinical conditions;

it is of interest that 'jake-paralysis', in which the principal disturbance affects the motor system, is caused by a compound that inhibits 'non-specific' cholinesterase : tri-orthocresyl phosphate.

DEGENERATION AND REGENERATION

There is now much evidence to suggest that there is a continuous flow of material along the axone away from the soma of the nerve cell. Thus observations upon living nerve fibres have shown the presence of moving granules, whilst other support for this view has come from experiments in which nerve fibres have been cut or constricted.

When a nerve is cut across, the peripheral segment degenerates and, in the case of a mammal, ceases to conduct impulses after about three days. The Wallerian degeneration that is seen consists of a segmentation of the fibre first into long ovoids and then into progressively shorter segments. All parts of the fibre are affected at about the same time (Gutmann & Holubář, 1950). These changes suggested to J. Z. Young a resemblance to the break-up of a long liquid cylinder under surface tension. Presumably the pumping of fluid along the axone normally counteracts this tendency (*vide* Young in Weiss, 1950). In the peripheral nervous system division of a nerve is followed by an outgrowth of fine fibres (*e.g.* 1μ diameter) into the peripheral stump. This tendency is manifested for long periods after the nerve has been divided or redivided, and it is associated with profound alterations of the metabolism of the neurone. It has been said that 'a long axis cylinder may contain a thousand times as much protoplasm as its cell body; and, during regeneration, axoplasm is formed at such a rate that the cell body must build several times its volume of protoplasm per day' (Gerard in Weiss, 1950).

Successful regeneration into the peripheral degenerated trunk may occur after many months, and once the axones have crossed the gap they may grow as much as 4 mm./day. These fine axones may increase in diameter, and one factor in this maturation depends upon the peripheral connections which they make. There is evidence that it is the fibres that have made successful peripheral connections that swell. The nerve fibres in their turn affect the sensory endings. Thus it has been noticed that the large 'corpuscles of Grandy' in the skin of the duck's bill may be used again when nerve fibres grow back into the area. If regeneration is delayed, however, they vanish, 'just as taste buds disappear when the nerves innervating them are sectioned and no regeneration sets in' (Boeke in Weiss, 1950). It is interesting that when full thickness skin grafts are made the tissue may become innervated by the growth of nerve fibres into the area from adjacent regions (*vide* Napier, 1952).

The axone may represent a large proportion of the nerve cell, and when it is divided histological alterations occur in the soma with which it has been connected. Different categories of nerve cells react in different ways, but one common response is a swelling up and loss of *Nissl substance*, a granular material that can be seen in histological preparations stained with aniline dyes. This change is associated with a loss of nucleoprotein ; indeed the Nissl substance itself may be nucleoprotein (*vide* Hydén, 1947 ; Bodian, 1947). Loss of nucleoprotein may also follow prolonged excitation of nerve cells ; any structural change caused by stimulation is of great interest for the light it may throw on the mechanisms of memory (p. 228).

VELOCITY OF CONDUCTION IN RELATION TO FIBRE SIZE

An electrical shock applied to a peripheral nerve may set up dis-charges in very many individual nerve fibres. Studies of the compound

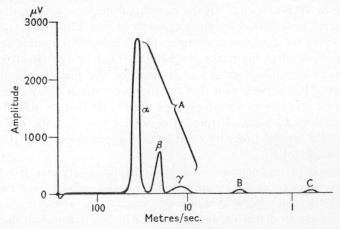

FIG. 1.6.—Different fibre groups : mixed nerve of frog. The graph has been constructed from records of compound action potentials recorded at a point some distance from the site of stimulation. Mammalian nerves show maximum rates of conduction greater than those of the frog's fibres. (Data of Erlanger & Gasser, 1937, modified from Bell, Davidson & Scarborough, 1950)

action potentials produced in this way reveals a series of humps which are related to groups of fibres with different conduction velocities (Fig. 1.6).

Erlanger & Gasser (1937) labelled the fastest group A, the next B, and the slowest C, and gave reasons for supposing that the fastest fibres were also the largest. The C fibres were, it appeared, unmyelinated. The A hump can be further subdivided into α, β, γ and δ groups.

The C group consists of unmyelinated axons whilst the B group represents pre-ganglionic sympathetic fibres. The conduction velocity of the B group (14-3 m./sec.) overlaps the lowest range of the A fibres (100-5 m./sec.), but the distinction has physiological significance, for the

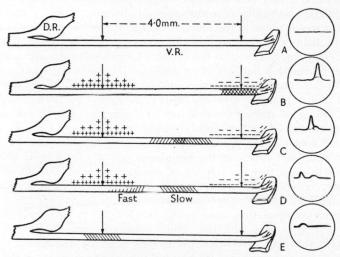

FIG. 1.7.—Ingenious method for 'gating' nervous messages. A ventral root, V.R., is seen attached to spinal cord on right, to dorsal root, D.R., on left. When a square pulse of current is applied to the electrodes excitation starts at the cathode and spreads along different fibres at different velocities. The impulses in the faster fibres reach the anode whilst the pulse is still being applied and are blocked (anodal polarisation). By the time the action potentials in the slower fibres have reached the anode the stimulus has ceased and these messages are able to proceed towards the periphery. On the right (A to E) is shown activity that might be revealed by appropriate recording on the face of a cathode-ray tube. (From Kuffler & Williams, 1953)

properties of the two types differ in important respects. Thus the action potentials are of longer duration in the B group (1·2 versus 0·5 msec.), whilst the after potentials (p. 108) also differ. In the B group the positive after potential is prominent, whilst the negative after potential is not seen (Grundfest, 1939). The C fibres are relatively resistant to asphyxia but are quite sensitive to the action of cocaine. Their properties are considered in detail by Gasser (1950).

The different properties of the various categories of nerve fibres enable the experimenter to excite the smallest or largest at will by suitable control of an electrical stimulus. One interesting way of studying the effects of small fibres by themselves has been devised by Kuffler & Williams (1953). By applying a square electrical pulse it is possible to arrange that the faster fibres are blocked by the currents around the anode whilst the slower impulses pass, for by the time they have reached this region the blocking current has stopped (Fig. 1.7). In considering the physiological significance of these various categories of fibre it is necessary to point out that some peripheral, and indeed central, nerve fibres branch and the subdivisions have smaller diameters than the parent axone. Furthermore, it may be found that fibres that perform similar tasks may have different velocities of conduction in different parts of the body. Thus the motor fibres to the muscles of the human hand do not conduct at more than 46-67 m./sec., whilst those supplying more proximal muscles may conduct twice as fast (Hodes, Larrabee & German, 1948).

The relationship between fibre diameter (D) and velocity of conduction (V) has interested a number of workers. Thus the relationships $V \propto D$, $V \propto \sqrt{D}$ and $V \propto D^2$ and other possibilities have been considered. Gasser (1955) has studied the structure of C fibres by electron microscopy and has confirmed earlier work showing that the axones are of much smaller diameter in the dorsal root between the ganglion and the spinal cord than in their course in the peripheral nerves. In these C fibres he was able to show that the velocity of conduction varied directly as their diameter. There would appear to be no reason to expect a single formula to be applicable to all situations, but it may be significant that recent measurements upon the squid axone (Hodes, 1953) have brought this tissue into agreement with the results obtained, using cats' myelinated fibres (Hursh, 1939). In both cases the data fitted the relationship $V \propto D$. In making his measurements Hursh used the outside diameter of the fibre, and thus included the thickness of the myelin sheath. The question of the relationship between fibre diameter and internodal distance is a complex problem (vide Rushton, 1951). No simple answer can be expected, but it is of interest that in regenerating nerve fibres the internodal distance may be shorter than normal without a significant alteration in the rate of conduction (Sanders & Whitteridge, 1946).

MUSCLE

The spread of electrical excitation through skeletal muscle appears to be similar in its mechanism to the spread of activity in a squid nerve fibre. The action potential is 'All-or-None' in type. The mechanical events follow the electrical after a very short latent period (1·5 msec.) and after a brief initial relaxation the contraction is initiated. It may, however, occasionally happen in mammalian tissue that a contraction, or 'contracture', may develop without concomitant electrical disturbances. This is sometimes seen in a cachectic patient when a muscle is struck with a tendon hammer; a local contraction may occur which is not associated with electrical signs of activity. One important change that may occur in muscles is the *myostatic contracture* (Adams, Denny-Brown & Pearson, 1953). If the bony attachments of a skeletal muscle are approximated and immobilised for a few days the muscle may become fixed at the length thus imposed upon it (*vide* Pollock & Davis, 1930 *b*). After a few weeks the muscle cannot be lengthened without structural damage. It seems likely that this alteration involves the elastic tissues of the muscle and that structural alterations of this type often become grafted onto positions primarily imposed by neurological abnormalities. At least the possibility of a myostatic contracture must be borne in mind when evaluating the tone of a limb which has been spastic for some time.

Owing to their small size it is more difficult to approach the problems of excitation in smooth muscle fibres. By means of micro-electrodes Bülbring (1954) has been able to show that in smooth muscle from the gut spikes do occur, but they represent only a very incomplete depolarisation of the cell membrane.

The striated muscle fibres are innervated in groups known as *motor units*. A number of muscle fibres are innervated from a single axone; the size of the motor unit defined in this way has been calculated by dividing the number of muscle fibres by the number of motor nerve fibres that are implicated. The problem is more complicated than this analysis would suggest, for a single muscle fibre may be innervated by more than one nerve fibre (Hunt & Kuffler, 1954). Evidently on the motor side, as on the sensory side, alternative pathways are available; should one fibre fail another may be able to control the musculature. That excitation may start at more than one site along the muscle membrane explains why it is that the shape of the action potential varies according to the part of the fibre from which it is recorded (Jarcho, Eyzaguirre, Berman & Lilienthal, 1952).

Since many muscle fibres are innervated by a single nerve fibre, it is not surprising that the potential that can be recorded from the muscles by *electromyography* varies according to whether a motor unit or a muscle fibre is active. The large and relatively long (10 msec.) potentials produced by activation of a motor unit may be recorded from electrodes placed on the skin over the surface of the muscle (Fig. 1.8 A). The currents are evidently due to the summation of action potentials from a number of muscle fibres. That

C

a muscle fibre may be innervated by more than one nerve fibre is, no doubt, the reason why the shape of the electromyogram alters when a nerve is partially paralysed.   Thus Pinelli & Buchthal (1953) blocked the ulnar nerve by cooling it and noticed that the potentials recorded from the motor units were more 'polyphasic' than normally.

A healthy muscle fibre is never entirely quiescent, for even when it is relaxed there is in the region of the neuromuscular junction a constant production of end-plate potentials that are too small to give rise to an action potential (Fatt & Katz, 1952).   When a muscle is denervated its fibres tend to become spontaneously active at a low frequency, and these contractions are accentuated by trivial manipulation.   This *fibrillation* cannot be seen through the skin and to study the electrical potentials it is necessary to insert needles into the muscle itself.   The discharges are of low voltage and of short duration (*e.g.* 20μV, 1 msec., *vide* Fig. 1.8 B). One interesting development in the technique of electromyography has been to use micro-electrodes inserted into human muscles through hypodermic needles (Norris & Gasteiger, 1955).

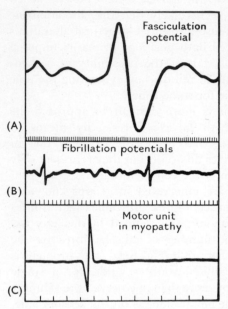

FIG. 1.8.—Some of the potentials that are seen in electromyography. (Time scales msec.) (From Sargent, 1950)

Fibrillation potentials are one aspect of the hyper-excitability of denervated striated muscles ; denervation also increases the sensitivity of the fibres to chemical agents.   Mammalian striated musculature is rendered 1000 times more sensitive to acetylcholine by denervation and it is sensitised also to potassium salts, adrenaline and nicotine-like compounds.   Denervated mammalian muscle may respond to an injection of aceylcholine by a prolonged contraction (Brown, 1937) which is not associated with maintained electrical discharges : a contracture (*vide supra*).   The hypersensitivity occasionally gives rise to curious effects, for a muscle, though denervated, may respond to substances circulating in the blood stream. Although these events have been well authenticated experimentally, they have received little attention clinically.

The occurrence of spontaneous discharges of motor units, or *fasciculation*, gives rise to a rippling of the surface of the muscle that has long been observed in *motor neurone disease*. Fasciculation may sometimes persist even when the motor nerve has been blocked ; the contractions appear to indicate that some part of the axone, or of the neurone, is hyper-excitable.

At times muscle fibres may degenerate and the order in which they do this need bear no relationship to their grouping into motor units. The action potentials of motor units therefore shorten in duration ; this finding may be of some value diagnostically (Fig. 1.8 C). In the group of conditions known as 'myopathy' the muscles usually degenerate with bilateral symmetry ; the degeneration commonly occurs in musculature of the face, trunk and extremities. Nevertheless, in some cases this condition is restricted to the extrinsic muscles of the eyes, suggesting, incorrectly, a lesion of the brain stem (Kiloh & Nevin, 1951).

Some information about the state of a muscle may be obtained by measuring its electrical excitability. By using currents of different durations it is possible to plot a *strength-duration curve* ; in general, the briefer the current the greater the voltage needed to excite. A great deal of attention in the past has been paid to measurements of 'chronaxie'. To estimate this the 'rheobase' is first determined, *i.e.* the strength needed to excite, using a current of indefinitely long duration. The chronaxie is the duration of the pulse needed to excite at a strength of twice the rheobase. Nerves have in general much shorter chronaxies than do striated muscles. Short lasting stimuli therefore tend to stimulate nerve fibres ; longer lasting pulses may stimulate muscle fibres themselves (Adrian, 1916). Naturally the effect of denervation is to reduce the sensitivity of brief electrical shocks ; in the older terminology the reaction to *faradic* stimuli is abolished, whilst the reaction to *galvanic* stimuli is retained or even accentuated. A normal muscle is most excitable in the region of its 'motor point', presumably because it is from there that current can most readily reach the nerve fibres supplying the muscle (Figs. 1.9 and 1.10). In denervated muscles no particular spot is found, on testing with skin electrodes, where the excitability is greater than elsewhere. Accordingly it follows that the changes in electrical excitability that are revealed by denervation will depend to an important extent upon the exact situation of the electrodes (Roberts, 1916).

There are many uncertainties in the clinical application of strength-duration measurements. By applying currents to the skin the shape of the pulses is inevitably distorted (*vide* Barnett, 1938 ; Moore, 1950 ; cf. Löfgren, 1953 ; Rothman 1954). In addition,

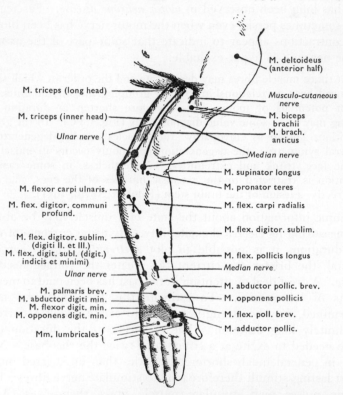

FIG. 1.9.—Motor points of upper limbs. (Reproduced from Purves-Stewart, 1945, after Erb)

the sheaths of nerve trunks are themselves substantial barriers to ionic movements and to the passage of electrical currents (*vide* Krnjevic, 1954). Even when these uncertainties are removed, under experimental conditions, by placing fine electrodes directly on single nerve fibres the results depend critically upon the placing of the electrodes with respect to the nodes of Ranvier. The chronaxie increases in between the nodes (Hodler, Stämpfli & Tasaki, 1952). Whilst, therefore, strength-duration curves can be of some practical value, electrical stimulation is not a highly refined method of testing function ; it yields less information than can be obtained by electro-myography.

Electrical stimuli may be used for therapeutic purposes. Thus the phrenic nerve may be stimulated when artificial respiration is needed : *Electro-phrenic Respiration* (Sarnoff *et al.*, 1951). Electrical stimuli may also be of use in preventing denervated muscles from undergoing extensive atrophy. Although the value of this treat-ment has been doubted, studies made during World War II

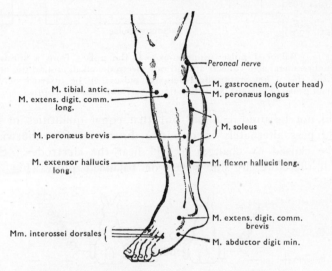

Peroneal nerve

M. tibial. antic.
M. extens. digit. comm. long.

M. gastrocnem. (outer head)
M. peronæus longus

M. soleus

M. peronæus brevis

M. extensor hallucis long.

M. flexor hallucis long.

M. extens. digit. comm. brevis

Mm. interossei dorsales

M. abductor digit min.

FIG. 1.10.—Motor points of leg. (Reproduced from Purves-Stewart, 1945, after Erb)

appear to have established unquestionably its usefulness (Gutmann & Guttmann, 1944 ; Grodins *et al.*, 1944 ; Jackson, 1945). It is interesting that electrical currents applied for a short time each day should prevent wasting, for the denervated muscle readily produces spontaneous contractions of individual fibres (*vide supra*). This fibrillation may be stopped by quinine and yet the denervated muscle may atrophy (Solandt & Magladery, 1940). Conversely, electrical stimulation may prevent atrophy and not abolish the fibrillation. Accordingly it has been concluded that fibrillation is not the cause of the loss of substance. Provided that a denervated muscle has not been replaced by fibrous tissue, satisfactory restitution of function may occur when the nerves again make contact, even though this is delayed as long as twelve months (Sunderland, 1950). Denervated muscle can remain electrically excitable for many years. When electrical stimuli are used for treating muscles it is desirable that it

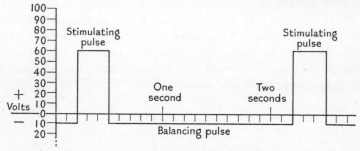

FIG. 1.11.—Balanced pulse stimulation. If the pulses from a stimulator are unidirectional acid collects around one electrode, alkali around the other. To avoid this a low-amplitude balancing pulse may be inserted between the main peaks of current, as in this figure. (From Mason, 1949)

should not be unidirectional but that equal quantities of current should pass alternately in opposite directions, for otherwise pain will be caused by changes of pH near the electrodes. Suitable stimuli, therefore, are sine waves, or 'balanced' pulses (Fig. 1.11).

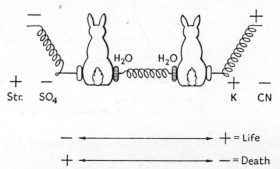

FIG. 1.12.—Iontophoresis. Depending upon direction of current flow the rabbits live or die. Either potassium is driven into one rabbit and sulphate into the other, or cyanide and strychnine respectively. Electrical currents in the body will be carried by whatever ions are available. Iontophoresis has been used as a way of applying drugs, but the technique is now rarely employed. (From Mitrinowicz, 1949, after Leduc)

Electricity has other applications in medicine. Thus drugs may be carried into the body by *Iontophoresis* (Fig. 1.12), or the heating effects of radio-frequency currents may be used, *Diathermy*. The currents that can be passed through the skin at radio frequencies are much greater than those that can be tolerated at lower frequencies; in long-wave

diathermy current of density of 75-100 mA/sq. in. may be passed through
the skin.   Such high-frequency currents do not stimulate nerve fibres,
presumably because the ions reverse direction before they can move far.
The relative ease with which these currents can penetrate tissues, together
with the fact that they do not directly stimulate nerves, explains how it is
that such high currents can be passed without discomfort.   Currents of
equal strength, or higher, are used to induce convulsions ; in *electro-
convulsive therapy* frequencies are employed (*e.g.* 50 c/s) many times (*e.g.*
10,000) lower than those used in long-wave diathermy and are slow enough
effectively to stimulate neurones.

ACCOMMODATION

It has long been known that an electrical current that rises
slowly may be less effective as a stimulus than one that increases
abruptly (*vide* Kugelberg, 1944).   This effect, as though the nerve
had a capacity of re-
adjustment to changed
conditions, is known
as ' accommodation '.
Some insight into its
mechanism has been
obtained by measure-
ments of the properties
of single nodes (Fran-
kenhaeuser, 1952).
With currents that rise
slowly a single node
may react not by the
abrupt discharge of an
action potential but by
a slow discharge that
precedes an action
potential of reduced
size.   Under normal
circumstances excita-
tion is facilitated by the
activity of neighbour-
ing nodes.

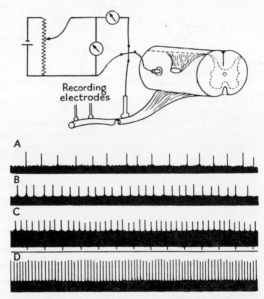

FIG. 1.13.—Discharge of anterior horn cell in
response to steady polarisation of spinal cord.
Currents: A, 5×10^{-7} amp.; B, 6×10^{-7} amp.;
C, 7×10^{-7} amp. ; D, 10×10^{-10} amp. (From
Barron & Matthews, 1938)

The degree to which different nerves accommodate varies
markedly.   There may even be differences between different parts
of a neurone.   Thus Barron & Matthews (1938) found that a steady

current passed through the spinal cord gave rise to a rhythmic discharge of motor neurones which was attributed to direct excitation
of these cells by the current (Fig. 1.13). Nevertheless, the motor
axones themselves classically show only a single response to a constant current. The axones of sensory nerves accommodate less than
those of motor nerves.

When a nerve is submitted to pressure or to some other injury
there is set up a condition in which *cross talk* may arise between
the fibres. The differences of accommodation between sensory and
motor fibres explain how it is that there can be the transmission of
impulses from motor to sensory nerves (Granit, Leksell & Skoglund,
1944), but not in the reverse direction. This would appear to be of
great importance in under-
standing the mechanism
of pain in many clinical
conditions, for instance
'sciatica' (prolapsed in-
tervertebral disc). Im-
pulses may reach pain
fibres from other active
filaments in the neighbourhood. The injury to the
nerve trunk appears to
increase the excitability of
the fibres; no doubt this
occurs because the healthy

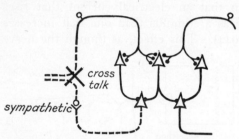

FIG. 1.14.—Causalgia. Suggested scheme of
its pathenogenesis. At the injured region
of the nerve efferent sympathetic impulses
can interact with sensory fibres and so
give rise to 'spontaneous' pain. (From
McCulloch in Foerster, 1949)

regions can discharge into the damaged area. If the fibres were
to accommodate to this their excitability would not be raised.

When a peripheral nerve is damaged a painful condition, *causalgia*,
may arise that is very distressing. The pain may arise spontaneously
and is usually described as a burning sensation. The patient may
say, for instance, that his skin in the affected region is 'mustard
red-hot', or his sensations may suggest that a 'red-hot file is rasping
the skin'. There is much evidence (*vide* Nathan, 1947) that in this
condition efferent sympathetic discharges are exciting sensory nerves
at the damaged region (Fig. 1.14, and see also Chapter 3, p. 63).

When the accommodation of a fibre is very low it is liable to
discharge impulses spontaneously. Kugelberg (1946) has pointed
out that:

'For many neurologists, the nerve fibre, even under pathological conditions, is merely a well-insulated cable, conducting impulses from one

point to another.   If its conductivity is broken phenomena arise which
can be ranged in the large clinical group, symptoms of deficiency.   This
view, however, proves to be inadequate to explain some phenomena from
another large clinical group, symptoms of irritation.   Paresthesias, muscular fasciculation, spasms, as well as pain in certain circumstances have
their origin in nerve fibres.'

An important rôle in regulating accommodation is played by calcium.
Brink (1954) has reviewed the complex actions of calcium upon
excitable tissues.   He states that : 'Sodium and potassium ions are
the principal current carriers in the membrane and their interchange
accounts for the action current.   In contrast, calcium ions seem to
affect primarily the constraints imposed upon these ionic movements.

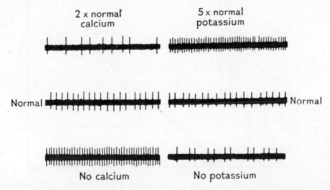

FIG. 1.15.—Discharge of ganglion cell in response to acetylcholine (40 μgm/cc.)
in Ringer's solution ('Normal') and when the content of calcium and potassium
is varied.   (From Bronk, 1939)

In other words, calcium ions react with and become part of the
surface structure of the cell.' Experimentally, reduction of the ionised
calcium may cause a nerve cell or muscle fibre to discharge spontaneously, or may increase the rate of pre-existing discharge (Fig.
1.15).

In man a lack of calcium in ionised form in the plasma leads to
tetany.   In this condition there develop paraesthesiae and muscular
cramps.

'The motor effect in the Trousseau phenomenon (Fig. 1.16) is a continuous contraction of the small hand muscles similar to the voluntary
contraction.   The impulse activity was found to consist in single or,
mostly, double spikes (more rarely of triple spikes) with a frequency of
7 to 16 per second, with a machine-like regularity' (Kugelberg, 1946).   In
dogs the tonic and clonic forms of tetany have been shown to depend

upon the integrity of the spinal cord. Thus section of the dorsal roots abolishes these features although the muscles may still fasciculate. On the other hand, impulses from pre-spinal centres do not appear to be essential for the phenomena (West, 1935). Sir Victor Horsley (1885) removed the arm region of the motor cortex from a monkey and found that the extremity although paralysed was invaded by the clonic movements that followed total removal of the thyroid (and doubtless parathyroid) tissue. The rôles of central and peripheral factors in human tetany do not appear to have been clearly defined, but in considering this problem some fascinating observations of Rosett (1924) may be considered. He found

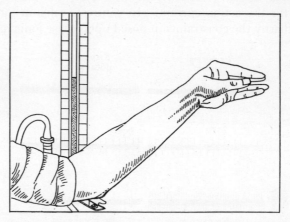

FIG. 1.16.—Trousseau sign. This patient had a low serum calcium which was associated with poor absorption of fat (steatorrhoea). The symptoms of tetany caused by hyperventilation are similar to those caused by a reduction in the serum calcium, and some have believed that hyperventilation provokes tetany by reducing the ionisation of calcium. The work of Schultzer & Lebel (1939) did not support this suggestion—the ionised serum calcium was found to be normal in cases of hyperventilation tetany, whilst the injection of calcium chloride intravenously did not relieve the condition

that the form of the rigidity induced by hyperventilation varied according to the posture into which the limb was placed. Thus a hand was fixed in a particular posture by bandaging and tetany was induced. The bandage was then removed and the hand was seen to retain the position in which it had been placed. The rigidity, therefore, is 'plastic' (p. 124). Rosett noted that in right-handed people the right hand was first affected, whilst the left hand was first involved in left-handed subjects. Involuntary movements (p. 391) were increased in intensity. Thus an 11-year-old girl who suffered from choreo-athetosis was asked to hyperventilate. 'From the very beginning until the end of the experiment the abnormal involuntary movements increased in amplitude and extent. In a few minutes every movable portion of the body was in motion in every direction, including torsion, until the picture became indistinguishable from a typical one of dystonia musculorum deformans' (cf. p. 395).

The repetitive discharges that may be set up by nerves or muscles often appear to depend upon the tissue being in a supernormal phase at some time after an impulse has been discharged. In large myelinated nerve fibres such a period of supernormality occurs after the relative refractory period and is associated with a negative after potential. Later a positive after potential is seen and this is accompanied by a diminution of excitability.

THE NEUROMUSCULAR JUNCTION

If two giant fibres (p. 3) are laid close together it can be arranged that an impulse started in one of the fibres will be transmitted to its neighbour. For this to be successfully achieved the second of the fibres should be in a hyper-excitable state. This can be achieved by bathing the junctional region in a solution low in calcium (Arvanitaki, 1942). In such an arrangement electrical currents carried by the ions of the surrounding fluid stimulate the second fibre. An artificial synapse (*ephapse*) has been formed. It might be supposed that similar arrangements held in the junctional tissues that occur naturally, but this is not the case. Special arrangements exist, perhaps, because 'the ordinary axon membrane is rather insensitive —it is an electro-receptor capable as a rule of responding to fairly large potential changes and amplifying them by some 10-20 db' [1] (Fatt & Katz, 1953).

In the case of the neuromuscular junction (Fig. 1.17) it is necessary to postulate a mechanism that involves the liberation of acetylcholine. Eccles (1953) has given the following account of the arrangements at the nerve muscle junction :

'An enzyme system, choline-acetylase, in the motor nerve-fibre manufactures acetyl-choline, ACh, which is stored within the motor fibre at a relatively high concentration. When an impulse passes along the fibre, a brief jet of ACh is liberated. Presumably this liberation occurs particularly freely from the non-myelinated nerve terminals. The liberated ACh diffuses across the junctional region to become attached momentarily to special receptors on the surface membrane of the motor end-plate. At the same time it is being rapidly hydrolysed by the specific cholinesterase

[1] Between 10- and 100-fold. The definition of a decibel (db) will be found on p. 266.

Very small amounts of Ach (10⁻¹⁷-10⁻¹⁵ mole) are enough to depolarize

threshold

that is concentrated at the end-plate surface so that its complete destruction occurs in a few milliseconds.) However, (during the brief period of its attachment, it rapidly depolarizes the surface membrane of the motor end-plate thus giving rise to the end-plate potential, henceforth e.p.p. Adjacent regions of the membrane in turn become depolarized by discharging into this sink at the junctional region. If this depolarization reaches a critical level, *i.e.* if the inward sodium current due to sodium-carrier activation becomes greater than the outward current due to potassium and chloride ions, a muscle impulse is generated adjacent to the end-plate region and propagates in both directions along the muscle-fibre, causing it in turn to contract.'

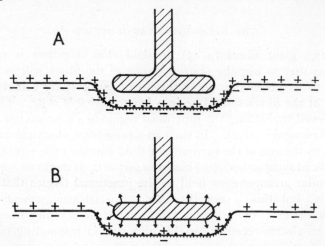

FIG. 1.17.—Neuromuscular junction. A shows normal polarised state ; B, partial depolarisation effected by acetylcholine. The muscle membrane at the end-plate region is especially sensitive to this action of acetylcholine, responding to a solution 1000 times as dilute as that needed for other parts of the muscle membrane. (From Eccles, 1953)

The work on the neuromuscular junction has thrown much light on the mechanism of the action of *curare*. This remarkable substance has long been known to cause a muscular paralysis without interfering with sensation; consequently the effect upon a conscious person is alarming. The drug was used in South America as an arrow poison. Curare blocks neuromuscular transmission by interfering with the effect of acetylcholine on the end-plate rather than by preventing the liberation of this compound.

The symptoms of *myasthenia gravis* resemble in some respects those that are produced by curarisation. It is natural, therefore, to ask to what extent the neuromuscular block in this disease depends upon mechanisms similar to those that have already been described. In this condition muscles that are used repeatedly become weaker and weaker ; finally, they can no longer be used until they have been rested (Fig. 1.18). The normal subject does not show this reaction except at a much greater number of repetitions (p. 363). Muscles that are weak in myasthenia gravis nevertheless react to direct electrical stimulation. Evidently the block is in the neuromuscular junction.

'In the electromyogram the most characteristic abnormality is the irregularity and eventual loss of voltage in the spikes of single units, presumed to be due to varia-tion in the number of fibers contracting to each nerve impulse (Fig. 1.19). When the nerve to the muscle is stimulated electrically by a rhythmical series of shocks the response fails progressively ("myasthenic reaction"). If a high frequency of stimulus is used (*e.g.* 200 to 500 stimuli a second) an additional pheno-menon is observed, namely a strong twitch to the first shock, followed by only a poor contraction (Pritchard). This is the Wedensky phenomenon, which means that the first impulse of the rapid series was the only one to excite

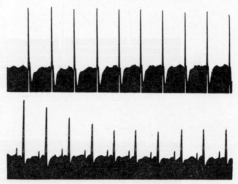

FIG. 1.18.—Reaction of normal (upper) and myasthenic muscle (lower) to repetitive electrical stimuli (25/sec.). Large deflections are EMG; shock artefacts, seen more prominently in lower trace, precede the EMG deflections. (Botelho, Deaterly, Austin & Comroe, 1952)

many of the fibers. It is observed only at a much higher frequency of stimulus in normal muscle, and was shown by Wedensky to be due to the rate of stimulus being so fast that each subsequent stimulus falls into the relative refractory period of the one before, then exciting only a subnormal impulse. The subnormal impulses, though insufficient to excite the muscle fiber, each set up yet another refractory period' (Adams, Denny-Brown & Pearson, 1953).

The muscles in myasthenia gravis react to acetylcholine given intra-arterially but do so less readily than do normal muscles (Engbaek, 1951), whilst the symptoms may be relieved, in part, by prostigmine and ameliorated also by potassium salts. These ob-servations would be compatible with the view that a curare-like compound was blocking neuromuscular transmission in this disease.

In keeping with this view is the observation that the infant of a myasthenic mother may suffer from myasthenia gravis for a few weeks after birth and then recover. Another fact that must be accounted for by any theory attempting to explain this disease is

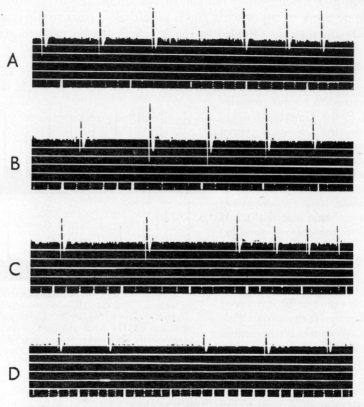

FIG. 1.19.—Myasthenia gravis. Electromyogram (needle electrodes) during voluntary effort. The action potentials, although believed to arise from the same motor unit, vary in size somewhat irregularly, and as the effort is continued decline, due to a failure of some of the muscle fibres of the unit, to respond. A, at start of contraction; B, after 40 sec.; C, after 80 sec.; D, after 170 sec. (Time 0·023 sec.) (Lindsley, 1935)

that by exercising one group of muscles the musculature elsewhere may become fatigued.

A related disorder is *Botulism*. The molecules of the toxin are large, having a molecular weight of 1 million. It may be necessary for an active fragment to be split off since there is a latency of many hours before the effects are seen. It has been estimated that as little as 0·05 mgm. of the toxin is lethal to man.   The muscles react normally to acetylcholine and the nerves transmit impulses.   The block at the neuromuscular junction appears to be due to the toxin interfering with the liberation of acetylcholine by the nerve terminals (*vide* Ambache, 1949).   A similar mechanism appears to be involved in the neuromuscular paralysis caused by *tetanus* toxin (Ambache, Morgan & Wright, 1949).

In some respects *myotonia* may be regarded as the converse of myasthenia gravis.   This condition may occur as a hereditary condition ;   it was first described by a Dr. Thomsen.   One of his sons suffered from the disease and when a Prussian army doctor refused

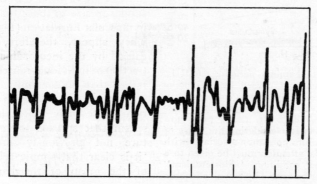

FIG. 1.20.—High-frequency oscillations ('dive-bomber' sounds), suggesting myotonia.   (Scale—10 millisec.)   (From Sargent, 1950)

to accept a certificate affirming this, Dr. Thomsen was prompted to write his monograph (for a recent account of the disease see Thomasen, 1948).

This disease may give rise to great difficulty in walking owing to the muscular spasm that accompanies voluntary acts, whilst 'if the patient stumbles or trips when walking or running, the additional effort to maintain balance commonly results in a spasm of the whole trunk and limbs, so that he falls to the ground as a rigid pillar'.   It has been noticed that :   'Small movements initiate myotonia only after prolonged rest, but any powerful effort sets up correspondingly severe spasm.   Blinking may occur naturally, whereas a strong closure of the eyes may initiate a spasm which continues for more than a minute after attempted opening' (Adams, Denny-Brown & Pearson, 1953).   Any muscle may be affected. Muscles that are involved will show a localised and persistent contraction on percussion, whilst repetitive electrical stimulation also may give rise to a prolonged contraction, though a single shock is inadequate. The difficulty in initiating movement may be due to the difficulty of relaxing antagonistic muscles. A related condition occurs in goats and there it is found that the delay in relaxation occurs even after curarisation and after the motor nerve has been severed and has degenerated.

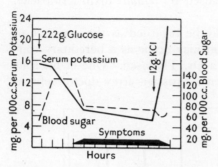

FIG. 1.21.—Familial periodic paralysis. Blood changes caused by the intake of glucose. Symptoms correspond to period when serum potassium is low and are relieved by taking potassium chloride. In considering the cause of a low serum potassium associated with paralysis, attention must be given to a hormonal condition, 'aldosteronism', that may be caused by a small adenoma of the adrenal gland (Conn & Louis, 1956). This disturbance may cause renal damage, hence the condition may falsely be regarded as chronic nephritis. (Figure from Aitken, Allott, Castleden & Walker, 1937, as modified by S. Wright, 1945)

The action potentials that can be recorded from such myotonic muscles are of brief duration and similar in size to those that occur in muscular fibrillation (Fig. 1.20). They appear, therefore, to be caused by the inco-ordinate contraction of individual muscle fibres rather than motor units. Quite apart from this effect, on relaxation there may be widespread spasm that spreads to musculature not previously involved: 'it is clear that simple relaxation of the grasp of the hand can alone set up an involuntary spasm in the forearm of whole limb, in flexors and extensors alike, more powerful than the original movement. . . . Such spasms are, in fact, the chief disability, for they are responsible for the sudden immobilisation of part or whole of the musculature which temporarily disables the patient' (Adams, Denny-Brown & Pearson, 1953). It has been supposed that this widespread spasm is a reflex initiated by abnormal proprioceptive discharges in the prime movers. Because of this constant overaction the muscles hypertrophy. In males the appearance, if not performance, may be Herculean.

Myotonia also occurs with a form of myopathy that develops in adult life, *dystrophia myotonica*. The reactions of the muscles appear to be similar to those in Thomsen's disease, showing defective accommodation; in response to a constant current a maintained contraction, rather than a twitch at 'make' and 'break', is the rule (Adie & Greenfield, 1923).

Somewhat similar disturbances may be found in muscles partaking in *muscular cramps* for other reasons. 'In true muscular cramps, parts of a contracting muscle will begin to show bursts of discharge at rates as high as 300 a second, and the disordered type of excitation rapidly spreads to affect more and more of the muscle fibers. . . . In such muscles spontaneous twitching of one or more fasciculi is common during repose, and the variable action potential of such twitches indicates that an irritable focus is present in the terminal branching of a motor unit, yet involves a varying extent of its network' (Adams, Denny-Brown & Pearson, 1953).

Disturbances may also arise in the muscles themselves. In *familial periodic paralysis* attacks of extreme weakness may be provoked by the administration of carbohydrate or by insulin. In either case potassium ions migrate intracellularly, and as a result the serum concentration falls (Fig. 1.21). During an attack the muscles are inexcitable to all forms of electrical stimuli. Muscular paralysis may occasionally occur in chronic nephritis, for the failure of the renal tubules may lead to an excessive loss of potassium salts in the urine.

Adams, Denny-Brown & Pearson (1953) in the preface to their treatise on *Diseases of Muscle* state that 'in our experience the problems presented by muscular diseases constantly lead us back to basic anatomic and physiologic considerations'. The data that have been presented in this chapter may serve to illuminate this remark.

D

CHAPTER 2

SOMATIC SENSIBILITY

Rather, indeed, than to a mosaic may the skin be likened to a sheet of water wherein grow water-plants, some sunken and some floating. An object thrown upon the surface moves the foliage commensurately with the violence of its impact, its dimensions, and with their propinquity to its place of incidence. Where the foliage grows densely, not a pebble striking the surface but will meet some leaf ; and beyond that or those directly struck, a number will be indirectly disturbed before equilibrium of the surface is re-established.—SHERRINGTON (1900).

THE LAW OF SPECIFIC NERVE ENERGIES

In making a study of the integrated activity of the nervous system it is logical to begin with the sensory receptors, for it is here that the stimulus, which initiates and controls so much of nervous activity, impinges on the nervous system. The development, both in ontogeny and phylogeny, of progressively more complex neural mechanisms, each of which influences and controls the activity of the more primitive neurone links, encouraged the notion that activity comes from within, or from what Hughlings Jackson called the highest level. In fact, without information obtained from sensory receptors, the most highly developed neural organisation is of no value.

Activation of an organism depends, therefore, on the receipt of stimulation. A stimulus may be defined as any change in the environment which is capable of exciting living tissue. In this regard we should remember that the environment is composed not only of the world outside us, but also of the world within. Alterations in the partial pressure of carbon dioxide in the alveoli of the lungs, or a rise in the blood pressure, or a change in the pH of the digestive juices, all constitute a change in the environment from the point of view of the nervous system. This inner world Claude Bernard described as the *milieu intérieur* in contrast to the *milieu*

34

extérieur with which we are more familiar. In the physiological laboratory we tend to use electrical stimuli for experimental work because they are easily handled, measured and controlled, but under more natural conditions such stimuli are rarely encountered.

In a primitive organism such as amoeba the whole of the body surface is excitable, for a touch at any point will cause the organism to withdraw ; we cannot distinguish any part of the body surface as being especially sensitive. With the development of more complex nervous mechanisms, however, certain structures have become morphologically distinct, and they serve a special function, namely, the receipt of stimuli from the environment. It is these structures and no others which are excited by stimuli, and which are called sensory receptors.

Sensory receptors can be variously classified. One such division is into :

(1) Exteroceptors dealing with the external environment. These can be subdivided into (*a*) the special senses and (*b*) the skin receptors.

(2) Interoceptors dealing with stimulation from within, also subdivided into (*a*) proprioceptors conveying information from muscle, tendons and joints, (*b*) visceroceptors carrying information from the viscera, and (*c*) specialised receptors such as baroreceptors, chemoreceptors and thermo-receptors which are sensitive to such things as change in the blood pressure, blood sugar and the temperature of the blood.

An alternative classification is into :

(1) Somatoceptors with subdivisions (*a*) exteroceptors and (*b*) proprio-ceptors, and

(2) Visceroceptors including the specialised chemoreceptors.

Both the anatomy and physiology of cutaneous sensibility have long been the subject of controversy. Since the time of Galen, touch, warmth and cold have been recognised as specific sensations, but pain was regarded, not as a separate sensation, but as a feeling state dependent on over-stimulation of other sensory modalities. Charles Bell (1811) first enunciated the Law of Specific Nerve Energies, but it was elaborated by Müller (1826), by whose name it is usually known. The law states that stimulation of a sensory end-organ gives rise to the specific sensation of that end-organ and to no other, no matter what the nature of the stimulus. Following this, Blix (1884), von Frey (1895) and Goldscheider (1898) studied sensation in the skin, and demonstrated that it is punctate in character (Fig. 2.1). By applying stimuli so as to stimulate one point on the skin at a time, it is possible to show that all regions are

not equally sensitive, but that certain 'spots' are particularly sensitive to one form of stimulation.   Another early finding was that
warmth applied to a cold spot gives rise to a sensation of cold ; a
finding that indicates that the type of sensation set up depends not
upon the nature of the stimulus but upon that of the spot.   In

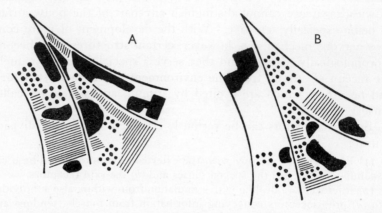

FIG. 2.1.—Showing cold spots A, and hot spots B, within an area on the palm of
the hand.   The sensation in each case was most intense in the black areas,
less intense in the lined and mildest in the dotted areas.   In the blank portions
no sensations were aroused.   To discover all the spots that can react to cold
it is necessary to make several examinations of the same area.   When this is
done it is observed that the localisation of the spots from which a cold reaction
can be obtained is very constant.   Some cold spots can be detected only when
the skin is warm.   (Bing & Skouby, 1949.)   After Goldsheider, reproduced from
Best & Taylor, 1939

considering the punctate nature of cutaneous innervation it is
important to bear in mind the three-dimensional nature of the
problem.   By the use of fine sharp needles Woollard and his pupils
were able to set up various sensations and to measure the depth at
which these were most readily aroused :

Table 2

Pressure	2-2·5 mm.
Warmth	1·75-2·5 mm.
Touch	from surface—2 mm.
Cold	1-1·5 mm.
1st Pain	0·25-0·5 mm.
(see pp. 43 and 64)	
2nd Pain	1 mm.
(see pp. 43 and 64)	

MORPHOLOGY OF CUTANEOUS AFFERENT ENDINGS IN RELATION
TO FUNCTION

To understand the problems of cutaneous sensation it is important to bear in mind certain anatomical features (*vide* Woollard *et al.*, 1940). In the skin are two nerve plexuses; the first lies deeply

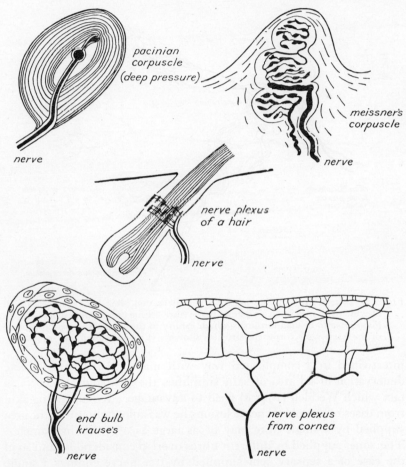

FIG. 2.2.—Diagrammatic representation of various types of cutaneous sensory receptors that have been described. (From Starling, 1941)

and in it nerve fibres approaching from all directions interweave in a complicated network. There is, however, no evidence of structural continuity between adjacent fibres. From this plexus fibres arise that pass towards the surface and participate in another nerve net lying in the upper part of the dermis. From this superficial nerve net free nerve terminals arise. Fibres may also arise from the deep net to innervate certain specialised sensory endings (*vide infra*).

In the case of free nerve endings, each fibre by branching eventually supplies an area of skin that is roughly circular. It is difficult to follow a single fibre through serial sections, for it is liable to be

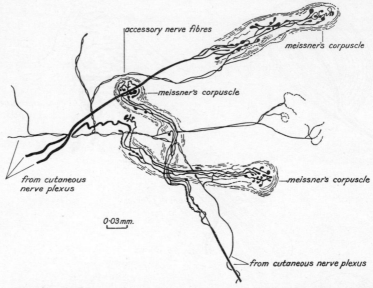

FIG. 2.3.—A scale drawing showing three closely related Meissner's corpuscles each of which is borne upon a separate nerve fibre. Fine unmyelinated nerve fibres giving rise to beaded terminals which ramify in the connective tissue capsule of the Meissner's corpuscles are also shown. (From Weddell, G., 1941 *b*)

intertwined in a complicated way with many others. Incomplete denervation of an area of skin simplifies the histological picture, a fact which Weddell (1941 *a*) used to advantage. By examining skin from cases of peripheral nerve lesions he was able to show that the area supplied by a single fibre may be as large as 0·75 cm. in diameter. The zones supplied by different fibres overlap considerably, and so in the case of a sensory spot supplied by free nerve endings a single spot is connected with more than one nerve fibre. In the case of the specialised nerve endings a single nerve fibre may, after its passage through the deep nerve plexus, supply only one receptor, or it may, as in the case of Merkel's discs, branch and supply several. The specialised receptors tend to occur in clusters, so, as with the free endings, a stimulus no matter how restricted is liable to excite several nerve fibres.

It used to be supposed that each type of skin sensibility was served by a category of sensory receptors that could clearly be separated on morphological grounds from all others. Von Frey in 1895 put forward the relationships which he believed existed in this way. In differentiating receptors in histological preparations of the skin it is often found that a particular ending does not fall clearly into one of the orthodox categories (Fig. 2.2). Nevertheless, before proceeding to discuss these problems in detail it is desirable to list the 'classical' relationships between ending and function :

Table 3

Receptor	Description	Supposed Function
Meissner's corpuscles	Spiral termination of sensory fibre in connective tissue capsule	Light touch
Merkel's discs	Cup-shaped disc-like structures	Light touch
Basket endings	Ramifications of nerve fibre around hair follicle	Light touch
Krause's end-bulbs	Complicated nerve-fibre network in spherical capsule	Cold
Ruffini's corpuscles	Encapsulated endings with a simpler network than in Krause's end-bulbs	Warmth
Free nerve endings	Lie just below epidermis or in its basal layer	Pain

Some of these relationships may well be true. Thus it is reasonable to believe that the endings around the shafts of hair follicles are disturbed when the hairs are displaced. It seems essential to postulate the sensitivity of free nerve endings to painful stimuli, for the number of encapsulated endings would not by themselves account for the closely packed distribution of pain spots. Again the paucity of warmth and cold spots would suggest that these modalities would be served by endings which also would be relatively sparse. Nevertheless there are clearly dangers in pushing such correlations too far. Are we justified in saying that Meissner's corpuscles are touch receptors *because* they are most plentiful in regions specially concerned with tactile appreciation, such as the hands, feet and face ?

How could the morphological basis of cutaneous sensation be placed on a more satisfactory footing so as to establish such relationships beyond question ?   It is clearly necessary to perfect the methods of testing the sensibility of the skin.   In clinical work, where time is often short, it may be necessary to restrict a sensory examination to simple procedures : touch, for instance, may be tested by a wisp of cotton-wool.   Such methods are inadequate for research on cutaneous sensation.   Von Frey introduced the use of hairs held in a wooden holder at one end and graded as to the weight needed to cause bending.   Von Frey's hairs (now often nylon strands) may be used to test touch and pain sensibility.   In the study of cutaneous sensation it may be noted that much has been learnt by the very intelligent use of very simple tools.   The introduction into clinical neurology of precise methods for mapping the skin was due to the efforts of Henry Head and Gordon Holmes (1911).   To establish the function of different types of receptor it is necessary first to map the skin as to its sensibility and then to remove ('biopsy') the piece for histological examination.

Investigations along these lines have been made by a number of observers since 1885.   Pendleton (1928) reviewed the earlier work and was himself unable to see Krause's end-bulbs under cold spots. His work points to the conclusion that the *unencapsulated nerve endings must serve not only pain but other modalities also.*

Weddell also made investigations along these lines.   His first studies seemed to support classical views.   Thus he mapped a cold spot on the forearm and then excised the piece of skin (Weddell, 1941 *a*).   Under the spot lay a group of structures which he identified as Krause's end-bulbs. Weddell also examined skin excised from patients with nerve injuries. In skin from an area in which a patient had perceived pain only he found a nerve net with naked nerve fibrils as terminals and no other receptors, whereas in skin from a touch-sensitive area he found specific receptors as well.   Weddell (1941 *b*) also thought that he had shown that a touch spot was associated with a small cluster of Meissner's corpuscles.

Weddell later was forced to the conclusion that his earlier results were due to technical imperfections in the methods of histological examination.   Thus encapsulated endings have been described in the cornea, but when this structure is examined in the living state, using illumination from a slit-lamp or by the use of phase-contrast microscopy, free nerve endings only can be discerned (Weddell & Zander, 1950).   In agreement with other workers (*vide* Gilmer & Haythorn, 1941), Sinclair, Weddell & Zander (1952) found that areas of skin may be sensitive to touch, warmth, cold and pain but contain no specialised receptors.   Hagen, Knoche, Sinclair and Weddell (1953) investigated skin from the finger, lip and abdomen. They noted that the hair-bearing areas had no specialised receptors. The hairless (glabrous) areas, on the other hand, had organised receptors in addition to the diffuse nerve net and the basket endings of the hair-bearing areas. The authors, however, were unable to classify these receptors according to the traditional morphological groups, but considered there was a smooth gradation from a simple to a complex structure. They believe that the morphological criteria, which were thought to distinguish one type of receptor from another, were artefacts produced by the histological methods used in examination.

On the basis of these and other observations, Lele, Weddell and Williams (1954) suggested that the free nerve endings in the skin are universal receptors, which respond by a burst of action potentials to all kinds of stimuli. The central differentiation between the various types of stimuli depends on the pattern of response from the sensory endings. Thus, they suggest that touch, prick, itch and sharp pain arise when a small number of fibres in any one stratum of the skin discharge simultaneously ; the lowest frequency of discharge gives the sensation of touch, the highest the sensation of sharp pain. When the endings in the superficial layers of the skin discharge and those in the deep layers are quiescent, cold is felt ; if the superficial endings are resting, while deep endings are discharging, warmth is perceived. They thus deny the validity of the doctrine of specific nerve energies, believing that it is the spatial pattern of discharge from sensory endings that determines sensory quality.

The histological findings are certainly of great importance but it must be borne in mind that in hairless skin (*e.g.* palm of hand) there certainly exist specialised encapsulated endings. Whilst it may be difficult to classify these structures along traditional lines, the simplest structures differ widely from the most complex. It is not unreasonable to suggest that this differentiation of structure has functional significance. Further, in deep tissues single receptors have been isolated and demonstrably react to a specific variety of stimulus. Naturally the sensory organisation of deep structures may be of a different type than that of the skin, but it is clear that the concept of the specificity of nerve endings cannot be denied for the body as a whole. In such discussions the case of the retina may be cited. There is very good physiological evidence for the existence of more than one category of cone, and whilst all cones are not structurally identical, they do not fall into separate categories on histological examination. Current methods of microscopy give limited information about the chemical and physical properties of the structures that are examined, and the newer techniques of histochemistry and electron microscopy do not appear to have been applied to the problems of the organisation of sensory receptors in the skin. Sperry (in Weiss, 1950, pp. 235-36) has pointed out that the end-organ tissues must 'possess a refined chemical differentiation far beyond what is visibly manifest'. He also points out that 'Neuronal specificity is presumed to arise by processes of cell differentiation similar to those that cause developmental differentiation in other tissues. In the nervous system, however, the result frequently is more subtle and involves no visible distinctions.'

CUTANEOUS PAIN AND TEMPERATURE SENSIBILITY

It has often been supposed that pain may be aroused by excessive stimulation of any type of cutaneous sensory receptor. Thus when a metal rod, heated beyond a certain temperature, is applied to the skin the initial sensation of warmth is followed by pain. Similarly an electrical shock applied to a touch spot will, if increased sufficiently in strength, become painful. Observations such as these do not, however, establish the 'over-stimulation' theory, for with increase of stimulus, neighbouring receptors may become involved; furthermore, a specialised receptor may have associated with it a naked nerve ending (Woollard et al., 1940).

By recording from the cutaneous nerve of a frog it is possible to pick up action potentials in response to touching the skin (Adrian, Cattell & Hoagland, 1931). These endings may also be excited by a jet of air, and if the jet is rhythmically interrupted, potentials may be discharged at a frequency much higher (e.g. 250-300/sec.) than is customary. If such a stimulus is applied to a living frog the animal responds but little, if at all. Although the ending has been 'over-stimulated', there is nothing to suggest reactions appropriate to pain. Other evidence that also favours the view that pain should be regarded as a separate modality of sensation comes from a study of situations where pain alone can be perceived. The centre of the cornea may approximate to this condition, which may be found also in skin that has lost a part of its innervation as a result of a peripheral nerve lesion (see, however, Lele & Weddell, 1956). Again regions of the body may be found from which pain cannot be elicited and yet are still responsive as regards other modalities. In the healthy adult the inside of the cheek opposite the second upper molar tooth is insensitive to pain, whilst with neurological lesions of the central afferent pathways similar insensitivity to pain is often found when sensitivity to tactile stimulation is preserved and may appear to be normal (see p. 58).

The evidence taken as a whole certainly supports Müller's doctrine of specific nerve energies, but the quality of pain may yet depend to some degree on the intensity of stimulation of a given pathway. Bishop (1943) studied the problem by exciting spots on the skin with an electric spark. He found that a given stimulus on repetition might gradually become painful whilst a single application was painless. In this latter case, as the same shock was being applied, the spread of current to other areas will be the same as with the repetitive stimulation.

After damage to a peripheral nerve, pain elicited from the skin may take on an unusually unpleasant quality. Much has been written on this subject. One view is that the arrival of impulses along fast fibres serving other modalities prepares the nerve centres for the receipt of pain signals. If pain signals arrive without warning their effects are exaggerated ; an unusual pattern of discharge has greater arousal value than a combination of signals to which the organism is accustomed. Gordon & Whitteridge (1943) measured the latency for the blocking of the alpha rhythm when painful stimuli were applied to the skin. In cases of nerve lesions with hyperpathia they found that the latency might be normal, indicating that some fast pain fibres were intact. Here again it seems necessary to modify to some extent a rigid interpretation of Müller's law.

When dealing with the mechanism of pain it is important to consider *latency*. Lewis & Pochin (1937) observed, as earlier workers also had, that when a needle was thrust into the skin there arose an *immediate*, followed by a *delayed*, pain. The interval between these two varieties of the sensation was greatest at the periphery of the limbs, whilst on the back close to the vertebrae the effects cannot be distinguished. This Lewis & Pochin (1937) took to indicate that two separate sets of peripheral nerve fibres, having different conduction velocities, were involved (see p. 65).

The way in which the sensory structures in the skin indicate the *temperature* of the skin surface has been the subject of many theories. Weber believed that a rising temperature was needed to stimulate the warmth endings, and a falling temperature to stimulate the cold receptors. Experiment shows, however, that when cold skin reaches equilibrium, and maintains a steady temperature, it still feels cold, suggesting that cold receptors are still discharging.

Moreover, when skin has been vigorously cooled by a cold object which is then removed, the skin continues to feel cold for a considerable time after its temperature has begun to rise.

Hering (1877) propounded another theory to overcome these difficulties. He believed that the skin acted as a thermometer, responding to increase above a standard as warmth, and decrease below it as cold, but that as the temperature rose or fell, the standard adjusted itself by rising and falling too. He did not explain how this alteration was achieved. The rise in standard as a result of heating meant that the cold standard must rise also, and Hering suggested that one type of receptor served both warmth and cold. Another theory was that of Ebbecke (1917); he supposed that it was not the temperature as such, but the temperature gradient across the tissue, that was the effective stimulus.

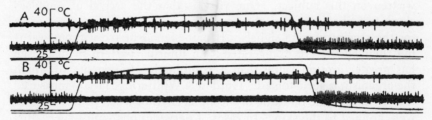

FIG. 2.4.—Simultaneous recording from a warm fibre in the chorda tympani (upper tracing of each pair) and a cold fibre in the lingual nerve (lower tracing of each pair) during a change of temperature from 23° C. to 38·5° C. and back. (From Dodt, E., & Zotterman, Y., 1952 a)

The most significant information as to thermoreception has come from the work of Zotterman and his colleagues. They have recorded the activity of single nerve fibres and their work enables, for the first time, a satisfactory explanation to be given of some of the earlier observations made on human subjects (*vide* Hensel & Zotterman, 1951 a, b, c and d, and Dodt & Zotterman, 1952 a, b). Two types of thermoreceptor exist in the tongue of the cat—a preparation that has certain technical advantages for this work. The *cold* fibres discharged continuously when the tongue was maintained steadily at a temperature within the range of 10 to 40° C. This discharge attained a maximum of about 10 impulses per second between 30 and 32° C., and decreased at higher and lower temperatures. There was, however, a second peak between 10 and 15° C. (Fig. 2.5). Heating the tongue surface at temperatures of 45 to 50° C. produced a further discharge in cold fibres (Fig. 2.6). This last observation accounts for the phenomenon of paradoxical cold, which had been noted previously, whereby heating a 'cold' spot gives rise to the sensation of cold. *Warmth* fibres responded at a lower frequency than cold fibres, and the discharge was somewhat arhythmic. Different fibres attained a maximum frequency of 1·5 to 3·7 impulses per second when the tongue was at a temperature of 37·5 to 40° C. ; the range over which they discharged was 20 to 47° C.

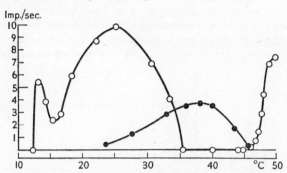

FIG. 2.5.—Graph showing the frequency of the steady discharge of a single cold fibre (open circles) and of a single warm fibre (filled circles) when the receptors were exposed to constant temperatures over the range of 10-15° C. (From Zotterman, Y., 1953)

Suddenly lowering the temperature produced a rapid rise in the frequency of impulses in the cold fibres, up to 140 impulses per second, which then fell to take up a new level of discharge at the maintained temperature (Fig. 2.4). The greater the drop in temperature, the higher became the frequency of the temporary increase in the discharge rate. Raising the temperature stopped all impulses in the cold fibres for a period, after which they reappeared at the

FIG. 2.6.—Recording showing the paradoxical discharge of a cold fibre during a rise of temperature from 38·5° C to 50° C. Time 20 c/s. (From Dodt, E., & Zotterman, Y., 1952 *b*)

new level. A rise in temperature produced a sudden increase in the discharge from the warmth fibres, the size of which was determined by the rate and extent of the elevation.

In the steady discharge of the two sorts of endings lies the explanation of the fact that warmth or cold may still be appreciated when thermal equilibrium has been reached. On the other hand, the adaptation that these endings showed explains how it is that the 'physiological zero' may be shifted some degrees, as Hering pointed out (*vide supra*). The shape of the response curve for cold receptors also explains how it is that after the skin has been substantially cooled the sensation of cold persists as the tissue is heating up.

Interesting quantitative studies of the sensibility of the human skin to alterations of temperature have been made by O'Connor & McCarthy (1952). They immersed one forearm of their subject in a water bath that was kept at a fixed temperature. The other forearm was in a bath the temperature of which was adjustable. A flat-bottomed copper tube containing water of known temperature was applied to a selected area of

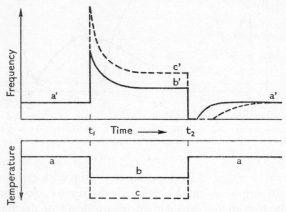

Fig. 2.7.—Graph showing the discharge of a single cold fibre at different changes of temperature. At a, the temperature and the frequency of discharge, a', are both steady. At t1 the temperature falls, causing a rise in discharge which then settles to a new steady level, b'. At t2 the temperature rises and the discharge ceases, gradually reappearing until it attains the former level. (From Zotterman, 1953)

the first forearm and served to give a standard sensation of warmth or cold. The copper tube was applied to the corresponding area of the second forearm and the temperature of the water that it contained was adjusted until the sensation matched the standard set up on the other side. The temperature difference needed to create a standard sensation of warmth fell as the temperature of the limb was raised within the range of 22 to 44° C. The cold sensitivity behaved in a more complex way, rising with increasing skin temperature to 26° C., then falling to a minimum at 31° C. and rising again to a new maximum at 34°, from which it fell steadily to the end of the range. These results show that as in the case of the cat's tongue so in the case of the human skin the effect of temperature on the cold receptors is complex, that on warm receptors relatively simple. It would appear likely that the thermoreceptors are rather similar in these two different tissues.

VARIETIES OF RECEPTOR AND SENSIBILITY : DEEP TISSUES

Tissues deep to the skin also contain sensory receptors which are of different morphological structure. Apart from proprioception there appear to be two modalities of sensation in the deep tissues, pain and pressure.

Deep pain, in contrast to pain aroused from the skin, is a dull, diffuse ache. It is subserved by *naked nerve terminals* of the same appearance as those seen in the dermis, but they form a much less dense nerve net than that seen below the skin, many fibres being isolated from their neighbours. Pressure is served by *Pacinian corpuscles* (Plate 2). These large structures, discernible with the naked eye, are found widely distributed in the body. They occur in deeper layers of the dermis, in tendon sheaths, fascia of muscle, periosteum, the serous membranes and the mesentery. They consist of a central core containing a thick myelinated nerve fibre with an expanded end. The core is surrounded by concentric layers of fibrous tissue so that in cross section it has a lamellated appearance. Such a structure might be adapted to subjecting the nerve terminal to stretch when pressure was applied to one side of the corpuscle.

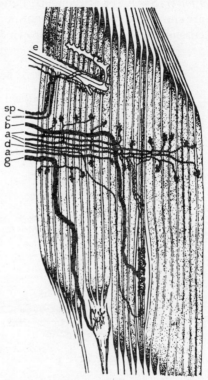

FIG. 2.8.—Diagram illustrating the sensory and motor innervation of mammalian muscle. a, Motor fibres. b, Fibre leading to annulo-spiral ending. d, Fibre leading to flower-spray ending. g, Fibre leading to Golgi tendon organ. sp, Sympathetic plexus. c, Myelinated pain fibre. e, Blood vessel. (Reproduced from Creed *et al.*, 1932)

The tendons of muscles have special end-organs, the *Golgi corpuscles*, associated with them. These endings consist of an encapsulated fibrous mass within which a nerve fibre ramifies. In the muscles themselves complex end-organs called *muscle spindles* are found. Each spindle is formed from a group of 1 to 12 muscle fibres

of narrow diameter. These fibres are enclosed at one zone in a connective tissue capsule; they are therefore referred to as being *intrafusal*. Each muscle spindle is supplied by a large afferent nerve fibre
that ends by twisting around the bellies of the intrafusal fibres (*Annulo-
Spiral* or Primary ending). In addition there may also be one or two
Flower-Spray (or 'Secondary') endings on the fibrous capsule that
are connected with finer afferent nerve fibres. (For more detailed discussion see Adams, Denny-Brown & Pearson, 1953, and Granit, 1955.)

DISCHARGES OF AFFERENT ENDINGS (*vide* Granit, 1955)

The difficulties of histological differentiation of endings in the
skin is one reason why many of the principles governing the activity
of afferent receptors were
established in the first place by
studies of fibres coming from
deep tissues. Adrian (1926)
recorded the action potential
in the sciatic nerve of the
frog when the gastrocnemius
muscle was subjected to varying degrees of stretch. He
applied various weights to the
tendon of the muscle, and
observed that the amplitude
of the nerve action potential
remained unchanged. The
frequency of the action potentials, on the other hand,
showed great change, for the
heavier the weight applied to
the tendon, and hence the
greater the degree of stretch
of the muscle, the greater the
frequency of discharge. The
frequency of discharge of impulses in the sensory nerve
was directly proportional to
the degree of stretch of the

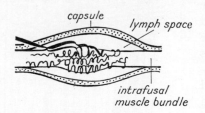

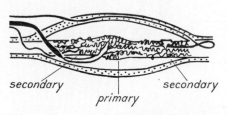

FIG. 2.9.—Afferent endings of muscle
spindles. The muscle fibres extend in
both directions far beyond the nuclear
bag—the region shown in these figures.
Cuajunco (1932) showed that the afferent
fibres of some muscle spindles are distributed to the spinal cord through more
than one dorsal root—they are 'pluriseg-
mentally innervated'. The muscle fibres
associated with the spindle receive a motor
innervation by which the sensitivity of
the afferent endings is adjusted. (After
Barker, reproduced from Granit, 1955)

muscle. Adrian & Zotterman (1926 *a*) repeated these observations in relation to a single stretch receptor. They used the

sterno-cutaneous muscle of the frog, which has only three or four stretch receptors, and by shaving down the muscle obtained a preparation containing a single receptor. They confirmed that the degree of stretch applied to a receptor has no effect on the size of the resultant action potential in the sensory nerve, but alters the frequency of discharge.

Adrian & Zotterman (1926 *b*) extended these observations to cutaneous sensation. They recorded action potentials from the plantar digital nerve of the cat, and showed that a light contact or pressure on the pad of the foot caused a discharge in the nerve. Increasing the pressure caused the discharge rate to rise, though the size of action potential was un-affected. They were thus able to confirm that the action potential in a sensory fibre obeys the 'All-or-None' law, and that its amplitude is in no way related to the intensity of the stimulus which evokes it. It is the frequency of discharge that is a function of the stimulus intensity, and not the size of the action potential.

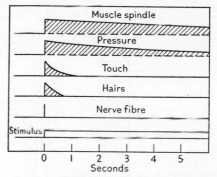

FIG. 2.10.—The response to a continued stimulus applied to a nerve fibre and to different types of receptors. Note the different rates of adaptation. (From Adrian, E. D., 1928)

The differences observed between the response of touch and stretch receptors illustrated a further principle governing the activity of sensory receptors, namely, that of *adaptation*. When a muscle spindle is stretched it begins to discharge and continues to do so indefinitely until the stretch ceases. When, on the other hand, a touch receptor is stimulated, there is an initial burst of action potentials, but, even though the touch is maintained, the discharge rapidly ceases. The touch receptor has adapted to the presence of the stimulus. Adrian (1928) illustrated (Fig. 2.10) the different rates of adaptation for the various receptors. Pressure receptors and pain endings, like those for stretch, adapt slowly in contrast to the rapid adaptation of touch. These differences serve an obvious biological purpose. As long as a muscle is under stretch, sensory information must be supplied to the spinal cord in order that a sustained response to the stretch can be maintained through motor fibres. Likewise, as long as a noxious stimulus is impinging on the body, so long

E

must there be pain to warn the organism of the threat to its integrity. Adaptation allows small changes to be registered, for the nerve fibres are not burdened with the need to respond to steadily maintained conditions. As the information that can be transmitted along a nerve fibre is limited by peak discharge frequency, this may be important. It is due to adaptation of tactile endings that a person is so rarely aware of the contact of his clothes.

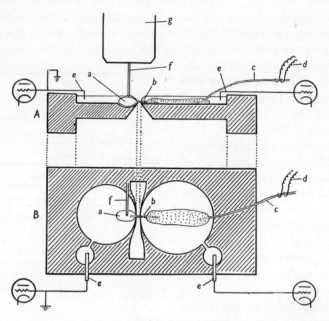

FIG. 2.11.—Diagram of the apparatus for recording potential in a single sensory receptor. A, Transverse section. B, Plan. a, Pacinian corpuscle. b, First node of Ranvier. c, Mesenteric nerve. d, Electrodes for anti-dromic stimulation. e, Recording electrodes. f, Rod for mechanical stimulation. g, Mechanical stimulator. (From Gray, J. A. B., & Sato, M., 1953)

The intensity of a stimulus is signalled to the sensorium in other ways besides the frequency of the action potentials. Thus, if a series of stimuli of the same duration is applied to a receptor, and the intensity of the stimuli are progressively increased, it may be observed that the duration of the discharge of action potentials after cessation of the stimulus will also increase. A stronger stimulus will also increase the number of receptors that discharge or, as it is said, are *recruited*. It is often found that the central effects of receptors from a wide area are additive; there may be 'central summation'.

A final principle governing the activity of sensory receptors is that of *accommodation*. If a stimulus is to excite a sensory receptor, it must at least produce a minimum degree of change in the receptor; furthermore, this degree of change must exceed a minimum rate. Thus, if the degree of change in the receptor is too small, no excitation will result; if the degree of change is great, but is achieved too slowly, there may be no resulting activation of the nerve fibre. The activity of a receptor may be considered as being due to a

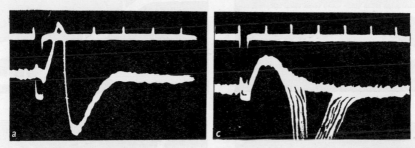

FIG. 2.12.— Separation of the phases in a receptor potential produced by mechanical stimulation. (*Left*) fresh preparation; (*right*) after procaine. The second phase has been lost but the first node of Ranvier is still excited (third phase) during some of the trials. The tracings represent approximately 20 records superimposed. The top trace signals the stimulant and 1 msec.-time intervals. (Reproduced from Gray, J. A. B., & Sato, M., 1953)

shift of ions across its surface. Deformation of the surface by physical agents precipitates such a shift, but there is a constant tendency to restore equilibrium. If, therefore, a stimulus is to cause a receptor to discharge, it must produce a shift of ions of sufficient magnitude and speed to exceed the equilibratory forces. If the rate of change is too slow, the receptor will accommodate to the change and will not discharge.

Though these various principles governing the activity of sensory receptors are well established, until recently little was known about the way in which the receptors initiate an action potential in a sensory nerve. Katz (1950), Alvarez-Buylla & Ramirez de Arellano (1953) and Gray & Sato (1953) have recorded the action potential in the sensory axone close to the receptor. Gray & Sato developed an ingenious experimental method (Fig. 2.11) and analysed this action potential. They utilised a Pacinian corpuscle which they stimulated mechanically with a rod, while recording the potential change between the corpuscle and its sensory

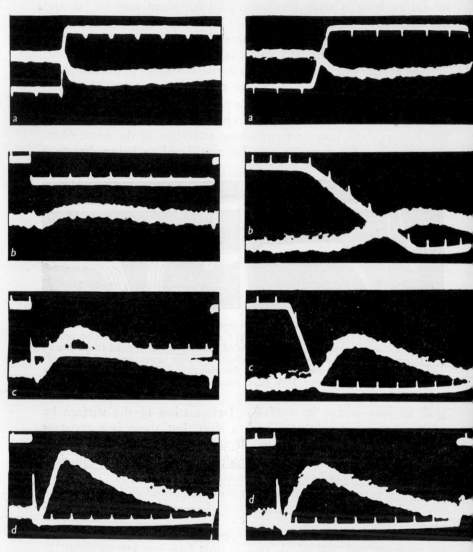

FIG. 2.13.—Change of receptor potential with increasing stimulus strength. a, is the effect of crystal movement recorded photoelectrically. b, c and d are records of receptor potential. Time marker gives 1 msec. intervals and also indicates stimulus strength by its displacement. (Reproduced from Gray, J. A. B., and Sato, M., 1953)

FIG. 2.14.—Change of receptor potential wit increasing rate of change of pressure. is crystal movement only, recorded photo electrically. b, c and d are records o receptor potential. Time marker grap (1 msec.) divisions indicate the strengt and rate of change of the stimulus. (Re produced from Gray, J. A. B., & Sato, M 1953)

nerve, after the first node of Ranvier. They found that the compound potential thus obtained has three components :

(1) The potential from the receptor itself ;
(2) That from the termination of the sensory nerve fibre in the corpuscle ; and
(3) The activity produced by the first node of Ranvier.

They showed that by treating the preparation with procaine or by removing sodium they could eliminate components (2) and (3) and leave the receptor potential in isolation (Fig. 2.12). To obtain the receptor potential a certain minimal stimulus was required, and thereafter increasing either the amplitude (Fig. 2.13) or the velocity (Fig. 2.14) of the mechanical deformation of the surface of the capsule increased the amplitude of the receptor potential until a maximum was reached, after which further increase of the stimulus was ineffective in producing more change. Increasing either the amplitude or velocity of deformation increased the rate of rise of the receptor potential as well as its amplitude. Repetitive stimulation correctly spaced would summate to give a potential of greater amplitude (Fig. 2.15), but if the stimuli followed one another too closely, there would be depression, as the second stimulus fell within the relative refractory period of the first.

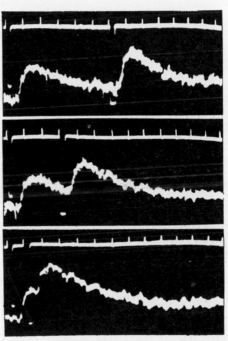

FIG. 2.15.—Summation of receptor potentials. Time marker in 1 msec. intervals also signals the stimuli. (Reproduced from Gray, J. A. B., & Sato, M., 1953)

The receptor potential was always of the same polarity irrespective of whether the stimulus was being applied to, or removed from, the receptor.

The second component in the compound potential, that produced in the nerve-fibre terminal, appeared abruptly when the receptor potential reached approximately one-tenth of its maximum. This second component immediately assumed its maximum value and, in contrast to the receptor potential, it did not undergo any further increase in amplitude with stronger stimulation. It thus obeyed the 'All-or-None' law, showing the characteristics of activity seen in nerve fibres.

Though the recording and analysis of these potentials have been a great achievement, their mechanism of production is still hypothetical. The most acceptable theory is that the surface of the receptor acts as a polarised membrane. Application of a current to the receptor, or distortion of its surface by mechanical stimulation, alters the permeability of the surface membrane, and allows a flow of ions. Potential change is thereby produced, and when it reaches a certain value will initiate a similar change in the attached sensory fibre, and so produce a nerve impulse.

THE ACTIVITY OF RECEPTORS IN MUSCLES AND
JOINTS : VIBRATION SENSIBILITY

The type of activity shown by the sensory receptors in muscle which have already been described (p. 47) was extensively studied by Matthews (1933). He identified various types of response ('A1', 'A2', 'B' and 'C').

A1 Fibres discharged whilst the muscle was being stretched and showed slow adaptation. If the motor nerve to the muscle was stimulated the discharge ceased during the twitch. This finding suggested that the fibre was connected with a flower-spray ending.

[Kuffler, Hunt & Quilliam (1951) were unable to identify fibres of this type, but this failure may perhaps have been due to technical reasons. At all events the subject is involved : a detailed discussion of the problems will be found in Granit (1955).]

A2 Fibres were also slowly adapting and discharged in response to passive stretching of the muscle. When the motor fibres to the muscle were stimulated the spindle ceased discharging, as did the A1 type. On the other hand, with shocks sufficiently strong to stimulate the motor fibres supplying the *intrafusal* muscle fibres, the discharge again started, which did not occur with the A1 category. This behaviour suggests that the fibre was connected with an intrafusal ending. If the small motor axones to the intrafusal fibres are stimulated, a discharge may appear in an ending that hitherto has been quiescent.

It is important to note that by stimulating these small fibres it is possible effectively to compensate for variations in muscle tension. Evidently a mechanism exists that enables the muscle spindle to maintain its sensitivity at widely differing muscle lengths : by the small motor fibres the range over which the A2 receptors can function is greatly extended.

B Fibres discharge in response to stretching of the muscle but, unlike those described already, their rate of firing is increased by activity of the muscle fibres. Their activity is not influenced by the small motor system supplying the intrafusal fibres of the muscle spindles. Accordingly they are believed to arise from Golgi tendon organs.

C Fibres are believed to arise from Pacinian corpuscles. Though Adrian & Umrath (1929) thought they were slowly adapting, it is now known (Gray & Matthews, 1951) that they are rapidly adapting end-organs. They respond by a rapid burst of action potentials only during movement, and cease to discharge when a new position is reached.

The sensorium receives information not only from muscles, but also from the capsules of *joints*. Thus Boyd & Roberts (1953) and Boyd (1954), employing the technique of recording from a single fibre preparation, and then excising the receptor to identify its structure, found two types of ending in the knee-joint of the cat. One was lamellated like the Pacinian corpuscle, though rather more elongated, and responded with a rapidly adapting burst of action potentials to movement in any direction. The other type of receptor was a spray type of ending, similar to the Ruffini corpuscle. These latter endings were slowly adapting, appearing to maintain their discharge indefinitely. They seemed to have a characteristic frequency of discharge for one position. If the joint was moved to a new position, these receptors gave a short rapid burst of potentials, and then settled down to discharge at a frequency characteristic of the new position. Thus any position of the joint was signalled by a characteristic frequency, and change of position by a rapid discharge from both the spray type and from the lamellated endings.

The threshold for perception of *vibration* [1] is lowest at a frequency of 200-300 cycles per second. When an oscillating bristle is applied to a touch 'spot' on the skin, or such a 'spot' is stimulated by a train of electrical sparks, a sensation of vibration is produced. When the skin is anaesthetised vibratory sensibility is impaired but not abolished (Weitz, 1939). If the skin sensation is left intact, and the deep tissues are anaesthetised, there is then a much greater loss of vibration sensibility (Newman, Doupe & Wilkins, 1939; Cosh, 1953). It seems, therefore, that receptors in both skin and deep

---

[1] More information about vibration sensibility will be found in Geldard (1953); see also p. 420.

tissues are capable of giving rise to the sensation of vibration, but that the latter are much more important in this regard. The receptors concerned are not specific for this modality, but repetitive stimulation of touch receptors in the skin, and the pressure endings in deep tissues, gives rise to the sensation of vibration. Such findings make it difficult to explain the isolated loss of vibration sense in some central lesions (*vide* Netsky, 1953). It may be, however, as Bishop (1943) has suggested in regard to touch and pain, that when impulses along a certain peripheral pathway reach a critical frequency, they are switched into different central connections. Thus, though there might be a common peripheral pathway for touch and vibration along a fibre normally subserving touch, there would be different central pathways, one of which could be damaged by disease while the other remained intact.

Fox & Klemperer (1942) studied the sense of vibration in a series of neurological patients using a device driven from the A.C. mains which produced vibration of an amplitude more readily reproducible than that obtainable with tuning-forks, the instruments usually used clinically. They found that section of spinothalamic tracts had little or no influence on the vibration threshold ; the important pathway lay in the posterior columns (see, however, Netsky, 1953). The sensibility was little affected by cortical lesions.

SENSORY FIBRES IN PERIPHERAL NERVES AND THE SPINAL CORD

The nerve action potentials produced by the various sensory receptors which have been discussed travel along the nerve fibres in peripheral nerves, and after passing through the posterior root ganglia enter the spinal cord via the posterior root. The behaviour of these action potentials in sensory nerve fibres is in no way different from that of a nerve impulse in any other type of fibre (see p. 1). The velocity of the action potential is proportional to the diameter of the nerve fibre (p. 14), and the work of Erlanger & Gasser (1930) and Gasser (1935) has shown that each sensory modality has its own particular range in the velocity spectrum. They observed that the compound action potentials obtained by stimulation of nerve trunk could have three major components which they named A, B and C, and that the A component could be further divided into alpha, beta, gamma and delta (see p. 15). The various sensory modalities which have been shown to be carried by the different fibres are :

A (myelinated): alpha—proprioception, vibration and impulses from
muscle spindles.

beta—touch, warmth

gamma—touch, cold

delta—touch, cold, pain

B (myelinated): autonomic efferent fibres

C (unmyelinated): slow pain

(Note the wide range of fibres used for tactile sensibility.)

Man in his embryological development shows a segmentation of mesodermal structures which is imposed on the spinal cord. There thus results a segmental arrangement of its afferent and efferent roots, and of the skin areas and musculature which each of these roots supplies. This segmental arrangement is best seen in the thorax and abdomen, where each nerve root supplies a narrow, more or less horizontal band of skin around the trunk. The limbs grow out as buds from the sides of the trunk and carry their segmental innervation with them. If the arm is held out horizontally from the side with the palm facing anteriorly, the remainder of the segmental pattern can then be seen, for the narrow dermatome strips run parallel to one another from above downwards. The lower limb buds arise in the same way, but the pattern is confused by subsequent rotation of the limb, so that the pre- and post-axial lines pursue a spiral course around the limb (see also p. 96).

The dermatomes in man have been studied by Head (1920), who observed the distribution of the eruption of herpes zoster, which invades the posterior root ganglion, giving rise to vesicles over the skin supplied by the affected ganglion, and by Foerster (1933), who studied the sensory changes when posterior roots were divided. The dermatomes, according to Foerster, are shown in Fig. 2.16. An important point made by Sherrington, who investigated the dermatomes in the monkey (1898 a), was that they overlapped to a considerable extent, and thus, division of one root in isolation rarely gives rise to any striking sensory loss (*vide* p. 91).

For many years diagrams of the spinal cord have often been reproduced that purport to show the routes taken by different types of sensory information in the white matter. Are these charts valid? In a particularly interesting set of observations on the cat Gaze & Gordon (1955) have obtained unexpected results. They recorded the activity of thalamic neurones in response to various varieties of stimuli applied to the body surface. By sectioning various parts of the spinal cord they arrived at the conclusion that in general all modalities can travel through all possible pathways. On the other hand, they found no evidence that any modality other than touch was mediated by the posterior columns, a finding that would fit in with the diminution, or abolition of pain sense, in man, by the operation of *lateral cordotomy*. The object of this operation is to divide the antero-lateral part of the white matter ; the efficacy of the procedure is an indication that in man, as in the cat, the main pathways serving pain do not run in the posterior columns. The operation does not abolish tactile sensitivity but small changes in threshold may be detected by the use of hairs of graded stiffness. 'We tell these patients that they will still be able to detect a mosquito when he alights, although they will not be able to feel him bite nor be annoyed by the subsequent itch' (White & Sweet, 1955).

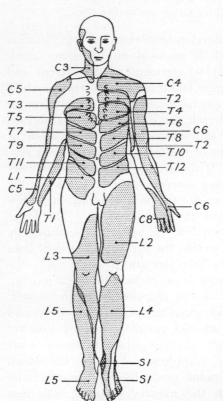

FIG. 2.16.—The dermatomes in man according to Foerster, redrawn by Lewis. (From J. F. Fulton, 1943)

White (1954) has urged that in the operation of cordotomy a fairly extensive division of the antero-lateral column should be made. Surgeons often prefer to operate on both sides of the spinal cord in order to make as complete a division of pain pathways as is practicable. Nevertheless, unilateral visceral pain may be abolished, sometimes at least, by division of the antero-lateral column on the opposite side only. Pain may sometimes persist even after bilateral cordotomy. White has recorded that after apparently satisfactory operative division muscle cramps may still be painful, burning pain may be felt in the rectum and perineum, and painful postural sensations may persist in a phantom limb. White suggests that these failures are due to pain impulses in the posterior columns, and he points out that in a conscious person pain may readily be elicited by stimulating or touching these parts of the spinal cord. The clinical evidence, therefore, suggests that the segregation of modalities in the spinal cord is less complete than was once thought.

There is evidence that fibres in both the posterior columns and in the lateral spino-thalamic tract are arranged according to their topographical connections (Fig. 2.17). Thus, in the posterior columns the fibres from the most caudal dermatomes are pushed progressively towards the mid-line by fibres entering from the more cranial dermatomes, so that in the cervical cord the fibres from the sacral region lie alongside the median raphe, and those from the lumbar, thoracic and cervical dermatomes are arranged in successive laminae from within outwards. In the spino-thalamic tracts the position is reversed, because fibres from the sacral region after crossing the cord take up a peripheral position in the tract, and the lumbar, thoracic and cervical fibres form successive layers from without inwards. Pressure

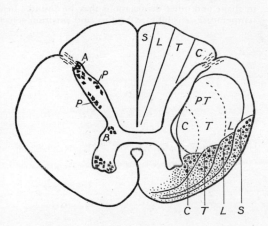

FIG. 2.17.—Cross section of the spinal cord at cervical level showing the lamination of the spino-thalamic tracts (stipled) and the posterior columns. *C*, Cervical. *T*, Thoracic. *L*, Lumbar. *S*, Sacral. *PT*, Cortico-spinal tract. (From Walker, A. E., 1940)

from an extra-medullary lesion will, therefore, tend to involve the sacral segments first and, as the lesion progresses, the sensory loss slowly spreads up the body. An intra-medullary lesion, on the other hand, expanding from within outwards, gives rise to what is known as 'sacral sparing', for it causes sensory loss in the cervical and thoracic dermatomes, but spares the sacral dermatomes until a late stage in its development. Furthermore, the enlargement of a syringomyelic cavity in the region of the central canal, where the spino-thalamic tracts cross, will cause loss of pain and temperature sensation, but spare the sense of touch, position and vibration which may in man partly travel by the posterior columns. There thus arises the so-called 'dissociated anaesthesia' of syringomyelia.[1] A fourth type of sensory disturbance is found in the Brown-Séquard syndrome and is caused by interruption of one-half of the cord. The sense of position and of vibration on the side of the lesion are lost below the level of hemisection, whereas pain and temperature sensibility are lost up to two or three segments lower on the opposite side. Owing to the interruption of descending pathways the syndrome shows signs of an upper motor neurone lesion also, on the side that has been damaged.

[1] The commonset type of disturbance in syringomyelia. The cysts are irregular in shape and other dissociations may be found—heat and cold sensation, pain and temperature sensibility, vibratory and position sensation (Netsky, 1953).

CHAPTER 3

THE APPLIED PHYSIOLOGY OF PAIN

I mention this case to point out the value and importance of recognising the precise distribution of the nerves of any part where a patient is suffering pain. I thought I might take the surface of the external ear as a pretty accurate illustration of what I intended to convey. Last July a patient came to me with earache. The pain was on the lower part of the ear—not the upper part, nor in the auditory canal. Looking at the neck, I saw a small swelling there, and the patient said, 'Oh, that is only a kernel which comes down sometimes. I have been under my surgeon's care for some time for the ear, but I am no better.' It struck me that the 'kernel', or gland, lying close to the second cervical nerve was the cause of the pain. Hemlock poultices were applied over the gland, and in a week or so the gland suppurated ; it was opened, and the painful symptoms disappeared. The patient had earache, and the symptoms were precisely expressed. There was no pain in the auditory canal supplied by the fifth nerve ; the part of the ear implicated was that connected with the auricular branch of the second cervical nerve. It was the recognition of the distribution of the nerves to the ear which gave me the opportunity of detecting the real cause of the painful symptoms.— JOHN HILTON (1863).

THE PAIN THRESHOLD

A SERIOUS difficulty encountered in studying pain is the extent to which responses to a painful stimulus depend upon the emotional state. It is necessary, therefore, to consider not only the strength of stimulus needed to produce discomfort (the pain threshold) but also the reaction to supra-threshold disturbances. Two people may, for instance, have identical pain thresholds, but one may show little distress under conditions in which the other responds vigorously. Pain thresholds are rarely measured under clinical conditions and it is often impossible to tell, from case reports, whether it is the threshold or the reaction that is abnormal. It is necessary, therefore, for the present to retain the terms 'hypoalgesia', 'hyperalgesia' and 'hyperpathia', although their ambiguity should be remembered.

Certain precautions must be observed in measuring the pain threshold. One method is to apply a weighted pin to the skin and ascertain the weight needed to cause pain. The skin is not, however, uniformly sensitive to such stimuli ; there are regions of low threshold (the pain spots) around which lie areas where heavier weights are needed. Thus throughout an experiment the same spot on the skin must be used for the tests, or stimuli must be applied at random within a demarcated area and the results subjected to statistical analysis. Another method that may be used is to expose a blackened area of skin to radiant heat and to measure the intensity needed to produce pain (Hardy, Wolff & Goodell, 1942). In interpreting the results with this technique it should be remembered that a change in the flow of blood through the skin will alter the effectiveness of a thermal stimulus, quite apart from any change at the sensory endings or in the nervous system. In assessing the action of drugs, therefore, this technique should be applied with caution (*vide* Cook, 1952).

In addition to these technical difficulties a person may be influenced by irrelevant considerations when deciding the point at which to say that he feels discomfort. Misleading results will be obtained if he is bored by the procedure or if he is trying to appear stoical. There is a more serious difficulty : it is usually impossible to avoid setting up other sensations. Thus with weighted needles the person is really being asked to decide when 'touch' changes to 'stab', with radiant heat to tell when a warm sensation becomes unpleasantly hot. He has to determine not whether he feels a stimulus but has to decide on its quality. By contrast the measurement of auditory or visual thresholds can be arranged so that the subject has no knowledge of the application of the stimulus except that gained through the sense being tested. In spite of these difficulties the pain threshold is reasonably replicable and appears to be of real value in assessing fluctuations in the state of the sensibility.

A number of factors are known to influence the pain threshold, and some of these are important from a clinical point of view. Thus Marshall (1953a), measuring the pain threshold with weighted needles, found that during a period of *ischaemia* the immediate and delayed pain thresholds behaved differently. There was little change for 15 minutes, but then the threshold for immediate pain began to rise whereas that for delayed pain fell (Fig. 3.1). Besides producing an alteration in threshold, ischaemia also affects the quality of the delayed pain, making it more prolonged and more unpleasant. The alterations in pain threshold during ischaemia produced by local pressure on the nerve are similar to those that follow the application of a blood-pressure cuff to the arm. It appears, therefore, that the threshold for delayed pain may be lowered by changes in the nerve trunk. That such an alteration of sensitivity does not necessarily involve alterations at the nerve endings is a matter of great theoretical importance. In this connection it may be noted that Lewis (1936)

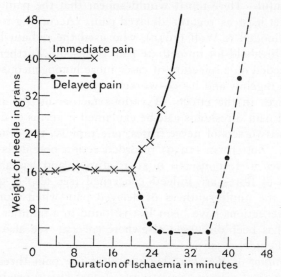

FIG. 3.1.—The threshold for immediate and delayed pain from an arm during a period of ischaemia. (From Marshall, 1953 b)

was able to produce hyperalgesia with a lowering of pain threshold by *faradisation* of a nerve trunk. The soreness persisted for some hours.

When a nerve is partially severed as a result of *mechanical injury*, there may arise a state in which the threshold for pain may be reached by light contact. Weir Mitchell (1874 a), in describing a case in which a splinter had been run into the median nerve, recorded that :

'Miss T. was thin and weak and singularly liable to sudden flushes or as sudden pallor. She slept with the hand propped up upon its ulnar edge, and awakened many times at night when it fell over or was touched by the bedclothes, while all day long she devoted herself to the task of shielding the part from every foreign contact. This anxiety to avoid having the hand touched, and the constant influence of pain, gave to her physiognomy a singular expression of suffering and vigilance, such as I have rarely seen since the terrible traumatic neuralgias of the late war.' Amongst the interesting observations that Mitchell made was that he could, by passing an electrical current along the course of the nerve, reduce the hypersensitivity and so enable the sense of touch to be examined.

In *peripheral neuritis*, such as may accompany alcoholism, the skin may become so sensitive that even the touch of bedclothes may be painful. Here too it would appear that the pain threshold is lowered, at least as regards delayed pain. According to Bigelow, Harrison, Goodell & Wolf (1945), who used the radiant-heat technique, the threshold for immediate pain is raised. Further observations are needed on a selection of cases more homogeneous than that available to Bigelow and his co-workers.

Differences in the effects of various factors on the immediate and delayed pain thresholds can be explained in terms of differential effects upon two sets of nerve fibres, one rapidly, the other slowly, conducting. Zotterman (1939) recorded action potentials in mammalian nerves in response to noxious stimuli and has shown that two groups of fibres are indeed concerned (see also p. 43). The increase in the unpleasantness of delayed pain when more rapidly conducted sensations have been lost is found in a number of conditions, and has been discussed elsewhere (p. 43; see also Weddell, Sinclair & Feindel, 1948).

Inflammation of the skin also can alter the pain threshold and produce a state of extreme sensitivity. Lewis (1936) produced such a state experimentally by applying a faradic current to the skin, and observing the development of a zone of altered sensibility. Light friction in this area was painful, and a needle prick produced diffuse, long-lasting pain. When the needle was applied to the skin at a standard pressure, he found that pricks were more frequently felt over the abnormal area than over the normal skin.

Lewis thought there might be a special anatomical system of nocifensor nerves, which liberated a substance into the tissues and produced this phenomenon. Such a system of special nerves has never been demonstrated anatomically, and it is now believed that the peripheral branching of axones provides a mechanism (axone reflex) whereby changes initiated in one peripheral branch of an axone can produce changes in another. These alterations may be associated with the liberation in the tissues, by any form of injury, of a substance which lowers the threshold of the pain endings.

Lowering of the threshold for pain is uncommon, except in peripheral nerve injuries and following damage to the skin. Lesions of the central nervous system sometimes appear to be associated with excessive pain on stimulation, but careful examination reveals that the threshold for pain is normal or even raised ; it is the reaction to pain that is exaggerated. Thus interference with the pain pathways, in the posterior roots as in tabes dorsalis, and in the spinal cord, raises rather than lowers the threshold for pain.

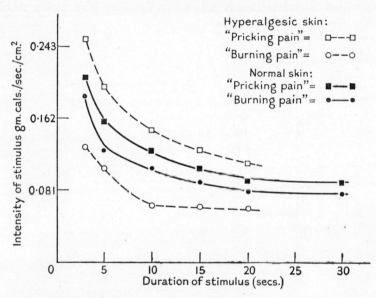

Fig. 3.2.—Comparison of thresholds of 'burning' pain to 'pricking' pain in a patient with hyperalgesia as a result of radiculitis. (From Bigelow, N., Harrison, J., Goodell, H., & Wolff, H. G., 1945)

Another disturbance in pain sensibility, which is often seen in tabes dorsalis, is delay in pain perception. A stimulus may be applied to the periphery of the limb, and an inordinately long interval, amounting sometimes to several seconds, may elapse before the pain is felt. Pochin (1938) suggested that this was due to selective destruction of the fibres responsible for immediate pain so that only delayed pain was felt. This viewpoint was supported by Ashby (1949) ; he pointed out that the delay was sometimes so great as to suggest that the faster of the C fibres also may be damaged. Sinclair & Hinshaw (1951) disagree with this interpretation, for they find a similar delay when a peripheral nerve is blocked with procaine,

F

an agent which is believed to block slow fibres preferentially; they believe that the delay occurs in the central rather than in the peripheral nervous system. The two interpretations are not, however, mutually exclusive.

The possibility must be seriously considered that impulses may travel in afferent fibres and yet only under certain circumstances, of relatively intense excitation, may a sense of pain be produced : *Subliminal Pain.* Bishop (1943 and 1946) is a protagonist of this view which is clearly closely related to the over-stimulation theory

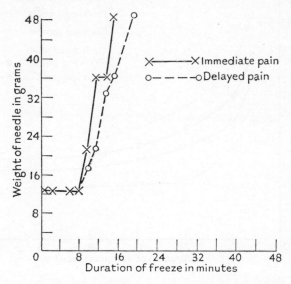

FIG. 3.3.—The threshold for immediate and delayed pain in a subject during freezing of the ulnar nerve. (Marshall, J., 1953 *b*)

of pain (p. 42). It has been suggested that a stimulus too weak to produce pain might yet provoke the discharge of impulses that travelled into the nervous system but were not consciously appreciated. There is a good deal to recommend such a view in certain situations. The heart, for instance, is insensitive to touch, as was shown by the observations of William Harvey on a young nobleman who had lost the bony structures from his precordium. Questioned by Charles I about the case, Harvey relates how :

'Instead of a verbal answer therefore, I carried the young man himself to the King, that His Majesty might with his own eyes behold this wonderful case : that, in a man alive and well, he might without detriment to the individual, observe the movement of the heart, and with his own hand even touch the ventricles as they contracted. And his most excellent Majesty, as well as myself, acknowledged that the heart was without sense of touch : for the youth never knew when we touched his heart, except by the sight or sensation he had through the external integument' (quoted from Wyatt, 1924).

Yet under pathological conditions, as in coronary insufficiency, the heart may give rise to distressing pain, both centrally along the sternum and also referred to the medial side of the arm. The most reasonable explanation is that impulses from the heart, normally concerned with cardiovascular regulation, can, under exceptional conditions, flow into the ascending sensory pathways.

Important observations have been made by Nathan (1953). In experimentally induced lesions he showed that ischaemia of a nerve trunk, unaccompanied by obstruction of the circulation to the periphery of the limb, caused a hitherto painless lesion in the territory of the nerve to become painful. He suggested that there might already be a subliminal discharge of painful impulses from the lesion, and that passage of these impulses through the area of increased irritability of the nerve fibres induced by ischaemia, might, by some unknown mechanism, cause the pain threshold to be exceeded.

Tickling is a sensation that appears to be mediated by the slowest of the A and by C fibres (Zotterman, 1939). Observations on this sensibility have been made on patients in whom the descending tract of the trigeminal nerve has been severed. On the affected side of the face pain sensibility is lost but the sense of touch is retained ; tickling cannot be felt on the analgesic side even when the inside of the nostril is stimulated with cotton-wool. An area of skin that has lost its sensitivity to touch may still *itch* if the pain pathways are intact, whilst when pain sensitivity is lost, as with a spinal cordotomy (p. 58), loss of itch sensitivity is invariable (White & Sweet, 1955).

PARAESTHESIAE AND COLD PAIN

Paraesthesiae are sensory phenomena experienced in a variety of conditions. Though commonly described as 'pins and needles', 'tingling' or 'burning', they are distinct from pain ; they may, however, conveniently be considered here. Experimentally paraesthesiae may be produced by subjecting a peripheral nerve to cooling, ischaemia or to mechanical or electrical stimuli. Clinically it is found that paraesthesiae may be produced by lesions within the central nervous system ; with lesions of the cervical part of the spinal cord acute flexion of the neck may provoke these sensations. Paraesthesiae are often an early manifestation of tetany (p. 25).

It is important to try to classify paraesthesiae. Merrington & Nathan (1949) made careful studies of the paraesthesiae which followed the return of the circulation to a limb deprived of its blood supply for a time (Fig. 3.4). They showed that these paraesthesiae arise as a result of ischaemia of the nerve fibres rather than of the sensory receptors, and that they could be divided into four groups.

(1) Thermal paraesthesiae. These consist of alternating sensations of cold and warmth. These paraesthesiae have been the subject of extensive study by Bazett & McGlone (1932).

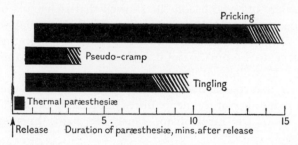

FIG. 3.4.—Diagram showing the onset and duration of post-ischaemic paraesthesiae. (From Merrington, W. R., & Nathan, P. W., 1949)

The sensations appear to be carried in the nerve fibres which serve thermal sensibility, as lesions which damage these fibres cause loss of the ability to experience thermal paraesthesiae.

(2) Tingling paraesthesiae. These consist of a fine vibrating or tingling sensation which is momentarily increased by firm pressure. They appear to be carried in nerve fibres which serve touch.

(3) Pricking paraesthesiae. These are characterised by a series of rapid, irregular, distinct pricks. They also are increased by firm pressure. The fibres which carry the impulses underlying these paraesthesiae appear to be those serving pressure.

(4) Pseudo-cramp. This is a feeling of tightness or tension which gives the subjective impression that the limb is being moved against the patient's will. On occasion, visible involuntary movements actually occur. The fibres which carry the sense of passive movement appear to subserve this type of paraesthesiae.

These paraesthesiae can be dissociated one from another by adjustment of the experimental conditions under which they are produced. Study of patients with lesions of the spinal cord has confirmed that tingling, pricking and pseudo-cramp paraesthesiae are carried by fibres which pass up the posterior columns of the cord, and do not go along the pathways serving pain.

Cooling may also induce sensory phenomena (*vide* Wolf & Hardy, 1941 ; and Kellgren, McGowan & Hughes, 1948). When a limb is immersed in water at 16° C. a dull, diffuse ache appears after a few seconds, rises to a peak within one minute and slowly dies away over a period of about four minutes. This *cold pain* is often accentuated in clinical conditions. A patient may have suffered an injury but

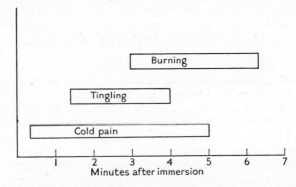

FIG. 3.5.—Diagram showing the onset and duration of paraesthesiae induced by cold water at 4° C. (From Marshall, J., 1953 *a*)

only notice discomfort when the limb is cold ; in the presence of a lesion in the deep tissues of a limb cold pain develops at a higher temperature than normal.

When cold pain has subsided, another sensation can be provoked by cooling the limb still further (Fig. 3.5). A diffuse tingling is felt which has been shown to arise, not in the sensory receptors, but in the nerve trunk. It is conveyed by fibres serving touch. Cold tingling can still be induced when ischaemic paraesthesiae have subsided.

The third sensation evoked by cooling a limb is an intense burning or stinging, which only appears at a temperature of 4° C. or less. It appears to arise in the nerve fibres concerned with pain from deep tissues.

Paraesthesiae occur in many diseases, though their relation to the experimental work which has been described is far from clear. In conditions such as Raynaud's phenomenon and acroparaesthesiae, ischaemia may be the important factor at work. In sub-acute combined degeneration of the cord, however, in which paraesthesiae are often a prominent and intractable symptom, the mechanism is obscure.

REFERRED PAIN FROM VISCERA, MUSCLES AND SKIN

It is a fact of universal experience that visceral disease is often accompanied by pain, but the mechanisms involved are by no means settled. When the gut is cut, pinched or burnt no pain is felt (*vide* Lenander, 1903); Hurst (1911), however, demonstrated that discomfort may be aroused by distending the intestine with a balloon. Normal contractions are not appreciated but pain may arise when, owing to obstruction, the tension in the bowel wall rises to an unusually high level. Of an operation on an umbilical hernia in a patient who refused anaesthetic, Mackenzie (1913) noted :

'I was able to break down numerous old and recent peritoneal adhesions, to detach them from the liver and bowel, to resect a piece of bowel and mesentery, and to stitch these structures without the patient experiencing the slightest sensation. But I found that he occasionally groaned with pain when I was not touching him, and watching to see the cause I found that the upper part of the resected bowel, which was laid on one side in a warm aseptic cloth, occasionally passed into peristalsis, contracting from a wide tube to a thick fleshy rod ; when this happened the patient groaned with pain. I asked him where he felt the pain, and he passed his hand invariably over the umbilical region.'

If the gut is inflamed it may be found that stimuli which are normally inadequate may be felt. Wolf & Wolff (1942) pinched and faradised normal gastric mucosa through a gastroscope and observed that the procedure was painless. They then applied mustard to the mucosal wall so that it became inflamed and oedematous ; pinching and faradising the mucosa was then acutely painful. It will be remembered that inflammation in the skin, whether produced by disease or experimentally, causes a lowering of the pain threshold to such an extent that stimuli, formerly painless, become painful. The experiments of Wolf & Wolff suggest that the threshold in the gut for pain produced by various stimuli can be similarly lowered.

The pain set up by irritation of one of the viscera may be felt, not over the organ, but at some relatively distant site : it is *referred*. There has been much discussion since the time of Ross (1888) on the mechanism of this false localisation. The debate has turned largely upon the rôle of other afferent information reaching the cord through the same segments as that from the inflamed part. Mackenzie (1920) believed that afferent impulses from a viscus irritated the cells which received afferents from somatic structures with the same segmental innervation. Impulses from these cells then travelled to the sensorium, where they were interpreted as having their origin in the appropriate somatic area of reference. Further, impulses from the area of reference, which were ordinarily nonpainful, became painful as a result of the increased excitability of the cell pool in the spinal cord. Thus, he explained the increased sensitivity of the skin to touch in the area of reference as being due to the visceral impulses, which enter the common pool and lower the threshold of the cells, which receive touch impulses from the skin. This is called a *viscero-sensory reflex*.

The question was studied by Doran & Ratcliffe (1954) in the case of the shoulder-tip pain referred from the diaphragm. They stimulated the phrenic nerve in a patient undergoing a block dissection of the neck for the removal of lymph glands. Shoulder-tip pain, similar to that found in patients with inflammation of the central part of the diaphragm, could be produced even though the nerves supplying the shoulder and neck had been divided. This 'crucial' investigation showed that impulses from the phrenic nerve *can* gain control of sensory pathways without assistance from messages arising in the skin. It is likely, nevertheless, that action potentials from skin afferents do facilitate the occurrence of referred pain when the peripheral nerves are intact. Thus in patients undergoing the operation of 'phrenic crush' Doran & Ratcliffe were able to show that the shoulder-tip pain could be produced by a smaller stimulus to the phrenic nerve when the cutaneous nerves were conducting than when they were anaesthetised. A person normally cannot know the position of his viscera, he cannot with the hand explore their structure as he can the cutaneous surface. Elsewhere it is pointed out that there is convergence in the sensory pathways (p. 399); evidently cutaneous and visceral fibres may share a single sensory channel. It would appear that the visceral impulses only use the 'party line' on exceptional occasions.

Mackenzie believed that messages from the viscera themselves could enhance the activity of the motor neurones in the segments to which the visceral afferent fibres were distributed: a *viscero-motor reflex*. Muscle spasm, however produced, can scarcely be overestimated as a cause of pain in many clinical conditions. The spasm of the abdominal musculature that follows distension of the pelvis of a kidney persists for several hours after the stimulus has ceased.

Morley (1931) has pointed out that pain in visceral disease may arise from endings in the viscera themselves, but that often it is irritation of the parietal peritoneum that plays the dominant rôle. The segmental level of innervation determines the site at which pain is felt in response to disten-sion of the viscus. Thus pain from the stomach is referred to the epigastrium, from the appendix to the umbilicus and from the colon to the hypo-chondrium. On the other hand, discomfort that arises from irrita-tion of the body wall varies according to the position of the diseased viscus. Such pain, in the case of appendicitis, may be felt in the mid-line just above the pubis if the appendix is in the pelvis, whilst if it is in the ileocaecal region, as is more common, the discomfort is in the right iliac fossa. Morley's work made it clear that Mackenzie's viscero-sensory and viscero-motor reflexes are, frequently at least, 'peritineo-cutaneous' and 'peritineo-muscular'.

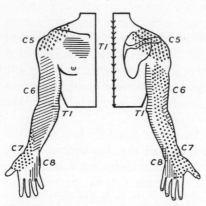

Fig. 3.6.—Deep pain produced by irrita-tion of muscles of arm. When hyper-tonic saline is injected into a muscle the distribution of the pain depends upon the segmental nerve supply of the fibres. The pain is deep and diffuse and does not correspond with the segmental innervation of the skin. Unless the pain is severe it is felt in only a part of the available segmental region. From rhomboids—crosses; from flexor carpi radialis—oblique hatching; from abductor pollicis longus—stippling; from third dorsal interosseous—vertical hatching; from first intercostal space — horizontal hatching (Kellgren, 1938)

It will be seen that when a sensitive viscus is stimulated by pressure applied to the abdominal wall the patient will be liable to feel—(1) pressure localised by endings in the tissues of the abdominal wall, and (2) pain that may be localised some distance away according to the segmental supply of the viscus. In general, the sensorium has a tendency to fuse these impressions and the pain may, under some circumstances, be felt as though it came from the area that has been pressed upon, even though the parietal peritoneum is not inflamed. Kinsella (1948) has reported a number of clinical observations showing that 'local sign' may be 'borrowed' in this way.

The deep tenderness associated with a gastric or duodenal ulcer is found at a point directly over the crater that can be seen radiographically. This is so even when there is no involvement of the peritoneum.

The *pain which arises from muscles* can be puzzling unless something is known of the physiological principles involved. Lewis (1938) wrote : 'I have noted that muscle pain is referred to a distance. Thus pain arising from the lower part of the triceps is often referred down the inner side of the forearm to the little finger ; from the trapezius it is usually referred to the occiput.'

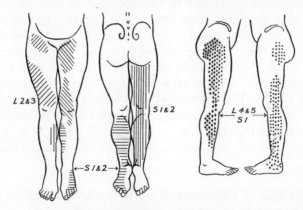

FIG. 3.7.—Deep pain produced by injecting hypertonic saline into muscles of lower limb. From sartorius (*right leg*) and from adductor longus (*left leg*)—oblique hatching ; from gastrocnemius—vertical hatching ; from first interosseous—horizontal hatching ; from tensor fascia femoris—crosses ; from peroneus longus—stippling (Kellgren, 1938)

Muscle pain has been extensively studied by Kellgren (1938, 1939). In quality it is less sharp but more diffused and prolonged than pain arising in the skin. Kellgren injected hypertonic saline into deep somatic structures, and observed that the distribution of the resulting pain follows a characteristic pattern, which is dependent on the segmental innervation of the injected structure. The musculature innervated by a single segment of the spinal cord is known as a myotome. A lesion may give rise to pain that is diffused throughout the myotome in which it lies. Knowledge of the segmental nerve supply enables the search for the source of the disturbance to be conducted along anatomical lines (Figs. 3.6 and 3.7). Kellgren (1939) has pointed out that 'pain arising from muscle may often fail to be recognised as such, and may be ascribed by the subject to other structures such as joints, teeth or testis'.

In the skin, as elsewhere, pain may be felt some distance from the site of the disturbance. This spread is important to remember when attempting to understand puzzling clinical symptomatology. Some light on the mechanisms concerned has been thrown by the observations of Sinclair (1949). He found trigger points in the skin, stimulation of which caused pain referred to another area ; the area of reference also showed altered sensibility. When he made a biopsy of the trigger point, he always found that a nerve trunk lay beneath it. Sinclair suggested that the reference of pain, and the altered sensibility, were due to branching of axones. Reference of pain to areas so remote that they could not be reached by axone branches of the stimulated nerve, might be due to branching of axones within the cord, the various branches making their exit by different roots. This does not explain why referred pain may be set up from otherwise analgesic areas following spinal cordotomy (White & Sweet, 1955). The discomfort may be referred to a symmetrical point on the opposite, normally innervated side, or elsewhere on the same side as the stimulus.

HEADACHE

A great deal of experimental work on the mechanism of head-ache has been carried out, especially by Wolff and his co-workers (1948). During operations under local anaesthesia, they stimulated various extra- and intracranial structures, and noted the patients' responses. They observed that the periosteum is moderately sensi-tive to painful stimuli, but the bone itself is entirely insensitive. Within the skull the important pain-sensitive structures are :—the venous sinuses and their tributaries, parts of the dura overlying the floor of the various fossae, and the cerebral arteries at the base of the brain (the internal carotid, the basilar, and their branches). The dura over the cerebral hemispheres, the falx and the tentorium cerebelli, the pia-arachnoid and the brain parenchyma are all insensi-tive. Stimulation of these structures does not give rise to pain nor, indeed, to any other kind of sensation.

The areas of reference of the pain from the sensitive structures were also studied. Stimulation of structures on or above the superior surface of the tentorium cerebelli caused pain referred to the oph-thalmic division of the trigeminal nerve. Stimulation of structures on or below the inferior surface of the tentorium gave rise to pain

over the back of the head and neck.   In the case of mid-line structures, the area of reference was bilateral, but pain from unilateral
structures was referred to the ipsilateral side.

The ependymal lining of the ventricles was also insensitive to
coagulation, compression and faradic currents.   A sudden change
of pressure within the ventricles was, however, accompanied by a
diffuse headache.   Thus a balloon was introduced into one lateral
ventricle, and then distended so as to stretch the ventricular wall.
This produced a diffuse pain in the frontal region of the same side.
Release of the balloon was accompanied by a transitory, intense
pain.   Distension of a balloon placed in the third ventricle had
similar effects, but the pain involved the whole of the head on both
sides.

Changes in the general *intracranial pressure* have also been
studied with regard to their effect on pain.   That lumbar puncture
is sometimes followed by headache has long been known, the headache being attributed to lowered intracranial pressure.   Wolff made
experimental observations on this phenomenon, by removing 20 ml.
of cerebrospinal fluid from normal subjects who were sitting erect.
He measured the pressure in the lumbar theca by means of a mano-
meter attached to a lumbar puncture needle in both the erect and
horizontal postures.   From the data thus obtained he calculated the
intracranial pressure at the vertex of the skull.   He showed that
following the removal of 20 ml. of cerebrospinal fluid the intracranial pressure at the vertex fell from −150 mm. of cerebrospinal
fluid to between −220 and −280 mm., and that this fall was accompanied by headache.   Tilting the subject from the erect to the
horizontal posture raised the intracranial pressure and relieved the
pain.   Similarly, restoring the intracranial pressure by injecting
normal saline solution relieved the headache.   Lowering the intracranial pressure, therefore, can produce headache, and is probably
a factor in the headache which sometimes follows lumbar puncture.
Wolff believes that the sag of the brain which follows disturbance
of the intracranial pressure relationships causes traction on the
vessels at the base of the brain and that this is responsible for the
headache.

A generalised rise in intracranial pressure does not appear of
itself to produce headache.   Thus, in some experiments on normal
subjects, the intracranial pressure at the vertex was raised from
−150 mm. of cerebrospinal fluid to between +680 and +830 mm.
for a period of two minutes without producing any pain.   In another

subject the pressure was raised to $+510$ mm. and kept there for ten minutes, but no headache developed. The distension of the ventricles by a balloon appears to produce headache, not because of the generalised rise in intracranial pressure, but because of the localised distortion of the ventricular walls. This latter mechanism is believed to be the factor responsible for the headache which is often associated with intracranial tumours. Cases of tumour with high intracranial pressure but without headache are well recognised. The observations of Wolff indicate that when headache does occur in cases of tumour with raised intracranial pressure, it is not the rise of pressure itself, but the local distortion of structures by the tumours which produces the pain.

That lowered intracranial pressure is not the only factor responsible for the pain following drainage of cerebrospinal fluid is shown by a further observation of Wolff. One subject had an initial vertex pressure in the erect posture of -165 mm. Drainage of cerebrospinal fluid was carried out and produced a headache at a pressure of -215 mm. Further drainage was done and then the patient tilted to an angle of $15°$ above the horizontal, which eliminated the headache. A further 10 ml. of fluid was then removed and the headache recurred, the vertex pressure being only -113 mm., which was higher than at the outset. Wolff concludes that the additional factor is dilatation of the intracranial veins to compensate for the reduction in volume of the intracranial content, this dilatation being painful. Further evidence in favour of this view is that compression of the jugular veins in the neck which raises the intracranial venous pressure and thus further distends the veins, aggravates a low-pressure headache.

The headache associated with changes in the intracranial arteries has been studied by the injection of 0.1 mg. of *histamine* phosphate intravenously. This substance causes dilatation of the intracranial arteries and an increase in the amplitude of the arterial pulsation which can be measured by the transmitted pulsation in the cerebrospinal fluid. The greater the amplitude of the arterial pulsation, the more severe the pain. Decreasing the amplitude of the arterial pulsation, either by reducing the arterial pressure or by raising the pressure of the cerebrospinal fluid, reduced the intensity of the pain.

Other aspects of the applied physiology of pain will be found discussed in other chapters. This short survey will, however, have indicated how important a knowledge of experimental investigations may be for an understanding of clinical conditions. Though many facts have been established, many important questions remain unanswered. A more fruitful field of research for physicians and physiologists would be hard to find, and it is to be expected that further advances in physiological knowledge will bring assistance to the clinician at the bedside.

CHAPTER 4

THE SPINAL CORD

A creature of very low intelligence, when aware of some large object in motion near it, makes a spasmodic movement, causing, it may be, a leap or a dart. The perceptions implied are relatively simple, homogeneous, and indefinite : the moving objects are not distinguished in their kinds as injurious or otherwise, as advancing or receding. The actions of escape, too, are all of one kind, having no adjustments of direction, and may bring the creature nearer the source of peril instead of further off. At a higher stage the dart or the leap is away from danger : the nervous changes are so far specialised that there results distinction of direction ; indicating a greater variety among them, a greater co-ordination or integration of them in each process, and a greater definiteness. If still higher animals, able to discriminate between enemies and not-enemies, as a bird which flies from a man but not from a cow, the acts of perception have severally become united into more complex wholes, since cognition of certain differential attributes is implied ; they have also become more multiform, since each additional component impression adds to the number of possible compounds ; and they have, by consequence, become more specific in their correspondences with objects—more definite. —HERBERT SPENSER (1900).

NEUROLOGICAL LEVELS

IT was Herbert Spenser the philosopher who gave to neurology the concept of levels, his general ideas being applied to this subject by John Hughlings Jackson (*vide* Fig. 4.1). Spenser wrote not only of the way in which complex organisations evolved, but of the way in which they disintegrate. According to him disintegration or 'dissolution' tends to retrace the events seen in the evolutionary process. Thus, in the case of the social system, disorder causes the greatest disturbances in the most highly evolved systems. Spenser wrote that 'the industrial and commercial processes that were co-ordinated throughout the body politic, are broken up ; and only the local, or

small, trading transactions continue. And each further disorganis-
ing change diminishes the joint operations by which men satisfy
their wants, and leaves them to satisfy their wants, as best they can,
by separate operations.'

In the evolution of the nervous system there has been a progressive encephalisation—progressively more complex correlation
centres are developed in the mid-brain, thalamus and cerebral
cortex.

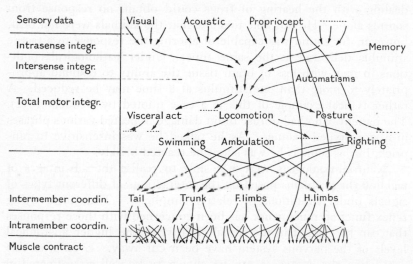

FIG. 4.1.—The concept of levels. 'We speak of functional systems of higher or
    lower orders, of dominance and subordination, of integration and analytic
    functions, and so on. Since more comprehensive functions operate through
    the activation of functional systems of lower order and more restricted scope,
    which themselves are composed of functional subunits of still lower order,
    integration and analysis proceed in steps. . . . Any given level operates
    through the selective activation and combination of unit functions of the
    next lowest level, each characterised by a high degree of stability, integrity
    and individuality' (Weiss, 1950)

Brickner (1948) discussing these problems has pointed out that 'in
the teleost,[1] the topmost, most complex, center of correlation is the tectum.
A single large cell, Mauthner's cell and its axon, appears to be sufficient
for most of the conduction from brain to spinal cord. As the brain
advances, even more inclusive integrating areas . . . develop and supersede
and dominate the integrative functions of the tectum.' Brickner also
points out that : 'When ventral fins become the legs of amphibians . . .
increased mesencephalization multiplies the functions of the extremities

[1] Bony fish, *e.g.* goldfish.

greatly beyond their limits in fishes. But this advance in complexity is minute compared to the multiplications produced by the human telencephalon, by which, for example, walking may become a tool for exploring African jungles, vocal sounds become speech, and vision the reading of meanings in the form of words.'

It is a function of the nervous system to vary response to an afferent signal according to contemporaneous events signalled through other channels. Yerkes (1905) in classical experiments dealing with the hearing of frogs could obtain no response from sounds alone. He was able to show that the animals were not deaf, however, for sound was capable of altering the response to a tactile stimulus delivered at the same time. Under pathological conditions in man with loss of brain tissue the ability to respond appropriately to more than one stimulus at a time may be reduced. A rather typical example of this is a case quoted by Bender (1952). The patient, who had diffuse brain damage, repeated various phrases in a stereotyped manner. As he talked he was insensitive to pinprick, but as soon as he was silent he reacted briskly.

Neurophysiologists were not slow to realise the advantages of tackling the problems posed by the interactions of different types of signals under conditions of relative simplicity. Thus in studying reflex function much work has been concerned with those responses that can be elicited in the spinal cord when the higher anatomical levels of the nervous system have been cut away. Even after this mutilation the responses can be shown to be well co-ordinated in many respects, and the responses that are aroused can usually be seen to be of biological significance in the intact animal. One important generalisation from the work of Sir Charles Sherrington concerns the reciprocal innervation of antagonistic muscles. In general, when a limb is moved, not only is there a contraction of the prime movers, but there is a relaxation of their antagonists. *Reciprocal innervation* is well seen in spinal reflexes and clearly is a mechanism of value to the organism ; its importance is in no way lessened by the possibility that in some movements there may be a simultaneous contraction of antagonistic muscle (*vide* pp. 390 and 178). Another reflex that may be mentioned is the flexor response. The application of a stimulus to the foot, which might, in the intact animal, be expected to cause pain, will cause a reflex withdrawal of the limb. Many reflexes have been described and some, such as the jump reflex, depend upon the excitation in correct serial order of different sensory receptors (Fig. 4.2).

Under normal circumstances more than one stimulus is likely to play upon the nervous system at once. It is clear that reflex effects must be graded according to the urgency with which they have to be performed. Thus it is found that the flexor response is prepotent over reflex scratching. The various reflexes may compete for the control of the anterior horn cells : *The Final Common Path*. Under certain circumstances the response of the spinal cord to two sets of incoming signals may alternate, according first with the response appropriate to one of the sets of signals and later with that fitting for the second.

To what extent can the nervous system be regarded as being composed of numerous reflex arcs interacting one with another?

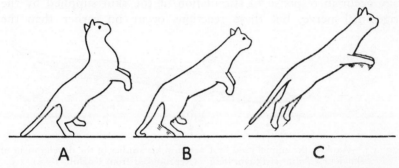

FIG. 4.2.—Jump reflex in hypothalamic cat; brought on by manipulating the animal's head and neck as shown in A and B in sequence. Jump is also dependent upon proprioceptive inflow from hind-legs. (From Guzman & de Pozo, 1953)

Other possibilities may be considered. Is the mammalian nervous system in any sense comparable to that of the sea-anemone (Pantin, 1952) in which simple reflexes are relatively unimportant and in which a response to a stimulus often consists of a prolonged change in the pattern of spontaneous activity? There seems little need to invoke such a conception where the spinal cord is concerned, but the responses of the cerebral cortex might provide a loose analogy.

A more serious challenge to the concept of 'levels' in the nervous system was provided by the work of Coghill (1929) who studied the development of the axolotl (Amblystoma, Fig. 4.3). At first, before the limbs have developed, the animal can curl up to one side or to the other, and a little later waves can pass backwards along the trunk and so propel the creature forwards through the water

G

(Fig. 4.4). It was found that when the fore-limbs developed they moved at first only when the trunk as a whole moved. Several days elapsed before local responses involving the limbs alone could be obtained. It appeared that localised reflexes were developed out of a complex pattern of movement affecting the body as a whole. Coghill's views have stimulated much important work and started a healthy scientific controversy. Much turns upon the order in which different reflex pathways become usable. The maturation of various neural routes may proceed in a different order in different animals. In the foetuses of placental mammals local responses of the limb musculature may be elicited by stimulation of the limb itself relatively early in development. Generalised movements may occur in response to stimulation of the skin supplied by the trigeminal nerve, but these reactions occur no earlier than the

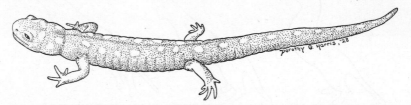

FIG. 4.3.—Axolotl, the animal used by Coghill in his studies of the development of behaviour. Adult is 15 cm. long. (Reproduced from Coghill, 1929)

reflexes confined to one limb (Barron in Weiss, 1950). It would appear, therefore, that, as far as the higher mammals are concerned, there is now no reason to give much weight to Coghill's view.

Ashby (1952, p. 137) has pointed out that :

'The views held about the amount of internal connection in the nervous system—its degree of "wholeness"—have tended to range from one extreme to the other. The "reflexologists" from Bell onwards recognised that in some of its activities the nervous system could be treated as a collection of independent parts. They pointed to the fact, for instance, that the pupillary reflex to light and the patellar reflex occur in their usual forms whether the other reflex is being elicited or not. The coughing reflex follows the same pattern whether the subject is standing or sitting. And the acquirement of a new conditioned reflex might leave a previously established reflex largely unaffected. On the other hand, the Gestalt school recognised that many activities of the nervous system were characterised by wholeness, so that what happened at one point was related to what was happening at other points. The two sets of facts were sometimes treated as irreconcilable.

'Yet Sherrington in 1906 had shown by the spinal reflexes that the nervous system was neither divided into permanently separated parts nor so wholly joined that every event always influenced every other.   Rather, it showed a richer, and a more intricate picture—one in which interactions and independencies fluctuated.   "Thus, a weak reflex may be elicited from the tail of the spinal dog without interference with the stepping-reflex" . . . "Two reflexes may be neutral to each other when both are weak, but may interfere when either, or both, are strong" . . . "But to show that reflexes may be neutral to each other in a spinal dog is not evidence that they will be neutral in the animal with its whole system

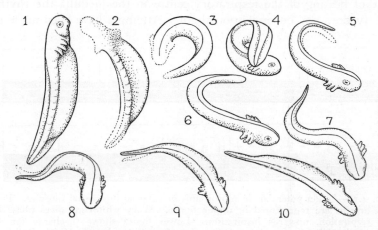

Fig. 4.4.—Early swimming movements in axolotl.   Animal at rest in 1, whilst 2, 3, 4, 5 and 6 show a coil to the left.   In 7 a flexure to the right has begun, whilst the original flexure is passing tailward, animal returns to resting posture by 10.   Reactions 1-10 lasted $\frac{3}{5}$ sec.   (Reproduced from Coghill, 1929)

intact and unmutilated."   The separation into many parts and the union into a single whole are simply the two extremes on the scale of "degree of connectedness".'

It should not be supposed that reflexes are restricted to the spinal cord, for similar mechanisms are found in the brain stem. Some of these responses involve reactions determined by the labyrinth.   These are considered elsewhere (p. 149).   Another set of responses is liable to be set off by loud sounds.   Thus the blink that often occurs when an unexpected noise is heard *may* depend upon fibres that pass from the superior olive to the facial nucleus.

Of greater importance are the respiratory reflexes, and they are of interest also, for they show the way in which the rhythmic discharge of a nerve centre (Fig. 4.5) may be modified by afferent impulses. The vagi carry information as to the distension of the lungs ; vagal stretch receptors are slowly adapting endings and discharge a stream of action potentials during inspiration. These messages are responsible for the cessation of the inspiratory act, and when the vagi are sectioned respiration becomes slower and deeper. In addition other afferent impulses arise within the thorax and can, under certain circumstances, also modify the respiratory movements (*vide* Whitteridge, 1950). Whilst the vagi influence the rate of beating of the respiratory centre in the medulla the rhythmicity does not depend upon them. Attempts have been made to

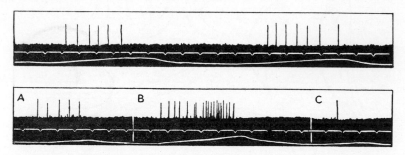

FIG. 4.5.—Action potentials in motor unit of external intercostal muscles. Two breaths are represented in upper figure. Wavy white line gives phase of respiration, upwards inspiration. Lower figure shows discharge for A, medium, B, deep and C, shallow breaths. Time $\frac{1}{5}$ sec. (From Bronk & Ferguson, 1935)

localise the position of the respiratory centre in the medulla by observing the regions from which respiratory responses can be obtained by stimulation (Pitts, 1946 ; Woldring & Dirken, 1951). The area is not well defined anatomically, it lies in the reticular formation. As is the case with other reflex mechanisms, the respiratory discharges may be modified by impulses descending from higher levels of the nervous system. Thus, for example, in encephalitis lethargica (p. 458) a wide variety of disorders of respiration may be seen (Turner & Critchley, 1925).

In contrast to this state of affairs in the respiratory system stand the arrangements for mastication in the cat. In the decerebrate animal jaw opening is a reflex response to broad pressure applied to the upper teeth and palate. The opening is followed by a strong rebound contraction of the jaw closers. In this way a rhythmic biting action can be maintained as long as a pabulum is between the teeth. Here is a simple example of 'feed-back' giving rise to an oscillation (*vide* p. 116).

From a practical viewpoint the analysis of reflexes has proved most important, for these responses, largely independent of the co-operation of the patient, enable numerous routes through the nervous system to be checked. Neurological disturbances may often be analysed fruitfully in terms of depression or excitation of reflex responses. Depression of reflex function is dealt with in detail later in this chapter ; as an example of a pathological disturbance caused by an exaggerated reflex the carotid sinus syndrome may be quoted (*vide* Fig. 4.6). This reflex normally regulates the blood pressure according to the pressure within the carotid sinus. It may be set off by inappropriate stimuli if

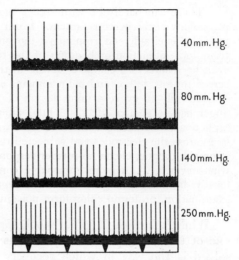

FIG. 4.6.—Discharge of single fibre from carotid sinus. Rate of discharge varies with pressure of blood. Time $\frac{1}{5}$ sec. (From Bronk & Stella, 1935, reproduced from S. Wright, 1947)

there are pathological changes in the vessel wall. Thus a patient may 'faint' due to the pressure of a tight collar on his neck. The faint is usually due to a reflex lowering of blood pressure (*vide* Engel, 1950).

SPINAL SHOCK

When the spinal cord is severed reflex function below the lesion is depressed ; in a few minutes in the frog, and over several weeks in man, some function gradually returns to the isolated segments. In the lower limbs responses involving the extensor muscles are more profoundly affected than those employing primarily flexor groups. Spinal shock is not due to disturbances in the blood supply to the spinal cord. Thus, if after recovery of reflex function following one transection a second cut is made, below the level of the first, depression does not reappear. Spinal shock is thought there-fore to be due to the withdrawal of impulses that flow down to the cord from the brain stem. These normally facilitate the action of the grey matter of the spinal cord.

Sherrington (1939, p. 121) left us with the following description of spinal shock :

'There can hardly be witnessed a more striking phenomenon in the physiology of the nervous system. From the limp limbs, even if the knee jerks be elicitable, no responsive movement, beyond perhaps a feeble tremulous adduction or bending of the thumb or hallux, can be evoked even by insults of a character severe in the extreme . . . a hot iron laid across thumb, index, and palm remains an absolutely impotent excitant, or able only to evoke a faint flexion of the thumb; the crushing of a finger has no greater effect. A huge afferent nerve, such as the internal saphenous, containing some five thousand sensory nerve-fibres, when laid across the electrodes and subjected to currents absolutely unbearable upon the tongue, elicits no further response, and probably no movement whatsoever. . . . A more impassable condition of block, or torpor, can hardly be imagined : its depth of negation resembles, to superficial examination, profound chloroform poisoning.'

Whilst the cause of spinal shock appears to be clearly established, one of the most interesting problems that remains essentially unsolved is the way in which recovery takes place. 'Our problem becomes then, not the explanation of the production of shock, but the explanation of the recovery, *i.e.* why these other paths open up under the changed conditions' (Pike, 1913).

It appears necessary to assume that in some way the excitability of the isolated spinal cord gradually rises, until the impulses coming in from the periphery are able again to elicit responses. The changes occur in spite of (or perhaps because of) degeneration of nerve cells in the grey matter. 'When the cord itself behind the trans-lesion is examined in microscopic section, severe and universal degeneration of perikarya is found in all regions except the ventral horn' (Liddell, 1934). Histological examination of an isolated part of the spinal cord has been performed by Tower, Bodian & Howe (1941) to ascertain the distribution of 'proprio-spinal fibres'. A transverse section above the area under investigation ensured degeneration of descending tracts, one below interrupted the ascending fibres whilst the primary sensory neurones were interrupted by division of posterior roots. Most of the intrinsic fibres left after these procedures were fine unmyelinated filaments. It is of interest that no muscular activity, such as fasciculation (p. 19), was observed in the muscles supplied by motor neurones within the isolated region.

The mechanisms concerned in the recovery from spinal shock are of more than academic interest, for a better understanding might lead to methods of speeding recovery from lesions of the central nervous system (cf. p. 214). In view of its importance this problem appears to have attracted relatively little interest (*vide* Lashley, 1938). There would appear to be two viewpoints, at the present time, that may be considered.

First it appears to be a general experience that the denervation of a structure increases the sensitivity of that structure to

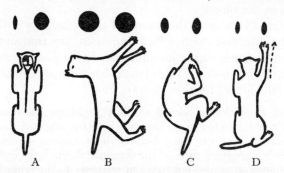

FIG. 4.7.—Following removal of left frontal lobe animal, allowed to recover, has equal pupils and adopts a symmetrical posture. Acetylcholine brings out latent abnormalities. Figures show characteristic attitudes at various periods *after* injection. Note unequal pupils soon after administration. A, before 'fit'—B, note asymmetry of posture in C. Movements of right fore-limb in D could be brought out by pressure upon pad of foot and may be the positive supporting reaction (p. 25), or may be analogous to the grasp reflex described in primates. These experiments were undertaken to attempt to investigate sensitivity of denervated neurones to acetylcholine, but the situation is complex and the tendency of brain bordering on a zone of injury to discharge epileptic waveforms must be borne in mind in the interpretation. (Reproduced from Stavraky, 1943)

excitation of various forms. Cannon formulated a 'Law of Denervation' as follows :—'when in a series of efferent neurons a unit is destroyed, an increased irritability to chemical agents develops in the isolated structure or structures, the effects being maximal in the part directly denervated'. Many examples of the principle are quoted in a book written by Cannon & Rosenblueth (1949). It has been suggested that the principle explains the recovery from spinal shock. 'Transection of the cord leads to degeneration of all the long descending pathways. This degeneration denervates partially or totally many spinal neurons. Supersensitivity to the effects of nervous impulses will not only develop in these denervated nervous elements, but may also become manifest in other cells, normally innervated by the now denervated neurons. This sensitisation leads to progressively greater efficacy of the afferent nerve impulses in conveying the direct or indirect, positive or negative, influences which they may exert on the motoneurons.' This effect may play a rôle in other lesions of the nervous system (Fig. 4.7). In connection with the 'Hypersensitivity Theory' it is interesting to observe that the 'toxaemia' associated with a bed-sore, or a urinary tract infection, may delay the recovery from spinal shock ; the excitability of the neurones of the spinal cord is evidently depressed by some agent circulating in the blood.

The second view as to the nature of the 'plasticity' of the spinal cord is that the ease with which impulses are transmitted along pathways involving synaptic junctions depends upon the use that has been made of that route. Eccles (1953) has been able to obtain some experimental support for this view (p. 229).

An observation closely related to these problems has been made by Teasdall & Stavraky (1953). These workers investigated the effects of electrical excitation of the basis pedunculi at various times after the posterior roots supplying one of the legs had been sectioned. At first the corresponding limb did not move in response to the stimulus ; when, however, the excitation was applied 5 to 47 days after that limb had been deafferented responses were evoked in the denervated limb more readily than on the normal side.[1] The workers concluded that 'section of the posterior nerve roots increases the excitability of the deafferented spinal neurones to nerve impulses reaching them via the corticospinal tract, this taking place after an initial depression of spinal activity'. It has been suggested 'that in sensory ataxia[2] an overactive response on the part of the deafferented spinal neurones plays a part in the exaggeration and disco-ordination of voluntary movements'. However this may be, it is evident that such changes of excitability occur and must be borne in mind in interpreting neurological syndromes.

Clinically an upper motor neurone lesion of abrupt onset is at first usually associated with flaccidity of the affected musculature. It is later, over a period ranging from hours to weeks, that spasticity is likely to develop (p. 382). This change may be related to the increase of excitability after a spinal transection. This is suggested by observations in which the spinal cord has been cut across on one side and then after a

---

[1] Sherrington & Denny-Brown investigated the effect of stimulating the motor cortex after section of posterior roots ; they were struck by the apparent normality of the responses to electrical stimulation of the motor cortex : 'Wild inco-ordination under willed action ; little or no abnormality under the action of the directly stimulated motor cortex.   A striking contrast' (Sherrington, 1931) (cf. p. 368).

[2] The form of ataxia associated with a loss of proprioceptive sensation (e.g. tabes dorsalis).

delay a complete transection has been made. The reflex recovery is more rapid on the side that has been paralysed (McCouch, Hughes & Stewart, 1943).

Quite apart from the restitution of function in the ways that have been considered there may also be a true regeneration of damaged structures. This regeneration is said to be absent in mammals (but see Windle, 1955). Hooker (in Weiss, 1950) has given a very brief summary of the experimental results in other forms of life.

'(1) in the teleosts, amphibians, and possibly birds, the spinal cord will frequently re-establish form and function after transection in early embryonic stages ;

'(2) in certain teleosts, at least, the spinal cord retains much of its regenerative capacity well into the adult period ;

'(3) in tailed amphibians, a similar retention of the capacity of the cord to regenerate is present for a varying time following metamorphosis ;

'(4) in amphibians which are tail-less after metamorphosis, the spinal cord may regenerate at least until the loss of the tail . . . ;

'(5) in all these forms, regeneration becomes less complete, both morphologically and physiologically, with increase in age . . . '

SPINAL LESIONS IN MAN

The occurrence of two world wars in one generation provided a stimulus for studying the medical problems that follow damage. to the spinal cord. With complete transection above the level of the phrenic motor neurones (C.3, 4 and 5), death will follow at once from asphyxiation, whilst with low cervical lesions the intercostal muscles will be paralysed but respiration will be maintained by the diaphragm. With cervical lesions below C.5 much may be learnt by studying the musculature of the upper limbs, for characteristic postures will be adopted according to which of the muscles remain active (Fig. 4.8).

One useful sign that may be produced even by incomplete lesions of the cervical region of the spinal cord is *Inversion of the Radial Reflex*.

Walshe & Ross (1936) who studied the reflex changes that are found with such lesions stated that : 'Whereas in amyotrophic lateral sclerosis with which these cases of cervical cord injury are commonly confused, the tendon jerks of the arms are uniformly, and sometimes considerably, increased, in these traumatic cases the various tendon jerks are varyingly affected : some are increased, some diminished or abolished, and one—the supinator jerk—may be replaced by finger flexion (inversion of the

FIG. 4.8.—Transverse section of spinal cord at C.6.   Abduction and outward rotation of the humerus.   Partial flexion of elbow.   Supination of forearm and flexion of hand.   Power was retained in the deltoid, biceps, brachialis anterior and supinator muscles.   As far as the arms are concerned, this condition is the counterpart of Erb's paralysis, sometimes found in newborn children as an obstetrical injury and caused by damage to the upper roots (C.5 and C.6) of the brachial plexus.   On the motor side the sharpness of the level will depend on the vertical extent of the motor neurones supplying different muscles.   The length of the cell columns is known to vary widely—being, for instance, particularly short in the instances of tibialis anterior and posterior and the long muscles of the toes.   Muscles which have such short columns are particularly likely to be permanently paralysed after an attack of poliomyelitis (Sharrard, 1955).   (Figure from Thorburn, 1887, reproduced from Foerster, 1936)

radial reflex).   Thus it is common to find the triceps jerk greatly increased, the biceps jerk normal or diminished, and the supinator jerk, on one or both sides replaced as described.'   Inversion of the supinator reflex is found with lesions at C.5.

It might be supposed that the level of a lesion of the spinal cord would readily be revealed by ascertaining which of the muscles remained under voluntary control.   The level revealed in this way may, however, be less well defined than might be expected, for the organisation of the spinal cord is longitudinal and the anatomical segmentation does not inevitably indicate corresponding functionally discrete subdivisions. Barron (in Weiss, 1950, p. 225) has pointed out that :

'The differentiation of the motor neurones appears to progress temporarily in a cranio-caudal direction without any evidence of segmentation ; those segmental features of the cord that do develop—segmental ganglia, sensory and motor roots—are imposed upon the neural structures by the adjacent somites and their derivatives, the sclerotomes.'

The motor nuclei of the anterior horns are not grouped segmentally but are divided into longitudinal columns (*vide* Sherrington, 1939, p. 139). Romanes (1953) has studied the significance of this grouping. He has pointed out that 'these structures are frequently ill-defined in adult mammals, consisting in regional densities in a scattering of cells in contrast to the clearly defined groups which exist in foetuses'. In the cat the division of the groups of cells is 'in terms of the joint or joints moved and not strictly in relation to the topographical position of the muscles or their neurovascular hila'.

Gowers (1886, p. 128) also was interested in these arrangements. He pointed out that : 'Most movements and muscles are represented in vertical tracts, and the whole anterior grey matter, at any one nerve segment, contains cells that are concerned with different movements. An extensive lesion of small vertical extent may thus weaken many movements, but abolish none.'

Just as the 'level' on the motor side may not be sharp, so similarly on the sensory side the overlap between adjacent dermatomes is great (Foerster, 1933), and an area of altered sensibility will intervene between normal skin and that from which no sensation can be elicited. Corresponding to the level of the lesion there may be root pains giving rise to a sensation that may be described as a sense of constriction in a girdle-shaped zone around the trunk.

Much experimental work on the spinal cord has made use of electrical stimuli delivered to individual dorsal roots. Caution is needed in the biological interpretation of the results that are obtained : 'To stimulate the whole of one single afferent root by itself is to do what Nature never normally does. So also to stimulate one continuous half or fourth of such a root is to do what is never done naturally. The end of a penholder pressed upon the skin anywhere—at least, anywhere on the limbs— excites contemporaneously single nerve-fibres scattered through two consecutive (in many cases three consecutive) spinal afferent roots' (Sherrington, 1939, p. 137).

The sensations that arise from time to time from the viscera are mediated by nerves that pass into the spinal cord, in many cases, at a number of different segmental levels.   Naturally, therefore, the loss of visceral sensation often fails to give much information about the level of a spinal lesion.   As an illustration of this the referred pain that can be set up by squeezing the testis [1] may be mentioned (*vide* Woollard & Carmichael, 1933).   When the posterior scrotal nerves are blocked the pain is felt in the 'maximal points of reference' of L.1 :—over the internal abdominal ring.   If also the genito-femoral nerves are blocked the pain is felt in the 11th thoracic segment and is lateralised to the stimulated side.   *In its migration the testis has obtained an innervation from more than one segment of the spinal cord, and in spite of its anatomical position some sensations may be aroused by pressing upon it in cases of spinal transection as high as T.11.*

After complete division of the spinal cord the musculature innervated from segments below the level of the lesion gradually regains reflexes and finally may develop some tone.   It has been usual to ascribe some prognostic significance according to the existence of 'paraplegia in extension' or 'paraplegia in flexion'.   It has been believed that extension of the lower limbs signified that the lesion was incomplete, but this appears to be unreliable.   There is no way available of telling, soon after a lesion has been inflicted, how extensive is the severence of the motor tracts.   Kabat (1952) has shown how easy it is to overlook a small flicker of voluntary movement that, with intensive physiotherapy, may be fanned into a useful degree of control.   He wrote that 'the demonstration of dormant motor function below the level of the injury to the spinal cord in patients who have had apparently complete paraplegia for a considerable period has been a relatively common finding in our series of patients'.   Kabat noted that with the restoration of some motor power sensation also might gradually return.

John Hilton (1863) reported the case of a man aged 21, who, following an injury to the cervical spine, was completely paralysed in both arms and legs.   There was also 'perfect loss of sensation in the lower and upper extremities, except indistinct sensibility on

---

[1] By contrast the ovaries are almost insensitive to handling.   The cervix and the fallopian tubes are, however, very sensitive, whilst the body of the uterus is less so.   From the uterus and cervix pain is referred to the abdominal wall half-way between the symphysis and umbilicus.   The pain of dysmenorrhoea may be relieved by blocking the iliohypogastric and ilioinguinal nerves with local anaesthetic.   The vagina itself is insensitive to heat (100° C.), cold (0° C.), touch, needle-prick and chemical irritants (Theobald, 1949 ; see also White & Sweet, 1955).   Pain from the pelvic organs may be the cause of backache, but little is known of the mechanisms involved.

the left side as far as the elbow'. He lived for many years and indeed died only as a result of another accident. He used to copy engravings by holding a camel's-hair brush in his mouth, three or four inches in length. Each line was made with the greatest accuracy and precision. Hilton remarked that 'this case forms a great encouragement to give every possible care and attention to the treatment of injuries of the spine, with the hope of obtaining the same happy result'. Nevertheless, until recently, most patients with complete transverse lesions of the cord were doomed to lie, almost to rot, in bed awaiting death from sepsis. They developed extensive bed-sores and intractable urinary infections. A dramatic change has occurred in the outlook for patients treated in centres where the lessons of World War II have been learnt (Guttmann, 1953). Bed-sores can be prevented by a régime that involves changing the position of the patient every 2 hours, day and night, to prevent the pressure of the body cutting off, for long periods, the blood supply to the skin. The rehabilitation involves exercises designed to strengthen those muscles that can usefully take over some of the functions previously performed by muscles from below the level of the lesion.

Great importance attaches to the latissimus dorsi, for it is inserted into the pelvis.

'The latissimus dorsi—that large muscle, with its segmental supply as high as C.6, 7 and 8—by-passes the spinal lesion in any transection of the spinal cord at any thoracic level and up to C.7, and thus connects the paralysed portion of the body with the remaining normal parts. In normal circumstances, the latissimus dorsi will adduct, retrovert and internally rotate the humerus. If, however, the shoulders are fixed by arm crutches or parallel bars, the mobilising part of this muscle is transferred to its insertion points on the thoracic and lumbar spine, the sacrum, and, most important of all, the postero-lateral rim of the ilium, and thus a pull is exerted on the pelvis which results in tilting the pelvis in an upward direction. Moreover, as the gluteus maximus, like the latissimus dorsi, also has its insertion on the lumbar fascia, the upward pull of the latissimus dorsi consequently results in extension of the hip by fascial stretch' (Guttmann, 1953).

Guttmann also points out that : 'It is obvious that the more distal the spinal cord lesion, the greater the number of muscles available with attachment to the pelvis, especially rectus abdominis and obliquus externus, in order to co-operate in the team-work to restore stabilisation of the pelvis, and thus postural adaptation in the spinal man'. The distal insertion of the muscles supplies proprioceptive information from segments of the body below the level of the lesion.

It will be seen that the necessity for the spinal man to lie flat in bed, or to sit up only when supported by pillows, is largely a myth. So successful was Guttmann's rehabilitation programme that numerous patients with complete spinal lesions are now earning their living at sedentary occupations. But systems other than the muscular must be considered in rehabilitation.

ACTIVITY OF SYMPATHETIC SYSTEM IN SPINAL MAN

When the spinal cord is severed above L.2 a part of the sympathetic outflow from the spinal cord is cut off from its connections with the brain stem, hypothalamus and cerebral cortex, whilst the

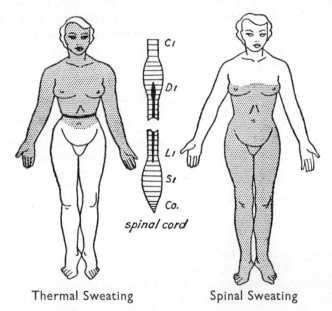

Thermal Sweating   Spinal Sweating

Fig. 4.9.—Distribution of thermoregulatory sweating compared with that brought out by the mass reflex. Lesion at T.8. Note overlap. (After Foerster, 1936, as redrawn by List & Pimenta, 1944)

whole of the outflow is cut off from this control if the lesion is as high as C.8. It is found, therefore, that below the level of the lesion there is a loss of sweating in response to heat (Fig. 4.9) and a loss of pilo-erection (goose flesh) in response to cold. The loss that is demonstrated in this way is not sharp, for the *sympathetic derma-tomes* are very large (Fig. 4.10) and overlap widely, in keeping with the fact that the white rami, emerging from the spinal cord between T.1 and L.2, supply the whole of the body. It has been observed that stimulation of a grey ramus causes movement of hair over one segment of skin, whilst stimulation of a white ramus causes movement of hairs over a number of segments. [Erection of the hair in the

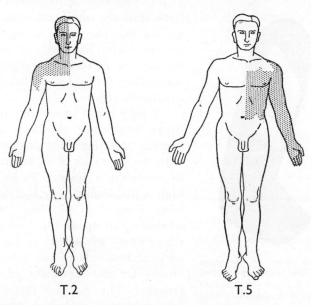

T.2   T.5

FIG. 4.10.—Sweating on stimulation of anterior roots (T.2 and T.5). Note the extensive areas under the control of these pre-ganglionic fibres. (From Foerster, 1936)

human being is an atavistic response serving no useful purpose. It corresponds to erection of the feathers in birds and to the movement of the spines of the hedgehog.]

There is no general agreement about the segmental supply of the sympathetic fibres from the spinal cord to different parts of the body, and differences may occur between different patients and between the two sides of a single patient. The following list has been compiled :

Head : T.1-T.3
Upper limbs : T.4-T.7
Trunk : T.5-T.12
Lower limbs : T.10-T.12

In contrast to this wide diffusion of pre-ganglionic sympathetic effects the pathways in the peripheral nerves do not appear to show more overlap than do the fibres conveying cutaneous sensation (Fig. 4.11).

Removal of various of the sympathetic ganglia which send fibres to the leg reveals a segmental pattern similar to that for sensation (Fig. 2.16, p. 58, cf. Keegan & Garrett, 1948). Richter & Woodruff (1945) have quaintly remarked : 'It is now known that the entire surface of the human body, like that of the sala-mander, is divided into regular seg-ments from one end of the longitudinal axis to the other'.

A high spinal lesion may not only upset temperature regulation by pre-venting sweating but also interferes with the responses of the blood vessels to autonomic changes. Patients with high spinal lesions may therefore feel faint, from drop of blood pressure, when they sit up, as did those patients who were subjected to extensive surgical removals of the sympathetic chains for the treatment of hyper-tension. The vascular bed available for responses operating from the carotid sinus is correspondingly re-duced. Lying in bed, the loss of much sympathetic control may be relatively unimportant; similarly, cats that have been subjected to total removal of the sympathetic chains may remain in good health under ordinary laboratory conditions (Cannon, Newton, Bright,

FIG. 4.11.—Loss of sweating caused by interruption of circumflex nerve by fracture of head of humerus. Area roughly corresponds to loss of cutaneous sensibility. Deltoid and teres minor muscles were paralysed also. A border of 'hyperhydrosis' is sometimes seen around an area dener-vated by a peripheral nerve lesion, particularly if pilo-carpine is used to promote sweating. (Reproduced from Guttmann, 1940)

Menkin & Moore, 1929). Such animals show deficient responses when subjected to some form of stress, failing, for instance, to protect themselves adequately against a drop of body temperature when exposed to cold. They also are more readily fatigued than normal by exercise (Hodes, 1939). Observations such as these show how cautious one must be before saying that a lesion of the nervous system is 'without effect', for the appropriate test situation may not have been devised.

In spinal man much of the sympathetic system may be out of reach of the control of the higher centres, but this does not mean that it is necessarily inactive. Responses come to light in the isolated spinal cord that are not normally seen, or are trivial when its connections with the higher centres are intact.

Such a response of the sympathetic system may be seen when a viscus such as the rectum or bladder is distended. There then may occur, after the stage of spinal shock has passed off, a *mass reflex*, in which there is a flexor spasm of the legs, sweating of the segments innervated by the isolated spinal cord, and contraction of the bladder and rectum. Other stimuli also may set off the response. Thus it may follow the application of a pin to the sole of the foot. As a part of the response the muscles of the body wall contract and increase the intra-abdominal pressure : then the bladder contracts (Denny-Brown & Robertson, 1933 b). The mass reflex is similar in its main features whatever has precipitated its appearance.

It was argued by Head that this represents a return of the spinal cord to a primitive state; this theory has been ridiculed by Walshe (1942 a) :

'The mass reflex consists of powerful bilateral flexion of the limbs, contraction of the abdominal muscles, evacuation of the bladder and an outburst of sweating. This response is not adapted to the strength or site of stimulation, but is maximal and unvarying, yet Head speaks of it as "an excellent answer to noxious stimuli in the lower animal"; able to respond only by a mass movement, the animal is "fixed in a position unfavourable to flight and crawls into a hole to die or recover". Such a creature, even if it could take the steps necessary to propagate its bewildered kind, which appears doubtful, could have no survival value, for on receipt of a stimulus which it could not localise from a stimulating agent whose nature it had no means of discovering, it could respond only by curling up and micturating.'

Is this criticism altogether fair ? After all, some animals (*e.g.* slug, hedgehog) do respond to danger by curling up (see quotation from Herbert Spenser, p. 78). We may, however, certainly draw the conclusion that it is dangerous to apply the doctrine of 'levels' without studying the facts of comparative physiology. It is true that disease processes may uncover mechanisms normally masked and seen in pure form only in more simple animals, but it is quite wrong to assume that because some response is seen in pathological

H

conditions it *necessarily* corresponds to that of a primitive creature. Riddoch & Buzzard (1921) have remarked that : 'The reactions laid bare by injury or disease cannot be looked upon as exact reproductions of modes of behaviour evoked under similar conditions at an earlier stage of human development. In spite of their modifications, however, they bear traces of their ancestry, and also of their relationship with analogous reactions in the intact individual.'

Hughlings Jackson suggested that there were three 'levels' of integration in the nervous system. This view was propounded at a time when knowledge of neuro-anatomy was much less advanced than it now is. Schiller (1952), discussing the concept of levels, has said that : 'Broadly speaking, Jackson's pioneering concept is still ours, namely that the highest, or most complex, processes of the association areas are the least rigidly organised and the most heterogeneous. But the hypothesis of three distinct "levels" was conceived at a time when it may have appeared possible to identify such levels with synaptic relays. Since then, the system of neuronal connections has revealed its most complex, extensively multisynaptic nature.'

Head & Riddoch (1917) were surprised that a patient with transection of the mid-thoracic cord complained of fullness of the head when his bladder was distended. It has become apparent from the work of Whitteridge & Guttmann (summarised in Guttmann, 1954) that the effects of distension of such a viscus may have far-reaching effects upon the autonomic system.

'The basic reflex response to bladder distension in all complete lesions above L.2, with intact, isolated cord, is vasoconstriction in the lower limbs, especially the toes, which is not limited to the skin and is mediated by the lowest part of the sympathetic outflow. Since, in these low lesions, there are large areas of the vascular bed left which can be utilised for vasomotor regulation, the vasomotor adaptation response to the vasoconstriction in the lower limbs is vasodilatation in parts above the level of the lesion, especially the fingers. It may be noted that, in distal lesions of the spinal cord, the increase of bloodflow occurring in the upper limbs as a readaptation response to its decrease in the lower limbs, also involves the vascular bed of the muscles. . . . In spinal transections at or above T.5/6, however, where the whole splanchnic outflow is situated below the level of the lesion, conditions are quite different. In these cases, vasoconstriction in the toes, due to visceral distension, is accompanied by vasoconstriction also in the fingers, and a steep fall in pulse volume in toes and fingers occurs. There is a very large rise in blood pressure, both systolic and diastolic. The pulse rate shows a marked drop and changes of rhythm are noted and the electrocardiogram may show an increase in the size of the U-waves. . . . However, even in these high lesions, an adaptive vasodilator mechanism is mobilised, to counteract the effects of vasoconstriction of even so large an area of the vascular bed. There is a marked vasodilatation in the upper trunk, shoulders, face and neck of patchy type, associated with congestion of the naso-pharyngeal mucosa, resulting in blockage of the nasal air passage.

'From a clinical point of view, knowledge of these responses of autonomic mechanisms in paraplegic patients is important, as these responses represent an alarm reaction of excessive activity of a viscus in the anaesthetic area of the body, and they may be the only indicator of impending abdominal catastrophe. On the other hand, the awareness of some of these phenomena, such as flushing, feeling of heat, etc., can be utilised for the re-education of the paralysed bladder and bowels and even sexual function.'

It will be seen that the effects of a transection of the cord differ from the results that would be expected from a mere loss of function. It is interesting to note that the sympathetic system can be truly paralysed by an intrathecal injection of a local anaesthetic (Sarnoff & Arrowood, 1947). In this way it is possible to paralyse the pathways mediating sudomotor and vasomotor regulation and the sense of pin-prick without disturbing motor power, touch, position or vibration sense.

NERVOUS CONTROL OF MICTURITION

The muscle of the various parts of the urinary apparatus depends to a very varying degree upon the integrity of the spinal cord. Thus the external sphincter, which is composed of striated muscle, is inevitably paralysed when the cord is transected, whereas the ureters may appear to behave normally. Fullerton made some observations of the state of the ureteric orifices in patients soon after the onset of transverse lesions of the spinal cord :

'The ureteric orifices were inspected through a cystoscope after an intramuscular injection of indigo-carmine had been administered in order to observe more easily the urine issuing from them. Several cases with complete lesions of the cervical and dorsal segments were examined, and his conclusions were :

(1) Peristalsis of the ureters continues, as evidenced by the rhythmical discharge of urine from them.

(2) Normal movements of the lips of the ureteric orifice take place, as shown by its visible systole and diastole.

(3) The tone of the uretero-vesical sphincter is maintained and the valve is competent' (quoted from Holmes, 1933).

It should not be supposed that the movements of the ureters and their orifices are independent of nervous control, however, for Learmonth (1931) has shown that on faradising the peripheral end of the presacral nerve there may be a powerful contraction of the orifices to pinpoint size.

The bladder itself is supplied with afferent fibres that set up sensations of distension and of pain, and which form connections with the spino-thalamic tracts (Nathan & Smith, 1951). Iggo (1955) studied the responses of afferent fibres from the bladder of the cat. Activity was recorded in response to *tension* in the bladder wall; the units became active both when the bladder was passively distended and when the viscus actively contracted. The tension receptors behaved, in this way, similarly to endings that were investigated in the stomach, and it is of interest that, as Hurst (1911) pointed out, patients may be unable to discriminate between a small hypertonic and a large atonic stomach. In the case of the bladder it has likewise been noted that distension markedly lowers 'the threshold at which added spontaneous active contractions can produce sensation' (Denny-Brown & Robertson, 1933 *a*).

Nature is not parsimonious with the number of fibres that are used to convey information to the nervous system; furthermore, even in the periphery a multiplicity of routes may be found by which information can reach the spinal cord. In the case of the bladder some afferent fibres enter the sacral nerves but others ascend through the presacral nerve to enter the spinal cord as high as the lower thoracic segments (T.9 and below). Accordingly, 'Normal sensation of desire for micturition ("Harndrang") is regularly abolished by limited sacral lesions, though some sensation, usually unpleasant or painful, of imminent micturition may be retained' (Denny-Brown & Robertson, 1933 *b*).

The presacral nerves may be severed without seriously disturbing micturition, but are we therefore justified in assuming that they play no part under normal circumstances ? Learmonth (1931) has written : 'The sympathetic pathway from the bladder is not essential for the act of micturition. *It follows* [italics inserted by E. G. W.] as a corollary that by far the most important path for "reflex" fibres is the parasympathetic system. . . .' Section of the pelvic nerves does lead to a loss of tone of the bladder and to a failure of the voluntary control over micturition, but inevitably the *efferent* fibres to the detrusor muscle are destroyed. Learmonth's point might be established by investigating the effects of sectioning the dorsal roots of the sacral nerves, but no observations upon this point appear to have been made upon human subjects. Barrington (1915) studied the effects of dividing the posterior sacral roots in cats and his results are in keeping with the view that these pathways do contain fibres of pre-eminent importance for control of the bladder. 'This operation is constantly followed by a lax condition of the bladder which is more marked than after section of both pelvics or than after transection of the cord. . . . The retention of urine after division of the sacral dorsal roots never alters from the day of the operation to that on which the cat is killed.'

Similar results were reported by Dees & Langworthy (1935). They found that section of the posterior sacral roots in cats led to chronic retention of urine, the bladder enlarging up to ten times its normal size. The retention may have been due, in part, to spasm of the internal sphincter, for they found that the bladder emptied automatically when the sympathetic nerves also were divided.

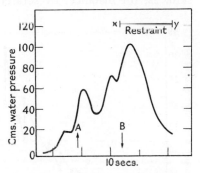

FIG. 4.12. — Normal micturition. Curve shows increase of bladder pressure and at A sphincters open. Subject tries to stop micturating during the period x-y, and at B the sphincter closes, whilst soon after the pressure in the bladder begins to fall. Bladder is smooth muscle but appears to be directly under the control of the will. (From Denny-Brown & Robertson, 1933 a)

When all the nervous connections of the bladder are cut it regains, after a while, power to contract in response to being distended; the emptying is, however, incomplete. It is possible that the act of micturition may on the efferent side normally involve both the pelvic and sympathetic nerves, the former controlling the contraction of the detrusor, the latter the relaxation of the internal sphincter (cf. Fig. 4.12). When it is remembered that the external sphincter, supplied by the pudic nerves, also has to be relaxed at the correct time, it will be seen that moderately complex integrative actions are called for by the central nervous system. Barrington has shown that a number of different reflex arcs are implicated in micturition.

It is not surprising, in view of these considerations, that disturbances of micturition are frequently found in neurological patients. One useful investigation is to perform a *cystometrogram*

(Fig. 4.13) by measuring the pressure in the bladder when it is filled to varying extents (*vide* Voris & Landes, 1940).

Disturbances of the bladder are a serious problem in patients with lesions of the spinal cord. If the transection is complete the bladder behaves at first as an inert bag. As it fills there is only a slight rise of pressure. The patient, if unrelieved, suffers from 'retention with overflow'. Under favourable conditions the nervous, although not the voluntary, control is gradually re-established. Contraction of the bladder may then be brought about by stimuli applied to the skin, as, for instance, by scratching the sacral region. This reflex response may be of value in rehabilitation, for it may enable the bladder to be emptied at times that are convenient. Naturally the reflex does not develop if the lesion involves the terminal segments of the cord. With the passage of time the responses of the bladder may become brisk; the 'automatic bladder' may empty itself when only slightly filled.

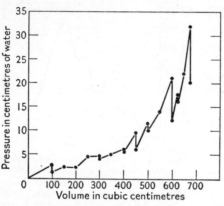

FIG. 4.13.—Normal cystometrogram. As bladder is filled so pressure rises. Each vertical fall of pressure indicates adaptation at constant volume. (Denny-Brown & Robertson, 1933 *a*, reproduced from S. Wright, 1947)

Just as the stretch reflex of skeletal muscles may be brisk or sluggish so, depending upon signals coming into the sacral segments of the spinal cord, the response of the bladder reflexes may be modified (*vide* Langworthy, Lewis, Dees & Hesser, 1936). It has sometimes been presumed that the stretch reflex of the bladder would be affected in any given patient in the same way that the stretch reflexes of the striated musculature are changed, but this is an over-simplification. Watts & Uhle (1935) could find no relationship between the type of cystometrogram and the position of a tumour of the brain, but it is known that quite small frontal lesions may sometimes give rise to incontinence and to little else. In any case, it should be realised that factors other than nervous reflexes can influence the cystometrogram. Thus if, by exteriorising the ureters, the bladder is kept small the mechanical properties of its wall change and it is less readily able to accommodate large quantities of urine.

The bladder produces electrical potentials when it contracts, as does other smooth muscle; attempts have been made to derive information about the state of the bladder by recording from electrodes placed within it (Alexander, Garvey & Boyce, 1954). It is uncertain whether all possible sources of error have been eliminated in these investigations. It may be noted also that the uterus produces slow potential changes when it contracts in labour. Rhythmic waves are generated once every three seconds and there are, in addition, slow drifts (Steer, 1954).

One important function of the presacral nerve, or at least of those filaments within it that arise from L.1, is concerned with *ejaculation*. Learmonth (1931) stated that:

'It has been shown that stimulation of the sympathetic nerves to the pelvis leads to expulsion of semen from the ejaculatory ducts, as a result of contraction of the musculature of the seminal vesicles, and to expulsion of secretion from the prostatic ducts, as a result of contraction of the unstriped musculature which permeates the gland. It is of great physiological interest that, following sympathetic neurectomy, male patients have found that although they could perform the sexual act, and although they experienced a psychical orgasm indistinguishable from the normal, ejaculation did not occur . . . the sensations constituting the orgasm are not directly associated with contractions of the musculature of the seminal vesicles and ejaculatory ducts.'

SYNAPTIC ACTION (*vide* Eccles, 1953)

Much was learnt about the activity of the spinal cord by Sherrington before data were available about the physico-chemical nature of the nerve impulse and synaptic action. Sherrington's analysis was couched in terms that did not invoke the action potential directly, and the Oxford School used the concepts of *central excitatory state* to describe long-lasting changes of excitability which could be demonstrated in reflex centres after stimulation of an afferent nerve (Fig. 4.14). Similarly, the inhibition of reflex activity which long outlasted the afferent volley that was its cause was described in terms of *central inhibitory state*. The time was not ripe for description of central excitatory state ('c.e.s.') or central inhibitory state ('c.i.s.') in physical terms (Fig. 4.15).

Microscopically the spinal cord is exceedingly complex. Lorente de Nó (1939 *a*) has pointed out that the primary sensory nuclei of the brain stem 'share with the posterior horn of the spinal cord the property of having a delicacy and complexity of structure not surpassed by any part of the nervous system, not even by the cerebral cortex'. Even the nervous system of an insect is extremely complex histologically, as Cajal has pointed out (*vide* Sherrington, 1951) :

'The complexity of the nerve-structures for vision is even in the insect something incredibly stupendous. From the insect's faceted eye proceeds an inextricable crisscross of excessively slender nerve fibres. These then plunge into a cell-labyrinth which doubtless serves to integrate what comes from the retinal layers. Next follow a countless host of amacrine cells and with them again numberless centrifugal fibres. All these elements are moreover so small the highest powers of the modern microscope hardly avail for following them. The intricacy of the connexions defies description.'

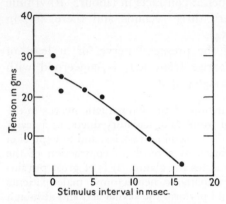

FIG. 4.14.—Flexor reflex. Response of tibialis anterior to two just threshold shocks delivered to different cutaneous nerves. When the stimuli are synchronous summation is greatest but some summation is evident with an interval between the stimuli of more than 10 msec. That weak stimuli in different nerves may add their effects is referred to as 'spatial summation'. (From Creed, Denny-Brown, Eccles, Liddell & Sherrington, 1932, as redrawn in S. Wright, 1947)

Synaptic conduction is unidirectional, at least in vertebrates (p. 4 n.). That excitation should proceed in one direction but be blocked in the reverse might be expected in view of the desirability for the nervous traffic to be routed along one-way pathways. Much work has been done on the effects of discharging impulses 'antidromically' back to the cord along efferent pathways. Changes of excitability may occur and may be due to the excitation invading the bodies of the motor nerve cells (*vide* Eccles, 1953). One difficulty encountered in interpreting the results of antidromic stimulation is that many efferent axones in the central nervous system give off collateral branches which run back into the grey matter (p. 119).

The complexity of the arrangements in the central nervous system is such that it is reasonable to consider first the *autonomic ganglia* that lie outside the central nervous system, for there it is more easy to control the excitation of the nerve cells. It is now possible to do better than to say that 'the synapse is, physiologically, a convention to describe the polarity of conduction in the nervous system of higher animals . . .' (Lashley, 1929). In a classical summary of work in this field Bronk (1939) pointed out that :

'The cells of a sympathetic ganglion are naturally excited by trains of impulses coming to the synapses from the central nervous system over varying numbers of fibers and at frequencies which wax and wane as the

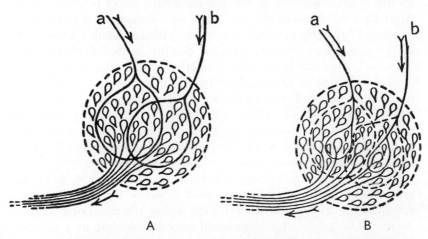

Fig. 4.15.—Motor neurone pool. Effect of excitation of two afferents. The overlap or convergence of their effects upon the anterior horn cells may give rise to 'occlusion', A : effect of simultaneous activation of both is less than algebraic sum of separate effects. Alternatively the 'sub-liminal' fringe may lead to 'facilitation', B—neurones become excited when both afferents are active that do not fire with either separately. (From Creed, Denny-Brown, Eccles, Liddell & Sherrington, 1932)

activity of the centers fluctuates under the influence of afferent stimuli. . . . Inasmuch as the frequency of impulses in the post-ganglionic neurons grades the response of the effector organ, it is important to know whether the frequency of impulses discharged from the centers is modified by transmission across the synapses of the ganglion.'

In attempting to answer this problem many workers have applied rhythmic electrical stimuli to the pre-synaptic fibres and have sought to discover corresponding fluctuations on the efferent side. At frequencies below 20/sec. synchronised volleys of impulses develop trains of impulses at like frequency in each of the post-ganglionic fibres (Bronk, 1939). The 'old and much-debated' problem regarding the modification of the frequency of discharge by the ganglia cannot be answered in this way, however, because under normal conditions the discharges in various pre-ganglionic fibres is far from synchronous. 'A ganglion cell receives the terminations of many pre-ganglionic fibers. Normally these several fibers conduct from the centers to the synapses trains of impulses, which are of different frequencies in the different fibers. The simultaneous arrival of impulses at a cell is therefore only a chance occurrence.'

There is now much evidence to suggest that a nerve cell is only excited when a number of the pre-ganglionic fibres become active. According to Lorente de Nó (1939 a), 'synaptic transmission is "optional" for any neuron ; therefore, without detailed knowledge of the anatomical and physiological conditions that determine the "choice", it cannot be predicted whether stimulation of fibers of a certain nerve, or of a certain pathway, will result in transmission ; nor can it be predicted through which anatomical channels the transmission, if at all, will be effected'. It is certainly true that under normal circumstances ganglion cells discharge at a rate that is not directly related to the frequencies of discharge in the pre-ganglionic fibres.

As in the case of the neuromuscular junction (p. 27), so in the sympathetic ganglion there are good grounds for believing that acetylcholine transmits the excitation across the junctional region. As might be expected, transmission may be blocked in a number of different ways. Paton (1951) lists the following mechanisms of ganglionic block :

(1) Interference with the release of acetylcholine, this is the state of affairs with procaine injections, or with a deficiency of calcium in the fluid bathing the ganglion.

(2) The acetylcholine may be prevented from acting upon the ganglion by some drug which is itself inactive. Curare, tetraethyl-ammonium and hexamethonium act in this way, causing 'block by competition'.

(3) The ganglion cell may be the site of a long-lasting depolarisation so that it can no longer respond to acetylcholine. This is the type of block induced by nicotine, a block that is preceded by a period of excitation. Nicotine has played a large part in the development of our conceptions of the autonomic nervous system, for with its aid Langley was able to localise the sites of synapses.

Now that hypertension is being treated by ganglion-blocking

agents the importance of basic information of this type can scarcely be over-emphasised.

Transmission through *synapses in the central nervous system* has been studied by Lorente de Nó (1939 *a*). He studied the transmission of impulses, initiated by a shock delivered to the floor of the fourth ventricle, to the oculo- motor nucleus. He found that transmission through to the motor axones depended upon suitable facilitation of the pathways involved. If an impulse was discharged it occurred with a synaptic latency that was found to be rela- tively constant (0·5-0·9 msec.). The strongest stimuli produced the shortest delay. Following a stimulus the 'c.e.s.' of the centres was raised for many msec. and he attributed this to re- peated bombardment of the synaptic junctions by impulses that had circulated in reverberating chains (Fig. 4.16). Lorente de Nó argued that prolonged facilitation of this type could not be explained by 'open chains', delay pathways that did not reverberate, but this question must be regarded as still being open to dis- cussion (p. 231).

Recently the discharge of *motor neurones* has been studied with the aid of micro- electrodes thrust through the cell membrane (Fig. 4.17). It appears that the cell may continue to respond normally under these circumstances ; the fine point of the micro- pipette does not inactivate the excitatory mechanisms. This technique has enabled a much clearer picture to be obtained of the events that lead up to the discharge of an action potential by the cell.

With the intra-cellular electrode it is possible to detect the arrival of a volley of impulses at the motor neurone even though an impulse is not discharged by the cell. The potential revealed is analogous to the end-plate potential of the neuromuscular junction ; it is known as the *post-synaptic potential* ('p.s.p.'). It varies in size according to the size of the stimulus that is applied on the afferent side,

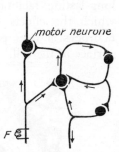

FIG. 4.16.—Scheme to explain facilitation. Stimulus delivered to F in floor of fourth ventricle may be inadequate by itself to excite the motor neurone in the third nerve nucleus. A second stimulus of the same strength delivered at an appropriate interval may, however, be successful. Evi- dently the first shock has changed con- ditions or raised 'c.e.s.' Figure sug- gests that this could be accomplished by a reverberating chain of neurones so that motor neurone is excited both directly by the second shock and indirectly by the reverberation started by the first. (From Lorente de Nó, 1935)

and if the potential reaches a critical value an action potential is discharged. If the afferent volley fails to produce a motor neurone discharge the post-synaptic potential decays away over a period of a few msec. This work supports Lorente de Nó's view that long-lasting facilitation is due to the existence of pathways by which the effects of excitation are delayed to reach the motor neurones at later periods rather than to persistent changes at the surface of the cell.

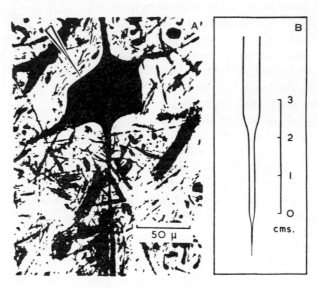

Fig. 4.17.—Microphotograph of motor neurone and its axone. Just about to penetrate the cell is shown a micro-electrode consisting of a fine glass tube drawn out to $\frac{1}{2}\mu$ diameter at the tip. Insert shows main shaft of micro-electrode. (Reproduced from Eccles, 1953)

Following the discharge of an action potential by the motor neurone there is a *negative after potential* of 5-10 mV. which slowly decays over some msec. The negative after potential in other tissues is indicative of a period of enhanced excitability and it is interesting to find that this is probably the case with the motor neurone also. The discharges of motor cells are normally relatively low in frequency (*e.g.* 10/sec.) during a voluntary act, but at times double spikes occur, the second following within a few msec. of the first. It may be assumed that the second spike is discharged at a period of supernormal excitability (Hoff & Grant, 1944). When this mechanism comes into play it often does so at the start of a

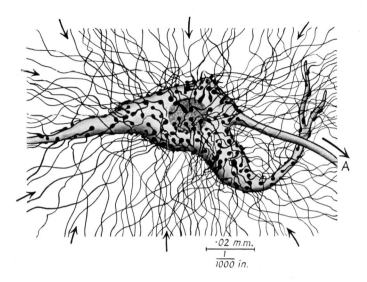

·02 m.m.

$\dfrac{1}{1000}$ in.

Single anterior horn cell showing the 'boutons' on the surface of the perikaryon. After a model by Haggar & Barr, reproduced from Young (1951*b*)

Plate 3

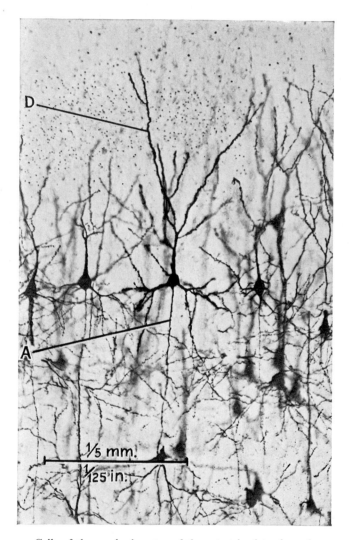

Cells of the cerebral cortex of the cat stained to show the
receiving dendrites (*D*) and the axones (*A*) along which the
output is sent to other regions. The method of staining
colours only a selection of the cells (about one in 50); if all
were fully stained the network would be very much more
dense. Reproduced from Young (1951*b*)

Plate 4

movement and the double spikes cause an increase of tension that is more rapid than otherwise would be the case.

The negative after potential is followed by a voltage drift of opposite sign. This *positive after potential* builds up to a maximum of about 5 mV. in 10-15 msec. and then decays, reaching zero after about 100 msec. The positive after potential is associated with a reduction in the excitability of the motor neurone, and it appears to explain the regular rhythmic response at about 10/sec. that is seen when the cells are excited by asynchronous bombardment which happens, presumably, during most voluntary actions. The higher the intensity of this bombardment the earlier in its recovery cycle will the motor neurone be discharged. This mechanism may be regarded as a device for converting the information from the spinal cord into a form suitable for the control of muscle. The mechanical properties of muscle fibres are such that the strengths of contraction would not be adjustable if the rates of discharge of the motor cells were substantially higher. Irrespective of the rate of discharge of sensory receptors the discharge of the motor neurones is kept on a sliding scale of frequencies suitable to match the information into the muscle (*vide* Marshall & Walsh, 1956).

Earlier in this chapter the views of Hughlings Jackson were considered. The various levels of which he wrote have been compared with the Houses of Parliament. It is interesting to consider in the light of more recent knowledge the 'democratic' or statistical nature of the control of the motor neurone. It has been estimated that there may be as many as 1300 end-bulbs on a single anterior horn cell (*vide* Plate 3). These endings may be either excitatory or inhibitory, and according to current conceptions the state of excitation of the neurone is determined on the basis of a majority 'vote'. The excitatory endings add together their post-synaptic potentials whilst, as is now known, the inhibitory fibres produce potentials of opposite sign (*vide* Eccles, 1953). The neurone will discharge, it appears, when the net effects of the pre-synaptic endings have depolarised the surface membrane to a certain critical value. By way of comparison, it may be noted that whether or not an Act of Parliament is passed or rejected depends upon the balance between the ayes and naes. Grey Walter has suggested that the nervous system should now be compared, not with a telephone exchange but with a totalisator—an instrument for working out the odds in favour of a given course of action.

CHAPTER 5

POSTURE: THE LABYRINTH

Obviously a great deal depends on the course of the pathways from the receptors to the motor nerve cells. We turn right or left when the stimulus is one-sided, because the signals enter the central nervous system from that side and are not evenly distributed ; and we react differently to a sound or a light because the signals come by the auditory and the optic nerves and follow a different route. In less highly organised animals—sea anemones, for instance—each group of receptors may serve a particular group of muscle fibres ; the connections are fixed and there is no central integration. But in the vertebrates there is a great deal of integration, and that means that the connexions and the route travelled by the signals can be varied considerably. . . . The afferent and efferent pattern are partly related by anatomical connexions, but there is an intermediate region where the connexions are sometimes open and sometimes closed and where a great variety of transmission is possible.—ADRIAN (1954).

THE STRETCH REFLEX : PHYSIOLOGICAL TREMOR

THE limits to movement are ultimately anatomical ; the flexion or extension possible in one of the joints of a limb is restricted by bony prominences and by ligaments. Under normal circumstances, however, physiological mechanisms come into play to prevent structural damage. In pathological conditions these agencies may fail and the joints lose their protection. Thus in tabes dorsalis the afferent fibres are damaged and joints may be forced beyond their normal limits without pain being aroused. Over the years repeated minor traumatic events may disorganise a joint so that its normal architecture is scarcely discernible, a Charcot joint.

The nervous system must have mechanisms for limiting the contraction of the muscles to extents that are not likely to injure tendons, ligaments and bones. Large forces are nevertheless exerted ; it has been estimated that in the act of chinning the bar the biceps

exerts a force of half a ton. Mechanisms must be at hand to counteract applied forces if these are likely to break up a postural set. In
addition, arrangements have to be made to counteract the force of
gravity and information as to the position of the vertical must be
obtained. Finally, if the animal has fallen over, or has been asleep
or resting, arrangements must be made to get it into a position
normal for an alert creature.

Basic amongst the postural mechanisms is the *stretch reflex*, a
response to signals transmitted to the spinal cord from muscle
spindles (Fig. 5.1). It has been described thus :

'If the tendon of a healthy muscle is drawn upon by an antagonistic
muscle or by the manipulation of the investigator or by the movement of
a joint in response to gravity, the
muscle actively resists the extending
force. A muscle which has been
paralysed by section of its motor-nerve
or of the ventral or dorsal roots
supplying it, does not actively resist and
behaves like a piece of non-contractile
tissue such as skin. The muscle is
flaccid. The resistance, however, from
a muscle in full connexion with the
nervous system is a reflex contraction,
"the stretch reflex"' (Creed, Denny-
Brown, Eccles, Liddell & Sherrington,
1932).

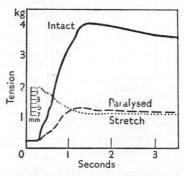

FIG. 5.1.—Response of intact and
paralysed muscle to stretch.
(Modified from Liddell &
Sherrington, 1924)

The stretch reflex is important
in determining the *tone* of a muscle.
'In Greek medicine the healthy tautness which our muscles,
even when not engaged in executing a movement, still keep, was
likened to the tension of a tuned string, and spoken of as τόνος'
(Sherrington, 1951). Tone is difficult to evaluate quantitatively for,
due to its dependency upon the stretch reflex, the tension exerted
by a muscle will be related to the way in which the limb is moved.[1]
In physics a well-known principle—that of uncertainty—points out
that it is impossible to measure a system without at the same time
altering it. Max Planck (1936) has pointed out that 'every measurement, whatever the method of its employment, invariably interferes

[1] Pollock & Davis (1932) devised a method for measuring tone, and their
results are instructive. In normal subjects the principal resistance was of an
elastic nature, like a spring, whilst in Parkinsonism viscous properties (treacle-
like) were developed.

more or less with the event to be measured. . . .' Muscle tone
can be evaluated only by some mechanical means, as by moving the
limb and observing the resistance that is encountered. The reaction
of the muscles will depend both upon the speed and the extent of
the movement. For this reason there are, at times, disagreements
between clinical observers as
to whether a limb does, or
does not, show an increase in
muscular tone. We may conclude by agreeing with the
'indeterminists' (*vide* Max
Planck, 1936) that 'it looks as
though it must be impossible
to distinguish between the
"event in itself" and the
apparatus by which it is
measured'.

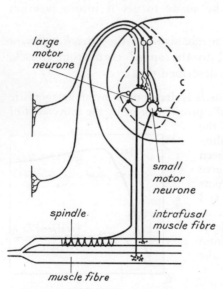

FIG. 5.2.—Stretch reflex. The discharge
of the small motor neurone controls the
length of the fibres of the muscle spindle
and so 'sets' the stretch reflex to stabilise
the muscle at a particular length. The
efficacy with which this stabilisation is
achieved depends upon the facilitation
that the stretch reflex obtains from other
sources. It may be modified both by
cutaneous stimulation (2 fibres from
the skin are shown) and by signals
descending from higher centres. (Modified from Eccles, 1953)

These considerations may
be illustrated by some observations of Weddell, Feinstein &
Pattle (1944). In studying the
electromyogram in hemiplegia
these workers found that although the musculature might
appear quite clearly hypertonic when tested clinically by
manipulating the limb, nevertheless in one position the
musculature might be electrically silent. If the limb was
moved a very small amount
discharges would immediately
commence. By contrast, in
Parkinsonism (p. 393 and p. 428) the rigid musculature was found
to be contracting in response to a steady stream of impulses no
matter what the position of the limb.

The stretch reflex can be looked upon as a feed-back or '*servo*'
system, the contraction of the muscle being regulated according to
the extent needed to prevent the fibres being elongated substantially.
Numerous electrical and mechanical devices (Tustin, 1950) use
similar systems as control devices, and priority in this field is ascribed

to the governors on steam engines (Clerk Maxwell, 1868). The flow of steam into the cylinder is regulated by a valve that is worked off the shaft. If the rate of rotation of the shaft falls more steam is supplied and the change thereby counteracted; similarly if the speed rises less steam is supplied and again the rate is controlled. In this system there are two main factors to be considered. First there is the level at which the rate is set, and secondly there is the efficacy with which changes may be counteracted. In the stretch reflex the small motor fibres control the length of the intrafusal elements and exert a variable degree of 'bias' upon the muscle

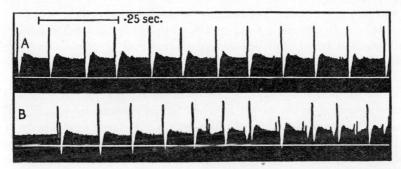

FIG. 5.3.—Discharge of quadriceps muscles of decerebrate cat. A, at rest; B, as the limb is passively flexed. The record is taken at the start of the motion and the activity of the motor unit recorded in A is seen to accelerate in B, whilst another motor unit (small spikes) which hitherto has been silent is brought into play. These records taken by means of needles thrust into the muscle portray the activity of a very small fraction of the whole; similar events are taking place at the same time at other points. The result of this activity is to oppose the force that is being applied to the limb. (From Adrian & Bronk, 1929, as re-drawn in S. Wright, 1945)

spindle (p. 54). Thus the discharge of the small motor fibres alters the length at which the afferent endings start to discharge. In this way the nervous system controls the point at which the stretch reflexes come into play (Fig. 5.2). The efficacy with which small degrees of stretch are counteracted is determined by the ease with which afferent impulses can elicit motor discharges (Fig. 5.3). This is a function of the grey matter of the spinal cord and depends in large measure on the balance of descending inhibitory and excitatory impulses.

In summary, therefore, the activity of the small motor fibres is principally concerned with the position of the limb, whilst the excitability of the grey matter ('loop gain') determines stability.

I

The stretch reflex in one muscle will stabilise a joint effectively only if the muscle that is involved operates against a force acting in the opposite direction, for otherwise, whilst movement in one direction will be prevented, movement in the opposite sense will be unopposed. The force may be provided by gravity but in general there is an alternative system for ensuring stability, for stretch reflexes may be found also in the antagonistic muscles. These responses can probably be obtained from all of the skeletal musculature; the only striated fibres from which they are known to be absent are the extra-ocular muscle (McCouch & Adler, 1952; Daniel & Whitteridge, personal communication). Stretch reflexes may even be present in the musculature of the face (Kugelberg, 1952).

It is a characteristic feature of feed-back systems that the overall result is largely independent of fluctuations of efficiency of the effector elements. Thus, in the steam engine, should the pressure of steam fall, the valve will open further and tend to maintain the rate of rotation of the shaft. The contractile power of a muscle will vary according to the extent to which it has recently been used and to the prevailing metabolic conditions. Quite large fluctuations of efficiency may be offset by the operation of the stretch reflex, for the afferent impulses ('error signals') will cause the motor units to be driven to a greater or lesser extent as required. Fluctuations in muscular efficiency may therefore largely be compensated as long as the muscle is operating under conditions which allow of some functional reserve (p. 363).

It must be pointed out, however, that there would appear to be no means of compensating for fluctuations that may arise in the sensitivity of afferent endings.

One further consideration may be mentioned that is concerned with the problems that arise when the afferent impulses are transmitted along a number of different pathways to the grey matter controlling muscular action. There may result but little alteration in the operation of the system from the destruction of one of the alternative routes. It may be necessary to interrupt nearly all the pathways that carry error signals in order to modify the operation of the system.

These points are relevant to the problem of the *treatment of spasticity*. This common neurological condition may cause great disability (Fig. 5.4). If the legs are rigidly extended the patient may have great difficulty in getting his heels on the floor and may similarly have trouble in raising the ball of his foot from the floor during

walking. If there is also adductor spasm he will not readily be able
to separate his thighs, and in taking a step he will be impeded by
the difficulty of getting the toes of one foot from behind the heel
of the other ; under these conditions extreme exertion may be
involved in a single movement forwards (*vide* Frazier, 1910). In
patients who are bed-ridden, extreme spas-
ticity, particularly of the flexors of the lower
limb, makes nursing extremely difficult. No
pharmacological agent has yet been found with
a sufficiently selective action upon the stretch
reflex to be entirely satisfactory. It is true that
the drug Mephenesin ('tolserol', 'myanesin')
does reduce spasticity (*vide* Kaada, 1950), but
it is liable to interfere also with other functions
of the nervous system. When necessary,
therefore, the treatment of spasticity usually
has to be surgical.

One approach to this problem has been to
divide the *posterior roots* that receive afferent
impulses from the affected musculature. This
therapy is rational, for the increase of tone is
due to an increase in the sensitivity of the
stretch reflexes, but for a satisfactory result
to be achieved it is necessary to destroy the
majority of the pathways concerned with proprioceptive discharges. There is little or no
effect discernible from the section of a single
posterior root ; for the relief of spasticity in
the limbs Foerster (1913) found that it was
advisable to cut no less than five of the roots.
In the arm he cut those between C_4 and T_2
but left C_6, whilst in the leg he cut from L_2
to S_2 but left L_4. In some cases it has been
found that the relief of spasticity uncovers a
degree of voluntary control that has previously

Fig. 5.4.—Spastic child
showing scissors gait
due to hypertonia of
adductor muscles of
thigh and tendency
for heel not to reach
the floor. (By per-
mission of Professor
R. W. B. Ellis & Dr.
T. T. S. Ingram)

been masked and which affords a gratifying therapeutic result.
Nevertheless this operation is now rarely performed, for the
extensive loss of sensitivity of the skin that is inevitable leads to
difficulties. The skin may break down and ulcerate and in bed-
ridden patients bed-sores may develop. For these reasons surgeons
prefer to treat spasticity by attacking the efferent side of the reflex

arc, cutting the anterior roots if the spasticity is widespread, or if it is prominent only in a restricted group of muscles they may section the nerve supply to these muscles peripherally.[1]

These observations upon the effect of posterior rhizotomy illustrate the caution that must be exercised in interpreting the effects that follow destruction of nervous tissue. The observation that a posterior root could be sectioned without disturbing spasticity might easily have led, incorrectly, to the conclusion that the root was not concerned in the maintenance of tone. Clearly, if there are several or more independent pathways concerned with the regulation of some variable (*e.g.* muscle tone), then it may prove very difficult to establish function by observations restricted to the effects of destruction. It is necessary to point out that these difficulties have not been, and still to some extent are not, fully recognised. Camis (1930), writing of the methods adopted by the eminent neurophysiologist Flourens, wrote that he 'followed the rule that, if a "Tactical Guide for the Physiologist" existed, among the many fundamental principles that can be recommended for attacking the problem of the function of an organ, the most elementary and the most general should be : to destroy the organ and observe the consequences of its absence on the general economy of the organism'. The need for care in interpreting the results of ablation experiments applies no doubt equally forcibly to other systems of the body, such as that of the endocrine glands ; but as in neurophysiology (p. 215), these considerations are rarely overtly stated and are frequently disregarded.

It is characteristic of feed-back systems that they become unstable under certain circumstances. In the case of the steam engine (p. 113) a change in speed may take some time to influence the steam coming to the cylinder. The velocity of the engine then tends not to be kept accurately stable but 'hunts' up and down at a frequency that is determined by the construction of the various parts of the system. Hallowell Davis (1950) has some comments that are pertinent in these respects :

'If a substance or state is regulated in the organism it is reasonable to expect that at least two abnormal states or "diseases" will be encountered clinically that can be recognised as failures of normal homeostatic regulation. One "disease" will represent too high, the other too low a level at which the regulation is maintained. A third disorder may

---

[1] For a fuller discussion of the treatment of spasticity see Guttmann (1953), who deals with the problems met with in spinal transection. The treatment of diverse disorders by posterior rhizotomy is described by Waugh *et al.* (1914).

be an abnormally wide fluctuation between upper and lower level. In the language of cybernetics we might say that the "thermostat", to use a specific analogy, gets set too high or too low or that the regulatory mechanism is underdamped and hunts too widely on each side of the average level.'

In simple electrical and mechanical servo systems a great deal of help in understanding the behaviour of the devices may be obtained by mathematical descriptions of the relationships ; in biology, however, the arrangements are usually complicated and mathematical treatments have so far found but a limited field of application (*vide* Kreezer, 1949). In studying the stability or instability of servo systems, however, a number of useful parallels may nevertheless be drawn between the methods used by the engineer and the procedures that have been adopted in the nervous system.

Both for precision of response and for stability it is desirable that the response of the effector system (*e.g.* muscle) should follow the error signals (*e.g.* from proprioceptors) as soon as possible. In servo systems the engineer tries to reduce the *delays* in his system as far as possible. In the nervous system parsimonious use is usually made of rapidly conducting fibres, for they are bulky for the amount of information that they carry. Thus to double the conduction velocity a fibre of twice the diameter will be needed (p. 16) ; this fibre will occupy four times the volume originally required. Nevertheless, in the case of the stretch reflexes the need for postural stability is such that on the afferent side the largest A fibres are used to carry the information from the muscle spindles, whilst on the motor side also large diameter fibres are employed. The cost in bulk of these arrangements is considerable. There are as many myelinated fibres in one optic nerve as there are in all the posterior roots on one side of the body. Delay is also reduced by the arrangements within the grey matter, for collaterals from the posterior root fibres reach to the anterior horn cells (p. 122) and some of the responses at least involve, in this way, only two neurones (Lloyd, 1943).

The long pathways to the foot and the hand, reckoning both the ingoing and outcoming routes, may amount to 2·5 metres. Assuming rates of conduction of 50 metres/sec. on both sides [1] of the reflex arc, it is clear that a delay of 50 msec. will be inevitable around the servo loop to the more distal parts of the extremity. There will also be some delay in the grey matter of the spinal cord, but the existence

[1] A low estimate. The actual values will depend upon the environmental temperature to some extent.

of direct connections to the anterior horn cells from the posterior root ganglia suggests that this time interval will be quite small (*e.g.* $\frac{1}{2}$ msec.) and can be neglected. That there are these direct pathways from the afferent to the efferent side should not lead to the belief that such 'short-circuiting' of the grey matter is inevitable in the stretch reflex. It is probable that other important routes exist that are longer and that involve a number of synaptic junctions (*vide* Magladery, Park, Porter & Teasdall, 1952).

A delay of 50 msec. in the stretch reflex suggests that, if due to an externally applied force the length of the muscle is increased, there will occur $\frac{1}{20}$ second later a reflex contraction that in its turn will lead to a relaxation after an additional $\frac{1}{20}$ second. Under certain circumstances this process might repeat itself indefinitely, leading to an oscillation with a frequency of 10 c/s.

There is another quite different reason for expecting a physiological tremor at 10 c/s. The recovery cycle of motor neurons is such as to suggest that this frequency will often be favoured [1] (p. 109). Whatever its cause, a rhythm at 10 c/s is often observable in records of the stability of fingers. It is an accentuation of this physiological effect that appears to give rise to the tremor seen in hyperthyroidism and in anxiety. A frequency of about 10 c/s is characteristic of the alpha waves of the electro-encephalogram, but this similarly appears to be fortuitous, for the tremor waves are not related in any direct way to the oscillations of the electro-encephalogram (Lindqvist, 1941).

Stability is improved by the use of *a number of independent pathways*. There is not one stretch reflex for each muscle but many; the activity of the various routes if asynchronous will effectively stabilise the limb whilst ironing out the oscillations that would occur if a single circuit only was involved. It is normally found that stretch of one muscle causes that muscle and that muscle only to contract, whilst if the muscle is subdivided into strips, then the stretching of one group of fibres may lead to a contraction of that group, and that group only. Under certain circumstances, when the excitability of the grey matter is altered, it may become apparent, however, that other pathways also come into play whereby the stretching of one strip of a muscle causes not only that strip but also the rest of the muscle to contract (Cohen, 1953). In addition to the coupling of stretch effects in the grey matter of the cord in this way, interaction is inevitable between different reflex arcs in

---

[1] Higher rates will tend to give a smooth rather than tremulous contraction (*vide* Marshall & Walsh, 1956).

the muscle itself, for the contraction of one motor unit will affect proprioceptive endings over a wide area. Some degree of synchronisation of different motor units is therefore to be expected (*vide* Buchthal & Madsen, 1950). Synchronisation may sometimes be identified electromyographically by the occurrence of spikes of different amplitudes that maintain relatively fixed intervals between one another. Occasionally one of the partners may drop out ; other evidence of synchronisation may be afforded by an abrupt alteration in the amplitude of a spike (Landau, 1951).

The mechanical coupling of the various reflex arcs through the muscle must be so close that what is surprising is not that some synchronisation should occur but that it should not be much more prominent. There is also evidence for electrical interaction between the different motor units of a single muscle (Merton, 1954 *a*) ; furthermore, even in denervated muscle the activity of the different fibres tends to get in step one with another (Landau, 1951).

Smooth movements depend upon the *asynchronous* activity of the different anterior horn cells, and it might be expected that special mechanisms would be found in the nervous system that would ensure that the inevitable synchronisation of different pathways due to mechanical and electrical interaction in the muscle would be kept at a minimum. There is some experimental support of this supposition. From the motor axones in the anterior horns collateral branches run back into the grey substance and make synaptic connection with internuncial neurones ('Renshaw cells') that in turn connect with the surfaces of neighbouring motor neurones. A single impulse in a motor axone leads to a repetitive discharge of the *Renshaw cells* and to a hyperpolarisation of the surfaces of the motor neurones. The effect of these changes is to depress the excitability of the other motor neurones, and whilst the depression is at its greatest within a few msec. of the discharge, some depression may be as long-lasting as 50 msec. (Eccles, Fatt & Koketsu, 1954). This mechanism is clearly a means of reducing the degree of synchronisation, for a discharge of one cell is associated with a temporary reduction in the level of excitation of neighbouring cells.

As might be expected, this inhibitory mechanism proves inefficacious when the level of excitation of the motor neurones is very high. It has long been known that when an intense voluntary effort is made the discharges to the muscles tend to synchronise at 40-50/sec. The electrical currents that can be led from the surface of a muscle during maximum voluntary effort may show rather regular sinusoidal waves at these frequencies, an effect referred to as the *Piper rhythm* (*vide* Adrian, 1947 *b*). The existence of these fluctuations may be inferred by the simple procedure of listening with a stethoscope to the contracting muscle. The occurrence of this rhythm does not interfere with the execution of skilled movements, for the fluctuations are too rapid to upset the stability of the limb.

Under pathological circumstances also, synchronisation may become more marked than is normal. On theoretical grounds it might be supposed that disturbances within the grey matter of the spinal cord might increase synchronisation either by damaging the Renshaw inhibitory mechanism or by allowing a greater degree of coupling between the various neural pathways handling the stretch reflex. It is certainly true that disturbances within the spinal cord

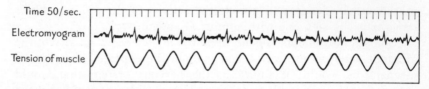

FIG. 5.5.—Clonus : electrical and mechanical records. The synchronisation of motor units was provoked by passively stretching the muscle. A flabby muscle transmits mechanical events poorly through its substance. Passive stretch may be expected, therefore, to increase the mechanical coupling of the different reflex arcs serving the stretch reflex. (Figure reproduced from Creed, Denny-Brown, Eccles, Liddell & Sherrington, 1932)

may increase the tendency for different units to discharge together ; this may occur, for instance, in poliomyelitis (*vide* Denny-Brown, 1949). It might also be supposed that lesions of the pathways descending in the white matter of the spinal cord might facilitate, under certain conditions, the spread of activity throughout synergistic motor neurones. Certain disorders of movement, such as athetosis and chorea (p. 391), resemble normal voluntary motions in that the discharge of the motor neurones is largely asynchronous, but both in Parkinsonism (p. 393) and in spastic limbs there is a greatly increased tendency for synchronous discharges to occur (Hoefer & Putnam, 1940 *a* and *b*). In the spastic limb this is to be expected, for the spasticity is the expression of an exaggeration of the reflex response to stretch. The tendency for the different motor units to get in step may be so marked that sustained oscillations or '*clonus*' may occur (Fig. 5.5). The frequency of these swings is sometimes low (*e.g.* 3 c/s), an expression perhaps of a tendency for polysynaptic stretch reflex pathways particularly to be hyperexcitable. A frequency as low as 3 c/s is not very different from the natural period of oscillation of a limb, thus the size of the swings may become quite large.

TENDON JERKS

The delay in the passage of information round the stretch reflex is the reason why it is possible to elicit tendon jerks. In an ideal servo system with no delay the contraction of the muscle would instantaneously match the applied force. The arrangements of the stretch reflex are adequate when changes occur relatively slowly but cannot deal successfully with rapidly applied forces. The tendon jerk is a response to a stimulus that has already faded before the muscle contracts. Tendon reflexes depend upon postural mechanisms, but they appear to serve no useful purpose; to the neurologist, however, the information that they yield about the integrity and state of the nervous pathways is of the utmost importance (*vide* Wartenberg, 1945).

It has been ascertained that a tap delivered to a tendon so small that the muscle is stretched only 10μ may nevertheless set up a detectable contraction. It often happens that the blow from a tendon hammer is supra-maximal for the reflex so that it may be found that uniform responses are obtained even though no special precautions are taken to keep the blow constant (Bucy & Buchanan, 1933). The sudden stretching of the muscle sets up a *synchronous volley* of afferent impulses that pass to the spinal cord, and it is of considerable interest that this synchrony is preserved on the efferent side of the pathway. At the muscle a large action potential can be recorded at the time of the contraction that represents activity in many fibres occurring at the same moment. After this spike potential the muscle is quiescent electrically; the asynchronous background activity that is normally present is temporarily abolished. This 'silent period' is caused by the cessation of impulses from the muscle spindles as the muscular contraction removes the strain placed upon these endings. Merton (1951) has pointed out that careful timing of the moment at which the afferent impulses start again is needed, for otherwise there might be set up a continuous series of self re-exciting responses. There is often some evidence for a small second contraction after the silent period.

Up to a point it seems that the nervous system may stabilise a limb by using information about its velocity rather than about its position.   A servo system that is set to bring the velocity of a part to zero is liable to be more stable than one which is set to stabilise position itself ; engineers frequently introduce stabilisation which is in part dependent upon velocity into their systems for this reason. That such an arrangement exists in the nervous system would be proved if there was evidence that muscular response was determined by the rate rather than by the extent of stretching of the fibres.

Such a state of affairs is perhaps not very uncommon, for it is frequently found that tendon jerks may be present in a limb that is hypotonic and that shows little if any evidence of a protracted response to stretching of one of the muscles. This is sometimes seen, for instance, during the recovery from spinal shock and under the action of various anaesthetics.   The reverse condition also is

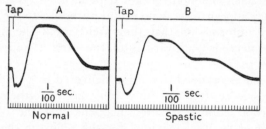

FIG. 5.6.—Knee jerk in normal subject and in spasticity. In the spastic limb the jerk is prolonged and shows undulations in the descending limb of the graph. These fluctuations may develop into a typical clonus, but in this record they are dying away. (After Pritchard from Walshe, 1929 a, re-drawn in S. Wright, 1945)

sometimes seen, namely an absence of the tendon jerks when posture is normal and where it may probably be assumed that the stretch reflexes to protracted tension are functioning normally.   This is found in Holmes-Adie's syndrome (p. 298).   In spastic limbs, on the other hand, the tendon reflexes may sometimes be unobtainable. This absence may be due to the spasticity bringing out virtually the full contractile powers of the muscles, but at times this explanation can scarcely be correct, for the hypertonia need not necessarily be extreme.

The *latency* of tendon jerks is very small when allowance is made for the conduction of impulses to and from the spinal cord. There are indeed grounds for believing that these responses depend primarily upon the integrity of the 2-neurone arcs of the stretch reflex.   Since nearly all of the latency of the reflex is consumed in the peripheral pathways it is evident that whilst changes in the excitability of the grey matter of the spinal cord may alter the number of motor units that respond to a given stimulus, they are unlikely to alter significantly the time at which the contraction occurs (Malcolm, 1951).

It should not be believed, however, that the whole, or even the main, reflex responses to mechanical stimulation of a muscle are dependent upon these short pathways through the spinal cord (p. 117). *Polysynaptic pathways* may be responsible for much of the sustained response to stretch. It is probable, however, that they do not normally contribute significantly to tendon jerks. Under pathological conditions this state of affairs may be altered, and it is probable that the prolongation of the knee jerk that may be seen in a spastic limb (Fig. 5.6) depends upon enhanced excitability of these polysynaptic routes (*vide* Pritchard, 1929) ; a similar explanation may hold for the 'hang up' knee jerks of chorea (*vide* Salomonson, 1920). Occasionally in a spastic limb the prolongation of the knee jerk lasts indefinitely ; onto the phasic manifestation of the jerk is grafted a change of posture. The stretch reflex has become set in another way (*vide* Viets, 1920).

LENGTHENING AND SHORTENING REACTIONS

As has been seen already (p. 113), the setting of the stretch reflex is determined by the discharge of the small motor fibres that regulates the length of the intrafusal fibres of the muscle spindles. It is now necessary to consider something of the ways in which this setting may be modified. When a spastic limb is forcibly flexed it is found, especially if the movement is rapid, that there is a sudden drop of the tension that is exerted. This sudden failure of the reflex is referred to as the '*clasp-knife*' *phenomenon*.[1] It is believed to be due to inhibition arising from stimulation of a group of receptors that may signal that the tension in the muscle tendon is rising to dangerous levels. McCouch, Deering & Stewart (1950) have been able to show that tendon spindles (Golgi organs) are indeed able to inhibit the knee jerk.

By manipulation a spastic limb may be 'encouraged' to take up a fresh position and the stretch reflex may become set at a different length, the 'lengthening' or 'shortening' reaction (Sherrington, 1909). By the operation of the stretch reflex the muscles can bear

[1] This reaction may be elicited, at times, in normal dogs whilst they are asleep.

different weights at the same length; by the operation of the lengthening and shortening reactions they may bear the same weight at different lengths (*vide* Rademaker, 1947).

These responses cannot be discerned in the normal human subject, no doubt because the posture that is adopted depends upon a multiplicity of causes, but the simplification of activity wrought by disease may occasionally leave the lengthening and shortening reactions intact whilst abolishing many of the other neural pathways competing for control of the musculature. These reactions may very often be elicited in hypertonic muscles, and Rademaker (1947) has made a special study of the responses in idiot children.

McAlpine (1924) described a case in which, following encephalitis lethargica (p. 458), the musculature on one side of the body showed these reactions particularly vividly. The limbs could be moulded into new postures by passive manipulation and these positions would be retained for long periods. When the limbs were put into positions that would rapidly have fatigued a normal subject the patient made no complaint. McAlpine stated that in one test the patient held his right hand above his head for half an hour :

'at the end of that time the patient did not complain of the least fatigue in the limb, and was at once able to carry out voluntary movements involving the right shoulder-muscles against resistance, without any appreciable diminution in the amount of muscular force'.

These observations suggest that the fatigue associated with the maintenance of an awkward posture may depend upon central causes. The reduction in strength of a maximal voluntary contraction as it is maintained may also be referred to as fatigue but depends upon changes in the muscles themselves (p. 363).

Reactions that may be related to those described by McAlpine (*vide supra*) can be produced experimentally either by lesions in the hypothalamus (p. 460) or by administration of the drug *bulbocapnine*. This substance produces immobility, with an increase in the resistance offered to passive movement. The body is maintained in attitudes which ordinarily would not be tolerated and it can be moulded into unusual positions that may be retained for long periods. There is extreme economy of movement. Lesions in the upper brain stem render animals hypersensitive to bulbocapnine, whilst the effect of the drug is not substantially altered by partial decortication, sympathectomy, or labyrinthectomy (Ingram & Ranson, 1934). It is perhaps not surprising that this drug which tends to 'freeze' the postural mechanisms should reduce the effects of labyrinthine stimulation (*vide* Babkin, Dworkin & Schachter, 1946).

There are other reactions by which stimuli arising in the limb may influence its posture. One of these reactions is the *magnet* response. This is a cutaneous reflex obtained most readily in decerebrate animals that also have been subjected to a removal of

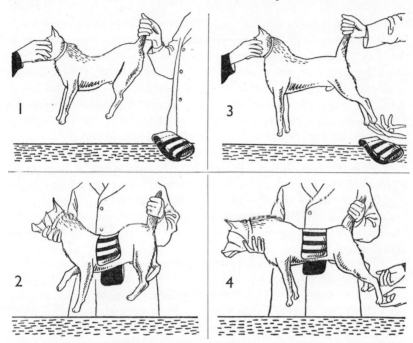

Fig. 5.7.—Magnet reflex, best seen in decerebrate animal from which the cerebellum also has been removed. The animal is supported by the head and tail (1) ; when a sand-bag is placed on its back the curvature of the spine is increased (2). When light contact is made with the soles of the hind-limbs they extend and become rigid supports, the magnet reflex (3). At the same time that the limbs extend the back is tensed and becomes able more easily to support the sand-bag (4). (After Rademaker from Bremer, 1932)

the cerebellum. The lightest touch to the soles of the paw causes an extension of the limb so that the paw follows the experimenter's finger as it is gradually withdrawn, as iron follows a magnet. A reflex extension of the limb also may follow stretching of the interossei muscles : this reflex is clearly of value in walking, for it enables weight to be carried by the limb as it comes into contact with the ground (Fig. 5.7). This effect, and the magnet response, are sometimes referred to as *Positive Supporting Reactions*.

The effects that have so far been considered are local reflexes; stimuli arising within the limb affect the musculature of that limb. It is now appropriate to consider the way in which these reactions are combined together in various patterns.

DECEREBRATE RIGIDITY [1]

Few experiments can be more unphysiological than those dealing with decerebrate rigidity, yet few have been more informative. An easy criticism of many experiments is to say that they are 'unphysiological', but this surely is a misunderstanding of the methods of science that consist in the bringing together of ordered bodies of data.   In any case, the results of experimental ablation of nervous tissue must have much to teach the neurologist.   The decerebrate animal is one in which the forebrain has been removed by a section of the midbrain.   A form of decerebration may also be achieved by depriving the forebrain of blood, but the procedure that is used, ligation of the basilar and carotid arteries, also cuts off the blood supply to a part of the cerebellum (Pollock & Davis, 1930 a).   The brain stem is relatively resistant to anoxia and therefore a rather similar result may follow the intravenous injection of cyanide (vide Ward, 1947).

The decerebrate animal does not move spontaneously, and has no tendency to right itself into a normal position if placed on its side.   It does, however, show an exaggeration of tonus that has been described as *reflex standing*.   In most decerebrate animals the exaggeration of tone is not extreme;   some of the more striking caricatures of standing that have been displayed represent decerebrate animals in which also there has been damage to the anterior lobe of the cerebellum (p. 178).   The increase in tone is due to an exaggeration of the sensitivity of the stretch reflexes, and it is most prominent in those muscles, such as the masseters and extensors of the limbs, that normally are called upon to resist gravity.   In the sloth decerebration often gives rise to flexion of the fore-limbs, in keeping with the fact that the flexors of the fore-limbs are in this animal antigravity muscles (Richter & Bartemeier, 1926; Britton & Kline, 1943).

[1] The term 'rigidity' is sometimes restricted to the type of hypertonia seen, for instance, in Parkinsonism, whilst hypertonia that shows the clasp-knife reaction (p. 123) is referred to as 'spasticity'.   It is this latter type of hypertonia that is present in the decerebrate animal, but long usage would render confusing the substitution of 'decerebrate spasticity' for 'decerebrate rigidity'.

The division of muscles into flexors and extensors is often difficult, for many muscles act not over one but over two joints. The
effect of a *two-joint muscle* upon posture
will depend on the activity present in
other muscles at the same time.   In
certain movements of the limbs extension at one joint is associated with flexion
at a neighbouring joint ; at such times
the existence of two joint muscles effects
a considerable economy as compared
with the metabolic cost of a similar
movement mediated by muscles acting
over single joints only (Elftmann, 1940).

From time to time reports have
appeared of patients who have displayed
features similar to those of decerebrate
rigidity in animals.   Such a condition
may, for instance, be caused by the
pressure of a pineal tumour upon the
midbrain.   Decerebrate patients lie with
their legs rigidly extended but the
position of the arms is more variable :
it may be recalled that in the human
being the upper limb may be called
upon to resist gravity in a number of
different positions.   Kinnier Wilson
(1920 *a*) believed that as in the monkey
(Sherrington, 1898) so in man true
decerebrate rigidity was accompanied
by extension and pronation of the arm,
but some patients that have been described have not shown these features
(Walshe, 1923 *b* ; Davis, 1925).   Clearly,
much may depend upon the level of the
transection and upon its completeness.
Fulton (1943) has suggested that when
the lesion is truly in the midbrain
extension and pronation is the rule,

FIG. 5.8.—Advanced, untreated
case of cerebellar tumour in
a boy.   The internal hydrocephalus has caused the head
to bulge above the ears.   The
rigidity is probably due to
functional *decortication* (p.
277) and the rôle of the
cerebellum is probably unimportant.   The decortication
cannot have been complete,
for he replied to questions
that were put to him. (Hughlings Jackson, 1906 *b*)

whilst when the lesion is higher flexion is to be expected (Fig. 5.8).
In the latter case the condition should be referred to as being
'decorticate' rather than 'decerebrate'.   There is certainly little

information about the pathways that must be severed to allow these forms of spasticity to occur. It might be supposed that occlusion of the basilar artery would give rise to decerebrate rigidity, but a study of 18 patients to whom this catastrophe had occurred showed (Kubik & Adams, 1946) that spasticity was exceptional—flaccid paralysis was the rule (see also Scott & Lennon, 1940).

Decerebrate rigidity is a release phenomenon and is caused by the withdrawal of normal descending impulses inhibitory to the stretch reflex ; it is not due to irritation at the level of the lesion for it persists indefinitely in the chronic preparation (Bazett & Penfield, 1922). Keller (1945), working on dogs, found that the lesion must be higher than the pons, whilst Sprague & Chambers (1953), using cats, found that sections as low as the rostral part of the trapezoid body were followed by hypertonia if the fastigial nuclei of the cerebellum and Deiter's nuclei were not damaged.

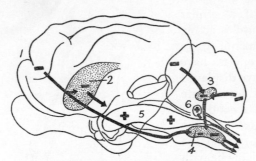

Fig. 5.9.—Pathways controlling muscle tone. Pathways descend to the spinal cord that can both increase and decrease muscle tone. The arrangements are less neat and less well understood than this diagram might suggest, but it does indicate some of the routes that must be considered in a discussion of hypertonia. Pathways causing a reduction of tone are 1, cortico-bulbo-reticular ; 2, caudato-spinal ; 3, cerebello-reticular, and 4, reticulo-spinal. Pathways increasing tone are 5, reticulo-spinal, and 6, vestibulo-spinal. (From Lindsley, Schreiner & Magoun, 1949)

According to Sherrington (1898 b) the hypertonia was not caused by destruction of the cortico-spinal tracts, for following a unilateral ablation of the forebrain of a cat the rigidity was homo-lateral. In human cases of hemiplegia caused by lesions within the internal capsule, however, the spasticity appears on the side that is opposite to the lesion. There would appear, therefore, to be important differences in the importance of crossed and uncrossed pathways in the cat and man.

There are grounds for believing that more than one pathway is concerned in these conditions (Fig. 5.8), but it has taken a long time to make much advance upon Sherrington's analysis. He found that he could not commit himself as to the nervous structures that were involved : 'continued experimentation still leaves me in doubt concerning the actual focus of origin of the rigidity . . .' (Sherrington, 1898 b).

The evidence that is at present available suggests that the *bulbar reticular formation* can influence the spinal reflexes in an inhibitory manner. Magoun & Rhines (1946) tested the effects of stimulating the bulbar reticular formation upon a variety of spinal reflexes. Both flexor and extensor reflexes were abolished, whilst in decerebrate animals stimulation of the bulbar reticular formation leads to a dissolution of tone, the limbs become flail-like. When movements were elicited by stimulating the motor cortex bulbar stimulation held these movements in abeyance. In man the pathways from the reticular formation to the spinal cord run in the anterior half of the lateral column (Hyndman, 1941). The tracts that are concerned in the maintenance of spasticity do not appear to be developed, fully at least, until some time after birth ; for this reason the effects of brain injuries sustained at parturition may not become apparent for a year or more (*vide* Kennard, 1940).

The facilitation of the stretch reflexes that is seen in decerebrate rigidity is due to an important extent to the barrage of impulses that reaches the brain stem through the vestibular nerves, and the rigidity is significantly reduced if the vestibular nuclei are destroyed (Fulton, Liddell & Rioch, 1930; cf. Sprague & Chambers, 1953). It is important, therefore, to consider the sort of information that the labyrinth supplies.

THE LABYRINTH

The word labyrinth is Greek for 'maze', or for 'a building with intricate passages'. The term is apt, for the organ is buried within the petrous bone and consists of a series of passages—the semicircular canals which are connected with two cavities—the saccule and utricle. Both the term saccule and the term utricle are diminutives—saccule of *saccus* (Latin), a sac—utricle of *uter* (Latin), a bag. Finally, the labyrinth connects with the cochlea by the ductus endolymphaticus. In spite of its small size the labyrinth plays an important rôle, for it supplies information to the brain about the position and movements of the head. This information is used as a basis for determining the postural adjustments which are necessary in the musculature of the limbs, trunk and eyes. It is not the only source of information about the position of the head in space ; both proprioceptive and visual sources of information also provide important cues about posture. These alternative sources of data become particularly important when the functions of the

K

labyrinth are disturbed. Many patients with labyrinthine disturbances are conscious of a disordered perception of space and they
may say that they feel *dizzy*. This term is applied to a number of
states associated with a feeling of confusion (*vide* McNally, 1953).
In Old English the term meant 'foolish' or 'stupid'. It is important,
therefore, always to attempt to discover whether or not a sense of
rotation was present, for such a sensation may plainly point towards a
disturbance of the labyrinthine system. The term 'vertigo' is applied
to such a sensation ; the word is derived from *vertere*, 'to turn'.

At times under experimental conditions the data concerning
position derived from the different sense organs will not correspond
(cf. p. 328). In this connection Wood's (1895) account of a 'haunted
swing' at a fair is interesting :

'On entering the building we found ourselves in a spacious cubical
room, furnished with a sofa, table, chairs, etc., a massive iron safe, and a
piano, together with other minor articles. But the most conspicuous
object was the huge swing, capable of holding forty or more persons,
which hung in the centre, suspended from an iron cylinder which passed
through the centre of the room. We took our seats and the swing was
put in motion, the arc gradually increasing in amplitude until each
oscillation carried us apparently into the upper corners of the room.
Each vibration of the swing caused those peculiar "empty" sensations
within which one feels in an elevator ; and as we rushed backwards
toward the top of the room there was a distinct feeling of "leaning forward",
if I can so describe it—such as one always experiences in a backward
swing, and an involuntary clutching at the seats to keep from being
pitched out. . . . The device was worked in the following way : The
swing proper was practically at rest, merely being joggled a trifle, while
the room itself was put in motion, the furniture being fastened down to
the floor. . . .'

Witkin (1949) seated a person on a chair that could be tilted in
any desired direction. The 'room' in which the subject was placed
was a large box, appropriately furnished, which itself could be tilted
as required independently of any slant of the chair (Fig. 5.10). Seated
erect in a backwardly tilted room the body may be perceived as
leaning forwards, whilst seated in a room inclined to the right the
body may be perceived as being inclined to the left. If the room
is rocked rhythmically, the person may feel that his body is swaying
in the opposite direction. In general, therefore, visual information
is used as the principal basis for orientation, and data from the
labyrinths and proprioceptive system are interpreted in this light.

When there is a *conflict of sensory cues* as to orientation the subject may complain of feeling ill and being dizzy. He may suffer also from headache, sweating and nausea. These symptoms are commonly found in patients with diverse diseases, and it is possible that in a substantial proportion of cases they stem from a disturbance of the systems concerned with the perception of position.

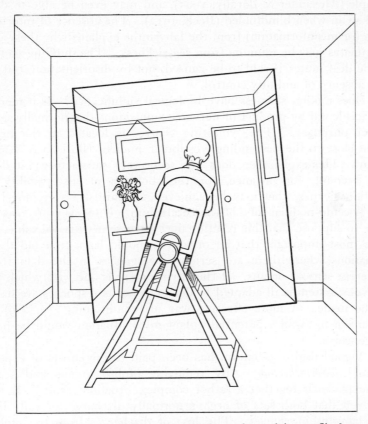

FIG. 5.10.—Tilting-room/tilting-chair experiment for studying conflict between visual and labyrinthine estimation of verticality. (Witkin, 1949)

Similar symptoms occur in *sea-sickness*, and it is clear that in a rolling ship, as in the experiments of Witkin, the nervous system may be faced with conflicting data (see review by Tyler & Bard, 1949). Seafarers are likely to base their orientation on visual cues, regarding the deck, for instance, as horizontal and stationary. With a swell on the sea the information from other sensory channels is incompatible with this interpretation.

In hereditary *deaf mutism* the labyrinths may behave normally and may even be larger than normal, but when, for instance, the condition has arisen from infantile meningitis, these structures may be functionless (Young, 1921). Deaf mutes with functionless labyrinths may, on land, estimate the vertical as accurately as normal people (Alexander & Bárány, 1905), and may even be able to dive and swim when blindfolded (Beck, 1912). The absence of information (or misinformation) from the labyrinths explains why these unfortunates may be immune from sea-sickness. The shuffling gait of some deaf mutes is said to be caused, not by disorientation, but by the absence of auditory control.

Does motion sickness have biological significance? Is it merely an accidental by-product of nervous connections that normally serve other purposes? The 'vomiting centre' is located in the brain stem close to the descending vestibular nucleus (Borison & Wang, 1949). This explanation does not seem very satisfactory; it does not account, for instance, for the abolition of susceptibility to motion sickness that may be achieved, in animals, by removal of the flocculo-nodular lobe of the cerebellum. It seems more reasonable to suppose that this reaction does have some survival value, for it is most important that an organism should learn to avoid those situations where there are serious divergences in the data from different sensory organs. If the environment is one with which the nervous system is ill adapted to deal, erroneous responses are liable to be made. A more effective way of 'conditioning' (p. 219) an organism to avoid a potentially dangerous situation would be hard to conceive.

A good deal of attention has been paid to the effects of experimental *labyrinthectomy*. By removing otolith organs and semicircular canals together a rather complex situation results. It will be seen that both sets of organs normally discharge tonically into the labyrinthine nuclei. The loss of discharges from the otolith organs might normally correspond to the head being tilted out of its normal position, whilst cessation of discharge from semicircular canals would correspond to rotation. Many of the otherwise puzzling sequelae of labyrinthectomy can be explained by assuming that the C.N.S. is operating to reduce the asymmetry of signals from the two sides. This principle is of use also in interpreting changes of bodily position caused by natural stimulation of the labyrinth.

The effects of labyrinthectomy are more profound in simple vertebrates than in those more highly evolved. Following unilateral labyrinthectomy, it is usually found that the head and eyes deviate towards the side of the operation (Dow, 1938 *c*). It is also found that there is a reduction in the tone of the homolateral limbs, a change that may be the result of the alteration in the position of the head with respect to the body, for when this is corrected passively the tone may be equal on the two sides once again (*vide* tonic neck reflexes, p. 151, & de Kleijn, 1923, Figs. 7 and 8). Because of these abnormalities of posture the animal tends to fall over towards the operated side, whilst when it runs or walks it travels in a circle deviating to the side of the lesion. The signs are accentuated, and are observable for longer post-operatively, if the animal is blindfolded during the examination.

The drift of the eyes to the side of the operation may be corrected periodically by quick flicks in the opposite direction ; there develops a horizontal 'nystagmus'. *Nystagmus*, although now restricted to rhythmic eye movements, did not originally signify this ; the term is Greek in origin and originally referred to sleep. During sleep, it may be noted, the eyes may roll to and fro in a smooth way as though driven by a slow pendulum ; this motion may commence as soon as the person drops asleep (Miles, 1929). The popular use of 'nodding' as a synonym for sleep may be remembered.

As time goes by these effects are less plainly seen; in some unknown way readjustment occurs to the new conditions. If after an interval the opposite labyrinth is destroyed the effects reappear in mirror image form, the head, for instance, deviating now to the newly operated side. The disturbances that are produced in this way by removal of the labyrinths one at a time may be much more severe than those that follow their simultaneous eradication. If the 8th nerves on both sides are sectioned at the same time in the dog 'the head oscillates in every direction ; it is very mobile and does not resist movements which are imparted to it. During walking the limbs are in slight abduction, the head describes oscillations of great amplitude . . .' (André-Thomas, 1910).

The effects of labyrinthectomy in the normal human subject are, naturally, unknown, but the labyrinths are occasionally destroyed or the 8th nerve sectioned to alleviate Ménière's disease (Cairns & Brain, 1933, and *vide infra*). The changes that have been reported after the operation are relatively slight—for a few days there is nystagmus which is principally horizontal but which has also a rotatory component. As in animals, the slow phase of this horizontal motion is directed to the side of the lesion. The movements are of greater amplitude when the person looks towards the opposite side, for there is then available a greater range over which the eyes may drift. The paucity of symptoms following section of the 8th nerve in cases of Ménière's disease may be due to destruction of tissue in the labyrinth having occurred with preceding attacks.

Ménière's disease itself is of interest for the light it throws upon the effects of acute disturbances of labyrinthine function. Some otologists recognise two forms, provisionally named the *canal type* and *otolithic catastrophe* (Tumarkin, 1936). The first is much the commoner. In it the patient is suddenly seized with vertigo and falls down, 'collapsing like an empty suit of clothes'. He keeps his head still, for any movement of it accentuates the vertigo. He has nystagmus, is nauseated and sometimes sick. In otolithic catastrophe the patient is suddenly thrown down, 'collapsing like the closing of a clasp knife': the rare fatal accidents that occur in Ménière's disease probably depend on this mechanism. Tumarkin wrote that :

'One of my patients declared that he was standing at his desk talking to a client and the next second he was flat on his back on the floor. Another man, a furniture remover, was standing in his van when suddenly he collapsed. His own words were that he thought one of the wheels must have fallen off and that the van had crumpled up. There is no loss of consciousness in these attacks, and my patients have never complained of nausea, faintness, sweating or other sympathetic symptoms. They do not complain of disorientation ; indeed there is hardly time, as the attack only lasts a matter of seconds and ends almost as quickly as it began.'

THE OTOLITH ORGANS (Fig. 5.11)

These interesting sense organs are represented widely in the animal kingdom, being found, with modifications, in invertebrates as well as in vertebrates. In one form they consist of tiny cavities lined with sensory epithelium, upon which rests an *otolith* or 'earstone'. The part of the cavity that is pressed upon determines which of the afferent nerve fibres will be active, and in this way the animal is provided with information about its orientation. The otoliths are usually produced metabolically and in some vertebrates (eel, plaice, young minnows) they are laminated—one ring per year. By contrast some invertebrates use particles which they pick up each time they moult ; this allowed Kreidl to investigate the functions of these organs. He supplied iron filings instead of sand. When he held a magnet above the animal it turned over as though the force of gravity was directed towards the sky. It should be remarked that an organ with such a 'plumb line' will give the position of the vertical accurately when it is not in movement, but erroneous indications are likely when it is subjected to *linear accelera-*

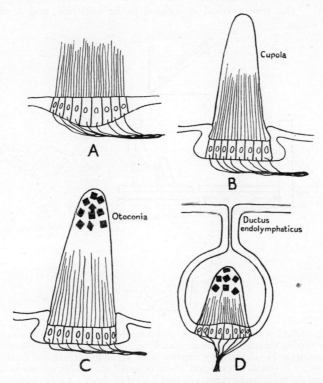

FIG. 5.11.—Evolution of otolith organs. A and B represent neuromast organs found in fish. C is a hypothetical intermediary form before the sensitive structure is enclosed beneath the surface to form an otolith organ, D. (From Pumphrey, 1950)

tion. If, for instance, the animal accelerates forward at 981 cm./sec./sec. the registration of the otolith organ may be expected to change 45° (Fig. 5.12). Similarly these structures are sensitive to centrifugal force. There is no easy way for the animal to overcome these ambiguities. When the aircraft engineer requires a referential plane he makes use not of a plumb line but of a gyroscope, a device that naturally has no biological counterpart.

The foregoing considerations help to explain how it is that motion may upset our sense of the vertical. Greenwood (1910) stated that :

'It is well known that from an express train moving round a curve houses bordering the line appear bent towards the carriages. . . . In rotation round a vertical axis, in an experimental modification of a "merry-go-round", the true vertical is judged to be inclined, and a plummet

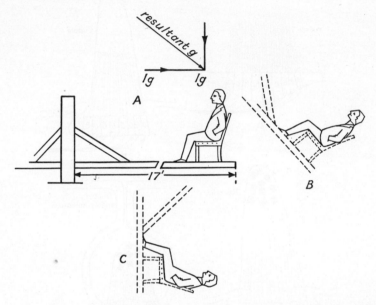

FIG. 5.12.—Effect of centrifugal force on estimation of vertical. Illusion of tilt of body during rotation in human centrifuge, *A*. *B* shows perception of tilting backwards at 45° induced by rotation with involving centripetal force equal to gravity *g*. *C* shows unexpected effect of small increment of rate of rotation. 'When the radial acceleration reached a level of about 1·5 g., a dramatic change occurred. The subject felt that he was motionless and resting on his back, the platform appeared vertical and motionless and the walls of the room were perceived as rotating around him. This phenomenon resembles that which an aviator may experience when in a spin.' (White & Benson, 1952)

which has taken up a position due to the resultant of the two forces, the vertical component of gravity and the angular horizontal rotational force, is judged to be really vertical; for instance, a pendulum will take up a position depending on the magnitude of these two forces and appear to be vertical (Purkinje)'[1] (Fig. 5.13).

[1] Greenwood is here referring to observations made by Johannes Evangelista Purkinje (1787–1869).

The otolith organs indicate the resultant of the forces, including gravity, that are acting upon the head and they give useful information about the posture that should be adopted. If a frog is placed on a tilting-board so that its head is raised, it leans forward and a similar change of posture occurs if it is subjected to linear acceleration forward. In both cases the centre of gravity is changed and the change is appropriate to ensure stability. The fact that the otolith organs are sensitive to gravitation and linear acceleration is not therefore necessarily a handicap (*vide* Tait & McNally, 1925). The reactions of the otoliths may prevent our 'feet being pulled from under ' us when a vehicle in which we are standing changes its speed (Fig. 5.14).

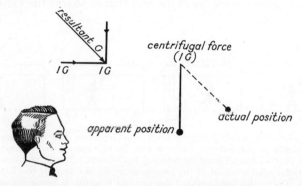

FIG. 5.13.—Incorrect estimation of verticality during rotation. Rotation causes pendulum, the bob of which is luminous, and seen against an otherwise completely black background, to swing outwards. This motion may not be perceived by the observer, for his own otolith organs will be acted upon by similar forces. (From White & Benson, 1952. After Patterson & Graybiel)

Mach (1875) placed a person on a large balance and noted the conditions under which, with the eyes covered, movement could be perceived as the balance swung up and down. The sense of rising came at or just before the top of the excursion, the sense of falling at or just before the bottom. The sensation was thus most striking when the acceleration was greatest ; a value of 12 cm./sec./sec. was needed to reach threshold. This figure is in satisfactory agreement with the thresholds quoted by Jongkees & Groen (1946) of 6-13 cm./sec./sec. The direction in which the linear acceleration occurs is said to have little influence on the values obtained.

An otolith organ is liable to be stimulated also by *vibration* (*vide* Löwenstein & Roberts, 1951). Relatively minor mechanical alterations of these organs may be expected to change their 'tuning' so as to respond preferentially either to tilt or to vibration. If the sensory cells adapt rapidly the structure will be insensitive to gravitation. In the frog some of the fibres of the vestibular nerve, perhaps those originating in the saccule, respond to vibration but not to head tilting (*vide* Ross, 1936).

In man the sensory epithelium does not cover the whole of the inner surface of the otolith cavities but is restricted to one region as in Fig. 5.11 (D) (*vide* Quix, 1925). The sensory cells bear hairs that are embedded in a jelly-like substance, the *otolith membrane*. Within this membrane calcareous particles may be found. The function of the organ evidently depends upon a difference in density between the membrane and the endolymph. Vilstrup & Vilstrup (1952) have taken advantage of the fact that in sharks the cartilaginous

FIG. 5.14.—Loss of stability during linear accelerations and decelerations. In a vehicle that is accelerating balance can be maintained by leaning forwards, in one that is decelerating by leaning backwards. If the acceleration is too abrupt, the readjustment of the musculature by the otolith mechanism is too slow as it is in this figure where the upright position is being maintained only with the aid of the strap. (From Starr, 1946)

skeleton enables the calcareous particles of the otoliths to be seen as sharp shadows on X-ray photographs of the head (cf. Fig. 5.15). They found that on rotating the head the otoliths moved almost as much. The membrane is able to shift in relationship to the sensory epithelium; the movements, although small (*e.g.* 2°), are still measurable.

The significance of the otolith organs can be investigated by observing the effects that follow their destruction, but the small size of these organs and the difficulty of obtaining surgical access are amongst the difficulties which the investigator encounters. It is not useful to attack the utricles directly, for to do so would inevitably disturb the functioning of the semicircular canals and render the results difficult to interpret. The *saccule* is further from the canals, however, and has been removed successfully in rabbits. After the operation the animals behave normally under most circumstances, but if the head is subjected to linear motion acting along an axis joining the ears equilibrium is lost (Jongkees, 1950).

The effects of excluding the influence of the *utricles* have been investigated in the frog by Tait & McNally (1934). These workers avoided damaging the labyrinth itself and accomplished their result by dividing the small branches of the 8th nerve. After sectioning the nerves supplying the *utricles* on the two sides the reactions of the animal to slow tilts was lost. Even when the table on which it had been placed was steeply inclined the posture was not readjusted. Writing of their results these workers said that:

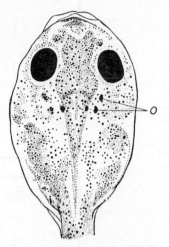

'The ablatory evidence so far available indicates with tolerable certainty that the organs of the labyrinth concerned in reflex adaptation of bodily posture to the field of gravity are the utricular maculae. . . . Their part is, presumably on the occurrence of some form of otolithic displacement, promptly to break up an existing postural set and as promptly to impose one that is physiologically more suitable to the changed inclination of the substratum.'

Precise knowledge concerning the way in which the otolith organs signal changes of position can come only from a study of the activity of single nerve fibres. Löwenstein & Roberts (1949) found that the sense endings in the maculae of the thornback ray normally show a *resting discharge*, the frequency of which is increased or decreased by positional changes. Two main types of receptor were found according to

FIG. 5.15.—Head of tadpole showing brain and otoliths, *O.* 'The larvae of Rana guntheri, when reared in a white porcelain dish, are light orange in colour, and the outlines of the brain remain visible to the naked eye and under the microscope for over a fortnight. Frequently we could see under the microscope the continual rostrad and caudad movements of a black particle in the fourth ventricle, indicating the existence of pulsation in the cerebrospinal fluid.' (From Wang & Lu, 1941)

whether the maximum of discharge was in the 'side up, nose up' or 'side up, nose down' positions. Their findings are of great interest, for they show that both the utricle and the saccule of this animal may respond both to fore-aft and to lateral tilts. The membrane of the utricle lies horizontally whilst that of the saccule lies vertically (Quix, 1925), and on the basis of these features it has previously been believed that the utricle was sensitive to fore-aft tilts whilst the saccule was sensitive to lateral tilts (Fig. 5.16).

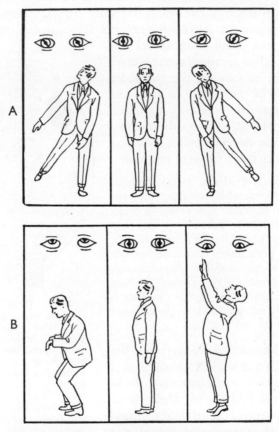

FIG. 5.16.—The two otolith organs are located in different planes. The membrane of the saccule is in the vertical plane, whilst that of the utricle is horizontal. It has therefore been supposed that stability in the lateral direction was dependent upon the saccule A, whilst fore-aft stability depended upon the utricle B. Modern electrophysiological investigations have thrown some doubt on these suppositions, showing that receptors having similar properties can be found in both the saccule and the utricle (Löwenstein & Roberts, 1949). It is, however, reasonable to try to ascertain in patients suffering from 'dizziness' whether they are particularly unstable when moved in a particular direction. For this purpose more use might be made of unstable platforms on which the patient is required to balance and which are connected to recording instruments. (*Vide* Wapner & Witkin, 1950.) (From Quix, 1925)

Direct data as to the performance of the mammalian otolith organs are lacking, but Adrian (1943) has been able to pick up responses of single units in the vestibular nuclei (Fig. 5.17). He found that there were two types of gravity-controlled response, those sensitive to fore-aft and those sensitive to lateral tilts. Whether or not these responses came from the utricle and the saccule respectively was not clear, but it would be important, in man, to attempt to identify a system concerned with tilts in the medial and another concerned with tilts in the lateral plane. Clearly, it may be expected that the symptom of unsteadiness may at times be caused by a disturbance of one or other of the otolith organs or of their central connections.

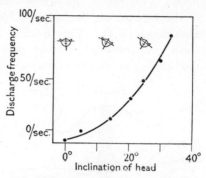

From time to time, indeed, disturbances of equilibration are much more prominent in some positions than in others. Similarly it may be found that nystagmus depends upon the position of the head in space (Cawthorne, 1954). In some cases of *positional nystagmus* it is hard to escape the conclusion that the otolith organs are playing a major rôle (*vide* Bárány, 1921), although it is possible that when this condition occurs in association with tumours that changes in the position of intracranial

FIG. 5.17.—Response of otolith organ of cat to lateral tilting of head. Responses picked up on one side of brain stem. Tilt downwards sets up discharges, the frequency depends upon the angle of tilt. Discharges are well sustained, showing little evidence of adaptation. (Adapted from Adrian, 1943)

structures may be responsible (*vide* Nylén, 1931). Positional nystagmus is very common in patients suffering from tumours in the posterior fossa ; in particular the presence of nystagmus that changes direction with changes in the position of the head argues strongly in favour of the presence of such a lesion rather than a forebrain tumour. It is likely that some of the 'dizziness' that may follow a head injury is caused by damage to the otolith organs as a result of a sudden acceleration (*vide* Phillips, 1945 ; Rådmark, 1944). It may be recalled that centrifugal force has been used experimentally by Wittmaack to detach the otolith membranes from the sensory epithelium in guinea-pigs. A similar mechanism might damage the utricle and saccule in a head injury.

THE SEMICIRCULAR CANALS

In mammals, including man, and in most other vertebrates, there are three of these canals on each side of the head, but in the lamprey, a primitive chordate, there are two canals only for each side, whilst in the hagfish there is only one. The understanding of the function of these organs has been greatly facilitated by a study of the structure of the jelly-like mass which is attached to the sensory hairs. This mass—the *cupola*—has been shown to stretch the whole of the way across the ampulla like a swing-door in its frame (*vide* Dohlman, 1935). This finding has been the result of observing fresh preparations; it was previously believed on the basis of the small size of the cupola in fixed histological preparations that the canal was not occluded. Actually the fit appears to be quite a tight seal (Fig. 5.18), as though the cupola is a little too big for the ampulla, and indian ink injected into one side does not readily pass into the endolymph on the other side of the obstruction. When the cupola is deflected from its mid-position a slight leak may develop, and it may be expected that one pathological condition that must occur is an insensitivity of the canals due to a leak in this mechanism.

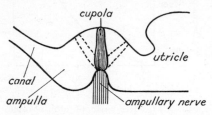

FIG. 5.18.—Structure of ampulla of semi-circular canal. The cupola reaches from its base to the opposite wall and normally is a tight fit. (From S. Wright, 1952)

Under these circumstances it will be evident that stimulation of the hair cells will depend upon the movement of endolymph in the canal driving the cupola out of its normal position; it appears to slide on the crista bodily rather than to bend (Vilstrup, 1950). Movement of the endolymph will occur when the head is subjected to angular acceleration or deceleration but not to rotation at an even tempo. To illustrate this fact a reply given by Eddington in *The Nature of the Physical World* to a related question may be illuminating :

"'You must find the journey between Cambridge and Edinburgh very tiring. I can understand the fatigue, if you travel to Edinburgh ; but why should you get tired if Edinburgh comes to you?' The answer is that fatigue arises from being shut up in a box and jolted about for nine hours ; and it makes no difference whether in the meantime I move to

Edinburgh or Edinburgh moves to me. Motion does not tire anybody. With the earth as our vehicle we are travelling at 20 miles a second round the sun ; the sun carries us at 12 miles a second through the galactic system ; the galactic system bears us at 250 miles a second amid the spiral nebulae ; the spiral nebulae . . . If motion could tire, we ought to be dead tired.'

The discharges of receptors of the semicircular canals have been studied by several workers (*e.g.* Ross, 1936; Löwenstein & Sand, 1940 ; Adrian, 1943 ; Zotterman, 1943). There is general agreement that at rest some of the endings may be spontaneously active. It is usually found that rotation in one sense increases the rate of discharge, whilst rotation in the opposite direction decreases the activity. If a steady angular velocity is maintained, then the discharge of the impulses returns to the resting value in about 20 seconds. This time interval corresponds with that found for the interval needed for the cupola when displaced to return, by virtue of its elasticity, to the mid-position ; accordingly it appears that the discharge is closely related to the position of the cupola at any given moment.

With these arrangements the registration of the extent of a rotation will not be accurate when this extends over many seconds. Under normal conditions, however, such rotations are but rarely encountered, and for the registration of short lasting movements the system is entirely satisfactory. The subjective estimation of the extent of a rotation is fairly accurate provided that the duration of the movement does not exceed 3 seconds (*vide* Egmond, Groen & Jongkees, 1949). When continued rotation is necessary, as when a dancer pirouettes, the head is not rotated steadily but is carried round by a series of accelerations and decelerations (*vide* Adrian, 1943).

One important function of the labyrinth is concerned with maintaining the direction of the optical axes stationary when the head moves. To be more precise, by the operation of certain *orientation reflexes* the image of objects upon the retina moves less than would otherwise be the case when the head moves. Both the otolith organs and the semicircular canals appear to be concerned in these responses, whilst there is also a contribution from receptors in the neck (*vide* de Kleijn, 1921 ; de Kleijn & Versteegh, 1924). Wendt (1936) studied the movements of the eyes of normal subjects during horizontal rotation of brief duration on a platform. He found a movement of the eyeballs that was sufficient to reduce to $\frac{1}{2}$ or $\frac{1}{3}$ the displacement of the retinal image.

After the compensation has taken place there is a tendency for the eyes to drift slowly back towards the mid-position. Evidently the function of the vestibulo-ocular reflexes is to maintain the rate of movement of images across the retina sufficiently small to prevent the definition of the visual 'image' that is sent to the brain being seriously blurred.

It is not difficult even without the use of special apparatus to convince oneself of the reality of the vestibulo-ocular reflexes. On staring fixedly at a naked electric light filament and then covering the eyes an after-image of the filament is seen (p. 316) that is probably due to prolonged disturbances of the retina where it has been stimulated. If now the head is rotated to one side or the other it will be observed that the after-image moves in the same sense but to a much smaller degree. Without the intervention of the vestibulo-ocular reflexes the after-images would move with the head to the full extent of the motion. Similarly when the head is inclined to one side it will be seen that the image is inclined to an extent that is much less than might be anticipated whilst the compensation for flexion and extension of the neck also appears to be substantial (*vide* Fischer, 1928).

Some idea of the importance of the vestibulo-ocular reflexes can be gained from the account given by Ford & Walsh (1936) of the symptoms following lesions of the vestibular nerves. One patient was a physician, aged 26, who had his right 8th nerve sectioned for the relief of Ménière's syndrome. 'When his head was immobilised, his vision was clear and there was no apparent movement of objects, but the least movement of the head made everything seem to move before him. Turning of the head to the right caused this phenomenon to appear in a more severe form than turning to the left. Several weeks later the patient could walk steadily if he was careful to avoid sudden movements of the head, but even then he found that his powers of ocular fixation were so deficient that he could not always recognise friends whom he passed in the hospital corridors, since their faces appeared to be in constant violent motion. If he would pause a moment and hold his head still, he could see clearly. The patient found that riding in an automobile caused the same phenomenon unless the road was quite smooth, for the least bouncing of the car made objects dance before his eyes.' Another patient whose case is reported by Ford & Walsh noticed, after section of both 8th nerves, that :

'Objects seemed to move before his eyes unless his head was kept perfectly still. Walking caused objects to "jump" before his eyes to some extent, but this did not interfere much with his gait. He found, however, that when crossing the street, he was apt to be very unsteady because he would have to turn his head to either side to look for approaching cars. Consequently he had become accustomed to hold his head very stiffly and to walk in straight lines looking directly before him.' Similar disturbances have been reported after inadvertent damage to the labyrinthine system by the drug streptomycin. 'Dizziness' is particularly noticeable on moving the head and the surroundings are seen either as blurred or as dancing. At first the gait is straddle-legged and in the dark the patient is almost helpless. Experiments on rabbits have shown that the drug attacks the canal rather than the otolithic mechanisms (de Kleyn & Deinse, 1950).

One useful method of testing the labyrinth would be to impart small rotations to the head and observe the efficacy of the vestibulo-ocular reflexes. The practical difficulties that are encountered have, however, led to other methods being adopted for clinical purposes. In the *Bárány test* the subject is seated on a rotating chair and is turned round once every two seconds.

With special apparatus it is possible to investigate the movements of the eyes whilst the subject is being rotated. Thus the eyes may be photographed with a ciné-camera mounted on the chair or they may be observed directly if the chair is fitted with the ingenious optical system devised by Hallpike, Hood & Byford (1952). It is necessary to prevent the subject seeing objects that would give evidence of his motion, for otherwise the effects of the labyrinth would be supported by optokinetic responses (p. 332) that would obscure a deficient response of the vestibulo-ocular system.

During rotation the eyes exhibit nystagmus with the slow phase in the direction that would be appropriate in order to maintain the position of images upon the retina relatively fixed; the type of nystagmus that is produced varies, therefore, according to the position of the head. If the patient looks vertically upwards the nystagmus will be rotatory, whilst if it is in its normal posture they will be horizontal. If the head is inclined towards one shoulder the eyes oscillate vertically between the superior and inferior margins of the orbit. Nystagmus continues as long as the cupola is deflected ; with uniform rotation the movements cease in 20 seconds.

It is not practicable normally to observe or record these eye movements in the ways that have been mentioned because of the complication of the apparatus and technique. In the Bárány test, therefore, the subject is rotated for 20 seconds at a uniform rate and

L

is then abruptly brought to rest. The reactions of the eyes [1] that are then seen are naturally those that would be appropriate for a rotation occurring in a direction opposite to the one that has just ceased, for the cupola will have been carried past its mid-position and will be pointing now in the opposite way. In keeping with this the subject experiences a sense of vertigo.

In order to test particular canals it is necessary to ensure that during rotation those under investigation lie in the plane of rotation. Thus to test the 'horizontal' semicircular canals the head must be brought forwards 30°, since only when this is done do they become truly horizontal (Fig. 5.19). Similarly, to test the 'vertical' canal the head should be bent forwards through 120°.

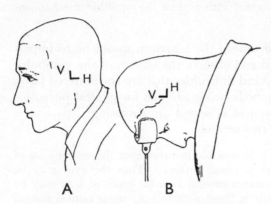

FIG. 5.19.—Stimulation of semicircular canals by rotation. To bring the horizontal canal into the horizontal plane the head must be bent forwards 30°, as in A. To bring the vertical canals into the horizontal plane the head must be bent 120° forwards or 60° backwards. The position shown in B will stimulate all 4 vertical canals and will give rise to a rotatory nystagmus. (From Best & Taylor, 1939)

It can be shown on physical grounds that the stimulus to the canals is not dependent upon the position of the axis of rotation as long as the same angular acceleration is achieved. Rotation is liable always to disturb the semicircular canals on both sides of the head and an abnormal reaction may therefore be difficult to interpret. These considerations show that methods of investigating the labyrinth that depend upon the stimulation of one side only (*vide infra*) are necessarily producing a situation to which the organism has hitherto been unaccustomed. The speed of rotation used in the Bárány test (180°/sec.) ensures that when the subject is stopped a very powerful stimulus is delivered to the cupola. Some workers believe that this stimulus is too strong and may temporarily damage the sensitive structures in the canals (*vide* Jongkees, 1952 ; van Egmond *et al.*, 1949). If the rotation is arrested in $\frac{1}{10}$ second the

[1] In infants a period of rotation in the horizontal plane is followed by head as well as eye nystagmus (Mygind, 1921).

deceleration is at the rate of 1800°/sec./sec., a very severe jolt. According to Tumarkin (1936), the Bárány method is 'rather like testing knee jerks with a sledge hammer'.

An alternative method of testing the canal system is to measure its 'threshold'. In normal people the sense of rotation may be produced by accelerations as trivial as 0·2 to 1·0°/sec./sec., but nystagmus cannot readily be detected unless the stimulus is at least 3°/sec./sec. (Hallpike, Hood & Byford, 1952).

Unilateral stimulation of the labyrinth may be accomplished *galvanically* by placing one electrode on the mastoid and another electrode on some other part of the body. The exposed labyrinth is extremely sensitive to electrical currents responding to a fraction of a microamp (Löwenstein, 1955). This extreme sensitivity may indicate that as is the case with other receptors the hair cells may be stimulated by 'generator potentials'. Mechanical deformation of the lateral line organs of fish set up electrical potentials, a fact that may be significant since these structures are related to the vestibular apparatus of other vertebrates (Jielof, Spoor & de Vries, 1952).

As a clinical test galvanic stimulation of the labyrinth is of somewhat limited usefulness for, when electrodes are applied to the skin, most of the current runs not through the labyrinth being tested but by other routes. It is not possible, therefore, to provoke violent labyrinthine reactions, or even to induce responses that can be detected at all, in bedridden patients. If, however, the patient can stand it is possible to make his balance sufficiently precarious to be upset with currents that are relatively weak and which are therefore painless (Blonder, 1937). If a person stands with his eyes closed and with his feet close together, current strengths of as little as 0·5–2·0 mA may normally suffice to cause him to fall (Dix, Hallpike & Harrison, 1949). It may be noted that galvanic stimulation affects the nerve terminals, and so when it can be applied it may indicate whether a defect lies in the mechanics of the labyrinth or in the nerve. The extent to which galvanic reactions depend upon the otoliths has not been established.

A more satisfactory test depends upon *caloric stimulation* of the labyrinth by running into the external canal water that is of higher or lower temperature than that of the body. This test depends upon the setting up of convection currents in the semicircular canals and is applied most successfully to stimulation of the horizontal canal. This canal bulges into the middle ear, whilst the vertical canals lie deeper. Naturally convection currents are set up most effectively when the canal under investigation lies vertically ; to bring the horizontal canal into the vertical the patient should lie down with his head propped up at 30°. Fitzgerald & Hallpike (1942) used this method extensively, and their technique is widely adopted, although it must be admitted that few can achieve results as reproducible as those obtained by these authors. They used water 7° C. above or below the body temperature (37° C.) and they ran it as a

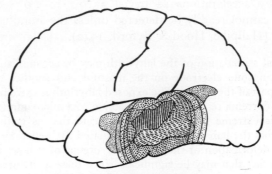

A. Labyrinthine Nystagmus

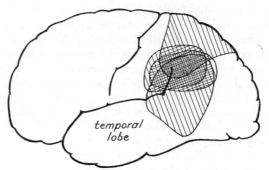

B. Optokinetic Nystagmus

Fig. 5.20.—A, directional preponderance of caloric nystagmus in cases of cerebral disease. The temporal lobe is implicated. Nystagmus, with its quick phase to the side of the lesion, is enhanced. B, directional preponderance of optokinetic nystagmus (p. 332). A different cortical region (supramarginal and angular gyri) is involved. Again it is nystagmus with its quick phase to the side of the lesion that is relatively enhanced. Each shaded area corresponds to one patient. (Carmichael, Dix & Hallpike, 1954)

steady stream into the external ear for 40 seconds. Under normal circumstances a nystagmus is produced that lasts from $1\frac{1}{2}$ to $2\frac{1}{2}$ minutes (measured arbitrarily from the start of the stimulation).

Quite apart from revealing unilateral damage to the labyrinth the caloric tests may show that nystagmus is more readily provoked to one side rather than to the other. Thus the reactions seen after stimulating the right ear with warm water or the left ear with cold water may both be enhanced ; in each case the nystagmus produced has its slow phase directed to the left. Similarly in another patient it may be found that responses to those stimuli that provoke nystagmus directed to the right (warmth to right ear, cold to left) may be relatively exaggerated. Such differences are known as '*directional preponderance*', and have some diagnostic value. If a cortical lesion is known to exist, the finding of directional preponderance to one side suggests that the temporal lobe on the same side is damaged (Figs. 5.20 and 5.21 and *vide* Fitzgerald & Hallpike, 1942 ; Carmichael, Dix & Hallpike, 1954). This result is in keeping with what is known of the cerebral representation of the labyrinth ; the area concerned is believed

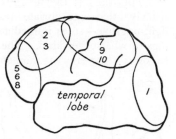

FIG. 5.21.—Areas of destruction of cerebrum in a series of patients with normal labyrinthine reactions. The temporal lobe is not involved. (Fitzgerald & Hallpike, 1940)

to lie close to the auditory cortex (p. 282) in the superior temporal gyrus. In cats the corresponding area has been shown to be connected principally with the ipsilateral labyrinth (Gerebtzoff, 1940). The impulses have been traced upwards along a route similar to that followed by the auditory impulses ; thus vestibular messages can be recorded both from the inferior colliculus and from the medial geniculate body (Gernandt, 1950).

SOMATIC EFFECTS OF LABYRINTHINE STIMULATION

The effect that the *semicircular canals* can exert upon the somatic musculature may be illustrated by considering the changes that follow rotation in the Bárány test. The most dramatic effects are obtained if immediately after rotation the position of the head is changed abruptly. If, for example, the head has been held during rotation in such a way as to stimulate the horizontal canals, then the after-effects that are experienced will be due to impulses arising in these same organs. If as soon as the subject is arrested the head is hyperflexed, then the subject will experience a sensation that he is falling to one side or that the floor is rising up to meet him, as might happen in an earthquake. The subject makes postural adjustments that are in keeping with these interpretations and may lean over, clutching the side of the chair in fear of falling. These reactions are quite inappropriate, and the experience may be alarming; they illustrate in an exaggerated form responses that may normally be set up from the semicircular canals. Tait has remarked that :

'This then is the first great characteristic of semicircular function, namely, that appropriate responses are made—quick, rapid, almost lightning-like—so as immediately to counteract sudden tiltings and jerkings of whatsoever kind. The canals are called into action by something sudden; their effect is momentary and evanescent' (Tait, 1926).

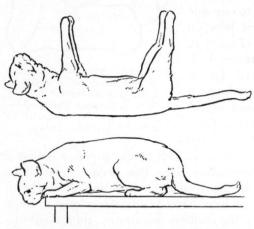

FIG. 5.22.—Change of extensor tone caused by labyrinth (decerebrate cat). This effect appears to depend upon the utricle. (Reproduced from Bell, Davidson & Scarborough, 1950)

When a person experiences a sense of rotation it will be found that voluntary actions are performed in a way different from normal. If he believes that he is rotating he will, if asked to point in a fixed direction, impart a movement to his arm to compensate for the motion of his body. This compensation may occur even if he is, in fact, still whilst experiencing the sense of rotation; thus after rotation in the Bárány test there will be reason to expect *past-pointing* in the direction of the preceding movement. On the other hand, the person may be aware that his sense of rotation is erroneous and modify his responses, trying, for instance, to keep his arm still. Past-pointing, therefore, is likely to be unreliable as a labyrinthine test, and indeed less than half of normal people past-point in the direction of preceding rotation, some past-point in the opposite direction (*vide* Dorcus & Mowrer, 1936).

The somatic musculature is also influenced by impulses from the *otolith organs*. A tonic influence is exerted and the position of the limbs is found to vary, according to the position of the head in space. The effect is most readily seen in the decerebrate animal, where the absence of spontaneous movements affords a favourable

background against which these responses can be seen. In quadrupeds it is found that the limbs are extended when supine, but that
they tend to flex when the animal is turned over into the prone
position (Fig. 5.22). In making observations upon these responses it
is important that the position of the head relative to the body should
not be changed, for if it is, the responses will be modified by messages
from receptors in the neck (*vide infra*). It is usual, therefore, to
make observations of this type with the neck encased in plaster of
Paris. Alternatively, the posterior roots of the upper cervical region
may be sectioned.

Very few observations have been made upon the tonic labyrinthine reactions in the adult human subject (*vide* Rademaker, 1935);
to rotate the whole body in the median plane through a wide angular
range without upsetting the position of the head in relationship to
the body is clearly an engineering feat demanding the use of a
tiltable couch. Observations have been made upon these responses
in children by de Kleijn (1923). The 4 children he investigated
suffered from amaurotic idiocy. Changes of limb posture were
observed, but the results with different children did not tally.
Further observations on this point are surely needed and could
easily be made in a hospital devoted to mental deficiency.

TONIC NECK REFLEXES

In addition to the position of the head affecting posture through
the otolith organs it also affects posture through receptors in the
neck (Fig. 5.23). These reflexes can be seen free from the complica-
tions of the otolith effects in animals that have been labyrinthectomised, and it is then found that turning the neck towards one side of
the body gives rise to an extension of the limbs towards which the
head is turned and a flexion of those on the opposite side. These
responses may be seen more readily in the decerebrate rather than
in the intact animal. Some of the receptors at least concerned with
these reflexes lie in the joints of the neck, especially the atlanto-axial
and atlanto-occipital joints (McCouch, Deering & Ling, 1951). The
effects of these endings are ipsilateral, for if the joints on one side are
denervated, the neck reflexes operate only in the contralateral limbs.

The importance of the neck reflexes may be illustrated in the
following way :

'Suppose a cat is standing in the middle of the room, and a mouse is
running on its right side along the wall. The optic and acoustic stimuli

act on the telereceptors of the cat's head, and make it turn the heavy head to the right. By this the centre of gravity of the fore part of the body is displaced to the right. At the same time tonic neck reflexes are evoked, by which the vertebral column is curved and the right fore-limb strongly extended, so that it carries the weight of the body alone and prevents it from falling. The left fore-limb has nothing to carry, and in harmony therewith this limb relaxes under the influence of the tonic neck reflex. At the same time the distribution of excitability in the motor centres of the spinal cord is rearranged by the turning of the neck, so that, if for some reason running movements begin, the limb which has no static function will always make the first step. In this way the moving mouse impresses on the cat through the mediation of tonic neck reflexes an attitude by which the cat is focussed towards the mouse and made ready

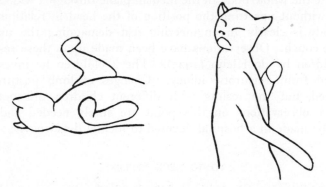

FIG. 5.23.—Tonic neck reflexes in decerebrate cat. (Reproduced from McCouch, Deering & Ling, 1951)

for movement. The only thing the cat has to do is to decide : to jump or not to jump ; all other things have been prepared beforehand reflexly under the influence of the mouse, which will be the object of the resulting jump' (Magnus, 1925).

In the *newborn*, particularly in the prematurely born, the tonic neck reflexes can often be demonstrated (Pacella & Barrrera, 1940). A little later the eyes and head will follow a moving object, and in this way the tonic neck reflexes ('t-n-r') may be driven by visual information. Gesell & Amatruda (1945) have given the following account of these reactions.

'At 4 weeks, for example, the t-n-r attitude is held with sustained fixity, directed prevailingly either to the right or to the left. At 16 weeks, the attitude is more labile and is coming under optical as well as neck torsion control. In a favourable (normal) subject, one is able to induce now a right, now a left t-n-r response simply by passing the hand slowly across the infant's field of vision.   The infant responds with a shift of t-n-r attitude, as though he were an automaton under photo-electric influence.   This reaction indicates the neurological incorporation of optical controls. . . . In the fetal-infant the t-n-r attitude may be completely determined by proprioceptive neck stimuli.   Face but not gaze is directed toward the extended arm.   In the newborn post-fetal

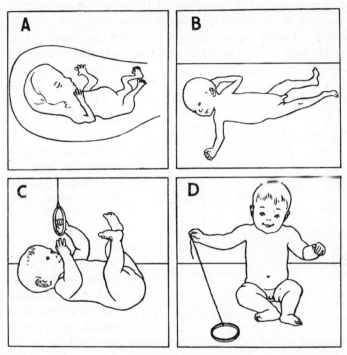

Fig. 5.24.—Changes in posture during development.   A shows symmetrical habitus of foetus ($11\frac{1}{2}$ weeks). B shows tonic neck reflex in premature infant (born at 28 weeks).   C, symmetrical prehensory activity in baby 20 weeks old.   D indicates greater versatility possible at 40 weeks. (From Gesell & Amatruda, 1945)

infant, visual fixation may be absent or rudimentary.   As the infant grows older the gaze becomes sustained for near objects and later it adapts to both near and distant objects.   At 10 or 12 weeks, he may regard his forearm and hand with transfixed attention.   At 20 weeks, his regard becomes versatile.   He makes a perceptual distinction between his hand and an object ; the asymmetric attitude gives way to a bilateral approach upon the object.   At 24 weeks, whether seated or supine, he makes a direct unilateral approach.   He reaches and grasps on sight.

'This new postural visual-manual-prehensory pattern is a landmark in the ontogenesis of behaviour. The infant has transcended the limitations of the archaic motor system. But from the standpoint of embryology, the new behaviour events have their developmental roots in the old. The t-n-r complex in a broad genetic sense is a matrix within which a wide array of postural and eye-hand co-ordinations are achieved and organised.'

As time goes by the responses of the musculature become more complex and in the adult the effects of the neck reflexes often pass unnoticed. Luhan (1932) showed that the responses could more readily be seen when the weight of the limb was counteracted by means of slings; the movements that he recorded were relatively small (*e.g.* 2·5 cm.) but quite definite. The neck reflexes are exaggerated in limbs that have lost their proprioceptive supply, as, for instance, when the posterior roots are severed (see discussion of paper by Pollock & Davis, 1930 *b*).

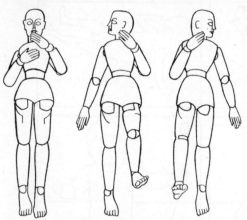

FIG. 5.25.—Posture of limbs in decerebrate rigidity in man and the effect upon them of rotation of the head. (From Walshe, 1923 *b*)

In testing for tonic neck reflexes under clinical conditions it is most satisfactory to arrange that the head is kept in the same horizontal plane, whilst it is slowly rotated so as to restrict any tonic effects to the neck receptors and avoid changing the gravitational stimulus delivered to the otolith organs. Tonic neck reflexes may sometimes be vividly demonstrated during the administration of a general anaesthetic, and similarly they may be seen in patients with decerebrate rigidity (Fig. 5.25). In cases of hemiplegia also the position of the paralysed side may be affected by turning the head to one side or to the other, whilst the reflexes also may change. The Babinski response (p. 373) may be more readily obtained when the head is turned away from the side that is being tested (Walshe, 1923 *a*).

In addition to the changes that have been discussed above which follow rotation of the head towards one or the other side of the body, other responses are found that depend upon the extent of flexion or extension of the neck. Flexion of the neck so as to bring the chin towards the chest gives rise to flexion of the fore-limbs and extension of the hind-limbs. These effects are most satisfactorily demonstrated in the labyrinthectomised decerebrate animal. If the labyrinths are left intact it is necessary to consider the interplay between the responses due to the otoliths, that affect all four limbs similarly (p. 150) and these neck reflexes. In this instance the effects add together as in an algebraic sum, so that when the head is bent downwards in the decerebrate cat there is a marked flexion of the fore-limbs and a partial extension of the hind-limbs,

FIG. 5.26.—In decerebrate animal posture depends not only upon labyrinth but also upon position of head with respect to body. The outcome depends on the extent to which the tonic neck reflexes support and antagonise those effects that are mediated by the labyrinth. In man correspondingly, the reactions to tilting vary according to information the C.N.S. has as to posture. Zador (1938) studied the reactions of normal subjects when placed on a tilting-platform. If they were on all fours and tilted, head-end downwards, the arms extended and buttressed the trunk (*en arc-boutement*), but if the subjects were seated the arms flexed. It is a function of the nervous system to vary the response to a given sensory stimulus according to other relevant data

whilst when the neck is extended there is a marked extension of the fore-limbs and a flexion of the hind-limbs (Fig. 5.26).

Afferent impulses do not, however, always add their effects together in this simple manner ; at times a particular combination of signals will evoke a response that would not be suspected from a study of the effects of one form of stimulus taken by itself. This point may be illustrated by some observations of Brain (1927), who was interested in the *flexor position of the upper limb in hemiplegia*. If a hemiplegic patient gets into a posture that is unstable the limb may extend so powerfully that it cannot be passively flexed.

'It is remarkable to observe the conversion of a limb which the patient could not voluntarily extend into a rigidly extended prop capable of supporting for a time the weight of the upper part of the body.' Brain remarked that 'in physiological terms, extension of the upper limb is reflexly evoked by impulses derived from the labyrinths and the muscles and joints of the spine and hips'. That either set of impulses alone is ineffective was shown because 'in the supine position flexion of the limb and spine no longer evokes extension of the affected upper limb but increases the flexor tonus. It is, in fact, only when the position of the head in space and the position of the neck are such as are naturally associated with the quadrupedal attitude that flexion of the limbs and spine evokes extension of the upper limb.' Here is a clear example of a truth that psychologists have long realised, that the reactions of a system taken as a whole cannot necessarily be deduced from the reactions of the sub-systems of which it is composed.

Another reaction that probably depends upon joint impulses was studied by Bieber & Fulton (1938). In the monkey (Macaque) a slight rotation of the pelvis may alter the position of the hind-limbs. Rotation 15° to the right, for instance, caused an extension of the right hind-limb and a flexion of the left.

RIGHTING REFLEXES

Many of the reactions that have been considered so far appear to be concerned with preserving the *status quo*. Reactions come into play to oppose applied forces or to prevent an alteration in one part of the body disrupting the whole attitude (Magnus, 1925). It is now necessary to consider what happens when these mechanisms fail and the animal falls over, or wakes from sleep. In each instance a radical alteration has to take place in the position of virtually all the parts of the body in order to re-establish an attitude that is a satisfactory one for an alert creature.

The reactions that are capable of re-establishing normal posture after it has been lost are known as righting reflexes. An important part in them is normally played by the otolith organs. They enable the head to be orientated into its normal position and therefore, as a secondary result, they may bring into play tonic neck reflexes. The labyrinths orientate the cat as it falls through the air (Fig. 5.27).

In addition vision may play an important rôle. The human being uses many visual cues for orientation, the rabbit none. In the human being the features of the environment considered significant will depend largely or entirely upon learning, but this is not necessarily the case with other forms of life. Thus fish adopt such a position that the two eyes are equally illuminated ; a carp, placed between two unequally bright lights, takes up a slantwise position (Thibault, 1949). A simple mechanism such as this could well be mediated by genetically determined neural structure.

Other righting reflexes depend upon information derived from nerves supplying the *skin*. Maxwell (1923) has pointed out that a dog-fish that has been deprived of its labyrinths does not right itself when placed belly upwards in the water, but 'such a fish rights itself promptly as soon as it comes in contact with the bottom of the aquarium'. Similar reactions are found in mammals (*vide* Maling & Acheson, 1946). A monkey from which the cerebral hemispheres have been removed and which has also been deprived of its labyrinths will nevertheless right itself, using as information the unequal distribution of pressure on the body. If a board of about the same weight as the body is placed upon the animal, the head may not be lifted off the ground. Under normal circumstances the information derived from the skin may be used to orientate the head towards the vertical, but even if the head is immobilised the cutaneous information may still be of significance, for it may set into action righting movements on the part of the musculature of the trunk.

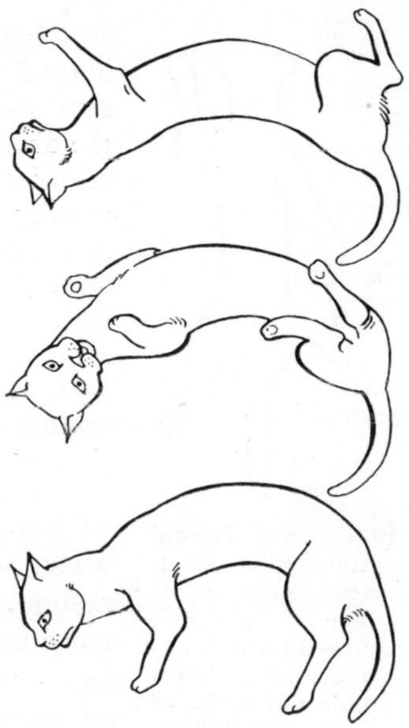

FIG. 5.27.—Movements of cat righting itself as it falls. The reaction depends upon the integrity of the labyrinth (Muller & Weed, 1916). After Rademaker & Ter Braak, 1936, reproduced from Fulton, 1946

Information derived from the skin is used also in the *contact placing* responses that have been studied by Bard (1937). If a cat is blindfolded and its nose is allowed to touch the edge of a table, the fore-limbs will immediately be brought up onto the table top. Similarly, if the dorsum of one front paw is touched by the edge of the table, then the limb will be moved so as to carry some of the weight of the animal. Similar cutaneous reactions may be very important in man.

ANATOMICAL BASIS OF POSTURAL MECHANISMS

Some of the reactions that have been described are dependent solely upon spinal pathways. This is true of the stretch reflex and of the magnet reaction, 'local segmental' responses. Other postural reactions may be seen in the spinal animal; thus when one limb is hurt it flexes and the other limbs take up such positions as would be expected to stabilise the animal (Fig. 5.28).

That the lumbar regions of the spinal cord normally exert a control over the fore-limbs may be seen also, for in the *Schiff-Sherrington* experiment the division of the spinal cord in the thoracic region of a decerebrate cat gives rise to an increase in the rigidity of the fore-limbs. This inter-segmental influence is mediated by large cells in the ventral horn of the spinal cord, the 'Border cells', that send their axones upwards rather than into the ventral roots (Sprague, 1953). Even if the fore-limbs have been de-afferented by section of the posterior roots rigidity appears when the cord is transected (Stella quoted by Moruzzi, 1950; cf. p. 177.

FIG. 5.28.—Painful stimulation of left foot causes extension of ipsilateral fore-limb and contralateral hind-limb and flexion of contralateral fore-limb. This attitude enables stability to be retained (Sherrington)

The reactions of the body as a whole are organised anatomically around the labyrinthine system. The *vestibular nuclei* extend over a considerable distance up and down the brain stem, and there appears to be a certain amount of segregation of function within the various subdivisions of the nuclear system. The fibres from the utricle and saccule have destinations that are, in part, distinct from those of the semicircular canals (Lorente de Nó, 1933 *b*). Thulin (1953) has investigated the effects of a stimulation of the various vestibular nuclei upon the somatic musculature. He has found that ipsilateral effects were predominant and could be obtained from all of the subdivisions, whilst contralateral effects were restricted to the medial vestibular nucleus. The effects of damaging the vestibular nuclei are said to be similar to, although more severe than, the effects of labyrinthectomy on the same side. Even after a bilateral labyrinthectomy damage to the vestibular nuclei gives rise to disturbances of posture (Ferraro, Barrerra & Blackeslee, 1936). In man it has been reported that damage to the vestibular nuclear complex of one side may give rise to sudden symptoms similar to those due to peripheral vestibular deficit, even though the labyrinth on the same side has previously been destroyed.

Tonic labyrinthine responses affecting the limbs can be seen in the decerebrate animal and do not depend upon the integrity of the midbrain. The vestibulo ocular reflexes may be mediated in part by the *medial longitudinal bundle* (*vide* Muskens, 1914), but as was first shown by Lorente de Nó (1933 *a*) (*vide* Szentagathai, 1950), this route is not the sole one concerned. If the medial longitudinal bundle is divided it may yet be possible to elicit nystagmus by stimulating the labyrinth. No comparable observations appear to have been made upon patients with similar lesions, but there is a report by André-Thomas (1924) of the effects of such a lesion on the *voluntary movements of the eyes.* Although vertical movements were unimpaired the eyes could not be moved from side to side at all.

It may be noted that a similar effect may follow lesions in the neighbourhood of the 6th nerve nucleus.

'It is well known that inability to move the eyes to one side is frequently associated with disease in the lower and dorsal portion of the pons Varolii, especially when it extends to the neighbourhood of the abducent nucleus of the same side. A lesion, for instance, in the region of the left abducens nucleus may make the patient unable to move either eye to the left of the middle line, that is to contract the left external rectus and the right internal rectus muscles. But these two muscles are innervated from two different nuclei about 3 cms. apart, and the root fibres proceeding from them nowhere come together in the brain stem. It is therefore necessary to assume that these two nuclei are connected by association fibres which distribute the exciting impulses to the cells of both' (Holmes, 1921).

Spiller (1924) also studied a patient who was later shown to have a lesion interrupting the posterior longitudinal bundle on both sides. Although the patient could converge and use her lateral recti normally, she could not bring either of the medial recti into play when attempting to look to the side.

With the exception of the visual righting reflexes, and of the contact placing reactions that in mammals depend upon the integrity of the cortex, the righting reflexes are well seen in the decorticate animal. In the lower vertebrates the auditory and visual signals are dealt with principally by the inferior and superior colliculi, and it is perhaps not altogether surprising that even in the mammals the midbrain should remain very important from the point of view of

postural mechanisms.   Nor is it surprising that when the midbrain is stimulated wide fields of the somatic musculature should
be affected as though the mechanism underlying attitude was being
reset.   It is illuminating to contrast these responses with the frag-
mentary movements elicited by stimulation of the motor cortex.
On stimulating the *tegmentum* the ipsilateral fore-limb flexes whilst
the other arm extends.   The head turns towards and the spine
arches to, the side that has been stimulated.   The lower limbs also
may move, but in a less stereotyped manner (Ingram, Ranson,
Hannett, Zeiss & Terwilliger, 1932; cf. Brown, 1915).

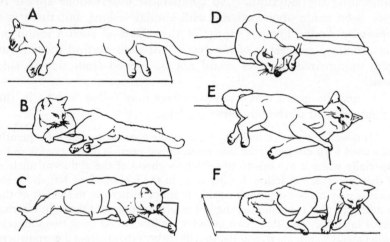

FIG. 5.29.—Righting activity of low decerebrate cats after d-amphetamine. A,
   typical posture of low decerebrate cats placed in side position before d-
   amphetamine; B to F, a series of postures achieved by low decerebrate cats
   placed in side position after d-amphetamine. (Reproduced from Maling &
   Acheson, 1946)

At one time it was believed that the *red nucleus* was a particularly
important part of the midbrain postural mechanisms, but there is
little evidence that it is of much importance in this respect in the
monkey (Keller & Hare, 1934), and whilst a rubro-spinal tract
probably exists in man it is certainly small (Stern, 1934) (*vide* p. 192
and Fig. 6.20).

That labyrinthine and cutaneous righting reflexes in general are
present in the thalamic animal and absent in animals that have
been decerebrated should not necessarily lead to the conclusion that
the neural circuits pass through the midbrain.   It may merely be
that facilitation of these responses is lacking in the decerebrate

animal. Maling & Acheson (1946) have studied this problem pharma-
cologically. They have found that the administration of the stimulant
d-amphetamine caused cutaneous righting responses to appear in
decerebrate and even spinal animals (Fig. 5.29). Their work illustrates again the caution needed in interpreting the results seen after
nervous tissue has been destroyed (p. 11 and p. 96).

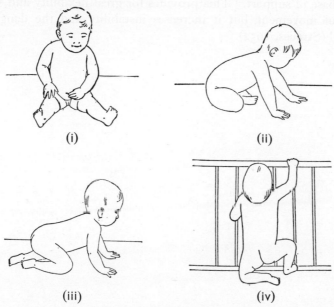

(i)   (ii)

(iii)   (iv)

FIG. 5.30.—Postural control normally possible at 40 weeks. Zador (1938) showed
that the responses of infants when placed on a tilting-table were often qualita-
tively different from the reactions of adults. Thus there may, for instance,
be a symmetrical alteration of the posture of the limbs even when the tilt is to
one side. At 3 months there develops a tendency for the arms to be extended
as a cross ; this effect lasts until the infant is about 8 months old. As the
child grows, one set of patterns of equilibration is replaced by another. During
the second and third years the postural responses are strikingly exaggerated.
(Reproduced from Gesell & Amatruda, 1947)

The foal can run a few hours after it is born, whilst the guinea-pig
has been compared with the goddess Minerva who, when born, was
ready for immediate action. In contrast the human baby remains
helpless for months. We may suppose that in the case of the horse
and cavy the reactions needed for equilibrium to be maintained are
simpler than in the case of the biped and can more readily be provided for by stereotyped 'built in' neural circuits. In the human
being it seems that what can and cannot be done has to be discovered

M

by *experience in infancy* (Fig. 5.30).   It may be that the limits of safety as to stability depend, in man, to a large extent upon learnt reactions (*vide* Lyons & Brickner, 1931).

The nervous system of the human being appears to gain knowledge of what can and cannot be done by a series of painful falls in infancy.   In man 'the centre of gravity is elevated high over the small base of support.   This provides for great flexibility and variability of movement, but it increases instability and the danger of falling' (Strauss, 1952).

CHAPTER 6

THE CEREBELLUM

Perhaps the most colourful figure in the story of the cerebellum is that of Luigi Rolando who, as a young man in the chair of anatomy at the provincial University of Sassari in Sardinia, carried out single-handed and alone a series of experiments in which he described the effects of cerebellar ablation in animals ranging from reptiles and fish to mammals. In all these forms he found disturbances of volitional movement and he was the first to insist that cerebellar removal in no way affected the 'mentality' of the animal and that such lesions were entirely without sensory sequelae.—FULTON (1949).

THE LABYRINTHINE REPRESENTATION

INGVAR (1923) has avowed that 'no homogeneous sensory area in the nervous system ever develops by means of marginal appositions; the differentiation always takes place in the centre'. This principle appears to be valuable in understanding the way in which the cerebellum has differentiated. This organ is seen even in primitive vertebrates, and in them its connections are principally with the vestibular system.

'In water-living forms, such as the salamander, the vestibular and lateral line systems are of great importance in coordinated movements of swimming. The brain centers of these sensory systems are accordingly enlarged and part of this central apparatus extends forward on each side of the rostral end of the medulla oblongata as the auricle. The two auricles are joined by a commissure which includes, in addition to direct VIII root fibres, as in Petromyzon,[1] also secondary fibres' (Larsell & Dow, 1939).

Edinger (1906) pointed out that 'the degree to which the cerebellum is differently developed varies according to equilibratory needs . . .' and he states that the hagfish, 'myxine which lives either quite

---

[1] The lamprey.

parasitically in other fish or firmly attached by its sucker to stones, has in effect no cerebellum'.

Ingvar (1923) stated that :—'The cerebellar cortex, with its uniform histological structure in all vertebrates, develops according to the same principles. In my comparative studies I found many signs that its marginal regions, that is, the regions situated at the base of the organ immediately above the fourth ventricle, are the oldest parts from a phylogenetic point of view. They vary little during development and their phylogenetic differentiation is very limited. They take no part in the intricate expansion found in higher animals,

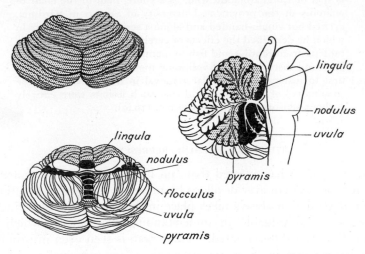

FIG. 6.1.—Supposed extent of 'vestibular floor' of cerebellum in human being—black areas. (Modified from Brown, 1944)

the culmination of which is the building up of the human cerebellar hemispheres (see Fig. 6.1). It is therefore necessary to consider the central parts of the cerebellar cortex separate from the border areas.' This area, referred to by Ingvar as the *vestibular floor*, receives fibres from the vestibular nerve and vestibular nuclei. The regions concerned are the most anterior and the most caudal parts of the cerebellum—the lingula, the uvula, the nodulus and the flocculus (Fig. 6.2). Referring to experimental studies of the cerebellum, Ingvar (1928 *b*) stated that :—'The vestibular floor is located very deeply in the cerebellum and entirely hidden by the organ *in situ*. It is therefore mostly spared in the experiments owing to technical difficulties.' Actually as early as 1894 Ferrier & Turner had succeeded in removing the 'posterior part of the vermiform process' from a monkey and had noted that whilst the animal was able to sit up without support on the day after the operation, nevertheless 'it was seen on several occasions, though apparently undisturbed, to fall over on its back'.

Russell (1894) in his work on the cerebellum of dogs also investigated the effects of lesions of the *posterior part of the vermis*. After the operation, 'as the animal made attempts to walk, each succeeding step taken with the fore limbs resulted in their being raised higher and higher from the ground, the animal as it were attempting to find solidity in mid air, at an increasingly elevated level, until the forepart of its body is raised so high that the dog falls backwards'. In some respects the behaviour was reminiscent of a circus horse walking on its hind-legs. It is very remarkable that a quadruped should in walking fall backwards in the way that Russell describes.

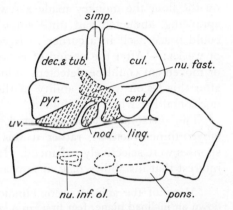

Fig. 6.2.—The 'vestibular floor' (cat). Shaded region gave electrical responses when the 8th nerve was stimulated. Collateral anatomical evidence indicates that these responses would be related to vestibular rather than auditory fibres. (From Dow, 1939)

Relevant perhaps to these questions are the studies of Mussen (1931). This worker destroyed a part of the posterior vermis of cats, and whilst the brunt of his lesions fell upon the pyramis, this area is so close to the vestibular floor ('pyr.', Fig. 6.2) that his results may be considered here. When the animal was held erect and suddenly let go it fell backwards. Mussen remarked that :

'The test that gave the most information was to hold the cat in the erect position with its hind feet on the floor and slowly pull it backward. It then became immediately apparent that some disturbance in equilibrium was present, for the animal allowed itself to lean backward resting in the investigator's hands, with legs relaxed and dragging, so that when suddenly let go it naturally fell backward. That the lesion involves backward balance alone was shown by the ability of this animal to jump from a chair to the floor without any indication that forward equilibrium was disturbed.' It may be noted that Mussen also investigated the effect of lesions of the anterior vermis and found that there resulted a tendency to fall forwards. There is some evidence that in man also falling forwards may result from lesions of the anterior, falling backwards from lesions of the posterior of the vermis (Ingvar, 1923).

Further information about the effect of lesions of the posterior part of the vermis was obtained by Dow (1938 a), who studied the effects of removing the nodulus and uvula from monkeys. After the operation there was a disturbance of equilibrium that became evident when the animal walked. Propped up in the corner of a cage, such an animal could eat a banana with no ataxia, but 'when on the floor the monkey made a few hesitant steps forward with a sprawling, abducted gait until some object could be grasped or it could brace itself in a corner'. Recovery took place over a period of weeks :—'After the period of recovery no abnormality of posture or movement could be detected. One of the last things to reappear after this lesion was the ability of the monkey to walk on a narrow horizontal bar when blindfolded.'

The instability, while it lasted, was not caused by a loss of labyrinthine reactions, rather it was found that some of these responses were selectively enhanced. It is a matter of great theoretical interest that instability may, it appears, be caused in this way.

'Many of the animals were blindfolded and observed as they slid down an inclined plane, feet first, in a lateral position. During the acute stages of the disequilibration animals subjected to this test were often observed, on reaching the floor after sliding about 3 feet (91 cm.), to lurch and sometimes fall toward the inclined plane in a direction opposite that in which the momentum was carrying them. A normal monkey subjected to such a procedure on the first trial always adjusted the extension of the extremities to counteract perfectly the momentum of the body and, without any noticeable swaying to either side, immediately walked away. A bilaterally labyrinthectomised animal did not have any reflex extension of the extremities under these conditions and always fell away from the inclined plane as a dead weight ; at times it rolled completely over away from the plane' (Dow, 1938 a).

In the child one not uncommon tumour is the medulloblastoma (*vide* Cushing, 1930). This tumour may arise from the nodulus itself and often remains hidden from the surface. Cushing, writing of his experiences, stated that in the majority of cases 'at least a small nubbin of the tumour has been brought to view . . . by drawing up the herniated tonsils from the foramen magnum and parting them so that the region of the calamus can be inspected'.

It is not surprising that these tumours disturb the vestibular floor of the cerebellum before upsetting other systems.

When this occurs there is pronounced difficulty in walking, although movements of the extremities may be executed, in bed, with but little disturbance. That this may be so has long been recognised. Thus Nothnagel (quoted by Luciani, 1915, vol. iii, p. 459) remarked that 'when the patient lies on his back in bed the leg movements are made quickly and certainly the subject has a clear idea of their position and manages to place one limb actively in exactly the same place to which the other has been brought passively'.

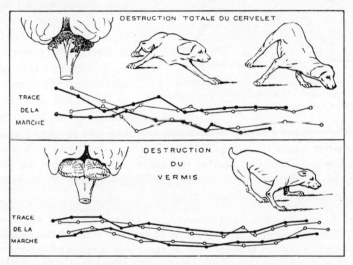

FIG. 6.3.—Effect of destruction of whole cerebellum (*above*), and of vermis (*below*). (Reproduced from André-Thomas, 1940)

Patients who show these disturbances of gait are said to be suffering from *trunk ataxia*, although it may be supposed that sometimes the difficulty really lies in the inability of the limbs adequately to support the full weight of the body [1] (*vide* p. 176). It is weakness of the legs rather than the ataxia of the trunk that appears

---

[1] A pure form of trunk ataxia may be seen in the snake where the situation is simplified by the absence of limbs. Dickinson on removing the cerebellum found that 'Snakes presented failure of lateral balance, and when the lateral connections were left on one side, they twisted into a corkscrew shape and revolved' (*vide* Russell, 1894). 'In the adder, the undulations which constitute the mode of progression of this animal, and which are so regular and so nicely coördinated, become irregular and incoördinated. "The animal does not advance at all, and the vain efforts which exhaust it do not enable it to change its position."' André-Thomas (1910), quoting Flourens.

to be responsible for the failure of dogs to walk after removal of the cerebellum (Fig. 6.3). Luciani (1915, vol. iii, p. 437), recording his observations, stated that :—'This inability to stand upright and walk may last four weeks. During this time, however, if the animal can lean the flank of the operated side against a wall, it is able to stand upright and make regular steps. Further, if thrown into water, it keeps itself quite well on the surface, maintains its equilibrium, and swims with perfect co-ordination.' Magendie also remarked that 'I kept a water-dog from which I had removed the cerebellum ; he made hardly any progressive movement during all that time except when I placed him in water' (quoted from Schäfer's *Textbook of Physiology*, 1900).

FIG. 6.4.—Dog with right half of its cerebellum removed. (Reproduced from Sharpey Schäfer's *Textbook of Physiology*)

When the whole of the cerebellum on one side is destroyed the animal arches its neck and trunk with the concavity to the side of the lesion so that the head and tail are approximated (Fig. 6.4). Russell (1897) described this posture following lesions of the inferior peduncle. He noted that the animal resists attempts to make it lie straight and, speaking of the instance of a left-sided lesion, he notes that :

'If this resistance is forcibly overcome and the animal is placed to lie on its right side, it quickly rolls on to its left side directly the restraining force which is exerted to keep it on its right side is taken off. Sometimes so suddenly and vigorously does it roll over to the left side that it may, as it were, overstep the mark and roll over once or twice before coming to rest on its left side.'

Actually these changes in Russell's experiments may have been due to coincidental damage to the vestibular nuclei (Ferraro & Barrera, 1935), but it is likely that such effects can, on occasion, be truly cerebellar (Turner & German, 1941). The posture is one into which an animal would place itself when rotated on a turn-table. It is logical, therefore, to ask whether *vertigo* occurs as a result of cerebellar lesions. The observations of Stewart & Holmes (1904) showed that this is the case, and that the sensation often differs from that caused by labyrinthine lesions :

'In both intra- and extra-cerebellar tumours the sense of displacement of external objects in front of the patient is from the side of the lesion to the opposite side.   Thus if the tumour be on the left side the apparent movement of objects is from left to right.   In intra-cerebellar tumours the subjective rotation of self is always from the side of the lesion to the healthy side, that is in the same direction as the apparent movement of external objects.   In extra-cerebellar tumours the subjective rotation of self is always from the healthy side towards the side of the lesion, that is in the opposite direction to that of the displacement of external objects.'

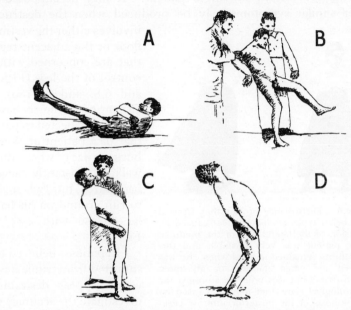

Fig. 6.5.—Trunk ataxia.   In attempting to perform acts that normally depend upon the co-operation of many muscles the patient with a cerebellar lesion is severely handicapped, as in the patient illustrated here (A, B and C) who was studied by Babinski.   A shows attempt to sit up ; the muscles of the trunk have not contracted, so that when the flexors of the hip come into play the legs and not the body are lifted from the ground.   B, the trunk does not follow the legs ; note the tendency to fall backwards, very reminiscent of cats with lesions of the posterior vermis (p. 165).   This tendency to fall backwards is seen also in C, which may be compared with the posture of a normal subject looking upwards, D.   (Reproduced from André-Thomas, 1940)

As might be expected from such symptoms, *nystagmus* is often present when there is a lesion of the cerebellum.   It is probable that nystagmus occurs when the middle of the vermis is involved. Nystagmus is not restricted, it would appear, to lesions of the vestibular floor.   It is interesting in this connection to consider a statement of Horsley (1906) : 'The coaptation of eye movements with those of the limbs in locomotion of the body by means of the limbs is, theoretically, a fundamental physiological fact in man and the higher animals'. Horsley regarded the control of the eyes by the cerebellum as being of pre-eminent importance. 'The *antecedence* of eye movements in all skeletal muscular actions is well recognised. . . .'

Whether the disturbance of gait results from a true trunk ataxia (Fig. 6.5) or from the inability of the lower limbs to support a heavy load may vary from patient to patient. It may be supposed that rather similar symptoms may be produced when the destruction involves either the vestibular floor or the adjacent regions that are concerned with the control of the legs (Figs. 6.7 and 6.8, and p. 180). In either case the behaviour might be expected to parallel that of a patient of Weisenburg (1927) who, during walking, constantly staggered backwards, but 'when asked to run around on his hands, he did so with ease' (cf. Fig. 6.6).

FIG. 6.6.—Disturbance of gait that showed cerebellar types of disturbances caused by a lesion of the lateral part of the medulla. The patient was very unstable and this instability remained marked when she was seated and when she was on all fours. Disturbances of this type are amongst the neurological signs that may be caused by thrombosis of the posterior inferior cerebellar artery. (*Vide* Goodhart & Davidson, 1936.) (Reproduced from André-Thomas, 1910)

In patients believed to be suffering from trunk ataxia it would appear desirable to investigate the accuracy with which the legs may be moved in bed, not only under normal circumstances but when weights are fixed to the feet. It is when a limb is loaded that cerebellar deficit is seen most prominently. A complementary investigation would be to investigate the responses when sitting on a tilting-table with the arms folded in front of the body and the eyes closed. These two tests might decide if a disturbance of gait is truly an ataxia of the trunk. The nature of the disturbance of the gait varies according to whether the whole trunk is implicated or whether the disturbance is restricted to one or other of the limb-girdles. Weisenberg (1927) has made the following suggestions as to the way in which patients should be examined:

'A cerebellar patient, when asked to walk across the stage, will take advantage of every sense so as to correct his difficulty in walking. The gait is distinctly modified whether the eyes are open or shut, or by sounds. When walking with the eyes open, the deviation will be at once corrected, or with the eyes shut by the sound of the voice. The cerebellar gait is best demonstrated with the eyes blindfolded and without any sound.'

'When the entire trunk is involved there is the greatest disturbance in the gait and in the station, and frequently such patients are unable to stand up, or, in attempting to walk, will fall in almost any direction. On the other hand, if the pelvic-girdle is involved alone the trunk is held rigidly erect and the legs are pushed forward from the pelvis, giving the impression that the trunk goes after the legs. In extreme cases the patient cannot walk even with help, and, when assisted, the trunk is held rigid and the legs are thrown out in almost any direction. In such cases the upper limbs are usually held partly outstretched and semiflexed at the elbows in an attempt to balance. On the other hand, if the shoulder-girdle alone is implicated the patient usually stands very well and walks almost normally—although he has a tendency to spread his legs apart— but in his station he is likely to fall, and, when walking will lurch usually in a certain direction, giving the impression that the trunk leads, and whichever way it goes, the legs follow.'

'An excellent way to differentiate between pelvic-girdle and shoulder-girdle asynergy is to have the patient get up from a recumbent posture. In his efforts to do so, while his hands and feet are extended, if the pelvic-girdle is involved alone, there is a distinct to-and-fro swaying of this part, the shoulder-girdle remaining stationary. The contrary is present when the shoulder-girdle is involved.'

That trunk ataxia should take different forms suggests that the regions of the cerebellum concerned with equilibration may show some differentiation of function. There is some experimental evidence for this view. Carrera & Mettler (1947) found that the effects of removing the uvula and nodulus differed from the results of removing the flocculus on each side. They stated that :

'Nodulo-uvula monkeys walked with the 4 limbs abducted, the anterior stiffly extended and the posterior flexed, the buttocks being carried upon or very close to the floor. Following floccular removal, the animals walked with the legs extended and the arms slightly flexed (as a "fighting bull"). The same pattern was present during running but under such circumstances the monkey deviated alternately to one and then to the other side, finally falling forcibly to the floor or hitting against the wall. . . .'

The authors found that the behaviour of the monkeys reminded them of a person trying to ride a bicycle for the first time. It seems likely that further progress in this field will be dependent upon

using electrical methods to ascertain whether, as some have supposed, different parts of the labyrinth project to different parts of
the labyrinthine floor (*vide* Ingvar, 1923).

The system under consideration relays through the fastigial
nucleus to the labyrinthine nuclei of the brain stem, and it is
interesting to note that when these connections are severed disorientation may occur (Ferraro & Barrera, 1936). Monkeys subjected to this procedure are liable, when they jump, to turn 'back

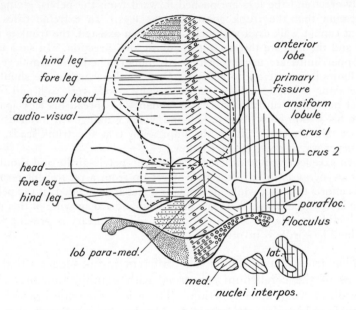

Fig. 6.7.—Connections of cerebellum. *Left half: Afferent.* Dots for vestibular,
horizontal lines for spinal. Pontocerebellar projections reach all areas except
flocculonodular lobe. The inferior olive and its associated nuclei project to
the whole of the cerebellum; these connections accordingly have not been
indicated. *Right half: Efferent.* Circles for vestibular nuclei, oblique lines (/)
for nucleus medialis (fastigii), other oblique lines (\) for nucleus interpositus
(globose and emboliformis), vertical lines for nucleus lateralis (dentate).
(From Ranson & Clark, 1953. After Jansen & Brodal)

flips'. They show changes similar to those following lesions of the
vestibular nerve or nuclei on the opposite side. This could be
taken as further evidence that the cerebellum restrains the action
of the labyrinthine system. Dow (1938 *a*) had noted that after a
unilateral lesion of the vestibular part of the cerebellum the animals
fell to the opposite side, a sign that also could be explained by
a 'release' of the ipsilateral labyrinthine system. It is not clear

to what extent the exaggeration of labyrinthine reactions is indiscriminate. Nystagmus resulting from rotation, mediated by the semicircular canals, may be either unchanged or enhanced after lesions of the cerebellum (Dow, 1938 *a* ; Spiegel & Scala, 1942), whilst the ocular reactions that depend upon the excitation of the otolith organs may be altered, giving rise to *positional* nystagmus (cf. p. 141).

It should not be supposed that the vestibular part of the cerebellum is autonomous. Although there is but little evidence for the presence of long-association fibres in the cerebellum (Dow, 1942), this region is linked through the fastigial nucleus with the whole of the rest of the vermis, and, as will be seen (p. 178), parts of the cerebellum other than the vestibular floor can modify labyrinthine reflexes. As is evident from a study of Fig. 6.7, 'there undoubtedly exists an overlapping at the cerebellar cortex of the different afferent fibre systems' (Ingvar, 1928 *a*). Dow (1939) found that by stimulating different afferent systems, evoked potentials of different sign and shape may be recorded from the same point on the cerebellar hemisphere. The same author (Dow, 1942), reviewing the problems of cerebellar organisation, said that 'sharp boundaries of functional importance may not exist in the cerebellum'. These uncertainties are a reflection of the organisation of the nervous system itself. Certain connections are regularly made between the afferent and efferent fibres of a neural mass, but between others transmission is optional and depends upon coexistent circumstances. It is necessary, therefore, continually to scrutinise the ways in which an organ such as the cerebellum can be regarded as being composed of a number of sub-systems.

THE INFLUENCE OF THE CEREBELLUM ON THE STRETCH REFLEXES

The anterior lobe of the cerebellum is known to be concerned with the regulation of muscular tone. The rigidity of a decerebrate cat can be 'dissolved' by *faradic stimulation* of this part of the cerebellum. Denny-Brown, Eccles & Liddell (1929) remarked that :

'When the cerebellum of a decerebrate, but otherwise intact, animal is stimulated, and the reactions are observed by clinical inspection, inhibition of all anti-gravity muscles is most apparent.' These workers also commented that : 'When the level of decerebration is well precollicular, it is common to find that cerebellar stimulation elicits a sharp flexion of the elbow joint, flexion (dorsi-flexion) of the wrist, abduction and extension of the digits and protrusion of the claws. The attitude of the forelimb is just that which is found in the "rampant" animals of heraldry.'

At the end of a period of stimulation the posture alters ; there is *rebound* to a position diametrically opposed to the one adopted during the excitation. Thus a rampant animal may 'strike' by the elbow becoming extended, the wrist and fingers flexed.

Hare, Magoun & Ranson (1937) have contrasted the results of stimulating the midbrain (p. 160) with those that are seen on stimulating the cerebellum. The 'tegmental posture outlasts the stimulus for some time but the cerebellar reaction is immediately reversed to a persistent posture that is often the mirror image of that of the first phase'. The rebound phase may last as long as 5 minutes. Clark (1939) used implanted electrodes to stimulate the cerebellar cortex of conscious cats, and he also noted a pronounced rebound to a mirror-image posture at the end of the period of stimulation. Magoun, Hare & Ranson

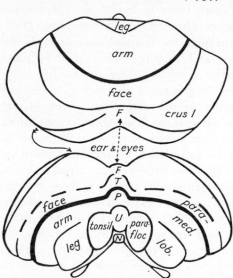

Fig. 6.8.—Hypothetical plan of human cerebellum. Somatotopic areas of representation have been made to correspond with those found in experimental animals (from Hampson, Harrison & Woolsey, 1952)

(1937) have found that this period is shortened if the limb that is being observed has been deprived of its afferent nerve supply by section of posterior roots. Evidently the rebound posture is retained, partly because of a 'myotatic appendage', a lengthening or shortening reaction (p. 123). Results such as these might lead one to suppose that two systems were present in the region being stimulated. This view would appear to have received rather strong support by the finding that, whilst inhibition of extensor tone is the usual result of stimulating the median part of the anterior lobe, an increase of rigidity usually follows stimulation delivered more laterally (Hampson, Harrison & Woolsey, 1952). The results obtained do depend, however, upon the nature of the electrical stimulus and reverse of the effects may follow an increase in the frequency of the shocks without any other alteration of their characteristics. Moruzzi (1950), who has studied this problem, believes that 'every Purkinje cell of the anterior vermis may be inhibitory or facilitating according to the frequency of its discharges', but this point cannot be regarded as being finally settled (*vide* Snider, 1952).

If care is taken to use electrical stimuli that are close to threshold, it may be seen that the effects are restricted to one region only of the musculature. This localisation corresponds to that known to

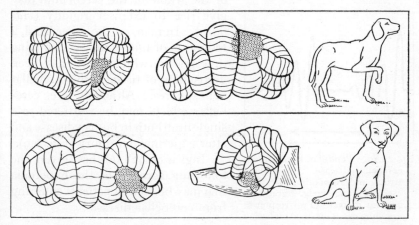

FIG. 6.9.—Persistent abnormalities of posture and movement in the right fore-limb (*above*) and hind-limb (*below*) following cerebellar lesions. (Reproduced from André-Thomas, 1940)

exist for the afferent fibres reaching the cerebellum, where the body is represented anteriorly, and also posteriorly on each side (cf. Fig. 6.8) (*vide* Hampson, Harrison & Woolsey, 1952). That there may be these striking effects from stimulating the cerebellum suggests that alterations of muscular tone might be expected to follow destructive lesions. If there is unilateral damage to the medial cortex of the anterior lobe of a decerebrate cat, there is ipsilateral extension and contralateral flexion of the limbs (Sprague & Chambers, 1953). Reversal of this posture follows if the lesion is extended to implicate the fastigial nucleus. Miller (1926) investigated the effects of removal of much of the cerebellar cortex on one side, sparing the anterior lobe. The fore-limb on the side of the lesion, he stated, 'customarily assumes a characteristic posture, being flexed so that the elbow forms a right angle, the paw advanced forwards ; I have called this the "hand-shake position", since it reminds one of a trained cat giving its paw'. If now the lateral cerebellar nucleus is stimulated, there is a further flexion of the ipsilateral fore-leg.

In interpreting results of such experiments it is important to be aware that the effects may depend both upon the region of the cerebellum that is involved and upon the species that is used for the investigation. In birds, removal of the cerebellum causes an enhanced activity of the anti-gravity musculature and the animal stands upon its talons (*vide* Bremer, 1932). In the cat, also, removal of the whole of the cerebellum may give rise to extensor rigidity (*vide infra*). In man, on the other hand, a reduction of tone is the usual finding in cases in which there has been destruction of tissue in the cerebellar hemispheres. Although rare, cerebellar effects may be restricted to a single limb both in human disease and after experimental injury (Fig. 6.9).

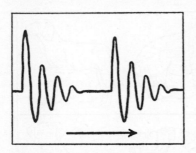

Fig. 6.10.—Pendular knee jerk in cerebellar disease. After being struck and responding the limb oscillates passively, gradually coming to rest. Two responses are shown. This is evidence of hypotonia, but similar responses can be obtained in normal, well-relaxed subjects. (After Holmes, 1917)

Ingvar (1928 *b*) has given the following account of the hypotonia that may be seen in patients suffering from cerebellar disease :

'In cases of cerebellar ataxia the impaired limbs behaved more or less like dead things attached to the rest of the body. . . . It is a quite striking fact that the impaired extremities are much more affected by the force of gravity than the normal limbs, in spite of the absence of definite signs of paresis. "If either the arm or the leg be seized and shaken, it is found that the more distal segments of the affected limb flop and swing about in an unnatural, inert manner, like the arms of a flail. While the oscillations of the normal limb are limited by the elastic tension of the muscles that are stretched, those of the affected limb can be felt to swing till the joints lock and their bony and ligamentous structures prevent further movement. The affected arm swings about inertly as though it were attached to the shoulder by a string" (André-Thomas).' (Cf. Fig. 6.10.)

Evidently the mechanisms that maintain the stability of the limbs are disturbed by cerebellar lesions (Fig. 6.11) and it is interesting therefore to enquire to what extent these disturbances result from an alteration of the stretch reflexes. Decerebrate rigidity depends under normal circumstances upon these stretch reflexes and upon their facilitation by descending impulses from the brain stem (p. 128). The rigidity is not seen in a limb that has lost its afferent connections with the spinal cord by section of the posterior roots. Pollock & Davis found that this was not the case if the animal in addition to being decerebrated was also decerebellated. The animal was then still rigid, often markedly so ; the tonus no longer depended upon the stretch reflexes.

These findings would suggest that when the cerebellum is removed the stretch reflexes are 'switched off', whilst other influences

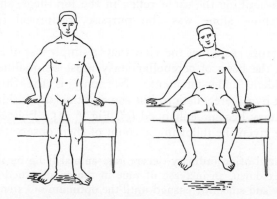

FIG. 6.11.—Lesion of right side of cerebellum. Note the instability of the right arm ; unlike the left it does not act as a prop at the moment when the patient sits on the bed. It is interesting to recall the statement of Walshe (1921) that 'all the component symptoms of cerebellar ataxy are nothing more than the manifestation of loss or impairment of postural tone. . . .' (From André-Thomas, 1940)

become more effective than usual in exciting the anterior horn cells. There is now good experimental evidence that this is indeed the case. Granit, Holmgren & Merton (1955) have shown that decerebellation prevents the *small motor fibres* that supply the muscle spindles from being active. The stretch reflex can, therefore, not be set to stabilise the limb in the usual way. Those pathways which impinge upon the main anterior horn cells will have automatically an enhanced influence over the control of the musculature because their effects will not continually be counteracted by the efforts of the stretch reflex to maintain the *status quo*.

One response that is exaggerated by decerebellation is the *magnet* or 'Stütz' reaction. Light pressure on the pad of the foot may

N

bring out a rigid contraction of the limb (p. 125). Whether this reaction bears a particular relationship to any specific part of the cerebellum does not appear to have been investigated, but it has been noted following lesions of the vestibular floor (Ferraro & Barrera, 1936; Dow, 1938 *a*). The reflex is of interest because in fixing the limb as a rigid pillar antagonistic muscles may contract simultaneously (cf. Sherrington, 1913). Pollock & Davis (1927), who deal with the question of the co-contraction of antagonistic muscles at some length, state that 'Schoen, in describing the "*Stütz-reaction*" in the fore-legs, noted simultaneous contraction of antagonistic muscles when fixation of joints was the purpose of the reflex. Pritchard, describing the same reflex in the hind-legs, showed that when stretching alone was the purpose, reciprocal innervation occurred.'

Walshe (1927) said that the view that 'a simple loss of all postural reactions is the basis of cerebellar ataxy must be qualified'. This is now evident understatement. Not only is the Stützreaction brought out by decerebellation, but some of the labyrinthine reflexes themselves may become enhanced (cf. Fig. 6.12). Pollock & Davis (1927) have given the following account of their observations :

'If the head of an ordinary decerebrate animal lying on its side was turned vertex down, an increase of tone in the outstretched extremities rather slowly and smoothly ensued until the optimum of extensor rigidity was produced. If the head of a decerebro-cerebellate animal was turned vertex down, the fore-legs were thrust forward suddenly with great force and with unsheathing of the claws. The force of this tonic contraction was so great that often the whole body was displaced. Its sudden appearance was tetanic, startling and entirely dissimilar to anything observed in an ordinary decerebrate preparation. The rigidity in the extremities was so marked that passive flexion could be performed only by the greatest force.

'Immediately following removal of the cerebellum the head assumed an attitude of extreme opisthotonos. If it was passively flexed the rigidity in the extremities, the fore-legs especially, diminished and a position of semiflexion was assumed. . . . When the labyrinths were destroyed in such an animal the opisthotonos entirely disappeared.'

Opisthotonos and rigidity were features seen by Luciani in his experiments on pigeons and referred to as indicating a state of 'functional exaltation'. The labyrinthine reactions of Pollock & Davis and the accentuated responses that Dow saw in animals sliding down an inclined plane (p. 166) are probably dependent upon

excitation of the otolith organs.   There has been no attempt, so far,
to test the otolith system in human cases of cerebellar disease.   The
reactions to stimulation of the semicircular canals may be normal
(*vide* Holmes, 1917).

SUJET NORMAL   LABYRINTHIQUE

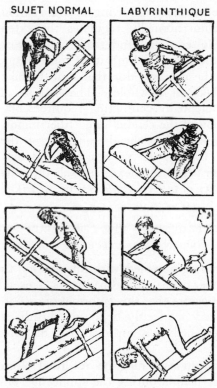

FIG. 6.12.—Reactions to tilting in a normal subject and in a patient deprived of
   the labyrinths.   Experiments on animals suggest that the cerebellum can hold
   in check or accentuate labyrinthine responses.   Zador (1938) made detailed
   study of the responses of patients with diverse neurological lesions when tilted
   on a table.   Appropriate reactions were not obtained when both labyrinthine
   nerves were destroyed, but the results when one alone was intact were variable.
   In keeping with animal observations Zador found that cerebellar lesions may
   increase the reactions to tilting.   Thus the patient may fall *towards* the inclined
   plane.   In tabes, however, normal responses may be obtained.   (Reproduced
   from André-Thomas, 1940)

In cats the crucial area that must be destroyed to obtain the
results reported by Pollock & Davis lies in the anterior lobe ; according to Stella (quoted by Moruzzi, 1950) it is the culmen and
lobulus centralis that are important.   To what extent the control

of these responses is mediated by fibres reaching to the vestibular nuclei is not clear ; there exist direct pathways from the cerebellum to the reticular formation of the midbrain that also must be considered (Whiteside & Snider, 1953). Here again, as in the case of the vestibular floor itself (p. 166), we have evidence that vestibular reactions may be enhanced following decerebellation. This suggests that the cerebellum normally regulates the extent to which the musculature is allowed to fall under this type of control. The needs for stability on the part of a limb itself must frequently need to be reconciled with the necessity for that limb to take part in actions stabilising the body as a whole. The seeking of a compromise between these potentially conflicting requirements is no doubt an important function of the cerebellum. Sherrington indeed referred to the cerebellum as 'the head ganglion of the proprioceptive system', whilst 'Lorente de Nó has well said that the cerebellum does not so much perform reflexes as exalt the activity of some and depress the activity of others' (*vide* Strong, 1926).

THE PATHWAYS LEADING TO THE CEREBELLUM FROM THE SENSE ORGANS AND CEREBRAL CORTEX

The cerebellum is provided with information that is brought to it through a number of anatomical pathways (Jansen & Brodal, 1954). It has become apparent that this information is not exclusively proprioceptive as was once tacitly believed. Furthermore it has been shown that the cerebellum is supplied with data from certain of the cranial nerves.

Conspicuous responses may be recorded electrically from the surface of the cerebellum during the application of *cutaneous stimuli* (Adrian, 1944 a). The results of experiments of this type have revealed that there is on each side of the anterior lobe a topographical representation of the same side of the body (Fig. 6.13). Further back there are two other areas, one in each paramedian lobule, and here again there is a topographic representation of the parts of the body surface. Each of these areas in the paramedian lobules is connected with points on both sides of the body.

In addition to these arrangements the cerebellum receives information from the *eye and the ear*. The pathways concerned in these responses may pass through the superior and inferior colliculi (Snider & Stowell, 1944). It will be seen (Fig. 6.13) that the regions to which these sense organs project lies, appropriately, towards the regions of representation of the head in the areas that have just been described, in the centre of the cortical surface.

Besides obtaining information from the afferent systems the cerebellum receives *large projections from the cerebral cortex*; it is indeed the great development of the cortical connections that has given to the human cerebellum its particular form. The projections from the cerebral cortex come from a wide area; those from the

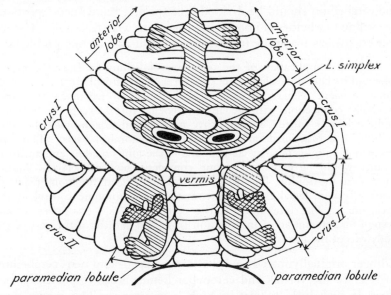

FIG. 6.13.—Tactile receiving areas in cerebellum of cat. The anterior of the projections is concerned on each side with the corresponding side of the body. The receiving areas in the paramedian lobules are each related to both sides of the body. Much of the cerebellar cortex is hidden; in man only about 15 per cent is visible on the surface (Kraus & Weil, 1926). It may be supposed that exploration of the hidden regions would reveal further details of topographical organisation. (From Snider, 1952)

frontal lobe pass in the medial part of the cerebral peduncle, those from the parietal, occipital and temporal lobes pass in its lateral part (Sunderland, 1940). These projections relay in the pontine nuclei and pass to the cerebellar cortex on the opposite side.[1] Points within the sensorimotor area of the cerebral cortex are connected systematically with points on the cerebellar cortex, the leg region of the cortex being connected with a part of the cerebellum to which

[1] The pontine nuclei receive also fibres ascending from the spinal cord (Jansen & Brodal, 1954).

afferent impulses from the leg project and so on. There are some grounds for believing that the representation of the body in the anterior lobe is connected principally with the main motor and sensory areas of the cortex, whilst the paramedian representation is concerned mainly with the secondary sensory and motor areas which lie close to the Sylvian fissure (p. 402 and p. 384, and *vide* Hampson, 1949).

These findings do not support Larsell's (1937) suggestion that the cerebellum should be divided into 'palaeo-' and 'neo-' portions according to whether or not spinal projections were traceable. Hampson (1949) has made the following comments about this problem :

'Larsell's application of the term neocerebellum to Ingvar's middle lobe and its lateral developments (the cerebellar hemispheres) . . . needs some revision. There is anatomical evidence for existence of pontocerebellar connections with the entire cerebellar cortex except the flocculonodular lobe.[1]   Indeed, it may prove more useful to subdivide the cerebellum on a functional rather than on an anatomical basis. Thus the absence of spino-cerebellar connections to the lobus medius and ansiform lobules would be explained if one considers that these recent studies show that the middle lobe seems to subserve head functions (such as hearing, vision, facial expression, somatic and automonic control of the eyes, etc.). The remainder of the cerebellum . . . comprises a dual system for integration of information from and control of the rest of the body except the head.'

Edinger originally introduced the terms palaeo- and neo- cerebellum to refer to the vermis and cerebellar hemispheres respectively, but there is now little to justify such a grouping. The words were re-used by Larsell, but now it appears that 'the Larsell classification . . . is no longer tenable' (Woolsey & Settlage, 1950, but cf. Jansen & Brodal, 1954).

The areas considered so far do not encroach upon the cerebellar hemispheres and the functions of these regions remains enigmatical. The cortico-pontine connections that reach to Crus I and II come from the cingulate gyrus (Snider & Eldred, 1951) and these regions may be concerned in autonomic functions. It is still necessary, however, to account for much of the lateral part of the cerebellar hemispheres, regions that do not appear to receive information from any of the sensory systems.

The function of the cerebellar cortex was investigated by Horsley & Clarke (1908), but their work is remembered rather for the

---

[1] *Vide* Brodal & Jansen (1946).

first use of a 'stereotaxic' method of stimulating structures within the cranium (Fig. 6.14). From their experiments they concluded that the cerebellar cortex was 'relatively inexcitable'. It is the function of a nervous system to respond to specific combinations of signals in time and space, and so it is not surprising that as in the cerebral cortex so in the cerebellum certain regions should be 'silent' to

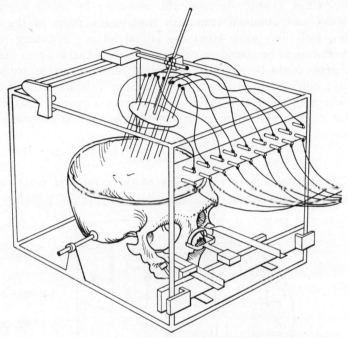

FIG. 6.14.—Light stereotaxic instrument for use at neurosurgical operations. (Marconi Instrument Co. After the design of Dr. S. Sherwood)

electrical stimulation. It is not as earlier workers supposed, that the cerebellar hemispheres are inexcitable, but that the key fashioned by the artificial stimulus is not able to turn the lock of the synaptic arrangements with which the cerebellum is connected. Speaking of this type of problem in the nervous system Hebb (in Delafresnaye, 1954, p. 308) has pointed out that :

'Electrical stimulation of a neural mass may mirror its neural function or not, depending on the arrangement of fibres in it. It seems that we must recognise two types of transmission in the CNS. Where fibres are essentially parallel (those originating together in one small region conducting to one other small region, so that they can act effectively together) gross stimulation may approximate what happens physiologically. But stimulation within a tangled network, where normal function requires independent or asynchronous firing, might simply prevent normal transmission, with a "busy-line effect".'

A failure to demonstrate responses to electrical stimulation of the cerebellar hemispheres may, however, be due to the use of anaesthesia. Clark (1939) overcame this difficulty by using implanted electrodes and obtained responses from many parts of the cerebellum, including some from the lateral lobes. Speaking of the interpretation to be placed on such experiments Clark wrote that the movements could be regarded as 'actual responses to an artificially induced sum of "proprioceptive information", the movements being identical with those that would follow from a posture that would present to the cerebellum a similar body of normal proprioceptive impulses'.

'CEREBELLAR FITS'

The question of the excitability of the cerebellar cortex arises again when considering the occurrence of fits in patients with

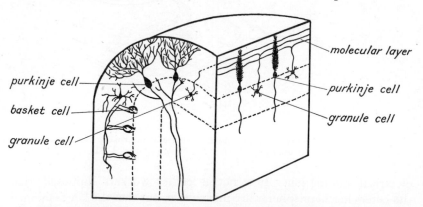

Fig. 6.15.—Section of cerebellar cortex showing structures seen along axis of folium (*right*) and at right angles (on *left*). Note orientation of dendrites of Purkinje cells ; in their orientation they resemble the branches of a vine on a trellis. Note collateral branches of axones of Purkinje cells. Degenerative processes commonly attack the Purkinje cells predominantly but occasionally it is the granule cells that suffer most (Norman, 1940). (From Ranson & Clark, 1953)

cerebellar tumours. Examination of the cerebellar cortex histologically shows a remarkable structure that is uniform throughout the organ (Fig. 6.15). Evidently much the same process is being performed in the different regions on the different types of signal being handled. The axones of the 14 million *Purkinje cells* send collateral branches back to form synaptic connections with neighbouring cells. It has been supposed that these branches are excitatory rather than inhibitory and that they may, therefore, give rise to *avalanche conduction*, excitation at one region setting up excitation that spreads widely. Speaking of the mechanisms that might be used to produce movements starting smoothly Ruch (in S. S. Stevens, 1951) says that 'this could be accomplished by cascading, or, in neural terms, avalanche conduction, in which dichotomising neurons synapse with several neurons the axons of which in turn dichotomise'. If such spreading excitation was a characteristic feature of the activity of the cerebellum, it might be supposed that fits would occur commonly with lesions of the organ.

FIG. 6.16.—Position during a 'cerebellar' seizure. 'The attitude . . . is a caricature, with gross exaggeration in some particulars, of the attitude depicted in a snapshot of a man or a child running very fast. In running very fast the extensor muscles of the spine are in strong action to prevent the forwardly-inclining trunk from collapsing—to save the runner from tumbling on the ground with his face downwards ; the opisthotonos in tetanus-like seizures is a gross exaggeration of the activity of the extensor muscles of the spine in swift running.' (From Hughlings Jackson, 1906 *a*)

The rôle of the cerebellum in *epilepsy* must be regarded as uncertain at present (*vide* Ramsay Hunt syndrome, p. 196). Tumours within the cerebellum are sometimes associated with fits in which there are transient periods of exacerbation of muscular tone (Fig. 6.16). Such tumours are liable, however, to press upon numerous structures and to damage the forebrain by obstructing the circulation of cerebrospinal fluid. For these reasons this type of fit is now usually regarded as being due to a transient decerebration or decortication (p. 127). These tonic fits are not the only variety to be seen with cerebellar tumours ; indeed a wide variety of epileptic manifestations have been observed (Webster & Weinberger, 1940), but again it is uncertain to what extent these fits depend upon activity in the cerebellum itself. Actually there is little experimental evidence for the spread within the cerebellar cortex of epileptic discharges. If one point is stimulated electrically, and after-discharge

produced, it is found that the cortex only a short distance away
(*e.g.* 4 mm.) has not changed its electrical rhythms (Dow, 1938 *b*).

In spite of these observations the activity of cerebellar neurones
may be profoundly altered by the administration of convulsants;
the observations of Brookhart, Moruzzi & Snider (1951) have shown

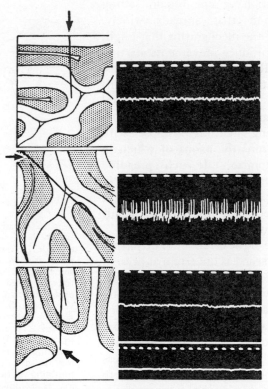

FIG. 6.17.—Localisation of electrical activity in anterior lobe of cerebellum. On
left, diagram of folded cerebellar cortex, with micro-electrode tracks ; on right,
electrical activity, with control to show noise level of amplifiers in the lowest
section.   Both spikes and waves appear to arise from Purkinje cell and/or
granule cell layers.   Time 25 c/s.   (Reproduced from Brookhart, Moruzzi &
Snider, 1951)

that under the action of strychnine the rate of discharge of individual cerebellar cells may rise to several hundred impulses per
second (cf. Fig. 6.17).   The connections between the cells, unlike
those in the cerebrum, do not facilitate the massive synchronous discharge of spikes that can break through synaptic barriers and discharge into the motor system.   Under the action of strychnine the

cerebellum produces waves that are much slower than those of its
normal activity, and they are sinusoidal rather than spike-like in
shape (*vide* Johnson, Walker, Browne & Markham, 1952). Since it
seems that 'avalanche' excitation does not occur, the possibility must
be considered that the collaterals from the axones of the Purkinje
cells are inhibitory to the discharge of neighbouring neurones. The
mechanism, in this case, would parallel that known to exist for the
comparable situation of the anterior horn cells (p. 119).

THE EFFECTS OF DAMAGE TO THE CORPUS CEREBELLI AND ITS AFFERENT CONNECTIONS

The massive cortical projection to the cerebellum is interrupted
by lesions of the *middle peduncle* ; it is not therefore surprising that
such lesions give rise to gross disorders of movement. Ferrier &
Turner (1894) give an account of their observations of a monkey.
The day after the section of the left middle peduncle the animal
'lay prone and exhibited great swaying of the body and a sprawling
gait on attempting spontaneous movement'. The animal tended
to fall backwards and to the left. It is surprising to what a large
extent the symptoms that follow such lesions improve as time goes
by. 'At the end of a month the animal had practically recovered
from its unsteadiness of equilibrium, but still exhibited oscillatory
movements of the left arm on volitional exertion, and the movements
of the left leg were awkward in progression.' Turner & German
(1941) also studied the effects of section of the brachium pontis. At
first the animals showed a curvature of the head and trunk to the
side of the lesion (cf. Fig. 6.4). More enduring was a disturbance of
walking, the movements of the fore- and hind-limbs were not
correctly related to one another.

This type of disturbance was noticed by Meyers (1919) in dogs with
lesions of the cerebellum itself. He trained the animals to pull a small
cart containing a kymograph on which records were obtained of the
movements of various parts of the animal's body. Meyers comments
that : 'In both, man as well as quadruped, there is a synchronous diagonal-
ism in each pace, an anterior and its diagonally opposite posterior extremity advancing and receding together. If a man walks with a stick in
each hand the movements of his extremities are exactly similar to those of
a quadruped. . . .'

It is in *complex acts*, movements involving the participation of
many muscles, that cerebellar disorders show most prominently.

Movements may be said to be 'decomposed', that is they are split up into simpler fragments which are performed successively ; there is a failure of 'synergia'. As has been seen, damage to the cerebellum may interfere with the operation of stretch reflexes and accordingly acts which involve the fixation of several joints by postural contraction of the associated musculature suffer.

Other pathways that reach the cerebellum come from the *inferior olive*. This structure projects in a point-to-point manner with the various parts of the cerebellar cortex (Holmes & Stewart, 1908). 'The olivo-cerebellar projection is a precisely orientated one, the accessory olivary parts send connections to the anterior and posterior cerebellar lobes and the main olive to the middle lobe' (Wilson & Magoun, 1945).

The inferior olive is supplied with information from the brain stem and basal ganglia by the *central tegmental tract* and by fibres from the spinal cord that run in the spino-cerebellar pathways. The fibres from the inferior olive cross the mid-line and run into the cerebellum on the opposite side. It is not possible to remove the inferior olive without at the same time doing some damage to neighbouring pathways, but in the experiments of Wilson & Magoun (1945) this damage was minimal. They give the following account of the changes observed one month after unilateral *olivectomy* in the cat : 'In its cage the animal usually lay or squatted on the floor. On standing it often fell to the side of the lesion. A body and head sway was often present when these parts were off the floor, and, on feeding, the head bobbed back and forth into the dish. Intention tremor of the neck was also evident when the animal sniffed at the wall or floor, this act became converted into a series of pecking movements. . . . Tremor was never observed in the extremities. . . . Gait was ataxic, being decomposed into a series of deliberate movements, and was further complicated by a pronounced overflexion of the limbs contralateral to the lesion in stepping. This hypermetria became exaggerated by attempts to move rapidly and progress was frequently punctuated by falling to the side of the lesion.' In these experiments it is interesting that abnormalities of laryngeal movements were recorded, for damage to the inferior olives or their connections is believed to be the cause of a rare but interesting clinical syndrome : *Palatal myoclonus.*

'The disorder is defined as constant rhythmic movements of the palate and pharynx, varying in rate and amplitude, the rate being between

50 and 180 per minute. The movements may be synchronous with those of other organs, such as the larynx, eyeballs, and diaphragm. Once a patient has acquired this disorder the movements continue inexorably until death, although in some patients the movements may be halted during voluntary innervation, such as phonation and swallowing.' The movements are said to continue during both sleep and general anaesthesia (Bender, Nathanson & Gordon, 1952). It is possible that the extent to which speech is affected in conditions in which the cerebellum degenerates (Greenfield, 1954) depends upon the extent to which the inferior olive is implicated in the disease process.

These olivo-cerebellar fibres are amongst those cut when the *inferior peduncle* of the cerebellum is severed. The effects of this procedure are to reduce the tone, strength and reflexes of the musculature on the same side of the body. Movements of the ipsilateral limbs are inaccurately performed. Speaking of their observations on the effects of cutting the inferior peduncle Ferraro & Barrera (1935) stated that : 'It may therefore be expected, in view of the various contingents which enter the restiform body as it passes upwards, that the symptoms associated with lesions of it at various levels may vary. The intensity of the disturbances increases as the lesions lie more cephalad, but no new symptoms appear.' It is interesting that in these experiments no intention tremor (*vide infra*) was seen.

THE SIGNIFICANCE OF 'INTENTION TREMOR'

It is the function of the static postural mechanisms to 'freeze' the musculature into a certain attitude, one which is stable. In studying movement we are really considering the ways in which these postural sets may be broken up and replaced by others. For rapid movements it may be assumed that it is often necessary to 'switch off' the postural mechanisms and let the body fall momentarily, catastrophe being averted by a subsequent movement or by re-establishing under changed conditions the stabilisation of the limbs and trunk. Rapid movements, it may be assumed, are initiated through the descending fibres that control the anterior horn cells supplying the voluntary musculature (Fig. 10.5, p. 368), but towards the end of movement it is clearly necessary for the small motor fibres to be brought into action to fix the limb in its new position. It may be supposed then that rapid movements are started by the large motor cells and are 'finished off' by the small fibres (Merton,

1953). The accuracy of a movement will in this way depend largely upon bringing into play the intrafusal fibres of the muscle spindles. As has been noticed, however, there is in cerebellar lesions a lack of these types of response. The hypotonia appears to be due to a failure of the stretch reflex ; the small motor fibres are quiescent. It is not, therefore, surprising that in cerebellar disease movements should be inaccurately performed, although the initial acceleration of the limb may be as great as normal (Marshall & Walsh : unpublished data).

After the initial movement the limb may come to rest for a short time some distance from the goal. This inaccuracy is classically referred to as *dysmetria*. Some inaccuracy with rapidly performed movements is found with normal people (*vide* Searle & Taylor, 1948), but is very much less marked than that shown in patients with cerebellar disease. If the inaccuracy is significant, the normal person makes a second movement that usually suffices to correct the misalignment. In cerebellar disease the correction needed may be larger and the corrective movement itself may be inaccurately performed ; thus a series of movements may occur as the subject attempts to move his limb into the desired position. These movements towards the end of the motion are known as intention tremor and constitute an important clinical sign (Fig. 6.18). It is important to realise that they are probably an exaggeration of a physiological mechanism that is attempting to compensate for shortcomings in the motor performance.

FIG. 6.18.—Intention tremor. Finger/nose test in patient with cerebellar disease ; the irregularities are most marked towards the end of the movement. (Modified from Lymans' photographs reproduced by Pullen)

Intention tremor shows up to varying degrees in the same patient at different times. André-Thomas (1910) studied this question on a patient suffering from a form of cerebellar degeneration :—

'When he was asked to place his finger upon his nose, the movement was executed differently according to whether it was spontaneous, rapid or slow. When the movement was executed spontaneously and naturally, it was done in several stages—it was not continuous. There was, so to speak, a certain degree of intention tremor. Also when the finger reached the nose, the hand was unstable and executed alternative movements of supination and pronation before reaching a state of repose. . . . If the movement was made slowly and carefully, it was practically executed correctly, continuously, and did not extend further than it should have. I the movement were rapid, the finger passed over the object and touched the cheek at the side of the nose ; this time it was very clearly out of proportion, and there was dysmetria. Dysmetria existed in all movements ; if he tried to take hold of a glass the hand was opened too far.'

Corrective movements imply that the system is 'error controlled' and it is probable that these movements are dependent upon one of the sensory areas of the cerebral cortex. Thus the misalignment may be perceived on the basis of proprioceptive, tactile, visual or auditory information. There is probably much truth in Collier's statement that the cerebellar patient 'walks with his cerebral hemispheres'. One patient who had a right-sided cerebellar lesion said of his movements : 'I seem to do it subconsciously on the left side, but on the right I have to think out each movement ; the arm comes to a dead stop and I have to think before starting again' (Holmes, 1922). That alternative sources of information are usually available about the accuracy of movement is probably the reason why cerebellar incoordination, in contrast to tabetic ataxia (Fig. 6.19), is made but little worse by closing the eyes. Nor is it entirely surprising when the cerebral hemispheres are extirpated and sensory data largely neglected that cerebellar tremor should not be seen (Fulton, 1936). A thalamic animal may be able to right itself and even to walk or run, and if it also loses its cerebellum these movements may still be accomplished without ataxia. In the thalamic animal, it may be remarked, movements are, literally, performed blindly and the sham rage that these preparations may manifest cannot be effectively directed against another animal or a person, for the cortical receiving areas of

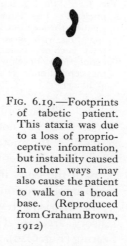

Fig. 6.19.—Footprints of tabetic patient. This ataxia was due to a loss of proprioceptive information, but instability caused in other ways may also cause the patient to walk on a broad base. (Reproduced from Graham Brown, 1912)

the special sense have been destroyed (p. 462). Walshe (1927) has aptly pointed out that '*There is no such phenomenon as cerebellar ataxy in the reflex preparation*'.

THE SIGNIFICANCE OF THE EFFERENT FIBRES THAT PASS TO THE CEREBRAL CORTEX

A cursory examination of the cerebellum suffices to show that the afferent pathways are more conspicuous than those leaving the cerebellum. It has been calculated that there are three times as many fibres entering as compared with those coming out of the organ. The great bulk of the fibres leaving the cerebellum of man arise in the dentate nuclei and travel through the brachium conjunctivum. They cross to the opposite side and pass through the red nucleus (Fig. 6.20) to ascend to the cerebral cortex on the opposite side. The pathways that have been most clearly established anatomically run to the sensorimotor cortex in the region of the central

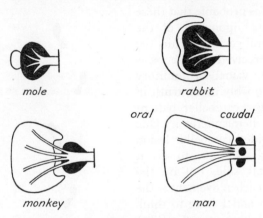

FIG. 6.20.—Phylogenetic development of the red nucleus. The large-celled portion becomes smaller, the small-celled portion larger. Corresponding with these changes the rubrospinal tract becomes insignificant, whilst important connections develop that are derived from the cerebellum. (From Brodal, 1948. After Winkler)

sulcus. These connections may be traced also by electrical means. Walker (1938 *b*) noted that there was an increase in the electrical activity of the motor cortex when the cerebellum was stimulated. There is also a return route from the areas representing particular parts of the body in the cerebellum to corresponding points on the sensorimotor region of the cerebral cortex (*vide* Fig. 6.21).

A surprising revelation has been that the cerebellum projects to sensory areas of the cerebral cortex concerned with vision and hearing (Fig. 6.22). As in the case of the sensorimotor strip, so it is those parts of the cerebellum that themselves receive the corresponding types of information that project back to the receiving

areas of the cerebral cortex. Fibres also descend in the reverse
direction. 'Thus it appears that much of the cerebellar cortex is
connected by two-way paths with the cerebral cortex and that the
connections are between regions of the two organs which are related
to specific peripheral receptor and effector mechanisms' (Woolsey &
Settlage, 1950).

What is the significance of these projections to the afferent areas
of the cerebrum ? It is usually said that cerebellar lesions do not
interfere with any form of sensibility, but this viewpoint may have
to be modified. When a patient with a unilateral cerebellar lesion
uses his affected arm to
lift objects they feel
unusually heavy ; this
disturbance is no doubt
related to the failure
of the stretch reflexes
(Holmes, 1917). Never-
theless, if the affected
hand is used to test
objects successively it
can differentiate as small
differences of weight as
normal. On this point
Holmes makes an in-
teresting comment con-
cerning a patient with
a left-sided cerebellar
lesion : 'the difference-

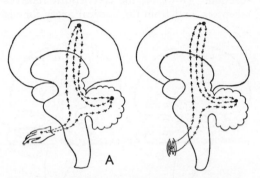

FIG. 6.21.—Dual projection of skin, A, and
possible dual projection of proprioceptors, B,
to cerebrum. As in the case of vision and
hearing, impulses reach the cerebrum not only
along direct pathways but also by being relayed
in the cerebellum. The cerebral areas in turn
project back to the cerebellum. (From Snider,
1950)

threshold for the affected limb was considerably smaller than in
the other . . . but this was explained by the fact that he had
been a mica dealer in Canada and accustomed since childhood to
"weigh" his wares in his left hand'.

Snider (1950) has rightly said that 'workers in this field have
been entirely too lethargic. . . .' Sjöqvist & Weinstein (1942),
working on chimpanzees, found that lesions of either the medial
fillet or of the superior cerebellar peduncle were without permanent
effect on the ability to discriminate different weights. On the other
hand, combined lesions of these pathways did produce a permanent
loss of the skill. Snider suggests that 'if sufficiently sensitive tests
could be developed, it is highly probable that similar results might
be obtained for the tactile, auditory and visual systems'. Could it

O

be that the pathways from the cerebellum are concerned with evaluating the error signals that are concerned with guiding movement ? Ruch in S. S. Stevens (1951) has written that :

'If simple analogies are sought, the cerebellum could be likened to the comparator of a servomechanism. It may receive from the cerebral cortex some representation of the command and from the muscles a representation of the resulting movement. These, compared, may result in a signal that is transmitted to the motor cortex, altering its signal to the muscles so as to diminish the error. In this capacity the cerebellum is acting as a feedback to stabilise one unit of the whole system of neural reaction. However, the cerebellum receives impulses from the distance receptors, and from the cortical areas for vision and audition. . . . Such an arrangement may mean that the cerebellum can compare the true input, the auditory or visual representation of the goal, and the proprioceptive indication of the limb's position.'

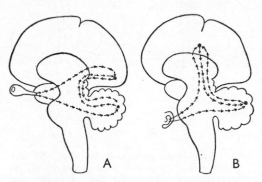

FIG. 6.22.—Dual projection of eye, A, and ear, B, to the cerebrum. In addition to the 'classical' routes through the geniculate bodies information from the eye and the ear is relayed upwards to the cerebrum from the cerebellum. The visual and auditory areas in turn project to the cerebellum. (From Snider, 1950)

Whatever explanations are put forward, it is necessary to take into account that intention tremor is absent or inconspicuous in lesions restricted to the inferior and middle peduncles. These movements appear in their fullest form only when the efferent pathways from the cerebellum to the cerebral cortex are damaged. Lesions restricted to the *superior peduncle* do sometimes arise clinically but are rare (Fig. 6.23) and do not always fall into the hands of the observant. Experimentally, lesions of the superior peduncle have been made by Walker & Botterell (1937) who worked on monkeys.

'To bring out the maximum deficit in motor performance the flexor tendons were sectioned in the wrist contralateral to the divided cerebellar peduncle in several cases. The animal was thus compelled to use the affected hand for feeding. . . .' In one monkey with a lesion of the left superior cerebellar peduncle it was noted that :
'Upon reaching for an object the movement of the left upper extremity

was definitely jerky, usually the animal missed the object, striking the
floor on either side of it, then corrected.   A slight fumbling occurred
after which the animal grasped the object and then carried it to his mouth.
Just as the hand was about to reach the mouth usually a fine tremor
occurred, then the object was placed in the buccal cavity.'   Walker &
Botterell also remarked that :

   'It is apparent that bilateral section of the superior cerebellar peduncles produces a severe and persisting inco-ordination of volitional
movement.   This disturbance is more than the arithmetic sum of the
disability produced by two unilateral sections of the superior cerebellar
peduncle.   The gait is a striking example of this fact.   Within a few
weeks the animal with a unilateral section of the superior cerebellar
peduncle is able to walk around without falling, whereas a monkey with
both superior cerebellar peduncles cut staggers and falls even after four
months.   Moreover, certain features which are slight in the unilateral

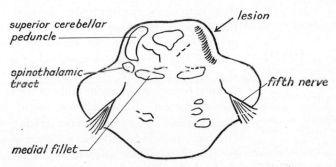

FIG. 6.23.—Lesion giving homolateral ataxia and heterolateral loss of pain and
    temperature sense.   The patient walked on a broad base with the left leg
    abducted and the left arm oscillating in a flail-like fashion.   'Emotional'
    movements on the right side of the face were impaired although 'volitional'
    movements were performed normally.   This dissociation of emotional from
    intellectual control is the converse of that commonly found in neurological
    patients.   (From Russel, 1931)

preparation become more prominent when both superior cerebellar peduncles are sectioned.   The tremor of the head and trunk is an illustration.
In unilateral preparations a nodding tremor of the head is present at
most for a few days, and in some cases may not occur at all.   By contrast,
the animal with both peduncles sectioned shows a severe tremor of the
head and trunk during the acute stage of the syndrome, and after some
months may exhibit the same tremor upon excitement or fatigue.'

   The bilaterality of the representation within the paramedian
lobule may explain how it is that bilateral lesions produced effects
much more severe than unilateral lesions.   In the cerebellum the
body is represented in more than one place (Fig. 6.13); it would

appear that, as in other parts of the nervous system, there are alternative pathways available for handling important signals. Much of the cerebellar cortex may thus be lost, and yet the permanent neurological deficit may be slight. The greatest degree of compensation probably occurs in lesions that have been present since birth ; almost complete absence of the cerebellum has been reported as a congenital anomaly (*vide* André-Thomas, 1910 ; Baker & Graves, 1931).

It has become apparent that not only does the cortex control the cerebellum but that the cerebellum in some way exerts an influence on the cortex. Russell (1894) found that after removal of the cerebellum on one side movements were produced more readily by excitation of the contralateral than ipsilateral motor cortex. He also noted that convulsive movements, induced by the intravenous injection of absinthe, were of greater amplitude in the limbs on the same side as the cerebellar lesion. He concluded that the cerebellum normally exerts an influence reducing the excitability of the opposite motor cortex. This concept might explain the Ramsay Hunt syndrome (Hunt, 1921). In this condition convulsive movements may be precipitated by afferent stimuli, such as those delivered by a tendon hammer (cf. p. 352). In some of these cases the only pathological findings have been an absence of Purkinje cells from the cerebellum.

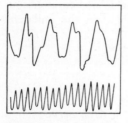

FIG. 6.24.—Interference with rapidly repeated movement in cerebellar ataxia. Ataxic limb (upper graph) compared with normal (lower record). The inability to perform rapid movements is known as 'adiadochokinesis'. (From Holmes, 1922)

There is, however, evidence that the cerebellum may increase the excitability of the cortex. Many years ago Rossi investigated the effects of exciting one side of the cerebellum on the excitability of the opposite motor cortex and concluded that the influence was excitatory. More recently Moruzzi (1950) has shown that according to the coexistent conditions cerebellar stimulation may either increase or decrease the effects of excitation of the motor cortex—but it is naturally difficult to ascertain to what extent these alterations are exerted at the cortex rather than, for instance, at the level of the spinal motor neurone. In view of the influences that play upon the motor cortex it is not altogether surprising that the rapid repetition of movement is poorly performed in patients with cerebellar lesions (Fig. 6.24).

Earlier in this chapter connections from the cerebral cortex to the cerebellum were considered, and the rôle of the cerebellum in controlling the postural mechanisms was discussed. It is evident that in many voluntary acts mediated by the motor cortex there is call for much postural readjustment. It may be assumed that the control exerted by the cortex over the cerebellum, and the influence that the cerebellum exerts, in its turn, over the postural reflex mechanisms, assist in these manœuvres. The system also works in the reverse direction, for through the cerebellum the postural mechanisms can modify the discharges of the motor cortex. It may be assumed that certain acts are barred, for they would give rise to instability. It is, therefore, wrong to regard the postural system as being dominated by the motor cortex, for movement that is performed must be regarded as being one that is both (1) satisfactory for the goal in view (cerebral cortex) and (2) does not conflict with the demands of the postural system for stabilisation (cerebellum and brain stem).

In balancing a ball on its nose the seal is supplied with visual and tactile information about movements of the object. It moves its head to keep the ball up, but the movements of the head involve readjustments in the trunk which may have to curve or lean over. At times the ball has to be allowed to fall because these adjustments have reached their limits, and if pushed further it would be the animal and not the ball that fell.

CHAPTER 7

THE CEREBRAL CORTEX: OLFACTION: ELECTRO-ENCEPHALOGRAPHY

At every stage of technique since Daedalus or Hero of Alexandria, the ability of the artificer to produce a working simulacrum of a living organism has always intrigued people. This desire to produce and to study automata has always been expressed in terms of the living technique of the age. In the days of magic, we have the bizarre and sinister concept of the Golem, that figure of clay into which the Rabbi of Prague breathed in life with the blasphemy of the Ineffable Name of God. In the time of Newton, the automaton becomes the clockwork music box with the little effigies pirouetting on top. In the nineteenth century, the automaton is a glorified heat engine, burning some combustible fuel instead of the glycogen of the human muscles. Finally, the present automaton opens doors by means of photocells, or points guns to the place at which a radar beam picks up an airplane, or computes the solution of a differential equation.—WIENER (1948, p. 51).

STRUCTURE

THE structure of the cerebral cortex [1] is known only as far as its grossest details, and therefore any discussion of it can hardly at the present time hope to describe function in terms of the details of the relationships between the neurones of the grey matter. Because of this shortcoming it is often useful to consider the function of the cortex in terms of mechanical and electrical analogies (*vide* McCallum & Smith, 1951 *a* & *b*). Even as to the main fibre tracts in the cerebrum there is but scanty knowledge. The earlier anatomists, by dissection, and by studying the myelinisation at different stages of development, believed that they had shown a rather intricate system of *long conducting tracts* linking different, and distant, cerebral zones (Fig. 7.1). Attempts have sometimes been made to ascertain

---

[1] 'Cortex' originally meant 'bark' (of a tree), whilst the synonym 'pallium' referred to a 'cloak'.

the function of various tracts by correlating the time at which they become myelinated with the development of function, but the supposition that tracts become functional only when they have become myelinated does not appear to have been proved. It is known, for instance, that reflex activity may be observed before any pathways in the nervous system become myelinated (Langworthy, 1932 *a*).

The existence of long fibre tracts in the cerebrum has, in recent times, received confirmation from another method of study ; these pathways may be demonstrated by the application of *strychnine* to

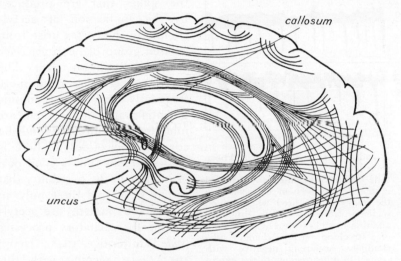

FIG. 7.1.—Long fibre connections of the cerebrum based upon observations of gross anatomy. (From Herrick, 1915)

the cortex. It is usual to apply the drug by means of small squares of filter paper, moistened with a solution of known concentration ; the liquid is coloured with a dye so that it is possible to tell how localised an area of the cortex has been treated. After a latent period of a few minutes the cells of the cortex discharge together giving rise to brief pulses of high amplitude : the *strychnine spikes* (Fig. 7.2). The occurrence of these potentials in distant regions of the cerebrum indicates a direct connection from the irritated zone to the regions from which the spikes are recorded (Fig. 7.3).

The relationships revealed in this way are complicated, but a summary of the longer connections that have been demonstrated is shown in Fig. 7.4. The absence of a connection in such a chart as this does not mean that connections do not exist, for some cells in the nervous system may not be susceptible to the action of the drug. Thus Frankenhaeuser (1951) could find no spikes on the application of strychnine to the olfactory bulb. It is possible, therefore, that the use of other excitatory agents would reveal other sets of connections.

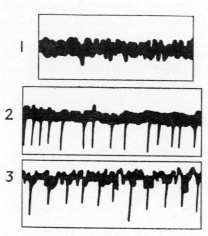

FIG. 7.2.—Strychnine spikes shown in 2 and 3; 1 is a control. These short lasting potentials of high amplitude enable connections to be traced in the nervous system by observing the areas that are 'fired' when a given region is treated with the drug. In addition to spikes the D.C. potential of a strychninised area changes substantially, becoming negative with respect to other regions to the extent of, for instance, 50 mV. As the area that has been treated becomes negative small spikes occur on its rising negativity; these are the discharge of the superficial layers. When the strychnine soaks into the depths the deeper layers begin to fire (McCulloch, 1949). (Figure after Dusser de Barenne & McCulloch, 1938, as redrawn in S. Wright, 1952)

There is some evidence that the spikes that are produced by the application of acetylcholine to the cortex arise from another group of neurones (*vide* Hughes & Robinson, 1951). The acetylcholine spikes recur more frequently than the strychnine potentials and unlike them are inhibited by atropine and by adenine nucleotides. There is at the present time a good deal of interest in the possibility that certain cells, and these only, in the nervous system use acetylcholine for excitatory processes (*vide* Whitteridge, 1948; Hebb, 1954). In keeping with this view Chatfield & Dempsey (1941) found striking regional differences in the reaction of the cortex to the topical application of acetylcholine after preliminary treatment with prostigmine. The drug increased the spontaneous electrical activity, and produced spikes in the auditory somaesthetic and motor regions of the cortex, but not in the 'association' (p. 283) areas.

Structurally the microscope reveals in the cerebral cortex a wealth of ramifying dendritic processes, a labyrinth of interconnections that defies description (Plate 4). These processes are shown by the use of silver stains, and in the staining procedure only long enough is allowed to enable a fraction of the possible cells to be seen ; if all of the cerebral cells were picked out the meshwork would be a densely matted black jumble. Any diagram that is produced represents, therefore, a considerable simplification (Fig. 7.5).

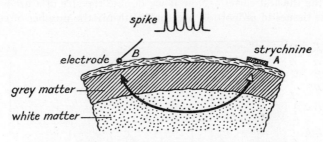

FIG. 7.3.—Diagram illustrating principles of strychnine neuronography. (From S. Wright, 1952)

The cortex, studied in this way, shows a number of horizontal layers ; this lamination suggests that neighbouring parts function in homologous ways.

The great wealth of fibre connections run vertically up and down rather than from side to side. It is estimated that of the 12×10^9 cells in the human brain, no less than $9 \cdot 2 \times 10^9$ lie in the cerebrum itself [1] (*vide* Herrick, 1926). These *numerous cells* allow a great number of alternatives to be 'considered' by the cerebrum ; the 'decisions' that are taken are represented by the states of excitation, or of quiescence of neurones in astronomical numbers. It is of interest in comparing the cortex of a mouse with that of a man to note that there is no evidence in the latter of any refinement of structure, the cortex seems to be built upon the same plan, but in man the number of cells is larger, and the area of the cortex is much greater (Lorente de Nó, 1939 *b*).

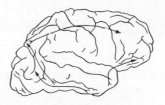

FIG. 7.4.—Long fibre tracts of the cortex revealed by 'strychnine neuronography'. (From Bailey, Bonin, Garol & McCulloch, 1943)

[1] There are 7×10^9 cells in the two human cerebral hemispheres, according to Shariff (1953). In spite of these astronomical numbers the cell bodies do not account for more than a fraction of the volume of the cortex—in man $2 \cdot 85$ per cent, in some lower forms 12 per cent. Dendrites and axones also must be considered, but most of the space is said to be taken up by glia (Gerard in Weiss, 1950, quoting figures of Bok).

These facts have a bearing on the proportion of the forebrain that is concerned with transmitting information to distant regions. Wiener (quoted by Ward, 1948) has pointed out that :

'the human brain is one of the largest of all, and of the large brains it has by far the thickest cortex. Now if we double the size of a brain keeping all gross tissues in proportion, we shall multiply the number of cells by 8

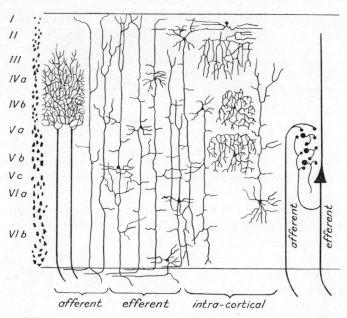

Fig. 7.5.—Microscopic structure of cortex. Nissl picture, showing only cell bodies, is seen on extreme left, whilst on extreme right is a greatly simplified 'wiring' diagram. A structure of this type clearly enables messages to be delayed to interact with those arriving at later periods (p. 230). Note the two types of afferent fibre, one of which terminates largely in layer 4, whilst those of the other type are connected to a number of different layers of the grey matter. (After Lorente de Nó as re-drawn by Brodal, 1948)

and the number of connecting fibres only by 4 since their length is also doubled. In other words, we have a relative deficiency of direct remote connectors between different parts of the brain. . . .'

A reflection of the great development of the grey matter of the cerebral cortex is to be seen in the folding of the surface of the cerebrum into sulci and gyri which increases the ratio of grey to white matter over what would otherwise be the case. The human brain, although highly convoluted, is surpassed in this by certain other mammals. The brain of the porpoise, for instance, is, macroscopically, more 'highly developed' than the human brain (Fig. 7.6), although microscopic examination shows that the grey matter is not richly endowed with cells (Langworthy, 1932 *b*).

A great deal of effort has gone into attempts to subdivide the surface of the cerebral cortex into different regions according to its

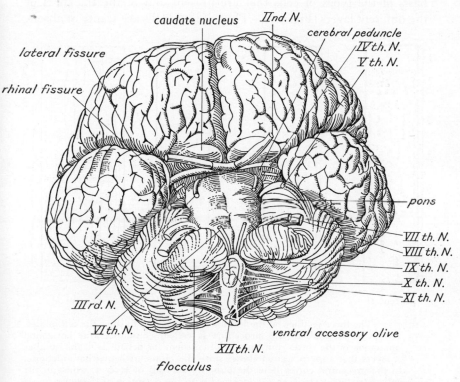

Fig. 7.6.—The brain of a porpoise from the ventral surface. The cerebral hemispheres are well developed and highly convoluted. The 8th nerve is larger than the optic nerve and the temporal lobes also are large. The structure labelled as the flocculus is probably in fact the paraflocculus. The flocculonodular (p. 164) part of the cerebellum is small in the cetacea (Jansen, 1950). Comparative studies throw into prominence structures and mechanisms the importance of which might not be grasped by a study of the human brain by itself. (From Langworthy, 1932 *b*)

microscopical appearances ; this study is referred to as *cyto-architectonics*. Some of the subdivisions leave no room for dispute. Thus in the occipital region there may be found a horizontal band composed of transversely running myelinated fibres. The cortex in that region is known, because of this, as the *striate* area, and it represents the primary cerebral receiving station for impulses from the optic radiations. In the cat, horizontal branches of the afferent fibres ramify in this 'stripe of Gennari' and form connections with other neurones over a surprisingly large area (O'Leary, 1941).

Other regions of the cerebral cortex are differentiated on the basis of the types of cells that are present and of the thickness of the different layers (Fig. 7.7). Thus, if large cells are scanty or absent

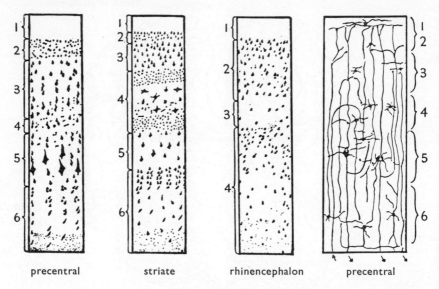

precentral   striate   rhinencephalon   precentral

Fig. 7.7.—The three sections on the left have been stained to show the cell bodies. The Nissl method, as this procedure is called, emphasises the horizontal lamination of the cortex, but there is often room for debate as to the number of layers that a given section shows since the limits are somewhat indefinite. In the precentral cortex note the large motor cells of layer 5, whilst in the optic (striate) cortex layer 4, concerned with the reception of the optic radiations, is greatly enlarged. In the rhinencephalon the number of layers is reduced. The section on the right of the figure was prepared with a silver stain and indicates that the majority of the interconnections of the cortex run radially. (Reproduced from Cobb, 1948)

and small cells only are seen, the cortex is referred to as 'koniocortex' or as being 'granular'. 'Konis' is Greek for 'dust'. By contrast the motor cortex contains some very large pyramidal cells.

The motor cortex is sometimes referred to as being the area 'gigantopyramidalis' as compared with the 'granular' regions lying further forward in the frontal lobe. This sort of nomenclature leads to confusion; it is an error to combine two different systems of classification as though they were synonymous. Thus a region of the cortex lying principally in front of the central fissure will, when excited electrically, give rise to muscular movements whilst certain structural features are found in approximately the same area.   In both cases, the limits to the areas are somewhat arbitrary, depending, for instance, in the case of the electrical stimulation, on the strength of the stimulus and upon the depth of anaesthesia.   In the case of the cyto-architectonic studies the limits are equally indefinite.   Speaking of cyto-architectonic areas in the frontal lobe, Campbell (1905, p. 234) wrote: 'But it is not to be denied that

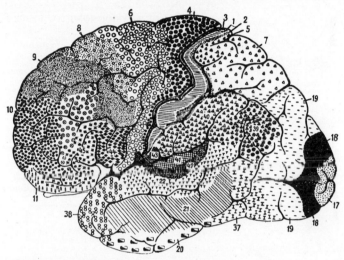

FIG. 7.8.—Subdivisions of cortex on the basis of cyto-architectonics.   Even more numerous subdivisions have been made than those indicated in this diagram, but the extent to which such parcellation is justifiable is debatable.   (After Brodman, reproduced from Fulton, 1943)

the structural variations are of a subtle description and only discoverable by a cautious examination of a large expanse of cortex in serial sections; for not only is the entire field enveloped by cortex showing the usual seven laminae to which I have made constant reference throughout this research, but the changes affecting these laminae are not of the gross character seen in other regions; moreover, the several subdividing lines of demarcation are by no means so sharp as the diagram indicates.   Therefore in putting an account of the lamination on paper it becomes necessary to use as a descriptive basis the appearances seen in portions of cortex lying towards the centre of each area,—that is, portions which may be regarded as typical—and to give point to the survey by adding comparative remarks concerning each type.'

The fact that one region should so often shade away into another should not mislead the student into believing that cyto-architectonic

divisions have no reality.   Few would quarrel with the statement
that 'cyto-architectonic study has given precious leads to physiologists but it has also misled them into accepting uncritically distinctions beyond the limits of probable functional significance'
(Bailey, 1948).   Le Gros Clark (1952) in this connection has remarked that 'the contrast between the pre- and post-central cortex

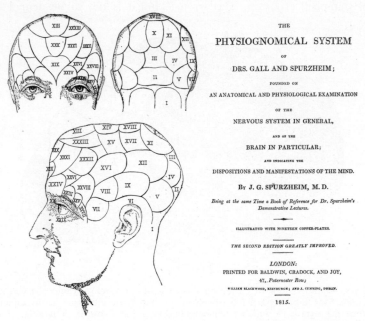

FIG. 7.9.—Title-page and frontispiece of an early volume on phrenology.   By
attempting to correlate mental 'faculties' with swellings of particular regions
of the head phrenologists drew diagrams of this type ; a debased version of
this type of activity now occurs at fairs.   The claims of the phrenologists
were not justified by their data but they did draw attention to the need for a
scientific study of criminology.   Reaction against the far-fetched claims of
the phrenologists led to the view, in the second half of the nineteenth century,
that the brain 'acts as a whole'

of the primate brain is . . . perfectly evident to anyone who takes
the trouble to examine appropriate slides'.   In examining such a
series of sections it is necessary to bear in mind differences in the
thickness of the cortex due to its folding ; just as a rubber tube
folded becomes thin at a convex fold and thick at a concave fold, so
the same changes occur in the gyri and sulci of the cortex.
    On the basis of structural differences, the cortex has been par-
celled into a quilt-work of areas (Fig. 7.8), comparable to the sub-

divisions made much earlier by the phrenologist (Fig. 7.9). The maps given by different observers differ very considerably, for the criteria by which one region should be separated depend upon the personal bias of the microscopist. Small clumps of cells might be regarded as being separate for architectonic purposes, but no one would wish to press the divisions to these limits. Lashley & Clark (1946) have pointed out that 'without exception students of architectonics have depended primarily upon intuitive judgement of the nature and amount of difference between areas'. These workers set themselves the task of learning to identify as many of the cytoarchitectonic areas as possible from sections.

When no evidence was given to them as to the part of the brain from which the section had been taken, they found that correct identification was possible for certain of the main regions but not for the lesser subdivisions.

Table 4

Regions Identifiable by Histological Characteristics (Neocortex)

Monkey brain (Ateles and Macaque), after Lashley & Clark, 1946

1. Frontal granular	5. Parieto-occipital
2. Precentral agranular	6. Temporal
3. Insular agranular	7. Striate
4. Post-central	

It seems that further progress in this field will only come through the introduction of new methods; it is quite possible that the study of the distribution of substances in the grey matter by histochemical techniques could provide a great deal of information. As it is possible to localise specific enzymes to specific types of cell in the retina (*vide* Hebb, Silver, Swan & Walsh, 1953), this should also be possible in the cortex.

OLFACTION

The cerebral cortex developed phylogenetically in connection with the sense of smell, and in some vertebrates the cortex is still largely concerned with this sense. Even in the case of the dog,[1] smell is perhaps of as great importance as vision, but in man, under civilised conditions, the sense of smell is neglected to a large extent, and the parts of the brain that developed in association with this sense (the 'rhinencephalon') appear in some measure to have

[1] 'The song of Quoodle' [G. K. Chesterton].

abandoned their original functions (p. 463) (cf. Berry, Hagamen & Hinsey, 1952). Smell is nevertheless still used as an important guide as to what is good to eat, and it can be used for many other discriminations if it is given sufficient practice, as by the North American Indians.

Hellen Keller (p. 417), who became deaf and blind in infancy, depended to a great extent upon the sense of smell. The American neurologist, Tilney (1929), gave the following account of what Miss Keller could accomplish :

'Miss Keller has an extremely sensitive olfactory sense. I may recite in this connection my experience with her in a drive from her home in Forest Hills to Garden City, a distance of about twenty miles. The windows of the car were open. It was a fresh crisp day in winter. I asked Miss Keller if she could tell me anything about the country through which we were passing, and her first observation was that we were then making our way through open fields. This proved to be the case, for the road ran through a golf course. Later, she said that we were passing trees. The road at this point made its way through a small grove. She then called attention to the fact that we had just passed a house with an open fire, and looking back I saw a small cottage with smoke pouring out of its chimney. She recognised at once when we turned off the main road to enter the Motor Parkway, and in the course of our drive along this road she declared that we were then passing a number of large buildings ; looking behind me I saw that we were actually in the vicinity of the several groups of structures constituting the Creedmore State Hospital for the insane. . . . Shortly after this Miss Keller called attention to the fact that we had just entered Garden City and were passing the plant of Doubleday and Doran, her publishers, which actually was the case. Her realisation of this fact, she told me, was due to her olfactory recognition of the ink from the presses of this publishing establishment with which she was familiar.'

In describing the importance of the sense of smell in her life, Helen Keller wrote :

'I wonder how many people are aware of the complex odours in a house that has been lived in for a long time. They give me a comfortable sense of hospitality. They suggest cheery winter fires and peace and sweet family intimacies. There are lingering scents of perfume and garments in closets and drawers, and appetising odours of cooking, which some people find extremely unpleasant, but which seem to me kindly.'

The *olfactory membrane* is situated in the upper part of the nasal cavity and from it fine unmyelinated fibres run into the olfactory bulb

(Fig. 7.10). The hair cells which are responsive to odours are the same ones that give rise to the axones that carry the information upwards.   In head injuries the sense of smell is sometimes lost, probably because the fine fibres are particularly vulnerable as they run through the openings in the ethmoid bone.   One illustrative case, quoted by Moncrieff (1944), was that of a man who had fallen from a horse twenty-seven years previously and had hit his head heavily on the ground.   After this he had completely lost the sense of smell.

'The strongest odours under his nose produced no sensation whatever, although the tactile sensibility of his nostrils was normal, and snuff occasioned sneezing and tickling.   He stated that he had also lost the

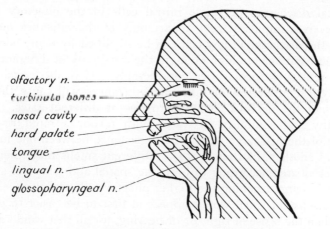

olfactory n.
turbinate bones
nasal cavity
hard palate
tongue
lingual n.
glossopharyngeal n.

FIG. 7.10.—The nasal passages. After Pfaffman, reproduced from Geldard (1953)

sense of taste as he could not distinguish one meat from another, whilst boiled onions, boiled apples and boiled turnips all appeared the same to him.   His palate could not distinguish the aroma of wines, although he could distinguish them a little by roughness or sweetness.   He could also recognise sweet, salt, bitter, and acid tastes. . . . Clearly the subject's sense of taste and common chemical sense were intact, but his sense of smell and with it the perception of flavour had been lost.'

On reaching the *olfactory bulb* the olfactory impulses meet their first synaptic junctions in the pathway.   At this stage there is considerable convergence; thus in the rabbit there are some millions of axones entering the bulb but only about 70,000 synapses.   Two cells, the mitral and the tufted, are involved in the pathways, and we

P

may consider that some special types of information are, at this point, selected to be passed backwards to the rest of the olfactory brain. There is evidence that there exist efferent fibres that run out from the brain to the olfactory bulb (Arduini & Moruzzi, 1953). It may well be that these pathways play a rôle in determining which types of information are passed backwards to the brain. Mechanisms of this sort may be important in other sensory systems (p. 273 and p. 414).

In some respects the olfactory bulb stands in the relationship to the olfactory receptors that the nervous elements of the retina stand to the rods and cones; no doubt the synaptic junctions within the bulb are concerned with sorting the information before it is sent to the higher centres. Adrian (1954) has studied the electrical discharges of single mitral cells in the olfactory bulb; each receives impulses from a part only of the olfactory mucosa. Whilst the discharge of any cell can be modified by many odours if the concentrations are high enough, the sensitivity of different units to different substances varies considerably. It is also certain that the physical properties of different substances will cause the discharges of the nervous elements to rise at different rates. Thus 'volatility and solubility in water both favour a rapid rise and decline of the discharge with little persistence between one inspiration and another' (Adrian, 1954). Different smells may, therefore, be differentiated according to both the spatial and temporal aspects of the discharge reaching the higher olfactory centres.

The sense of smell would appear at first to be easier to understand than the sense of sight or of hearing, for all that would appear to be needed for olfactory perceptions would be a collection of neurones that responded in one way to one pattern of excitation, and in another way to another. It must be remembered, however, that the way in which the sense organs are stimulated will depend upon the way in which the odour reaches the nostril. The respiratory flow of air affects principally the lower part of the nose, whilst the olfactory organ is tucked away at the top of the cavity; sniffing is a way of inducing turbulence and of forming eddies that carry the odorous particles upwards. The area presented by the olfactory mucosa is very great, for each cell possesses up to a thousand finger-like processes (2μ long, $0{\cdot}1\mu$ diameter); these projections can be seen with the aid of the electron microscope (Bloom & Engström, 1952).

In testing the sense of smell in man it is usual to attempt to measure *thresholds* for different substances (Wenzel, 1948). Many chemicals stimulate not only the olfactory organ, but the trigeminal receptors of the nose in addition ; for testing the sense of smell, irritants such as ammonia should be avoided. Allen (1937) investigated the rôles of the olfactory and trigeminal nerves in dogs and found that whilst certain substances appeared to stimulate only the olfactory organ, it was rather common for the trigeminal endings also to be affected.

Table 5

Acting only on Olfactory Endings	Acting on both Olfactory and Trigeminal Nerves
Cloves	Camphor
Lavender	Eucalyptus
Anise	Pyridine
Asafoetida	Butyric acid
Benzol	Phenol
Xylol	

Quite apart from this, some odorous substances stimulate endings on the tongue ; thus a patient who is anosmic may detect chloroform vapour because of its sweet taste, and he may also be sensitive to peppermint (Crossland, Miller & Bradway, 1928).

Quantitative olfactory tests are not easy to perform and it is not normally practicable to measure directly the concentrations that are involved, for the nose may be a more sensitive detector than are the methods available to the chemist. The figures that are quoted for the olfactory thresholds depend upon dilution techniques ; thus, for example, a known quantity of odorous substances may be evaporated in a room of known dimension. The sensitivity can be remarkable ; mercaptan (C_2H_5SH) can be recognised when there are only 4×10^{-8} mgm. of the substance per litre of air. On the other hand, the human nose is insensitive to many odours to which animals respond. Thus certain female moths can be shown to attract mates from long distances by liberation of odoriferous particles ; males will continue to besiege a place where a female has been kept even though she has been removed. If she is in a glass box and can be seen but not smelt, they are not attracted. To the human being these moths are scentless.

For the accurate study of olfaction it is necessary to eliminate unwanted odours : a difficult task. At one American University (Cornell) a special chamber or 'olfactorium' has been installed

(Fig. 7.11). The chamber consists solely of tempered plate-glass joined with polished stainless steel, and it is supplied with a generous quantity of carefully filtered air. The absence of furnishings, such

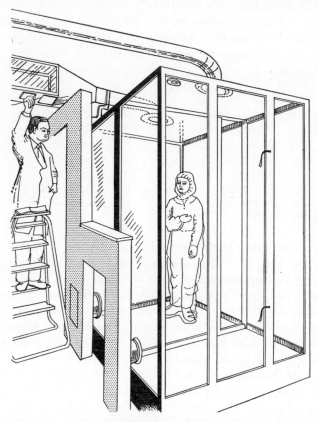

FIG. 7.11.—An olfactorium, a chamber designed to enable the sense of smell to be studied. The air in the chamber (175 c.ft.) may be changed six times per minute and the supply is carefully filtered beforehand. The observer when in the olfactorium wears an 'envelope' which is like an Eskimo's parka. 'It is made of an odorless plastic and it covers all parts of O's body and head except his face. Closely cropped hair and vaseline are rendered unnecessary by this covering—which facilitates the procurement of Os.' (From Foster, Scofield & Dallenbach, 1950)

as carpets and curtains, enables steam treatment of the chamber to remove successfully odours that have previously been introduced.

This degree of refinement has not been applied to the olfactory tests used for the investigation of neurological diseases; it is customary to use a simple bottle containing the odorous substance and pass the air into the subject's nose whilst he holds his breath.   The air may be introduced either as a brief blast or as a continuous stream, but care must be taken to ensure that the subject is really reacting to the odour and not merely to the stimulation of tactile endings by the impact of the air (*vide* Elsberg, 1937 ; Spillane, 1939).

There appears to be some degree of physiological *interaction* between the olfactory organs on the two sides of the nose.   Thus it is said that the smell of iodoform can largely be neutralised by the smell of pyruvian balsam applied to the other side.   In considering such interactions it is important to ensure that the air supplied to the two nostrils is not mixing in the pharynx and returning to the nose.   Elsberg (1937) felt that with suitable development olfactory tests would be a useful guide to the site of cerebral lesions, but unfortunately the commissural pathways concerned in these 'birhinal' responses are not known (*vide* Spillane, 1938 ; Brodal, 1947). Finally, it may be noted that if care is taken to avoid extraneous cues it is impossible to tell whether an odour arises in the right or left nostril, the sensation lacks 'local sign'.[1]

THE PROBLEM OF CEREBRAL MASS ACTION : THE EFFECTS OF CEREBRAL LESIONS

Certain functions are served by specific regions of the cerebral cortex and the details of these arrangements form a large part of the material presented in subsequent chapters.   It is also necessary to consider whether in some respects different regions of the cortex may be regarded as being 'equi-potential' (interchangeable in function).   We may consider the analogy of an electrical computing device, the elements of which may be used for a wide variety of different calculations, the use that is made of the parts depending solely upon the way in which the work is 'programmed'.

This problem has a bearing on the interpretation placed upon the

---

[1] 'It certainly makes no difference to the human nose whether the object it smells is short or long, round or square. . . . It is quite different with the bee, however.   A bee, whose feelers, in the darkness of the hive, touch an object in order to examine it . . . is bound to perceive the two different impressions of touch and of smell in very close association. . . . We may say that we ourselves, being accustomed to associate our visual with our tactile impressions from early childhood, are able to see "plastically" in exactly the same way as the bee can smell "plastically" ' (Frisch, 1954).   In vertebrates other than man olfactory local sign may be used.   Thus Parker (quoted by Moncrieff, 1944, p. 162) using dogfish found that after occlusion of one nostril the animals turned persistently to the opposite side.   Dogfish seek their food by olfaction and turn to the side with the greatest odour.

effects of *cerebral lesions*, for it is necessary to explain why the disturbances are most marked shortly after the injury has been inflicted and gradually get less as time passes. Some have held that other regions of the brain take over the functions previously exercised by the damaged area : that there is *vicarious function*. Alternatively damage to one part might disturb the activity of other parts with which it is linked by neural pathways—*diaschisis*. This might be due to the withdrawal of facilitation much as reflex depression follows section of the spinal cord. If the first explanation is correct, the functions served by the damaged area are correctly assessed by evaluating the deficit soon after the injury has been inflicted. Contrariwise if the second explanation is true these functions are best estimated when the fullest possible recovery has occurred (Lashley, 1938). These two possibilities must always be considered in evaluating the data obtained from a study of cerebral lesions with regard to the localisation of function in different cerebral sites. In addition it is necessary to consider that epileptic discharges set up close to the borders of a damaged region may upset the activity of areas of brain that are themselves quite healthy and far removed from the site of the injury ; sometimes the elimination of epileptogenic foci improves behaviour dramatically (p. 478).

It will have become apparent that the delineation of function on the basis of the effects of a lesion is fraught with hazards ; there is yet to be considered, however, a consideration that is perhaps even more important, it may be referred to as the *Principle of Alternative Pathways*.

This principle may be illustrated by the arrangements found in the auditory system. A person does not become deaf if he loses the cortical regions connected with the auditory pathways on one side, or indeed if he loses the whole of one cerebral hemisphere. It would nevertheless be wrong to assume that the regions that have been removed normally play no part in hearing, for the elimination of part of the opposite temporal lobe as well may now make him unable to hear the loudest sound (p. 280).

The reduplication of pathways in the nervous system mitigates the effects of brain damage. It is common to find, at post-mortem, areas of cystic degeneration in the brain caused by vascular disease that have not during life given rise to recognisable symptoms. It is only when the area of damage falls in a limited number of sites, such as the internal capsule or medulla oblongata, that the effects will be disastrous, or even detectable.

By analogy we may consider the arrangements that are now made in battleships to enable the electrical supply to be maintained even if part of the ship is blown away. One report of the arrangements reads as follows : ' Electrical supply in these ships depends upon the now universally adopted "ring main" system, which ensures the maximum degree of "damage control". The ship's generators, four in the case of a cruiser and eight in the case of a battleship, feed in current at various points and are independent of each other. The whole of the ship's supply can be controlled remotely from any one of up to five complete switchboards . . . each of these switchboards is a geographic representation of the ship, so that even a novice can follow its operation. Each part of the circuit is illuminated when current is present. The priority of each piece of apparatus is indicated by a coloured light on the switch. An operator attempting to keep the ship in action after part of the generating plant has been destroyed can thus see at a glance which circuits may be "shed" to avoid overloading' (*Daily Telegraph*, 23.12.52).

It is clearly wrong to assume that because a function may still be performed when a certain region is destroyed that this region normally plays no part in the activity under consideration. These considerations are simple but nevertheless are less widely appreciated than would be desirable. Thus in an interesting set of experiments Marquis & Williams (1938) showed that the vaso-constrictor response to pain (p. 482) could still be obtained when the cerebral hemisphere on one side had been damaged, and a similar result was obtained by Williams & Scott (1939) who investigated a patient from whom the whole of the cerebral cortex on one side had been removed. In both instances the authors came to the conclusion, unjustifiably, that the cerebral cortex was not concerned in the responses.

In addition to mitigating the effects of damage the presence of alternative pathways dealing with the same information may be important from another point of view. By replicating the transformations to which messages are subjected, conclusions may be reached with greater security than would be the case if all depended upon the vagaries of a single neural circuit. It is customary in some electronic calculating machines for the computations to be performed simultaneously, in duplicate by different parts of the apparatus. If the results tally, the next step in the mathematical treatment proceeds automatically, but if the results differ, then a warning signal is sent to the engineer in charge. By performing the same set of operations more than once, greater reliance can be placed upon the results.

In studying the localisation of functions in the nervous system it may therefore be necessary to consider the results not only of single but also of multiple lesions, for otherwise the effects of the alternative pathways may be misleading. The number of observations that could be made in this direction is legion. In the past, cases that showed more than one lesion at post-mortem have usually been discarded for the purposes of serious investigation, whilst it is just these categories that may prove to be the most rewarding material; they are, in any case, in the majority. Rather similar arguments have led the statistician R. A. Fisher (1935) to suggest that in the design of experiments, contrary to popular impression, it is better to arrange to modify more than one variable at a time :

'In expositions of the scientific use of experimentation it is frequent to find an excessive stress laid on the importance of varying the essential conditions *only one at a time*. The experimenter interested in the causes which contribute to a certain effect is supposed, by a process of abstraction, to isolate these causes into a number of elementary ingredients or factors, and it is often supposed, at least for purposes of exposition, that to establish controlled conditions in which all of these factors except one can be held constant, and then to study the effects of this single factor, is the essential scientific approach to an experimental investigation.'

'The modifications possible to any complicated apparatus, machine or industrial process must always be considered as potentially interacting with one another, and must be judged by the probable effects of such interactions. If they have to be tested one at a time this is not because to do so is an ideal scientific procedure, but because to test them simultaneously would sometimes be too troublesome, or too costly. In many instances . . . this impression is greatly exaggerated. Indeed, in a wide class of cases an experimental investigation, at the same time as it is made more comprehensive, may also be made more efficient, if, by more efficient we mean that more knowledge and a higher degree of precision are obtainable by the same number of observations.'

On many charts of the brain large regions are labelled as *silent areas*. As has been seen, a failure to attribute specific functions to particular areas may merely indicate that there are alternative routes that the information may follow. There is another possibility; appropriate tests may not have been tried. There is unlimited scope for extending the methods of clinical examination by techniques used in special sense physiology.

An analogous situation to that of the 'silent' areas of the cerebrum may be met with in other fields of biological study. Thus mice treated with the 'benzedrine' show little alteration when kept separately, but if a number of treated animals are kept together in the same cage there develops peculiar aberrations of behaviour. The running of one animal excites another to run, and so on, as a chain reaction (Chance, 1947). Similarly, in investigating the effects of frontal lesions it may be desirable to study animals in groups in order to understand the effects of the operation more fully (p. 477, Fig. 12.22). The human being also lives in society, and man's forebears probably hunted in groups. 'The sub-men seem to have been gregarious running animals, less like the solitary great apes than the baboons' (Wells, 1944). The effects of brain damage in man can, in some instances, only adequately be described in terms of changed social behaviour.

So far the alternative paths that have been considered have related to one and the same system. Actually a perception is usually built up from information arrived at by a number of distinct methods. It has sometimes been found that the performance at some task is affected by lesions of the cerebrum and that the impairment that is seen depends more upon the extent than upon the site of the lesion. This was the case in the experiments of Lashley (1929) on the ability of rats to run through *mazes*. In running a maze a rat may use a number of cues from different sensory organs : kinaesthetic, tactile, visual, olfactory and perhaps auditory and labyrinthine. Experiments such as Lashley's therefore require the most careful scrutiny before it can be concluded that the different regions of the cortex are in truth equi-potential (p. 213).

This point may be illustrated by considering another performance, that of *mating*, to which, also, different types of sensory information normally contribute, no single category being vital. The work on the male rabbit has been reviewed by Bard (1939). Bilateral labyrinthectomy is without effect. Olfaction, vision and hearing may be destroyed in the same animal without seriously interfering with sexual activity. The whole of the neocortex may be removed and yet coitus is effectively accomplished. Nevertheless, removal of the neocortex together with the olfactory bulbs destroys the capacity for mating. In discussing these results Bard concludes that the male rabbit requires 'for the excitation of sexual behaviour either the specific olfactory influence of the rhinencephalon or the neocortical mediation of visual, auditory or somesthetic sensibility'. It is clearly most important 'to determine the relationship between a defect produced by a cerebral removal and any accompanying specific sensory deficit. Unless this is done one runs the risk of prematurely or erroneously referring the defect to the absence of some non-specific cerebral function and, if so inclined, of invoking, simply from want of sufficient experimental analysis, the concept of "mass action".'

Enough has been said to show that the interpretation of ablation experiments is by no means easy. It is not very difficult to ablate a part of the cerebral cortex, but it is often difficult to design satisfactory tests for the loss of function. It may be even more difficult, on the basis of the data that accrue, to draw incontrovertible conclusions as to localisation of function. Tentative views based on the results of ablation experiments should be tested in other ways, by, for instance, electrical recording from, or stimulation of, the part concerned.

THE CEREBRUM AS A 'PREDICTOR': PLASTICITY

Information that is received at one moment through the sense organs is used to control behaviour at some time in the future. The implications of this may first be considered in terms of an analogy : the control of an anti-aircraft gun by radar signals giving the position of a hostile aeroplane. It would be of little value to direct the gun exactly towards the target, for the shell would inevitably burst some distance behind. For control to be effective it is necessary to attempt to predict the most probable course of events in the future. One simple assumption would be that the aircraft would continue to travel at the same velocity and in the same direction, whilst a more refined prediction might take account also of any acceleration or deceleration and of any curvature in the path of the plane. There are limitless 'laws' that might describe the path taken, and some are closer approximations to what such a plane is likely to do in a given set of circumstances than are others. Similar predictions must be made by the nervous system, for the information from the sense organs is out of date by the time it reaches the cerebral cortex ; the delay ranges from a fraction of a second to thousands of years in the case of the stars. Some of the predictions made by the nervous system will depend upon genetically determined structure, but in man much will be decided by past experience. Thus in cricket the probable behaviour of the ball has been learnt and the way in which it is likely to travel can be judged. The stroke that is delivered to the ball will have to be organised as an act on the basis of visual information received some tenths of a second before the ball reaches the bat.

Frolov (1937) has pointed out, in the following terms, the close relationship that exists between the mechanisms of learning and the ability to react more rapidly, to anticipate events :

'The mechanism of the coupling of new connections is of tremendous service to the higher representatives of the animal world. In the process of the continual struggle for existence it is obvious that the *time* when a reaction begins is throughout a matter of great moment. Every second gained is of enormous significance. It is extremely important for a hungry animal that it should react to food as soon as it appears in its field of vision, for it is obvious that if it does not do so other animals in the neighbourhood may seize the prey before it, for which an incessant struggle is always taking place.'

Learning makes the organism adaptable to a changing environment. Fish live in a medium which is nearly constant as to temperature and composition. Compared with the situations likely to be encountered by animals living on land the events likely to be of importance to fish can, in general, be predicted by procedures that are both more simple and more likely to be applicable over long periods of time. The more numerous the factors that may play upon an organism the greater is the need for its behaviour to change rapidly, for otherwise it is liable to be overtaken by disaster. Conversely, the greater the adaptability of the individual of the species the more success there is likely to be in existing under diverse conditions. It is due to the cerebrum that man is able to exist (if not to live in great prosperity) from the polar regions to the tropics.

Learning as a form of prediction may be seen with *conditioned reflexes*. These responses represent an elementary variety of learning established under controlled conditions in the laboratory. Their study was due in the first place mainly to the distinguished Russian physiologist Ivan Petrovitch Pavlov, a man who put his whole effort into advancing knowledge of the nervous system. It has been reported that on one occasion in 1917 one of his assistants was late for an experiment, having been held up by the street fighting that then was in progress. Pavlov asked, 'Why are you late, sir ? What difference does a revolution make when you have work in the laboratory to do ?'

Pavlov showed that it was important to control the way in which the stimuli were presented and to exclude extraneous stimuli that might interfere with the responses. He found that in order for a conditioned reflex to be set up, the new stimulus must precede the stimulus that set off the inborn reflex. Thus a dog was exposed to a metronome ticking and then was given food. After a number of trials of this sort the metronome was sounded by itself and salivation followed automatically ; a conditioned reflex to the metronome had been established. If the metronome was sounded only after the food had been given no conditioning took place. Numerous stimuli could be linked with a variety of inborn reflexes, and even with other but already established conditioned reflexes.

These facts bear upon medical problems in various ways (*vide* Gantt, 1944); of particular interest are the 'cardiac neuroses'. In these conditions the cardiovascular system shows a 'conditioned irritability to normal stimuli' and it is certainly true that cardiovascular responses may readily be linked with new stimuli by the conditioned reflex technique. Thus Beier (1940) set up a conditioned rise of blood pressure and of pulse rate to the sound of a buzzer by presenting the stimulus to the subject whilst he pedalled on a bicycle ergometer. Experiments of this sort show that there are in the cortex great numbers of pathways that can be opened up with suitable training.

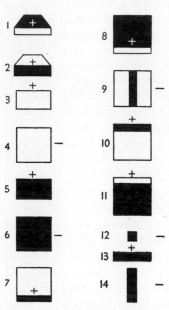

FIG. 7.12.—Equivalent stimuli for a habit of jumping in the rat. The animals were trained to jump towards a platform with the pattern shown in 1. When the habit had been established they were tested with the other patterns. Plus signs indicate rats jumped to the patterns shown, whilst minus signs indicate that they did not respond. (From Lashley in Murchison, 1929)

The conditioned reflex technique has proved of great value in analysing the nervous system experimentality. It enables, for instance, the effects of lesions of different pathways to be evaluated when considering messages from the organs of special sense. 'Theoretically you can answer for animals, by tests of discrimination or by observation of conditioned reflexes, any of the questions about sensory or perceptual capacities that have been answered for human beings by the use of the introspective method' (Boring, 1932). An example of the use that can be made of the conditioned reflex technique is afforded by the careful investigations that have been made into the hearing of dogs and cats (Dworkin, Katzman, Hutchison & McCabe, 1940). A motor response was used whereby when correctly trained the animal could gain meat from a rotary feeder. Both dogs and cats were shown to be most sensitive to notes between 5000 and 8000 c/s as against 2000 to 3000 c/s in the case of man.

When a conditioned reflex is set up to one form of stimulus there follows automatically a tendency to respond to a number of other stimuli that bear some relationship to the one that has been used (Fig. 7.12). In testing for sensory discrimination it may therefore be necessary to train the animal to react towards one stimulus and not to react towards another, rewarding one form of behaviour, and punishing the other.

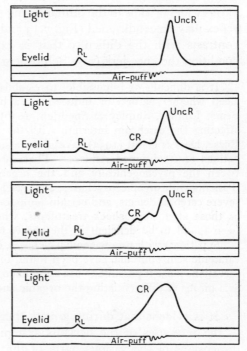

Pavlov stressed the need for complete isolation of the animal from the observer and used sound-proofed chambers to exclude unwanted sounds. It was shown to be important to use intervals between successive stimuli long enough to enable the responses to any one stimulus to be evaluated without interference from the effects of its predecessor. Conditioning is most readily achieved if there is a simple relationship between stimulus and reinforcement. These principles are perhaps the

FIG. 7.13.—Conditioned reflex of human eyelid. Puff of air brings out reflex closure, whilst light causes at first only a slight reflex response. By preceding each puff with the light stimulus a conditioned reflex is established, CR, whereby the lid starts to close before the puff reaches it; eventually the conditioned and unconditioned reflexes fuse smoothly together. The effect of this is to anticipate the occurrence of the stimulus. The small initial reflex response to light persists independently. (After Hilgard & Marquis, as re-drawn in Fulton, 1943)

most enduring feature of the work on conditioned reflexes; it is interesting that it is the methodology that has survived whilst Pavlov's theories as to the mechanisms involved at a cerebral level have not stood the test of time and need not be examined in this book.

As has been seen, Dworkin, Katzman, Hutchison & McCabe

(1940) used a motor response in their work on hearing, and indeed many workers have preferred to condition a movement rather than a glandular response such as the secretion of saliva. It has been found that the ease with which various responses can be conditioned varies widely ; thus in the human being the ease with which the blink reflex may be conditioned (Fig. 7.13 and Hilgard & Campbell, 1936) contrasts with the difficulty that is experienced in attempting to condition the knee jerk (*vide* Schlosberg, 1928).

It is difficult, or impossible, to establish conditioned reflexes during sleep whether natural or induced by a barbiturate drug (*vide* Cohen, Sears, Lindley, Shipley & Snedden, 1936). Similarly disease processes affecting the cerebrum interfere with the formation of these responses. Reese, Doss & Gantt (1953) have given a summary of the clinical investigations of conditioned reflexes. There are pronounced differences between the psychogenically and the organically determined psychoses. 'Patients with organic psychoses, such as Korsakoff's alcoholic dementia, severe cerebral defects, and certain temporary cerebral disturbances, such as those after some shock treatments, when studied in this way, have been found to be deficient in the ability to form conditional responses, while patients with psychogenic psychoses, even severe conditions, such as catatonic schizophrenia, have been found to retain this ability. Such observations make it possible to use a modified conditional reflex examination as a means of differentiating the organic and the psychogenic psychoses.'

It is evident that during *growth* there must be a slow alteration of the responses of the nervous system to allow for the changing dimensions of the various parts of the body, and even at a spinal level readjustment may have to take place to allow for the altered times taken up in conducting the action potentials through the lengthening peripheral pathways. Wagman (1954) studied the latency in the human being of a reflex affecting one of the muscles of the calf. As growth occurred the latency of the reflex increased progressively, in fact it varied directly with the size of the individual.

Further evidence as to the plasticity of nervous responses may be obtained by studying conditions in which the arrangements of the peripheral nervous system are altered so that motor discharges evoke unaccustomed responses from the musculature. In the operation of *transposition* a muscle is inserted into a fresh site so as to alter its action. Wrist drop caused by radial nerve paralysis is sometimes treated by transposing a part of the forearm flexor musculature to act as an extensor of the wrist, whilst a similar operation occasionally performed is to take the biceps from the hamstring group and use it to compensate for paralysis of the quadriceps. Sperry (1945) in a masterly review has stated that :

'On the whole it may be inferred from the literature that with practice man is capable of dissociating the action of individual muscles from associated muscles so as to adapt the action of a transplant to its new position in at least the simplest voluntary movements. This is easier in the arm than in the leg. The problem after muscle transplantation in man is not so much "is any readaptation possible?" as "to what extent is readaptation possible?" Readjustment apparently is not automatic but depends upon the learning process, and consequently is more apt to be found in slow, protracted, simple, deliberate, voluntary movements than in rapid, unpractised, complex, involuntary, surprise reactions.'

It is uncertain to what extent readjustment occurs to comparable alterations on the *sensory side* of the nervous system. Douglas & Lanier (1934) studied the changes in cutaneous localisation on stimulating a pedicle skin flap which was moved from the upper to the lower lip without interrupting the original nerve supply. At first the patient felt that the upper lip had been touched when the flap was stimulated but eventually he became adjusted to the new arrangements ; some nerves from the surrounding skin may have grown into the grafted area. More interesting is the report of Purdy (1934) who studied the sensations aroused by stimulating skin that had been transposed from the palmar to the dorsal surface of a digit after an accident ten years previously. The sensations were still referred to the volar aspect of a non-existent first phalanx. A single touch at the suture line felt double, one dorsal and one ventral with the finger in between. 'When a fine point was moved along the dorsal side of the finger in the direction of the end, there was an apparent discontinuity in the movement at the instant of crossing the suture line. At this moment the point seemed suddenly to cease its movement along the dorsal side ; it apparently "popped up" on the volar side and began to move in the opposite direction.'

Purdy also makes the following statements that bear upon the problem of the 'phantoms' that patients may experience after an amputation of a part of the body (p. 424). 'Ordinarily . . . the injured member feels like a perfectly normal and complete finger. When, however, he (the patient) was asked to plunge the finger into a vessel of cool water, he reported a very curious effect. According to his impression, the dorsal side of the terminal phalanx was now very definitely missing ; the finger felt as if a large slice had been taken out of it. Evidently, the stimulation of the whole surface by cold furnished a vivid background in which the absence of the part which lacked peripheral representation could be perceived as a definite gap in the sensory field.'

The adaptation of the nervous system to 'crossed lines' on both the motor and sensory side is limited even in man and is more difficult to achieve in the monkey (Sperry, 1947 a), whilst in the rat mal-adaptive responses may persist indefinitely (cf. p. 328 and

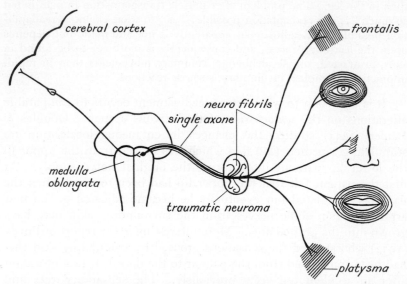

FIG. 7.14.—Following section of, or damage to, the facial nerve the fibres on regenerating have little chance of reaching their former destinations. Furthermore, the regenerating axones branch so as to supply, in some cases, a wide field of musculature. No amount of plasticity in the higher centres can compensate for these difficulties, and any small movement of a part of the face on the normal side is liable to be accompanied by a widespread contortion of the other half of the face. Patients may, therefore, profit from cultivating a 'dead pan' face, portraying as little expression as possible to minimise these difficulties. (From Fowler, 1939)

Fig. 9.21). It is, however, difficult to generalise, for adaptation may more readily be achieved with some crosses than with others. Under certain conditions peripheral nerves are damaged and the axones, on *regenerating*, are liable to form connections which are entirely different from the ones that they had hitherto. For instance, when the median nerve is severed the axones growing down across the cut have little chance of reaching the same muscles in the hand to which formerly they were connected. When a single nerve supplies a number of different muscles having diverse functions the results after regeneration are less satisfactory than when the supply is restricted to a single muscle, the fibres of which all have essentially the same function. Quite apart from the difficulty of arranging that after re-education the motor neurones come into play in sequences appropriate to the motion that is intended, another disturbing factor has to be considered. *Regenerating fibres may branch* and supply muscle strands throughout the region (Fig. 7.14) ; if the strands normally serve different functions no amount of central readaptation can be expected to compensate for the changed relationships in the periphery.

Some of the difficulties that are involved in attempts to readjust to such altered conditions may be seen after recovery from paralysis of the oculomotor nerve, the fibres of which supply a number of muscles that have very different actions. Downward rotation of the eyeball is normally associated with a corresponding movement of the upper eyelid. After regeneration of a damaged oculomotor nerve the lid may be stationary or may even move upwards : a 'disjunctive' movement (*vide* Bender & Fulton, 1939).

The facial nerve similarly supplies muscles that under normal circumstances combine to work together in a wide variety of ways. After damage to this nerve [1] (Fig. 7.15), especially if there has been disruption of part of its substance, involuntary facial movements occur which have been described in the following terms by Sperry (1945) :

FIG. 7.15.—Right facial paralysis. The mouth is pulled over to the healthy side. Owing to the paralysis of the orbicular oculis muscle the palpebral fissure is wider on the right side, and the lids may not close when the patient sleeps. Patients with this condition sometimes suffer from ectropion, an eversion of the lower lid which is pulled down by the weight of the cheek. Note the absence of the naso-labial fold on the paralysed side. (Re-drawn from Fowler, 1939)

'Three types of functional disorder have commonly been recorded after regeneration of the completely disrupted facial nerve. First, mass contractions, *i.e.* inability to individualise the contraction of the various

---

[1] Similar disturbances occur in the absence of a gross lesion of the facial nerve. This 'hemi-facial spasm' may be due to 'cross-talk' (*vide* p. 24) between different fibres of the nerve (*vide* O'Donnell, 1953).

Q

muscle groups. Different facial expressions or separate movement of the lips and eyelids are impossible; the patient can only contract *en masse* the entire musculature of the affected side of the face—except for the frontalis muscle, which for some reason usually fails to recover any function. Second, facial tics, purposeless brief twitchings of the re-innervated muscles. These tics may be confined to a few muscles or may be present in most of the reinnervated region. Third, contracture of the facial musculature. All the recovered muscles tend to show a sustained active contracture which in some cases may result gradually in a permanent anatomical shortening of the muscles. The contractures become more pronounced when facial expression and tonus is heightened on the normal side of the face.

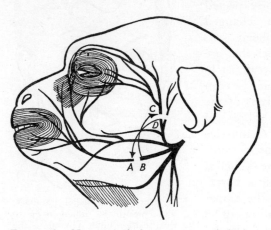

FIG. 7.16.—Nerve trunk for eye was switched to lips and that for lips was made to innervate eye. When healing had occurred re-education was successful and there were no tic-like movements of the face. (From Fowler, 1939)

'All three of the above functional disturbances may be attributed to the same fundamental cause, namely, the persistences without central adaptation of the original functional properties of the various facial axons after they have branched and become redistributed at random throughout the array of facial muscles. When, for example, isolated movements of the lips are attempted, the axons originally terminating in the lip muscles are activated, but because these axons have been widely redistributed among the facial muscles there results, instead of separate lip movement, a mass contraction throughout the affected side of the face. When automatic blinking movements of the lids on the affected side would occur normally, the brief flicks of muscle contraction, instead of being restricted to the eyelid muscle, appear in other muscles about the face and are called facial tics. Whenever any muscle would normally be activated all muscles tend to be activated. Every muscle is thus kept in a prolonged state of contraction throughout those periods when any muscle at all would be active under normal conditions. This means that individual muscles get much less chance for complete relaxation and are kept instead in a persistent state of contraction most of the time.'

Denny-Brown & Pennybacker (1938) investigated these disturbances by electromyography : one interesting finding was that high-frequency discharges occurred at irregular intervals. This activity would appear to correspond to the discharge of impulses intended for certain fibres in the orbicularis oculi that are concerned in brief bilateral movements of the lids. These units, involved in blinking and in the corneal reflex, are discharged at frequencies up to 180/sec. Different fibres are recruited when sustained contraction is needed (Gordon, 1951). It is often fruitless for patients with these disturbances to try to cultivate normal facial expressions ; they may be advised rather to develop a 'poker-face' so as to reduce the contrast between the two sides. Facial spasms may become less marked if they voluntarily inhibit the tendency to blink (*vide* Figs. 7.16 and 7.17).

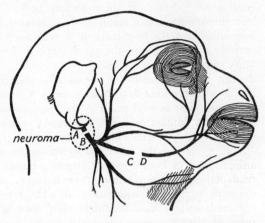

FIG. 7.17.—Following section of the facial nerve at A-B and regeneration tic-like movements of the face are liable to develop. Their cause is peripheral and is due to branched axones ; excitation that would formerly have reached only one of the facial muscles, such as the orbicularis oculi, spreads now throughout the musculature of the affected side of the face. Section of one of the branches and stimulation of the cut ends gives the following results. Stimulation of end D causes contraction of the lips and nose, whilst stimulation of the central end C causes contraction of all the muscles of the right side of the face, including the muscles moving the ears, the platysma and the frontalis. Stimulation of C on the other side of the face causes no response. (From Fowler, 1939)

In view of these difficulties following regeneration of the facial nerve itself it is not surprising that when a foreign nerve is crossed onto the distal stump of the facial nerve, to treat an intractable paralysis, that normal facial expressions should again be unattainable. Such crossings give rise to unwanted 'associated' movements of the face ; thus when the tongue is moved, the face may screw itself up if the hypoglossal nerve has been used. Sperry (1945) gives the following account of this work :

'The most extensive investigation of the late results of facial nerve substitution have been carried out by Ballance. One of the first to attempt a clinical application of nerve crossing, he soon became displeased with the hypoglossal or spinal accessory crosses because of the associated movements which regularly resulted. The associated movements were so distressing to the patients and persisted so tenaciously as to mar seriously the effect of the operative treatment. Consequently he and his collaborators conducted extensive experiments on more than a hundred baboons, monkeys, dogs and cats, trying successfully all the additional nerves of the neck which could be crossed to the facial nerve, hoping to find one that would produce satisfactory motor recovery with little or no associated contraction. Many of these varied nerve crosses were tried also on human patients. As a result of their extensive experiences, it was finally concluded that the best method of treatment was to avoid nerve crosses entirely and to attempt the more difficult procedure of repairing in the bony canal the damaged facial nerve itself. . . . Ballance stated that we do not know whether the associated movements produced by crossing the facial nerve ever disappear or not. Certainly they regularly failed to disappear after several years in the experimental animals, and their persistence in human patients for many years without any appreciable improvement has been well authenticated.

'In summary, the results of crossing the facial nerve in experimental animals and in human patients indicate that very little central nervous readaptation occurs. The reports in recent years have tended more and more to admit the inadequacy of what few voluntary movements are regained, and to state definitely that even in the most successful cases there is always a complete lack of any recovery of natural emotional expression. It must not be assumed, however, that this acknowledgement of the failure of the crossed nerves to give up their original central associations and take over new ones suited to their terminations implies that such nerve cross operations are no longer justified. It is true that whenever possible it is much better to restore function by re-uniting the two ends of the facial nerve itself, but when this is impossible, or when it is a matter of relieving facial spasm, nerve crossing may still be indicated because the restoration of muscle volume on the affected side of the face in itself produces a worth-while improvement in facial appearance, particularly when the features are in repose.'

Little is known of the physiology of the learning process, but there are a number of facts that point to some structural change as being responsible for long-term memories. Thus the electrical activity of the cerebrum is radically altered in refrigeration,[1] concussion, sleep, electro-convulsive therapy and deep anaesthesia ; yet when the patient recovers he does not forget his identity or his friends. It seems necessary to suppose that the fresh pathways that

---

[1] Dogs and human beings enter a narcotic state when their body temperature is cooled to 30° C. ; no permanent neurological effects are found on rewarming unless the brain has been cooled to much lower temperatures (Callaghan, McQueen, Scott & Bigelow, 1954 ; Parkins, Jensen & Vars, 1954).

are opened up by learning involve some structural alteration at the synapses (Hebb, 1949). Lashley in 1929 stated that 'we have today an almost universal acceptance of the theory that learning consists of a modification of the resistance of specific synapses within definite conduction units of the nervous system' (see also Young, 1951 a).

Some experimental evidence that points in this direction has been obtained by Eccles (1953) who has investigated the effects of repetitive stimulation upon the subsequent behaviour of spinal reflexes over many hours. He states that 'relatively enduring enhancement of reflex function occurs after a burst of repetitive stimulation (post-tetanic potentiation) and on the contrary prolonged disuse leads to defectiveness of synaptic function, which, however, can be partially restored, at least for many hours, by repetitive activation'.

These results raise the question as to whether the spinal cord can be said to 'learn' and to what extent any such modifications of its responses bear upon the way in which it recovers from spinal shock (p. 85). Although no final answer can be given, it is of interest that there are reports in the literature which can be regarded as showing that conditioned reflexes can be set up in the isolated spinal cord. Shurrager & Culler (1940) combined electrical or mechanical stimulation of the tail of a spinal dog with a shock to the left hind-paw. The semitendinosus muscle which contracted at first only to the paw shock later came to respond when the tail alone was stimulated (see also Windle, 1955).

Quite apart from the possibility of changes at synaptic junctions in the learning process there is the problem of the region at which the memory 'engram' is laid down in any particular instance, for which later chapters need be consulted. Lashley (1950) has pointed out that learning represents much more than a simple coupling of specific receptors to specific motor units. This was indeed one of the conclusions of his earlier work (Lashley, 1929) from which is taken the following quotation, dealing with the behaviour of rats following spinal or cerebellar injuries :

'Animals which have learned the maze before the development of the motor inco-ordination continue to traverse it, although the manner of progression may be almost completely altered. One drags himself through with his fore-paws ; another falls at every step but gets through by a series of lunges ; a third rolls over completely in making each turn, yet manages to avoid rolling into a cul-de-sac and makes an errorless run. The behaviour presents exactly the same problem of direct adaptation of any motor organs to the attainment of a given end, which was outstanding in my earlier observations on the behaviour of monkeys after the destruction of the precentral gyri. . . . If the customary sequence of movements employed in reaching the food is rendered impossible, another set, not previously used in the habit, and constituting an entirely different motor pattern, may be directly and efficiently substituted. . . .'

Many clinical parallels could be drawn for comparison with these observations. As long as a sensory channel is available for estimating the progress made towards reaching a particular goal, the cerebrum will use any movements that it can command in an effort to reduce the gap between achievement and fulfilment. The ease with which patients can employ 'trick' movements may mislead the unwary into failing to detect paralysis of a muscle due to a peripheral nerve lesion (Pollock, 1919 ; Woods, 1919).

TEMPORAL ASPECTS OF BEHAVIOUR

As has been seen in previous chapters, it is probable that all 'decisions' that are taken within the nervous system depend upon the events that take place at synaptic junctions. For most purposes it may be considered that the events that determine whether an action potential will, or will not, be discharged are evaluated at the same moment ; the discharge will depend upon the coincidence of a number of contemporaneous events (spikes) in the afferent fibres. It is interesting that Boring (1933), summarising the work of experimental psychologists, also came to the conclusion that 'all "knowledge" is potentially spatial'.

In evaluating sensory messages it is important that the C.N.S. should be able to 'estimate' frequencies of discharge, for these so often will be an important guide to stimulus intensity. Quite apart from this, important features of the environment can only be detected if the nervous system is sensitive to the rhythm of discharges that signal environmental changes. Since the synapse may be looked upon as a 'coincidence detector' it might be supposed that temporal discriminations would be based upon the use of appropriate delay pathways.

A false idea of simplicity is often given by anatomical diagrams presented in many elementary books. Figures purporting to show routes that impulses take are often incorrect in so far as they show only the shortest of the pathways ; the routes indicated would afford no possibility for delaying some of the impulses to react with those arriving later. Along a number of these 'classical' pathways the existence of long chains of neurones may be inferred by the occurrence of electrical potentials at a substantial delay after the stimulus. Sensory information also passes to the cortex through reticular relays in the brain stem (Fig. 7.37 and *vide* Magoun in Delafresnaye, 1954).

Temporal delay can therefore be introduced in the nervous system by routing the information along channels of different length, involving differing numbers of synaptic junctions. Delay is also an especial feature of the action of the cortex itself where the number of possible pathways is so very great. These arrangements can be summarised in the language of the communication engineer by saying that the nervous system possesses *delay lines* (*vide* Uttley, 1954). It is not clear to what extent the delay pathways are pure relays in the sense that the human lateral geniculate body is a pure 'repeater station' passing on the information with a delay but with little other modification, and to what extent information of different categories interacts during the period of delay.

On the efferent side of the nervous system there is need to examine mechanisms that might determine the temporal sequence of events in a movement. Lashley (1937) has stated that :

'The least studied and most obscure problems of nervous organisation are presented by the temporal aspects of behaviour. Every action above the level of a spinal reflex involves time factors for which there is available no adequate explanation. Control of speed and duration enters into the simplest adaptive movement. Accurate timing of the separate components of an organised movement is as important as the spatial pattern. Most adaptive activities depend upon the serial release of a succession of movements in a pre-determined order, as in the production of a musical phrase or a grammatical form in speech.'

From time to time in neurological patients these timing mechanisms are disrupted. If the innervation of the limbs is disturbed, the muscles will not come into play at the right moments (*vide* Tilney & Pike, 1925), whilst if the cranial nerves are involved speech will be upset (*vide* Critchley, 1938).

The existence of 'delay lines' in the cortex may perhaps help to explain how it is that after the application of an electrical stimulus signals continue to circulate for some time.[1] An electrical *after-discharge* is normally found on recording from an area of the brain

[1] After-discharge from the cortex could be due alternatively to 'auto-rhythmicity' of cortical neurones (Bremer, 1953) or to *reverberating* chains of neurones ; the data at present available give little assistance at differentiating between these possibilities.

that has been subjected to a period of faradic stimulation, and it is perhaps significant in view of the importance of temporal order in movement that after-discharge tends to occur with the greatest facility in the motor cortex. Electrical after-discharge may be set up in the motor cortex without at the same time there being evidence of muscular movement; no doubt the occurrence of movement is dependent upon appropriate facilitation of 'down-stream' synapses (Fig. 7.34, p. 249).

When an area of cortex is stimulated, after-discharge may be recorded not only from regions close to the area that has been excited but also in other and distant parts of the cerebrum. The spread of after-discharge in this way is believed to indicate the existence of direct nervous connections to the regions that are secondarily set into activity; accordingly some workers have used the distribution of electrical after-discharge as a guide to the connections between different areas. Green (1953), for instance, was interested in the spread of epileptic activity from the hippocampus. Working on cats, he found that from the fimbriae of the hippocampus after-discharge could be followed into the temporal lobe.

Walker & Johnson (1948) make the following comments regarding the routes by which after-discharge may spread in the normal brain :

'The area stimulated not only influences the spread of the after-discharge but predicates the pattern of the dissemination. The self-sustained response may radiate to adjacent areas of the cerebral cortex or to distant areas without affecting proximate cortex. Symmetrical points of the contralateral hemisphere are often involved before the other areas of the ipsilateral half of the brain. To the opposite hemisphere the discharge passes by way of the corpus callosum . . . and to the distal parts of the ipsilateral hemisphere by long fibre tracts.'

Electrical stimulation of the cortex sometimes has given rise contrariwise to a reduction of electrical activity that spreads slowly (2-3 mm./min.). This spreading depression first described by Leão has attracted a good deal of interest but it may be an artefact which is dependent upon drying of the surface of the brain, for it does not occur if the brain is kept covered with mineral oil (W. H. Marshall, 1950). Spreading depression may be caused by a change in the calibre of the blood vessels; that it does not depend upon nervous pathways is indicated by the fact that it may cross a cut through the thickness of the cortex.

After-discharge is particularly easy to produce from a region of the cortex that is liable to give rise to epileptic fits. Indeed, Walker

(1949) has demonstrated that prolonged after-discharge may be a useful guide to the neuro-surgeon to establish the site of an epileptic focus at operation.

'The usual method of electroactivation consists of serial stimulation of representative points of the cerebral cortex, using sine wave current from 1·5 to 2·5 volts for five seconds. The electrical activity of the cerebral cortex, the motor responses, and the patient's subjective sensation at the time of stimulation are noted. If no change is observed in the electrocorticogram, after a one-minute interval, another point is stimulated and so on until the entire cortex has been mapped. An after-discharge for a few seconds, at the point stimulated, is considered within physiological limits. However, generally an area of cortex adjacent to the scar can be found which, on stimulation, causes a long lasting, spiky after-discharge. This epileptic discharge has been seen to persist for as long as twenty-eight minutes. In many cases, the sensory or motor aura which precede the patient's spontaneous attacks occur with this after-discharge. Occasionally, the electrocorticographic attack progresses to a clinical seizure. But, in some cases the individual does not have any motor or sensory concomitants during the electrocorticographic discharge' (Walker, 1949).

Experimentally, epilepsy may be induced by treating a spot on the cortex with *aluminium hydroxide*. After a period of some weeks the animal starts to suffer from focal fits, and on stimulation the experimental foci also are particularly liable to show prolonged after-discharge. Walker & Johnson (1948) commenting on these observations state that :

'the after-discharge, although beginning at one point, spread rapidly to all parts of the cerebral cortex, and instead of abruptly ceasing after a few minutes, died out at one point, but continued to fire at another. As the latter point stopped, a comparable area on the other hemisphere began again until the original area commenced once more and the cycle started all over. At times this "wandering after-discharge" would break out into what appeared to be a generalised electro-encephalographic seizure at the conclusion of which the circuit would start again. This self-propagating discharge has been continuously recorded for over two hours before it finally stopped.'

'The usual abrupt cessation of clonic activity in all regions sharing in after-discharge is a dramatic phenomenon not yet fully understood. ... Whatever the factors are which bring about the normal abrupt universal cessation of after-discharge, they appear to play a large rôle in epileptic activity.'

Evidently the localised lesions of the cortex produced by the aluminium hydroxide alter the excitability of the cerebrum ; perhaps by changing the *vascularity* of the grey matter the local metabolism is altered. There is some evidence that excessive neuronal activity is associated with an increase in the blood flow through the part of the cortex concerned ; a system such as this may be regarded as a homeostatic mechanism which minimises the changes in oxygen and carbon-dioxide tension that otherwise would occur. When this compensatory mechanism is exhausted the pH of the cortex falls (Fig. 7.18) and the activity ceases (Dusser de Barenne & McCulloch,

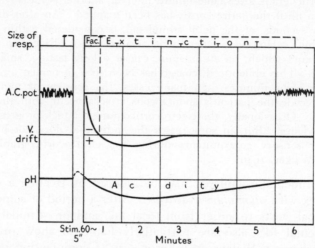

FIG. 7.18.—Changes in excitability of a point on the motor cortex following a period of electrical stimulation. The figure shows : top, size of muscular response ; next, spontaneous rhythms ; third, D.C. level of cortex ; fourth, pH. During the period of extinction the muscular responses are reduced, the cortex becomes positive with respect to other areas and it also becomes acid. Attempts to demonstrate D.C. drifts during sleep by recording from the human scalp have not succeeded (Davis, Davis, Loomis, Harvey & Hobart, 1939 a). It is known, however, that there are substantial D.C. changes during the course of a 'wave and spike' epileptic discharge. (From Dusser de Barenne & McCulloch, 1939)

1939) ; it may be that the action of the convulsant drug metrazol (cf. p. 239) is to be explained in part by an action upon this vascular mechanism, for under its influence the cortex although discharging actively remains relatively alkaline (*vide* Jasper & Erickson, 1941). Alkalinity favours the discharge of epileptic foci in the forebrain and hyperventilation has long been used as a provocative test for epilepsy. Other metabolic factors too influence these discharges ; thus the occurrence of fits may be the first clear indication of hypoglycaemia. The number of agents that can precipitate epileptic seizures is very great indeed. Little is known as to the specificity that various convulsants may perhaps display ; do particular agents tend, preferentially, to provoke discharges in particular regions of the brain ? The study of the electro-encephalogram (*vide infra*) may eventually answer this question and lead to a better understanding of these effects than can be obtained by clinical investigations alone (p. 376).

ELECTRO-ENCEPHALOGRAPHY
(*vide* Hill & Parr, 1950)

The electrical activity of the cerebrum may be recorded not only directly from the cortex ('electro-corticography') but also through the scalp (Figs. 7.19 and 7.20). This technique is known as electro-encephalography, whilst the records obtained are called electro-encephalograms (cf. telegraphy and telegram). The normal disturbances in the electro-encephalogram consist of a sequence of waves that recur with a frequency of between 8 and 13 c/s ; they were first described, in 1929, by the Austrian psychiatrist, Berger. These waves, known as the *alpha rhythm*, always show some irregularity ; their amplitude varies from cycle to cycle as does their duration and shape. The activity at any given instant can never be accurately superimposed upon the record of activity taken at another time. Nevertheless the general features of the activity from any one person are rather constant ; records taken at intervals usually resemble one another sufficiently closely to be easily differentiated from those of other people. Similarly the records taken from identical twins closely resemble one another.

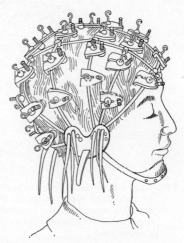

FIG. 7.19.—Technique used in electro-encephalography. The figure illustrates one of the methods that is used for making connections with the scalp. It is desirable to treat the skin with ether before applying the moistened electrodes in order to make efficient contact

The waves tend to occur in bursts or 'spindles' (Fig. 7.21), gradually building up and then slowly getting smaller or becoming unrecognisable.   As the alpha waves are normally most prominent when the eyes are closed, Adrian & Matthews (1934 *b*) suggested that the rhythm was produced by neurones normally concerned with vision.   Adrian (1944 *b*) showed that a visual field that is patterned is more effective in abolishing ('blocking') the waves than one that is plain, and it has been suggested that the alpha rhythm itself plays some special rôle in vision (Pitts & McCulloch, 1947 ; Walter, 1950).

Although this may prove to be the case, the following facts must be taken into account.   Firstly, any relationship between the alpha waves

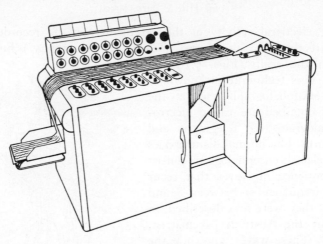

FIG. 7.20.—A modern electro-encephalograph using eight independent amplifiers for recording simultaneously from different parts of the head.   The paper, which is stored in the central compartment of the instrument, is pulled along, whilst the pens inscribe the tracings.   (By permission of Edison Swan Electric Co.)

and visual perception can hardly be an essential one, for in some apparently normal subjects the alpha rhythm cannot be detected, whilst in others who do possess a rhythm it is found that the waves are uninfluenced by visual stimulation (Redlich, Callahan & Mendelson, 1946).   Not uncommonly indeed it is found that the alpha rhythm may even continue whilst the subject reads aloud (Bates—personal communication and author's personal observations).   Secondly, the visual reaction time appears to bear no relationship to the amplitude, or to the phase, of the alpha rhythm at the moment of stimulation (Walsh, 1952).   Thirdly, observations dealing with the perception of patterns have also failed to support the idea that there is a direct relationship between the alpha waves and visual perception (MacKay, 1953 ; Walsh, 1953).   It may be noted that visual stimuli are not the only means of reducing the size of the waves. Touch—particularly if it is unexpected—also may be effect-ive ; sounds also may, on occasion, block the rhythm. Anxiety and mental arithmetic may be equally effective.

During operations upon the human brain the opportunity is presented of applying electrodes to the surface of the grey matter itself, and the records that can be obtained are valuable as a guide to the surgeon when he attempts to remove epileptogenic foci.

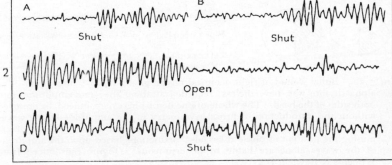

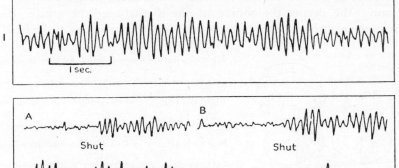

FIG. 7.21.—The alpha rhythm. 1, At rest with eyes closed ; 2, effect of opening and closing eyes. In A and B closing the eyes brings out the waves, whilst in C opening the eyes abolishes the waves. In D the subject has been in total darkness for some minutes with his eyes open ; shutting the eyes now makes no difference to the rhythm. Only a minority of people show the alpha rhythm as clearly as in these figures. (Adrian & Matthews, 1934 b, reproduced from S. Wright, 1945)

Observations made under these conditions have shown how great a barrier the skull and dura are to electrical signals ; the cerebrospinal fluid, on the other hand, is a good electrical conductor. It follows from simple electrical theory (vide Adrian & Matthews, 1934 b) that currents which are generated by a small part of the brain will spread out over considerable areas on the surface of the head. The mistake should not be made, therefore, of assuming that a rhythm which is recorded from two electrodes on the surface of the scalp is necessarily generated by the underlying tissue. Adrian

& Yamagiwa (1935), experimenting on a cadaver with artificially generated signals, obtained direct evidence for this extensive spread of current; more recently electrical recordings from patients subjected to the operation of hemispherectomy have shown that waves of considerable amplitude may be recorded from the side of the head from which the hemisphere has been removed (Marshall & Walker, 1950; Obrador & Lorramendi, 1950) (cf. Fig. 7.22). It follows also that disturbances that are produced deep within one hemisphere may be recordable at the surface in the electro-encephalogram; the deeper the source of the disturbance the greater the symmetry of the waveforms recorded from the two sides of the head.

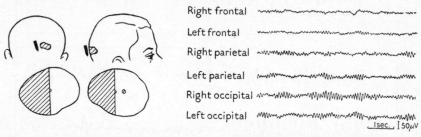

FIG. 7.22.—Bullet wound of right occipital region giving rise to hemianopia. The alpha rhythm was, nevertheless, recorded at about the same amplitude from both sides of the head. The whole of one hemisphere may, indeed, be removed without the introduction of gross asymmetry in the amplitude of the waves on the two sides. These facts point to the extreme importance of determining the position of phase reversals; deductions based upon the amplitude of the waves alone are liable to be erroneous. (Figure reproduced from Williams & Reynell, 1945)

Electrical rhythms recorded from the cerebral cortex might be expected to behave as *travelling waves*, in which case the disturbance would spread over the cortex and this spread would take a measurable time. If the identity of the disturbance was retained as it travelled, it would be possible to show that corresponding features occurred at different times in different regions. Under certain circumstances waves have been recorded which do indeed appear to travel through the neuronal meshwork of the cortex for short distances. Adrian (1936) recorded spikes from the cortex of a rabbit under the action of a convulsant and found that they travelled at a velocity of 10-40 cm./sec. Just beyond the region invaded by the travelling wave the normal spontaneous activity of the cortex continued unchanged. Burns (1951) has made observations upon the spread of activity in an area of the cortex of the cat which has been separated from the rest of the cortex. He found that following an electrical shock activity was induced that spread at a rate of 10-20 cm./sec.

The pathways through the cortex that travelling waves may follow are not immutable but change from time to time. Adrian &

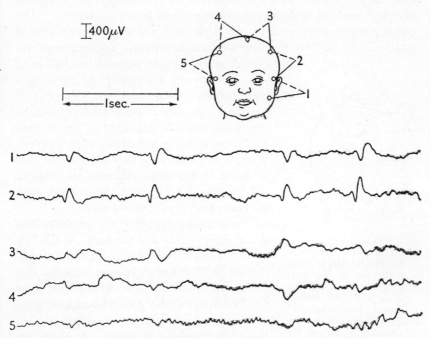

Fig. 7.23.—Spike discharge in anterior temporal region. Baby 18 months old suffered from fits starting in the right side of the face. Focus for spikes as determined by phase reversals is at electrode common to channels 1 and 2. X-ray examination with the introduction of air into the cranium to outline the ventricular system pointed to an atrophic process in anterior part of left temporal lobe

Matthews (1934 a) studied these problems with the aid of a convulsant drug, thujone. They state that :

'The sudden or gradual shifts in direction are not surprising if we assume that the cortex behaves under thujone like a mass of cells as closely linked as are the muscle fibres of the heart. Spontaneous beats may arise now from one point and now from another or the origin may shift progressively without affecting the rhythm. Similar changes often take place in the spontaneous beats produced in skeletal muscle fibres bathed in NaCl solution.'

Under certain conditions travelling waves may be propagated through the cortex without the mediation of neural pathways, the excitation being carried by electrical currents as in the artificial synapse (p. 27). Libet & Gerard (1941) studied these problems using frogs. 'The isolated frog brain continues to manifest essentially stationary rhythmic potential oscillations, and under the influence of drugs such as caffeine, slowly travelling potential waves.' The caffeine waves continued to travel through the cortex even after it had been treated by nicotine to abolish synaptic transmission and even after all nervous connections had been severed between adjacent parts by a complete transection of the brain. Waves that travelled regularly along fixed routes in the cerebrum might be expected to repeat their waveform rather exactly from cycle to cycle. With few exceptions this is not the case with the spontaneous rhythms recorded in the human E.E.G., and the disturbances are comparable to *standing waves*.

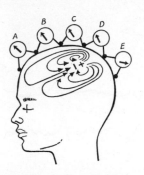

FIG. 7.24.—Origin of alpha rhythm, after Adrian & Matthews (1934 b). The deflections in amplifiers D and E are in opposite directions; the records show 'phase reversals'. Such phase reversals are a useful guide to the origins of electro-encephalographic rhythms

Berger suggested that the production of the alpha rhythm is a function of all areas of the cortex, whilst on the other hand Adrian & Matthews (1934 b) believed that the waves arose from generators of restricted size situated in the parieto-occipital areas of the two hemispheres. Using a sagittal line of electrodes it is possible to show that normally there is a *phase reversal* in this region (Fig. 7.24) and, furthermore, the waves are normally of low amplitude in channels connected to the frontal regions. Adrian & Matthews (1934 b) postulated that another ('mirror image') phase reversal would be present in the region of the frontal pole. This focus can sometimes be demonstrated if the chain of electrodes is extended onto the face so that the tip of the frontal lobe is adequately straddled (Walsh, 1954, and cf. Fig. 7.25).

For waves which have a wide distribution on the head it is to be supposed that the structures generating the rhythms lie on an axis which joins the regions at which the phase reversals are found. Accordingly among the most important features of an E.E.G. are these phase reversals (Fig. 7.23). The human eye can detect these relationships readily only under favourable conditions (*e.g.* slow waves of considerable amplitude showing highly consistent phase reversals between neighbouring channels). This limitation has suggested that instrumental assistance should be of value; Grey Walter's toposcope (Walter & Shipton, 1951) and Goodwin's correlator (Goodwin & Stein, 1948) are both designed towards this end.

It may be demonstrated that any given electrical field at the surface of the cerebrum (*e.g.* Fig. 7.26) could theoretically be produced by an

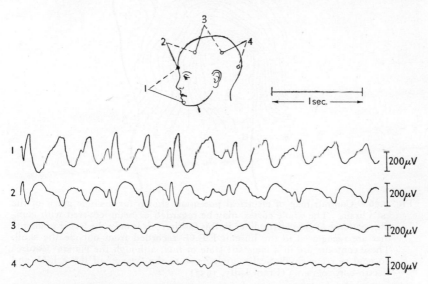

FIG. 7.25.—Epileptic discharge showing phase reversals between leads 1 and 2. In this case it was necessary to extend the chain of electrodes farther than is customary in order to observe the phase reversal. A record such as this would suggest that the frontal lobe was concerned in the production of these waves

infinite variety of generators differing in size, shape and position. It is salutary to be aware of this fundamental difficulty in E.E.G. interpretation. Of these limitless mathematical possibilities, however, some will be absurd from a physiological point of view. The structures cannot, for instance, be situated in the ventricular system of the brain. It is unfortunate that we are almost, if not totally, ignorant of the size of the systems producing disturbances in the E.E.G. In clinical work it is often necessary to attempt to determine the origin of a particular rhythm and it is usual to assume that only a small area of the brain is concerned. This assumption is normally found to give fairly satisfactory results. Disturbances which are recorded only from a restricted region of the cerebrum

R

are presumed to have an origin from the grey matter of the convexity of the hemisphere. Activity which is present in channels recording from a number of different regions of the head is presumed to have an origin from cortex which is situated some distance from the surface.

According to one Greek philosopher it is never possible to bathe in the same river twice, since the water of which the river is com-

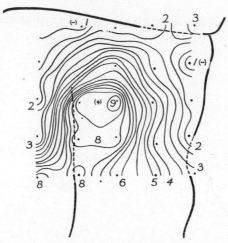

FIG. 7.26.—Contour map of electrical potentials shown for a single gyrus of the cat's brain. The whole cortex may be regarded as being covered with complex patterns of iso-electric lines in this fashion ; it is only the larger gradients that are recognised in the human E.E.G. recorded from outside the skull. These contours are in a constant state of flux, although the general features do tend to recur rhythmically, giving rise to the 'waves' of the E.E.G. and electro-corticogram. (From Lilly, 1953)

posed is constantly changing. Electro-encephalographic rhythms present comparable difficulties in definition, for they are always, to greater or lesser degrees, altering their characteristics. The waves may be classified according to their frequency, their spatial distribution and to the way in which they are modified under certain circumstances. Of these three criteria of classification that of frequency has been found to be the most useful :

Table 6

Frequency	Name
$\frac{1}{2}$-$3\frac{1}{2}$ c/s	Delta (δ)
$3\frac{1}{2}$-8 c/s	Theta (θ)
8-13 c/s	Alpha (α)
13-30 c/s	Beta (β)

Not uncommonly more than one rhythm may be generated at the same time. It may be possible to see, for instance, that in addition to the alpha rhythm delta waves are also present. When more than one rhythm is present the human eye may find it difficult to identify the various components and it may sometimes prove useful to pass the signals into a frequency analyser. In the Baldock & Walter (1946) analyser the output of an E.E.G. amplifier is split by a series of circuits tuned to different frequencies and the response is

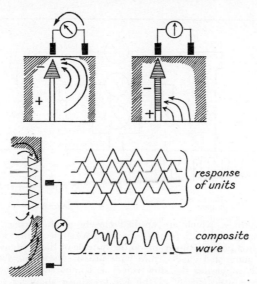

response
of units

composite
wave

FIG. 7.27.—The waves recorded in the electro-encephalogram are of relatively long duration and could be composed of summated effects of shorter duration produced by many neurones. This figure shows how a slow wave could be built up from a number of spike discharges. It is perhaps unlikely that spike discharges are the only, or even the main, contributors to the E.E.G., but the same principle could hold with other unitary potentials of short duration. (From Adrian & Matthews, 1934 a)

plotted on the recording paper superimposed on the original tracing. The various rhythms in the E.E.G. are irregularly modulated and each has a fairly broad distribution of energy. Frequency analysis has been criticised by some neurophysiologists (e.g. Forbes, 1950) because it is unlikely that the potentials generated by neurones are sinusoidal. This criticism can scarcely be taken seriously, for any method of classification of data is justified according to its convenience and utility. Different electro-encephalographic rhythms simultaneously present usually have different spatial distributions.

Thus the gradient of potential change may be greatest for the alpha waves in the parieto-occipital region whilst that for delta waves may be steepest in the frontal areas.

Knowledge of the physiological mechanisms underlying the production of waves in the E.E.G. is slender. Adrian (1936) stated that 'we do not know what kind of cortical activity is revealed by a given potential change, for we do not know what kind of activity is possible, what structures are responsible for the potential changes,

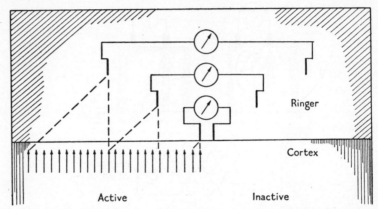

FIG. 7.28.—Electrodes which are applied closely to the surface of the cortex record potentials from a limited region, whilst electrodes which are more distant, as in a pool of Ringer, or on the outside of the head, as in the E.E.G., record the summated effects from wide areas. Recording from the outside of the skull emphasises the slow waves as compared with the faster. Thus there is often little energy in the E.E.G. above about 12 c/s, whilst with surface leads, and especially with micro-electrodes plunged into the grey matter, short lasting potentials are revealed. (From Adrian & Matthews, 1934 a)

or how excitations spread from one neurone to another'. The problem has proved to be extremely difficult; Li & Jasper (1953) have remarked that 'after over twenty years of study, the neurophysiological basis of the rhythmic oscillations in electrical potential which can be recorded from the cerebral cortex remains poorly understood'.

The size of the waves has suggested that they are the result of activity in a large number of neurones, and it was the view of Adrian & Matthews (1934 a) that they resulted from the summation of a large number of individual spike potentials (Figs. 7.27 and 7.28). A number of workers have attempted to verify this view by investigations on the exposed animal cortex. The earliest and still perhaps the most important work of this nature was performed by Renshaw, Forbes & Morison (1940) who investigated the activity of the cortex of the cat by using micro-pipettes as electrodes. These workers noted that the hippocampus may be considered as a form of simplified cortex, for one cell layer only, that of the pyramidal

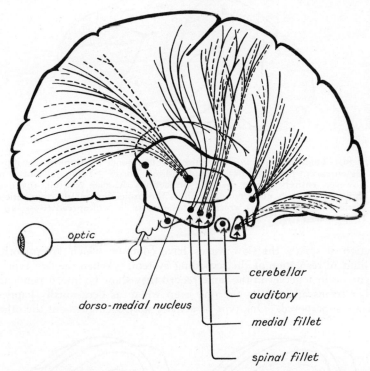

optic

dorso-medial nucleus

cerebellar

auditory

medial fillet

spinal fillet

FIG. 7.29.—Distribution of various pathways from thalamus to the cerebral cortex. The arrangements appear complicated because during development different parts of the forebrain have developed to different degrees and the original relationships have become twisted. Useful discussions of the thalamus are : Rose & Woolsey (1943), Droogleever Fortuyn (1953), Dekakan (1953). (Figure reproduced from Cobb, 1946)

cells, is highly developed. They therefore paid particular attention to the activity recorded from this region. Spikes could be recorded from the layer of pyramidal cells but not at other levels in the grey matter, whereas slow waves were recorded throughout the thickness of the cortex.

These workers concluded that 'a sharp distinction may be drawn between the axon-like spikes and the slow waves. Although we do not know what the slow waves signify in terms of the activity of neurones, no evidence has yet appeared to indicate that the latter are the summation products of numbers of axon-like spikes or other rapid components. No intermediate forms are seen. Though they have 10 to 100 times the

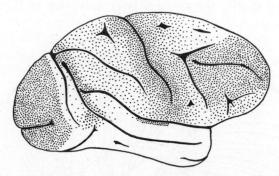

Fig. 7.30.—Thalamic projection to cortex. Note absence of stippling in temporal region except for small area around auditory cortex. Temporal lobe is not, however, entirely free of thalamic projections (Marsan & Stoll, 1951), and this diagram does not attempt to show the projections of the thin reticular nucleus of the thalamus which are believed to be widespread (Rose, 1952). (Reproduced from Walker, 1938 *a*)

duration of spikes, the slow waves have contours which are smooth to the limit of resolution of the recording system. When the two types of activity occur together in the same record they show no interdependence ; neither seems affected by the one even when, as occasionally happens, they are superposed. One type of activity may occur without the other.'

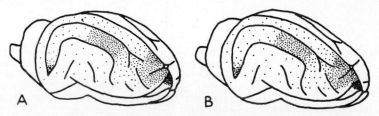

Fig. 7.31.—Distribution of recruiting response, A (electrical disturbance that is provoked by repetitive stimulation of certain thalamic nuclei) and of spontaneous waves of electro-corticogram, B, in the dog. The distributions are identical. (Reproduced from Morison & Dempsey, 1942)

At times spikes may be recorded both from the cortex (cf. Fig. 9.32, p. 347) and from the thalamus (Verzeano & Calma, 1954) that do bear a consistent relationship to the phase of the slow waves that are recorded from the same regions, but the evidence that is available does not suggest that the slow waves of the E.E.G. are merely the envelopes of summated spikes.

In principle any structure within the head capable of generating an electrical current may contribute to the E.E.G. Observations made whilst recording from the brain at different depths from the

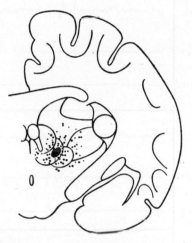

FIG. 7.32.—Fibre degeneration resulting from a lesion of the centre-median nucleus of the thalamus. Nauta & Whitlock (*vide* Delafresnaye, 1954) state that their work lends support 'to the neurophysiological concept of multi-synaptic conduction within the non-specific thalamic cell groups. Although long lines of conduction are not wholly lacking, an organisation of intrinsic association pathways in the form of chains of short neurones appears to prevail both in the longitudinal and transverse directions. Judging on the basis of fibre quantity it is noteworthy that longitudinal conduction within the non-specific apparatus would seem to be potentially more intensive in the rostral than in the caudal direction. This organisation would tend to place the centre median, as the most caudal element, in an optimum position to produce widespread excitation within the non-specific thalamic apparatus. It may be significant in this respect that the centre median appears to have diffuse efferent connections with all remaining non-specific cell groups, including . . . some contralateral associations, and, in addition, with almost the entire rostral half of the reticular complex of the thalamus. Furthermore the centre median apparently emits a massive fibre system to most of the ventral nuclear complex of the thalamus, including the entire extent of the n. ventralis anterior'

surface suggest that the waves originate in grey rather than in white matter (*vide* Hayne, Belinson & Gibbs, 1949), but the extent to which nuclear masses within the substance of the cerebrum, such as the thalamus, contribute directly to the E.E.G. is obscure. Destruction of the superficial layers of the grey matter of the cortex does not seriously interfere with the production of the slow waves (Murphy & Dusser de Barenne, 1941), but if the cortex is isolated by surgical section of all its nervous connections (Burns, 1951 & 1953) it becomes quiescent. At times in such undercutting experiments damaged regions on the borders of the isolated slabs of tissue

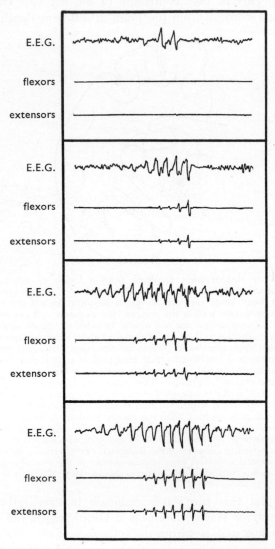

FIG. 7.33.—Correlation between duration of spike activity in E.E.G. (right fronto-central leads) and appearance of spikes in muscles of left thigh. As the epileptic discharge lengthens so the spikes that appear in the muscles become more prominent. With very short discharges in the E.E.G. there may be no corresponding disturbance in the muscles. (Modified from Dawson, 1946)

may discharge for a while and it may be this fact that explains why Kristiansen & Courtois (1949) believed that isolated cortex could generate normal electrical rhythms.

It is uncertain to what extent cortical rhythms are pulsed by discharges of the same frequency in fibres leading to the cortex and to what extent the barrage of afferent signals is merely facilitatory, the rate of the rhythms being determined by the state of the cortical cells themselves (*vide* Eccles, 1953). There is, however, evidence that cortical waves *can* be 'clocked' by sub-cortical structures. Electrical stimulation of certain thalamic nuclei, the *recruiting system*, gives rise to cortical potentials that increase in amplitude as the stimuli are repeated. The waveforms may closely mimic those that occur spontaneously as to shape and frequency whilst the distribution of the potentials in the two instances may be identical (Fig. 7.31).

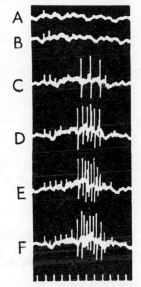

FIG. 7.34.—Electrical activity of internuncial neurones of spinal cord in response to shocks delivered to cortico-spinal tract. In records A to F the pyramids were stimulated by one to six shocks as shown by the small artefacts to the left of each tracing. One or two shocks (A and B) failed to set up discharges, whilst the more numerous the cortico-spinal volleys the greater the number and higher the frequency of the internuncial discharge. Time 5 msec. (Reproduced from Lloyd, 1941)

These facts have made it highly probable that the recruiting system is intimately concerned with the production of the normal E.E.G. and a great deal of work is at present in progress in an attempt to unravel the details of the structures that are concerned (*vide* Delafresnaye, 1954; and Fig. 7.32).

According to Starzl & Magoun (1951) the centre-median, intralaminar anterior, anteroventral, and anterior reticular nuclei of the thalamus form a functionally interconnected unit so that excitation of any part of the system sets the whole into activity. They remark that :

'By whatever means it is conducted, the influence of this thalamic recruiting system appears . . . not to be exerted indiscriminately upon the cortex as the term "diffuse" might connote. Instead, responsive cortical zones were found to be relatively specific and delimited, and were distributed in the frontal, cingulate, orbital, parietal and occipital associational regions. . . .

Each cortical region that is not preoccupied with sensory and motor functions in the strict sense thus possesses a recruiting focus, and a thalamic system capable of exerting such a mass influence upon the associational cortex would seem in a position to play a most important functional rôle.'

The recruiting system is not directly related to the handling of information reaching the cortex along the direct sensory pathways. This conclusion has been reached in a number of ways. Thus, for instance, Dempsey & Morison (1942) found that sensory responses occurred irrespective of the presence or absence of spontaneous waves, or of their phase, and they could be superimposed upon any phase of the response produced by stimulating the recruiting system.

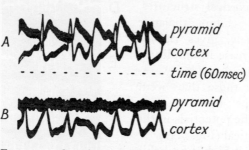

Dawson (1947 a) has been particularly interested in observing the potentials evoked in the *post-central gyrus* by stimulation of a somatic nerve. The potentials in the electro-encephalo-gram are usually so small compared with the spontaneous rhythms that special methods are needed for their detection. Devices have been invented that average successive responses to a series of stimuli ; the fluctuations that occur consistently after each stimulus are thus emphasised (see Dawson, 1953 ; cf. Brazier & Casby, 1952). Occasionally, the potentials set up by somatic stimulation may be relatively large ; Dawson (1947 b) studied a patient in whom the eliciting of a tendon jerk set up large potentials in the opposite post-central gyrus. Other sensory systems also may become hyper-excitable ; fits may sometimes be set off by flashing lights (p. 352) and, even more rarely, by sounds.

FIG. 7.35.—Correlation between electrical activity of motor cortex and discharges recorded from region of medullary pyramid. Note the relationship between the two curves in A. This relationship was not dependent upon passive electrical spread from the forebrain, for when the medullary electrode was pushed $1\frac{1}{2}$ mm. deeper, B, it recorded little or no activity. (Re-drawn, from Adrian & Morruzzi, 1939)

The spontaneous rhythms of the E.E.G. bear no direct relationship to muscular movements, although it has been reported that during a voluntary act the beta rhythm of the motor cortex is inhibited. At times, under pathological conditions, muscular jerks may occur in association with cortical spike discharges (Fig. 7.33). Spikes represent a form of *hypersynchrony* in which the cortical neurones tend to discharge simultaneously (Ecclin, 1944). Single spikes may occur in epileptic subjects without external evidence of any disturbance ; if, however, these potentials are rapidly repeated temporal summation occurs, the spinal centres are recruited and the muscles jerk at each discharge (cf. Fig. 7.34). Adrian & Moruzzi (1939) showed that an efferent discharge might be recorded, at the level of the medullary pyramids that was related to the discharge of spikes recorded from the motor cortex (Fig. 7.35). Several spikes at the level of the pyramid might correspond to a single one in the cortical discharge. Jasper (1949) has pointed out that cortical spikes (Fig. 7.36) are similar in form regardless of the cortical area from which they are obtained. 'To those who are familiar with the strychnine spikes (p. 199) . . . it would seem that the spikes of

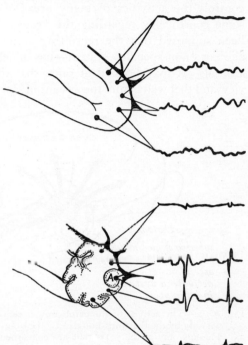

FIG. 7.36.—The most reliable sign of an epileptogenic focus is a spike discharge, but it is frequently difficult to detect these abnormalities when the recording is made through the skull. At operation the spike focus may be seen only when the electrodes are applied closely to the discharging focus. This figure shows that whilst slow activity was recorded from the tip of the temporal lobe the spikes were found only after a surgical resection had made it possible to explore the medial surface of the lobe. Phase reversals are clearly seen pointing to an origin for the disturbances in the region A. At this point the cortex was seen to be scared. (From Gastaut, 1954)

the epileptogenic lesion in man are comparable in almost every respect. It is surprising that their conduction along fibre tracts does not interfere to a greater extent with localisation studies of the focus of spike discharge although mirror foci are occasionally seen.'

CONSCIOUSNESS

The discovery that the somewhat ill-defined 'recruiting system' controls the activities of many areas of the cortex has stimulated some controversy regarding the 'centre of consciousness'. It has been supposed that the recruiting system—alias the 'centrencephalic' or 'non-specific' system—has much to do with the level of arousal. It may be said at once that there is much truth in this view and that well before the advent of electro-encephalography it was

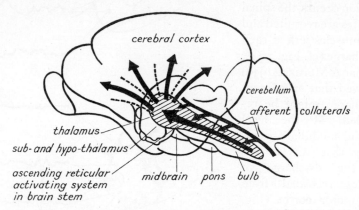

FIG. 7.37.—The activity of the cerebrum, as reflected in the E.E.G., is influenced not only by the thalamus but also by the brain stem even as low as the medulla. The anatomy of the parts that are concerned is confusing and is not defined with the exactitude that this figure might lead one to suppose. The 'reticular formation' is a mixture of grey matter cut across by fibre tracts. The term 'reticular' is derived from the Latin word 'reticulum' which is a diminutive of 'rete' meaning a 'net'. The reticular formation affords a route by which afferent information may influence the cerebral cortex independently of the main sensory pathways. (From Starzl, Taylor & Magoun, 1951)

known that the hypothalamus and upper brain stem were concerned with sleep. The idea of a 'specific' and a 'non-specific' system is not new. Lashley (1938) speaking of the effects of cerebral lesions wrote :

'There are many suggestions that every nervous function is dependent both upon a specific pattern of nervous organisation, such as the spatial excitation of a pattern of movement, and also upon the general level of non-specific excitations constituting central tonus. The specific character of amnesias produced by lesions in focal cerebral areas, together with the fluctuating severity of the defects suggests that the lesions destroy some dynamic or reinforcing mechanism which alters the level of excitability of the integrating or patterning mechanism without destroying the mnemonic traces.'

The question is hardly whether certain sub-cortical structures influence the reactivity of the cortex but to what extent more recent investigations have led to an increase in the precision with which these relationships are known.

In many of the recent discussions of this problem it has been assumed that the electro-encephalogram reflects the state of arousal. It is therefore worth pointing out that whilst such a relationship is

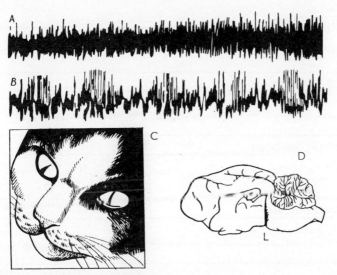

FIG. 7.38.—Effect of section of midbrain on cortical discharges. Before the section, A, there is little activity to be seen but rhythmic bursts appear after it has been made, B. The pupils are constricted, due to a severance of the descending sympathetic pathways, C. D shows position of lesion. It has been claimed that the waves are typical of sleep, but little delta activity can be detected. Roger, Rossi & Zirondoli (1956) have shown that the effects of brain-stem section on the E.E.G. depends in large measure on interference with centripetal discharges originating in the trigeminal nerves. (Figure modified from Bremer, 1953, based on earlier work of the same author)

often found (*vide* Fig. 7.38) there are authentic exceptions. It is true that during sleep, and during anaesthesia, the electrical activity of the brain alters in a characteristic manner according to the depth of unconsciousness. On the other hand, during carotid sinus syncope the only change observable may be some decrease in the amplitude of the waves (Forster, Roseman & Gibbs, 1942), whilst Dawson, Webster & Gurdjian (1951) have observed that unconsciousness caused by head injuries may fail to abolish the alpha rhythm. Gastaut (in Delafresnaye, 1954) has pointed out that not only may there be unconsciousness without slow waves, but (as is more widely appreciated) slow waves may occur without unconsciousness. Gastaut quotes the case of a girl who following a head injury showed for three years a rhythmic activity at 3 c/s. Writing of her he states : 'her psychic state is quite normal. Her powers of abstraction and attention are even well developed and she has a remarkable gift for mathematics.'

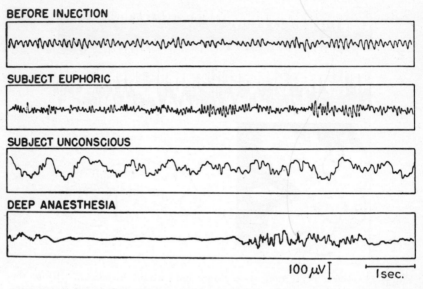

FIG. 7.39.—Electrical activity of brain (E.E.G.) during pentothal anaesthesia. The first effect is to cause the alpha rhythm to be replaced by faster activity (beta waves). With further administration of the drug slow waves become evident, and with deep anaesthesia bursts of activity alternate with periods of quiescence (suppression-burst activity). In the lowest part of the diagram the end of one burst is seen followed by a period of quiescence, then the cycle is repeated. Similar suppression-burst activity may be set off by under-cutting areas of the cortex, as in the operation of frontal leucotomy (p. 471) (*vide* Henry & Scoville, 1952). This figure is reproduced from Brazier (1951)

It may well prove that disturbances of consciousness depend upon rather extensive blocking of cortical areas by abnormal activity. It is often assumed that a rhythm that spreads widely over the hemispheres is being produced by a correspondingly large expanse of cortex. As has been seen, this view is fallacious ; there is no satisfactory way of estimating the size of a cortical generator from measurements of currents on the surface of the skull (p. 241). It is certain too that much will depend upon the particular sites of

abnormal response.   Bates (1953 *b*) found that consciousness was
lost during 'wave and spike' responses only when there was a
particular spatial distribution of the potentials over the head.   These
special complexes that are bilaterally symmetrical, and of high amplitude, should surely demonstrate that the 'centrencephalic system
is the centre of consciousness' if this was so.   Wave and spikes similar
in every way to those found in epilepsy may be produced by electrical

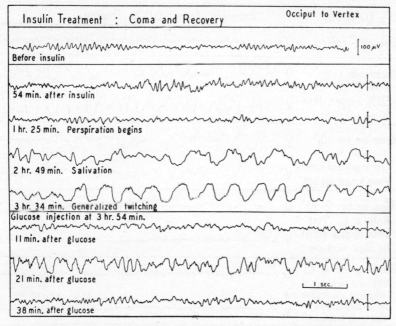

Fig. 7.40.—E.E.G.s taken during insulin treatment of a schizophrenic patient.
Connections occiput to vertex.   Dosages : insulin 44 units ; glucose 90 gm.
in 200 c.c. water.   Note the delta activity when the effects are most marked.
(Reproduced from Davis & Davis, 1939)

stimulation of the thalamus in cats (Jasper & Fortuyn, 1947 ; Hunter
& Jasper, 1949).   A person may respond to questions entirely
normally during a wave and spike burst.

It is important to be aware of the varied meanings applied to
consciousness.   Gowers pointed out that :

'The terms "conscious and consciousness" are used in two senses :
first to signify the subjective knowledge of the occurrence of mental processes ; secondly to designate the outward manifestations of such processes.   In medical language the term is chiefly employed in the latter

sense. A patient is said to be "unconscious", or to have "lost consciousness", when there is no spontaneous evidence of mental action, and none can be elicited by sensory stimulation. Hence the term "insensible" is often used in the same manner. Another confusion is introduced by frequent relative use of the word "conscious of" in the sense of cognition or knowing. Thus the delirious patient may be said to be unconscious of what is occurring around him, although he is not said to be unconscious' (quoted from Schiller, 1952).

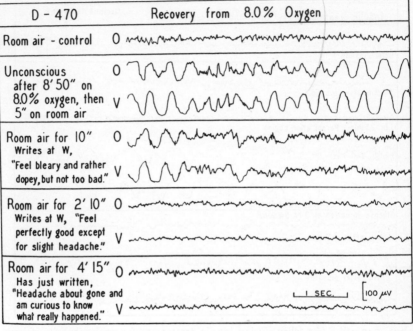

Fig. 7.41.—E.E.G. of normal subject showing changes induced by anoxia. Records from vertex, V, and occiput, O, taken simultaneously, the reference electrodes being on the ears. Note the presence of delta waves when the subject is unconscious. (Reproduced from Davis & Davis, 1939)

The selectivity with which various functions may be lost is the reason why there can be debate as to whether or not 'consciousness is present'. It might be supposed that if a patient can speak that he should be regarded as being conscious, and indeed when we say that a person is 'conscious of' a particular stimulus we usually mean that he can speak about the effects upon him of that stimulus. Nevertheless, even under these circumstances ambiguities can arise, as the following account of the now abandoned 'twilight sleep' anaesthesia shows.

'The peculiar quality of scopolamine-morphine was its effect on the memory. It wiped out all traces of memory. Although the patient might be aware of the actual pains and discuss them with those about her, and groan and scream with agony, she would retain no memory of what had taken place under the influence of the drug. But Krönig would not permit any member of the patient's family to be present because, despite the fact that the patient might have no recollection of her pain afterwards, her outcries might be just as bad as those of women who received no treatment. Not only laymen but even professional observers were thus led to doubt the efficacy of the drug. . . . Some critics argued that since Twilight Sleep did not actually do away with pain, it was misleading to call it Painless Childbirth. On the other hand, it was held that since there was no memory of pain, the doctors were justified in giving it the name. "If there is no memory of pain, it is equivalent to having no pain . . ."' (Robinson, 1946). Twilight sleep was abandoned, not because it was regarded as an inadequate 'anaesthetic' but because it was dangerous to the infant.

A comparable state of affairs may follow an epileptic fit, the patient reacting to his surroundings but later having no memory of what he has been doing, and the same effect may be seen after a blow on the head. 'Prize fighters have been known to fight several rounds, not as well as normally but following the major rules and going through all the motions of offense and defense, starting and ceasing each round by the bell, etc., but without recollection of the events at a later date. Football players have also been known to perform according to the rules of the game for many minutes without subsequent recollection of events' (Nielsen & Thompson, 1947).

Denny-Brown (1945), writing of concussion, made the following points :

'If the disturbance is severe, an initial stage of coma ("absence of any psychologically understandable response to external stimuli or inner need") is usual. Within a few seconds or minutes . . . simple mal-directed responses to painful stimuli or loud demands appear. This state is commonly called *semi-coma*. This is in time followed by a phase of automatic behaviour, called mental "confusion" in which responses of increasing appropriateness are made, but where there is disorientation in time, place and person.'

Something is now known of the mechanics of concussion (Holbourn, 1943), but it is not possible to be dogmatic about the nature of the physiological changes that are induced at a neuronal level. It is likely that synaptic conduction is rendered more difficult than normal ; following a blow upon the head there is little evidence
S

that the conduction in nerve tracts is impaired but the electrical threshold of supra-nuclear motor regions such as the tegmentum, hypothalamus and motor cortex is raised (Groat, Magoun, Dey & Windle, 1944). At the moment of impact there may be a traumatic discharge of neurones ; working on anaesthetised curarised animals Walker, Kollross & Case (1944) recorded a large potential at the moment of impact which they believed not to be an artefact. These workers regard the loss of reflexes after concussion as being comparable to the changes in reflex excitability that follow an epileptic fit. The view that trauma may discharge central neurones is not unreasonable ; the soma of a nerve cell may be readily stimulated mechanically (Alanis & Matthews, 1952).

Consciousness has many facets, and for this reason some have thought that the search for the 'seat of consciousness' was misguided. Clinical studies show that lesions at any level in the brain stem and diencephalon may on occasion give rise to unconsciousness (Cairns, 1952). Those who have sought to 'localise' consciousness have not always framed their problem clearly, and it is axiomatic that only unsatisfactory answers can be given to ill-thought-out questions. Dandy thought consciousness depended upon the territory of the anterior cerebral artery (Myers, 1951) whilst Penfield's 'Highest Level' is represented by the 'centrencephalic' system (p. 252). The number of discriminations with which the centrencephalic system can be concerned is probably much more limited than those possible at a cortical level as the number of cells is relatively small. Lashley (*vide* Penfield, 1952) spoke—

'a word of warning against the present tendency to ascribe very complex functions to the thalamus and brain stem. These are regions of relatively few cells and poorly developed internuncial systems. . . . The pulvinar of the monkey contains only 0·5% as many cells as does the parieto-temporal region, to which its fibres project. In man the ratios of cortical to sub-cortical cells are certainly much greater.'

It is unreasonable to suppose that all discriminations are served by a single restricted region ; indeed the greater part of this book is concerned with the way in which different regions and systems within the brain handle the various types of problem with which the organism is faced. The activity of various regions is, however, affected by the recruiting system. The brain deals in its different parts with summarised and selected information. Eddington points out in *The Nature of the Physical World* that the mathematician in considering the problem of an elephant sliding down a grassy hillside simplifies the complex happening to two symbols, a mass M and a coefficient of friction μ. Hallowell Davis (1950) has pointed out that :

'In nature's machines, ourselves, this thing we call consciousness would seem to be the very process of continual dynamic balancing of a set of summary reports. These summary reports are continually coming in from our sensory systems, from our memories and our bodily needs, and include our concepts of future action (calculations of probabilities). All of the information from each of these areas obviously cannot be assembled in one bit of brain tissue at one time. The information can only be assembled and interact in summary form and decisions are dispatched likewise in summary form to be elaborated as to details in the lower centres of the motor system.'

CHAPTER 8

THE AUDITORY SYSTEM AND TEMPORAL LOBES

Mundane nature is simply full of sound. Few events happen on the surface of our globe that do not simultaneously set up vibrations in some body or other, whether in rock or in timber, in water, or in air. Every raindrop that falls from the sky, every stream that hurries down the hillside, every wave that gathers and breaks, every branch or twig that falls from a tree, every obstructed gust of wind, every animal that steps on the solid ground or lands after a leap, sets up in the material environment, whether this be solid, liquid or gaseous, a whole series of molecular oscillations, violent or insignificant as the case may be. From their original focus these are promptly conducted in different directions, to die down in the end like the ripples from a splash in a still lake. All around us perpetual shakes and quivers are occurring. . . .—TAIT (1932).

AUDITORY THRESHOLDS

THE *sensitivity* of the ears, under favourable conditions, can be surprising. Wilska (1938) fixed a very light stylus to a human eardrum and observed, under a microscope, the motion for a low-frequency note at a high intensity level. He then reduced the intensity and measured the auditory threshold of the subject. By making an appropriate extrapolation he was able to estimate the least motion of the drum that corresponded to a just perceptible sound. Alternative techniques have been used by other workers and these methods have been summarised by Rayleigh (1926) and by Stevens & Davis (1938). Since the ear may be a more sensitive detector of air-borne vibrations than the physical instruments available it is in general necessary to measure the intensity of the sound at levels which are well above the auditory threshold, and then take steps to reduce the sound to known extents until it can only just be heard. The various measurements which have been made agree fairly well; under optimum conditions it is probable that the ear can respond to a movement of the tympanic membrane of as little as 10^{-8} cm. (Fig. 8.1). This distance is less than the diameter of the smallest of the atoms, hydrogen. Under normal circumstances, as may readily be observed, the use of two ears instead of one increases slightly the chance of detecting a very weak sound (*vide* Hirsh, 1948). Hughes (1937, 1940) has compared the

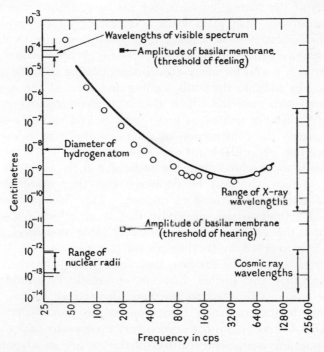

FIG. 8.1.—Sensitivity of ear. Movements of air molecules (curve), of ear drum (circles), and of basilar membrane (hollow square) at threshold. Data (Stevens & Davis, Wilska, and Békésy) were obtained by different techniques. They agree in showing that the movements are very small. Also shown is the movement of the basilar membrane at the 'threshold of feeling', *i.e.* sound level that causes pain. (From Stevens, 1951)

'monaural' threshold with the 'binaural' threshold and has found that the total energy for two ears is equal to the energy needed for one ear by itself irrespective of the actual division of energy between the ears. Hughes also found that the threshold of one ear is lowered by simultaneous stimulation of the opposite ear even when different frequencies are used.

It is exceptional for any ordinary room to be free of noise. The *sound insulation* provided by normal windows, doors and walls is far from complete, and sounds produced outside enter except under the most unusual conditions. Sounds within the room are not absorbed as soon as they meet a solid surface but are reflected with relatively slight loss of energy. In this way a sound started at one point may be reflected around the room many times before it is extinguished. The number of reflections varies, of course, with the contents of the room; curtains, for instance, absorb sound much more effectively than plain walls. By taking special precautions with the construction of a room it is possible greatly to attenuate those sounds which do penetrate. Sound-proofed rooms of this type are very useful for many experiments dealing with the auditory system. In addition the walls, ceiling and floor of the room may be treated with materials which absorb incident sound very effectively. A chamber treated in these ways is said to be 'anechoic'; unfortunately the construction of rooms of this type is expensive, and very few are available for experimental work.

Even in an anechoic room the molecules of the air are not completely at rest. It must be supposed that they move, owing to thermal agitation, in a random manner. This *Brownian movement* must set a limit to the sensitivity that is of value in any sound detector; the evidence shows, however, that this level has not nearly been reached by the human ear (cf. discussion in Wever & Lawrence, 1954). The ear has, however, probably reached such a threshold that any further increase of sensitivity would render audible noise transmitted to the ears along bony routes. There is a limit to the insulation from bone-borne sounds that can be achieved; Békésy (1949) has argued very ingeniously that a number of the puzzling anatomical features of the ear are an adaptation for reducing sensitivity to vibrations carried through the skull. Wever & Lawrence (1954) have suggested that 'Nature's expedient of isolating the hair cells of the cochlea from the circulatory supply' is important for the attainment of maximum sensitivity.

The rôle of the human *external ear* in hearing is debatable and when lost there is no striking disturbance of auditory sensitivity. It is sometimes said to be a sound reflector beaming sound into the external canal of the ear. This view is almost certainly incorrect, for an efficient reflector must have dimensions which are large compared with the wavelength of the sound. In the case of the pinna this situation is not, in general, found; the wavelength of a note of 1000 c/s, for instance, is about one foot (30 cm.). Various observers have, however, shown that the pinna acts as a screen for notes of high frequency which come from behind and Rayleigh noticed that the tick of a clock sounded duller when his back was towards the clock, as compared with facing the clock. The head itself acts as an effective screen only for notes of high frequency ; most sounds pass round the head and thereby reach not only the ear turned towards the source of sound, but also that which is turned in the other direction. This failure of sound to travel in straight lines is due to the process known as diffraction and is influenced to some extent by projections from the head such as the pinna and nose.

The remarkable sensitivity of the ear must clearly depend upon the efficient use of the available energy, and it appears that *the*

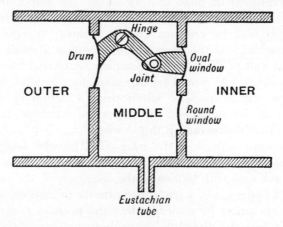

FIG. 8.2.—Functional diagram of middle-ear mechanism.
(Reproduced from Beatty, 1932)

middle ear is especially adapted to transfer the maximum of energy into the inner ear. When sound falls upon a semi-solid surface such as the skin most of it is reflected off again, very little is transmitted through (cf. Bárány, 1942). The *middle ear* transmits sound which falls upon the tympanic membrane to the oval window of the cochlea ; the energy which is picked up by the relatively large tympanic membrane is therefore available for driving the much smaller stapes. In addition the ossicles of the middle ear act as a lever which reduces the amplitude but increases the force acting on the oval window (Fig. 8.2). This rather elaborate middle-ear mechanism is, of course, not necessary in the case of animals which live in water for the vibrations which reach the surface of the body may be transmitted into the inner ear without difficulty. It is found that in fish the middle-ear mechanism has not evolved, whilst in those mammals such as whales, which in the course of evolution have again taken to living in water, it is found that the structures are modified and the external auditory meatus may not be patent. Again, in the snake, the single ossicle or 'columella' is fixed by a ligament to the quadrate bone of the skull. Accordingly the animal is insensitive to air-borne sounds ('deaf as an adder') but reacts to vibrations transmitted through the terrain.

This specialised middle-ear mechanism is, in man, rather a vulnerable area, being commonly damaged by infections. Another pathological process which is not uncommon is a hereditary tendency for an overgrowth of bone to immobilise the stapes in the oval window. This condition is known as *otosclerosis*. The deafness can only be overcome by creating a fresh pathway for the sound to enter the cochlea ; in the fenestration operation a small window is made in the wall of the horizontal semicircular canal (*vide* Wever & Lawrence, 1954). As would be expected the operation is followed by transient disturbances of labyrinthine function (p. 134). In addition to the immobility of the stapes the sensitive structures of the cochlea may degenerate in this disease.

Loud sounds may cause the intra-aural muscles (stapedius and tensor tympani) to contract, and when this mechanism is deranged, as may be the case with lesions of the facial nerve, the patient may complain of hyperacusis, a painful sensitivity to loud sounds. Subjectively a click may be noticed when the muscles contract whilst their activity may be directly observable in patients with large perforations of the ear drum (*vide* Wever & Lawrence, 1954). The contractions alter the ease with which sound can travel into the ear and thus by measuring 'acoustic impedance' the responses can be studied in the intact human being (Metz, 1951).

In pathological conditions in which the ossicles are damaged but the cochlea healthy it is found that the sensitivity to air-borne sound is reduced whilst that to sound reaching the ear through the bones of the head is essentially unchanged. In diagnosis use is made of *Rinné's test*. A tuning-fork is struck and held upon the mastoid until the patient signals that it can no longer be heard. The fork is then removed and held with the prongs near the external ear when, with normal hearing, it is heard again : a result known as a *positive* Rinné test. If, on the contrary, the tuning-fork cannot be heard by the air route after the bone-conducted sound has vanished, the test is said to be *negative* and indicates a disturbance of the middle ear.

The *Weber test* is also of value in diagnosis. The tuning-fork is struck and placed on the vertex of the head. In middle-ear deafness the sound is heard louder in the diseased ear whilst the reverse is naturally the case when the inner ear, or eighth nerve is the source of the mischief. The result with middle-ear disease is surprising and there seems to be no clear account of the physics of this reliable and simple clinical test (but cf. Littler, Knight & Strange, 1952). Just as the middle-ear mechanism readily transmits sound from air to the cochlea, so it may operate in reverse and is known to be particularly effective at radiating into the air sound energy transmitted through the bones of the head (Nikiforowsky, 1912, but cf. Oyer, 1955).

The human ear is most sensitive at about 2000 c/s, and very much more energy may be needed to stimulate it at frequencies near the upper and lower limits of hearing. The precise upper and lower limits are indeed rather difficult to define, for they depend, to some extent, upon the intensity of sound which is available for the test. It may, however, be said that there is little useful hearing below 30 c/s or above 16,000 c/s.

In small mammals the greatest sensitivity is at frequencies higher than those optimum for human hearing. In shoo-ing a cat away our effects on the animal may be comparable to those of a lion roaring on ourselves, for 's—' is a sound with much energy at the higher frequencies ; the same situation occurs when a snake hisses at a mouse.

In assessing hearing tuning-fork tests have many useful applications, but a more precise method is available in the pure tone *audiometer*. This is an electronic instrument which produces alternating electrical current, adjustable as to intensity and frequency, which is fed into headphones. It is usual to test the hearing of the patient at a number of different frequencies. The intensity of the sound is gradually increased until the patient signals that it can just be heard. The calibration of audiometers presents considerable technical difficulties which do not appear to have been entirely overcome. The trouble arises from the necessity of depending upon the use of arbitrary instead of absolute standards ; it is a weakness met with also in other instruments used in medicine. Because the measurement of the absolute intensity of a sound is difficult, it is usual in audiometry to specify the level in relation to some quite arbitrary value.[1] The range of sound intensities from

[1] Where absolute measurements can be made a reference intensity of 2×10^{-4} dynes/sq. cm. is adopted (*vide* Wever & Lawrence, 1954).

the least detectable to the greatest tolerable is very great (Fig. 8.3), so great indeed that it is conventional to use a logarithmic scale. The intensity of a sound is given in decibels (db.) and the value may be calculated by the formula 10 log I_1/I_2, where I_1 represents the intensity of the sound being measured and I_2 represents the intensity of the arbitrary standard source. The unit is a tenth of a bel, a measure which was found to be too large for practical purposes and which was named after Alexander Graham Bell (1847–1922), the inventor of the telephone. Bell was born and educated in Edinburgh but he left the city as a young man and his scientific work was done elsewhere. Deafness may, by means of the audiometer, be described as so many 'decibels loss' at a given frequency, meaning that the sound has to be increased that number of decibels above the normal until it is heard. It is usual in audiometry to take as standard intensity at each frequency the threshold value for a group of healthy young adults. Although audiometry is the most scientific test of hearing available at present for clinical work, it is well to bear in mind that the end point depends upon a subjective response by the patient. It is therefore desirable to test the reliability of the measurements by replication.

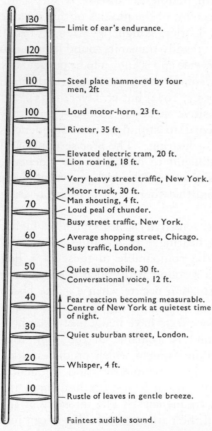

FIG. 8.3.—The ladder of noise. Each rung is 10 decibels above the rung below, *i.e.* each rung corresponds to a change of intensity of tenfold. (After Beatty, 1932)

Simple tuning-fork tests may enable deafness to be classified into 'conduction' or 'nerve' categories, but in the latter case they are inadequate to differentiate a lesion within the cochlea from one in the auditory nerve itself. By means of a 'Recruitment Test' this may, however, be possible.   With lesions within the cochlea 'the impairment of hearing present at threshold diminishes as the intensity of the stimulus is increased, until a point is reached when the sound is heard equally well by both ears. . . .' This is not the case with nerve lesions and thus recruitment may prove useful in the early diagnosis of an acoustic neuroma (Elliott & McKissock, 1954).   The recruitment test may be performed with an audiometer by switching the sound from one ear to the other.

The importance of different frequencies in understanding speech varies widely.   Frequencies below 250 and above 4000 c/s [1] may be removed with only slight loss of intelligibility, and Fowler (1942), in estimating loss of speech clarity from an audiogram, depends upon a system in which he weights the hearing loss (db.) in the following way :

Table 7

Frequencies (c/s)	512	1024	2046	4098
Weighting factor (%)	15	30	40	15

It is necessary to consider the contribution of both ears, for even with moderately severe deafness on one side there may be, from that ear, a significant contribution to clarity.   With nerve deafness the situation may be complicated by blurring ; speech frequencies may be heard, but if the threshold is raised by 45-50 db. the speech itself cannot be understood.

Audiometry may thus have, or come to have, a bearing upon the choice of *hearing aid* for a deaf person.   Hearing aids may be manufactured so as to have an increased sensitivity in a particular frequency range.   The useful limit of amplification in a hearing aid, however, is set by the occurrence of pain in the ear.   A person who is deaf may still experience pain when the sound intensity is very great, and the sensory endings concerned may be in the tympanic membrane and not in the inner ear.   Very great amplification cannot be utilised because sounds, except the weakest, will be increased to uncomfortable levels and the user will switch the instrument off. One method which offers some improvement is the technique of *volume compression*.   By this electrical system the amplification of the hearing aid depends upon the intensity of sound reaching the microphone, weak sounds being amplified more than loud ones.   It might be supposed that the greatest amplification of a hearing aid should be at those frequencies at which a loss was detected.   This

[1] Frequencies above 4000 c/s nevertheless do contribute significantly to the liveliness of speech and are particularly important for the sibilants. They are like the 'salt in the soup'.

view has been shown to be erroneous. It is better to put most of
the amplification into frequencies at which the hearing is still fairly
good, for the use of great amplification at frequencies at which the
hearing is poor leads to the occurrence of pain (Hearing Aids and
Audiometers, 1947). In practice it is usually found most satisfactory
to use a hearing aid, the amplification of which increases at the
higher frequencies.

The ear may be stimulated not only by sound but also by electrical
currents : the 'Electrophonic' effect (*vide* Flottorp, 1953). This curious
phenomenon has long been known and several different explanations
have been put forward to account for it. One of these supposes that a
mechanical vibration of the ear drum is set up by a condenser-like action
of the middle ear. The sounds are not loud and the electrophonic effect
has not been turned to practical use for aiding the deaf.

THE ACTION OF THE COCHLEA

The way in which sound is dealt with by the cochlea is of fundamental importance in understanding the auditory system.   Until

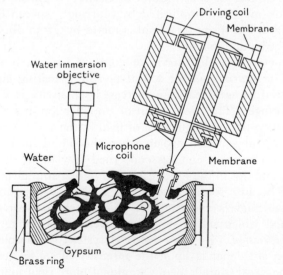

FIG. 8.4.—Direct observation of movements of basilar membrane.
(From Békésy in Stevens, 1951)

recently two main theories have been held. According to *Helmholtz's
theory* the cochlea behaved as a frequency analyser splitting the sound
into its component sine waves. Helmholtz believed that the fibres

of the basilar membrane were stretched so as to respond to different notes. The opposing view was put forward by Rutherford, Professor of Physiology in the University of Edinburgh. Rutherford supposed that the ear acted as a telephone converting the sound waves into corresponding electrical currents. The *telephone theory* is difficult to reconcile with the fact that the ear is sensitive to frequencies well above those that can be carried by individual nerve fibres. Detailed discussion of these two theories is now scarcely necessary since there has become available a wealth of facts which have clarified these issues.

Some of the most direct evidence about the performance of the cochlea comes from observing the movements of the basilar membrane in response to sound. Technically this is very difficult, for it is necessary to remove a good deal of hard bone before the cochlea can be inspected. Békésy (1949) in a masterly series of experiments has been able to cement a glass window into the wall of the cochlea and to observe the movements under stroboscopic illumination (Fig. 8.4). The basilar membrane is a transparent structure, but its position may be determined if fine particles of silver are introduced as markers. It is rather difficult to be certain that the operative procedure has not altered the behaviour of the organ, but it seems unlikely that the responses have been changed fundamentally. Békésy found that the vibration of the basilar membrane

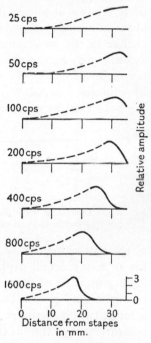

Fig. 8.5.—Amplitude of displacement of basilar membrane for different notes. (Békésy in Stevens, 1951)

was of considerable extent with all of the notes that he used, although there was one region at which the disturbance was greatest for any particular pitch (Fig. 8.5). The waves appeared to travel along the basilar membrane (Fig. 8.6). It has long been supposed that the basilar membrane behaved as a number of relatively independent resonators, but this view, originally proposed by Helmholtz, now seems scarcely tenable in view of Békésy's observations. Under direct microscopic observation the basilar membrane appears to be under no tension, and it does not gape if cut. According to the Helmholtz theory the fibres of the basilar membrane were likened to piano strings ; each element was supposed to have its own natural period of resonance. Resonance of this type cannot be expected in a membrane which is not under tension, and the observation that the waves are propagated along the membrane, and are not stationary, is also opposed to the conception of Helmholtz.

One type of deafness which is not uncommon is that in which there is a loss of sensitivity to high frequencies. Careful histological observations have shown that this may be the result of a degenerative change in the basilar membrane (Crowe *et al.*, 1934). High tone deafness may be correlated with a degeneration of the basal part of the organ of Corti. In animals similar lesions may be established by prolonged exposure to loud sounds. Another approach which has been used by a number of investigators is to destroy small parts

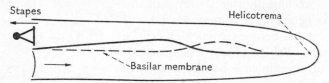

FIG. 8.6.—Travelling wave on basilar membrane. The cochlea has been uncoiled for diagrammatic purposes. (After Békésy from Stevens & Davis, 1938)

of the basilar membrane in animals. This may be achieved by the use of a fine dental drill (Fig. 8.7), but it is difficult to get a satisfactory measure of the resulting loss of hearing. One method which has been used is to measure the intensity of sound needed to elicit a reflex twitch of the pinna. Another technique depends upon the measurement of the electrical currents known as *cochlear microphonics* or the *Wever-Bray effect*. These remarkable currents which were first observed by two American psychologists (Wever & Bray) reproduce the waveform of the incoming sound up to a certain frequency. They can be recorded from anywhere in the region of the cochlea and are quite separate from the response of the auditory nerve occurring after a shorter latency (0·1 as compared with 0·5 msec.) and being more resistant to asphyxia. The cochlear microphonics are easily recorded in the guinea-pig and cat, but, unfortunately, they are too small to be of any practical use as a test of hearing in man. Their origin is uncertain but they may be a product of the hair cells of the organ of Corti (Fig. 8.8), and since they result presumably from mechanical pressure or deformation they have been compared with the piezo-electric effects familiar to students of physics.   Recently it has proved possible to record the responses of various parts of the cochlea by means of needles inserted through fine holes into various regions (Tasaki & Fernández, 1952).   It was found that microphonic potentials were developed in the basal turn to both high and low frequencies, whilst low

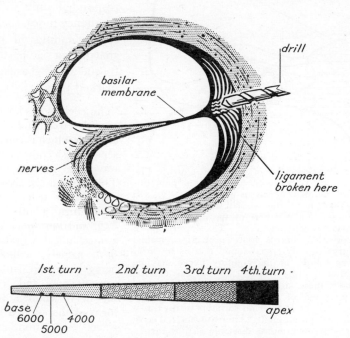

FIG. 8.7.—Experimental rupture of spiral ligament. These experiments were performed to test Helmholtz's theory. It was supposed that the fibres of the basilar membrane were kept tense, and therefore tuned, by the spiral ligament. Békésy's work has, however, shown that the basilar membrane is a lax structure. (Held from Beatty, 1932)

frequencies alone were effective at the apex of the organ.   These results parallel those of Békésy already described.

As has been the case in other similar problems, the response of the 8th nerve *taken as a whole* is difficult to understand, for a large number of separate effects are summated in a random manner.   The response does reproduce the waveform of the incoming sound (Derbyshire & Davis, 1935) for notes of up to about 3000 c/s ; and as it is difficult to believe that any separate fibre can respond as rapidly as that, it was necessary to suppose that the nerve fibres acted in rotation (Volley Theory). The situation has been clarified by the brilliant observations of Tasaki (1954). This worker has been able to record the activity of single neurones within the modiolus of the cochlea. He found that fibres which arose in the basal turn of the cochlea responded to notes of any frequency, whilst those from the apical end responded only to low-frequency tones, their response falling off rather sharply at a particular frequency. Tasaki remarked that :

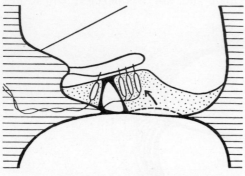

FIG. 8.8.—Structure of organ of Corti. The inner hair cells are provided with a 'point-to-point' set of connections with the C.N.S. On the other hand, the external spiral fibres which supply the outer part of the organ of Corti innervate many hair cells. This latter type of innervation affords more protection against injury. Dandy (1934) found that as much as seven-eighths of the auditory nerve may be sectioned without rendering the ear useless. Under these circumstances the *discrimination* of pitch and of intensity may suffer, although there may be little or no elevation of the thresholds for pure tones. (After Stevens & Davis, 1938—arrow indicates direction of movement)

'The cochlea has long been considered as kind of wave analyser which is capable of separating a compound sine wave into its components. This notion is, however, only partly true. In the basal turn a mixture of high and low tones causes a mechanical vibration *as such*, namely, without its being resolved into its components, and excites the nerve endings in the form of the applied mixed wave. Separation between the components occurs only as the mechanical wave (caused by the mixed tones) travels along the cochlea partition upwards and the higher frequency component decays more rapidly than the low one as they travel.'

If all primary neurones respond to low frequencies whilst only certain of them respond to high notes, an explanation is afforded of the fact that lesions of the nerve, not so complete as to cause total deafness, may give rise to high-, but not to low-frequency deafness.

SOUND LOCALISATION (*vide* Walsh, 1957)

Remarkable precision may be shown, under favourable circumstances, in the ability to localise a sound, an ability which depends on the use of two ears. One indication which is used by the brain depends upon the relative intensity of the sound on the two sides of the head, but this cue is likely to be of value only for notes of high frequency, or for sources close to one ear (Duyff *et al.*, 1950). Under most circumstances a more important clue is yielded by time differences, the sound may strike one ear a fraction of a second before it strikes the other ear. This time difference will be small; if the distance between the ears is taken as 6 inches and the velocity of sound in air as 1000 feet per second, it will be seen that a difference of 500 μsec. will separate the time of arrival of the noise on the two sides of the head when the source is situated on a line joining the ears (1 μsec. = 1 $\times$ 10^{-6} sec.). If the source lies in another direction the time interval will be smaller. Sound localisation, then, depends upon the evaluation of signals from the two ears, and this must be performed at some point in the nervous system where the pathways from the two sides come together.

It is worth noting that a connection between the two ears is known. This cochleo-cochlear pathway may be demonstrated electrically (Galambos, Rosenblith & Rosenzweig, 1950) by recording from an electrode on the round window. It is found that a click delivered not only to the ipsilateral, but also to the contralateral ear produces recordable potentials. A click delivered to the contralateral car depresses the neural response expected from an ipsilateral click delivered a short interval later. The conduction time across the pathway is at least 1 msec.

The use of time intervals as a cue to auditory localisation illustrates an interesting principle in sensory physiology which is met with in many different connections; nevertheless, the principle is rarely remarked upon and does not appear to have been named. Any given time interval is ambiguous since it corresponds to a source of sound located on either of two possible bearings. In locating a source of sound it is usual to rotate the head towards the side from which it appears to come. At the new position of the head the binaural time difference will be different and it also will correspond to two alternative bearings. The true bearing of the source of sound will, of course, be the one which corresponds in the two instances. It is thus apparent that the use of two cues in conjunction has enabled precise information to be obtained about the outside world, whilst either cue by itself could give only ambiguous information. It is necessary to disagree with Stevens & Newman (1934) who said that ' localisation is built up in experience, and . . . only unequivocal bases for localisation can become established as effective cues'.

T

THE AUDITORY PATHWAYS

Not uncommonly it is supposed that *the auditory pathways in the brain stem* (Fig. 8.9) act merely as conducting routes leading the messages to the cerebral cortex. This view is entirely erroneous.

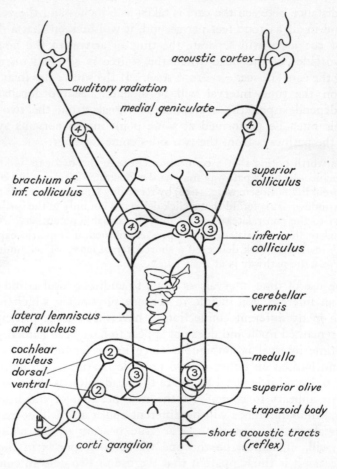

FIG. 8.9.—Connections of the auditory system. The 'order' of the neurones is indicated numerically. The cochleo-cochlear pathway has been omitted. (From Stevens, 1951)

The dorsal cochlear nucleus is a structure even more complicated than the retina or the olfactory bulb. All afferents from the cochlea make synapses in each of at least 13 distinct subdivisions of the cochlear nucleus complex; each fibre thus ends on a very large number of cells. The points at which the fibres terminate depends upon the part of the cochlea with which they are connected.

Galambos (1954) in an important review has concluded that 'in some, if not in all, of its 13 subdivisions, the geographical (spatial) correlate for frequency established at the basilar membrane is repeated in the first central nucleus. In other words, the cochlea is "unrolled" at the cochlea nucleus, not just once, but repeatedly.'

Physiological as well as anatomical evidence strongly supports the view that there is considerable 'reshuffling' of auditory information at the various synaptic junctions in the brain stem. Galambos & Davis (1943, 1944) described the results of studying the responses of single units of the auditory system and their first paper must be regarded as a classical contribution to physiology. These workers used fine micro-pipettes as electrodes; the pipettes were thrust into the auditory nerve between the internal auditory meatus and the brain stem. The units which they recorded arose, so they later came to believe (Galambos & Davis, 1948), from scattered nerve cells and not from the axones of the cochlear (primary) neurones. The activity that they investigated was therefore removed by one synapse from the response initiated by the hair cells of the cochlea. Each unit had a characteristic frequency to which it was most sensitive, although with loud sounds a given unit responded over a considerable range of frequencies (Fig. 8.10). As the intensity of the stimulus was increased there was an increase in the rate of discharge of the action potentials. Nevertheless, there was a tendency for the impulses which did arise to be set off at the same phase of the stimulus waveform on each occasion. Some of the units discharged spontaneously and it was sometimes found that notes of certain frequencies might stop this activity. It was even found that the discharge produced by one frequency might be inhibited by simultaneous stimulation by a neighbouring frequency. This inhibition was never found by Tasaki (1954) in his studies of the activity of the primary neurones, and is evidently the result of neural interaction at synaptic junctions. The information from the ear is subjected to further transformations at other points in the brain stem. Hilali & Whitfield (1953) have recorded by micro-needles from the brain stem of the cat. Some of the responses which they obtained seemed to come from nerve fibres and some from cells, in the trapezoid body. The discharges set up by sounds were remarkable for their irregularity, an unusual finding in any part of the nervous system.

Some of the auditory pathways run to the *superior olive* in the brain stem (Rasmussen, 1946). This nucleus is believed to be concerned in auditory reflexes and it gives rise to a bundle that crosses to the opposite side to reach the cochlea. This bundle may be responsible for the cochleo-cochlear effects described above (p. 273). Weisschedel (1938) studied the pathology of Huntington's chorea and was able to collect a series of cases in which both superior olives

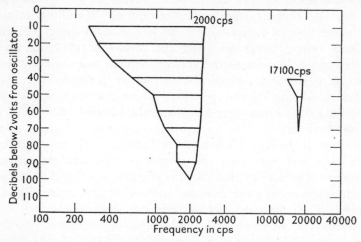

FIG. 8.10.—Response of single units of the auditory system to notes of different frequency. Each fibre had a characteristic frequency to which it was most sensitive. As the intensity of the stimulus was increased other notes became effective. (Galambos & Davis, 1943.) The units are believed to be second order neurones. (Galambos & Davis, 1948)

were degenerate. His cases had not been deaf but the reflex responses were not investigated. Deafness does sometimes occur with lesions of the brain stem, particularly with disturbances in the neighbourhood of the inferior colliculus, for in that region the pathways on the two sides lie close together (Sloane, Persky & Saltzman, 1943).

Galambos *et al.* (1952) studied the electrical responses of the *medial geniculate body* using micro-electrodes. Different units varied widely in the latencies of their responses to clicks (6-125 msec.). The authors remark that :—

'It has surprised us to encounter at the medial geniculate so much evidence for those functions that are usually assigned to the cerebral cortex.

It is apparent that there is reason to question a simple concept of afferent activity according to which prompt delivery of impulses to the cortex is its sole, or even its primary, function. The mechanism by which the substantial time delays are introduced and the function of these delays appear to be worthy of further study.'

In contrast to data from the peripheral nervous system—'a stimulus may inhibit rather than excite central neurons in the afferent pathway. Increased stimulus intensity may lead to reduction rather than to increase in neural response, and neural response may appear later in time rather than earlier.' Rather commonly units may be found which respond readily to noises and clicks, but are not activated by pure tone stimuli (Galambos, 1952).

In view of these electro-physiological findings it is perhaps not surprising that *even when the cerebral hemispheres have been removed responses to sounds may still be elicited.* Forbes & Sherrington (1914) studied the *acoustic reflexes* in recently decerebrated preparations. In one cat they reported that 'sharp hissing three feet from the right ear caused . . . a raising of the head, the head being carried to the right'. One common response to sound in the decerebrate animal was a lashing of the tail. Even more striking responses have been recorded by Bazett & Penfield (1922) who studied animals that had been decerebrated some days beforehand. These workers stated that 'the most effective sound was a small scratching noise, and an animal would often react promptly by raising its head if a piece of paper was crumpled up at a distance of one or two yards. These sounds are similar to those made by a mouse. . . . Animals would react to these slight noises even though there was a constant loud noise from the motors and stirrers to which no reaction was shown except when it was started after an interval of rest.' Dusser de Barenne (1933 b) studied a decorticate cat. The cat 'could be induced, especially when hungry, to walk and run promptly in the direction from which she was called', whilst Schaltenbrand & Cobb (1930) who studied another decorticate cat reported that the 'animal was very sensitive to sounds and turned the head even at the snapping of a finger nail. It always started to move and mew when the door was opened.' 'The animal often slept and then did not react to ordinary sounds. While awake she was extremely sensitive to sounds, the breath of the examiner was sufficient to cause a rotation of the head.'

Similar results have been reported by Bard & Rioch (1937). In three of the four decorticate cats that they studied certain auditory responses were easily obtained. 'A light whistling noise, the sound made by sand-paper rubbing against wood or other noises of high pitch and low intensity, evoked elevation and pointing of the ears, widening of the palpebral spaces and turning of the head toward the source of the sound. When-ever this response was repeatedly elicited, it became less marked and eventually disappeared, only to return after a period free from auditory stimulation of the adequate type.' In one animal a 'singular and very striking item of behaviour appeared during the later six months of the survival period. At times when the animal was allowed the freedom of a large laboratory room it was noticed that she followed one about. On several occasions she followed different observers out into a corridor, along it for a distance of from 10 to 20 yards and back again into the room. At other times it was impossible to obtain this response. . . . That the adequate stimulus was auditory seems certain. When following was evocable the responses to sounds were particularly brisk and she would often turn and walk or even run toward the source of a light whistle or of a scraping noise.'

Decorticate animals cannot therefore be regarded as deaf and their responses may even be appropriate for a particular signal in some circumstances. The hearing that remains after the extirpation is unlikely to be due to the activity of the medial geniculate body, for this structure is largely degenerate in these animals. It is probable that a number of auditory reactions are mediated by the inferior colliculus. This is an 'integrative structure of considerable complexity which discharges by way of the superior colliculus into the bulbar and spinal efferent systems' (Ades & Brookhart, 1950). It is said that there is a multiplication of the elements concerned with audition at successively higher levels, so that at the midbrain there are many more elements responding to a stimulus than at the level of entry of the 8th nerve. It would, however, be wrong to suppose that the inferior colliculus is essential for all auditory reflexes. Bazett & Penfield (1922) believed that the auditory responses that they observed in decerebrate cats were dependent upon structures in the ventral, rather than the dorsal, half of the brain stem (see also review in Woollard & Harpman, 1940).

Whilst it is difficult to believe that the basic organisation of the auditory pathways differs in the mammalia, nevertheless consider-able differences between species do appear from a functional point of view. Monkeys may show only startle responses to loud sounds (Karplus & Kreidl, 1914) after the loss of both cerebral hemispheres. Edinger & Fischer (1913) reported a similar finding in a child who lived for $3\frac{1}{2}$ years although there was a complete absence of both cerebral hemispheres and thalami and partial absence of one corpus striatum (Fig. 8.11). A loud noise caused the child to start, but no reactions suggestive of actual hearing were ever observed by the mother.

The loss of one cerebral hemisphere by itself does not result in deafness because of the bilateral nature of the auditory system. Both of the ears have connections with both of the temporal lobes. It has long been recognised that speech suffers much more profoundly in right-handed patients when the left rather than the right hemisphere is damaged. This fact leads to the concept of cerebral dominance ; in a right-handed patient the left hemisphere is said to be dominant. As Hughlings Jackson (1874) wrote :

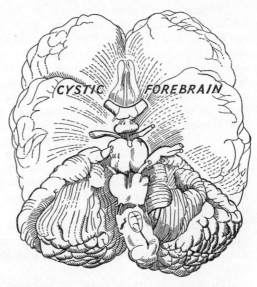

FIG. 8.11.—Brain of imbecile seen from below. The infant started in response to loud sounds but showed no other evidence of hearing. (Re-drawn from Edinger & Fischer, 1913)

'Prior to the researches of Dax and Broca it might have been supposed that the brain was double in function in either of two ways—(1) That action of both halves was required in any mental operation ; (2) That either half (indifferently) would serve alone. Neither of these opinions can now be held —with regard to words, at any rate. The two halves are not double in function in the sense that *both* are required for speech, since a patient can speak perfectly well when the *right* half of his brain is damaged, in whatever part the damage is, and however extensive it may be. Nor are they double in the sense that the two halves are such exact duplicates that *either* of them will do for speech, since extensive damage in a certain region of the *left* hemisphere will destroy speech altogether.'

The defect in aphasia usually concerns not only the production of speech but also most functions related to language to some extent. It is usual for patients with extensive lesions in the region of the left Sylvian fissure to have difficulty with the interpretation of sounds, being able, for instance, to comprehend simple but not complex sentences. Patients in whom this type of difficulty is the most striking aspect of the disturbance are said to have receptive, or auditory, aphasia. The loss of the temporal regions concerned with hearing on both sides of the brain is rather rare, but enough cases have been described in the literature to allow an idea of the type of defect to be ascertained. One case (Mills, 1891) of this type which illustrates some of these points concerned a woman aged 46.

'Fifteen years before her death she had an apoplectic attack which left her word-deaf but not paralysed. Prior to this first attack of apoplexy her hearing had been good, but after it she could not, by hearing, understand anything that was said to her. She could, however, hear music and sounds of various kinds; for instance when an organ or band had performed on the street she at times had called attention to the fact; and she had also come down from the second or even the third story to open the front door in answer to a knock. She could hear such sounds as a bell ringing and a clock ticking. These facts were elicited from her relatives through various statements made by them, chiefly spontaneously.

'When anyone wished to communicate with her it was done by means of writing or signs, as she had fully preserved her vision and was evidently not word-blind either for writing or printing.' She sometimes read the newspapers aloud and in so doing she had seemed to understand fully what she read but 'made a tangle of her words'. 'From the time of the first attack she had never been able to speak well, her words becoming "jumbled" or "tangled". From the description given of her manner of speech the defect was evidently a serious form of paraphasia and paralexia.[1] . . .

'Nine years before her death she had another and more severe apoplexy, after which her deafness increased for sounds as well as words until it was almost total. This seizure left her also with partial left hemiplegia, chiefly affecting the arm, and in this extremity, from the description, the paralysis was more marked below the elbow. . . . It was impossible to make her understand what was said to her, and so far as could be determined by repeated tests she was totally deaf; but notwithstanding her weakness, helplessness and deafness her face had a somewhat intelligent expression.'

Post-mortem examination revealed that the upper border of the temporal lobe on both sides had been destroyed by vascular accidents. The 3rd, 4th and 5th temporal convolutions were intact.

Because of the bilaterality of the auditory pathways (Fig. 8.9) it is exceptional, also, for subcortical lesions to cause deafness. A case

---

[1] Paraphasia = a defect of speech consisting of the substitution of incorrect words for those which would be appropriate. Paralexia = substitution of incorrect words during reading.

of this type has, however, been reported in detail by Le Gros Clark & Ritchie Russell (1938) in a woman aged 44 who suffered from two strokes. They record that all efforts to make her hear were unsuccessful. She could read and write without difficulty and could speak clearly and correctly in response to written questions. She had no difficulty in carrying out written instructions. 'I was right enough until after 10 o'clock at night when I began to feel queer and then I couldn't hear anything.' She died, and at post-mortem there was a bilateral thrombosis of the most laterally situated of the basal branches of the middle cerebral artery. There had resulted a destruction of the auditory radiations in the region of the external capsule on both sides.

In the anaesthetised animal the cerebral regions which receive afferent fibres from the auditory system can be mapped by recording the electrical responses of the exposed cortex (*vide* Bremer, 1953). Sound stimuli set up electrical changes which are larger, and appear earlier within the primary projection area than at other regions. The electrical changes which follow a click are complex, but the first phase is always surface positive and is believed to represent the arrival of impulses in the afferent fibres. The response may be reduced in amplitude if the auditory signals are repeated too frequently. Under chloralose anaesthesia the cat cortex responds a good deal less well to clicks which are repeated three times per second compared with once per second. The responses to pure tones are much less readily investigated and this has led to difficulties when attempts have been made to discover whether there is a localisation of different frequencies in different parts of the auditory cortex. One of the difficulties is associated with the inability to start a pure tone without, by the very act of switching the tone on, introducing other frequency components. A pure tone which is started abruptly will, if subjected to frequency analysis, show some energy throughout the frequency spectrum (Licklider in Stevens, 1951). A note started in this way may be expected to excite all regions of the cochlea, and under these conditions any localisation of frequency on recording from the cortex will be obscured. To get over this difficulty Woolsey & Walzl (1942) used not sound stimuli, but electrical shocks, which they delivered to the spiral ganglion within the cochlea. On recording the activity of the auditory region of the cortex they found a point-to-point localisation ; the basal turn of the cochlea was represented at the anterior end of the receptive strip and the apical turn was represented posteriorly.   In addition there was another region underneath the first which responded only when the stimuli were strong.   This second area was related to the cochlea in a manner which was opposite to that found in the first area ; the basal turn was represented posteriorly and the apical turn anteriorly.

More recently Tunturi (1950) has tackled the problem using refinements of technique which have set a new standard in cortical investigations.   He recorded the activity set up in the temporal lobes of anaesthetised dogs.   He applied strychnine to small areas of the cortex, thereby rendering more prominent the discharges in the areas under investigation.   He arranged that the notes used to stimulate the animal should increase in amplitude gradually instead

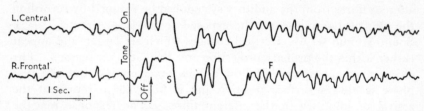

Fig. 8.12.—K-complex.   The sound increases substantially the activity shown by the E.E.G.   After a brief latent period slow waves, S, appear and in this case have overloaded the amplifiers.   At the same time a faster rhythm, F, which was not previously detectable, starts ; it persists for longer than the slow activity.   If the same stimulus is repeated at intervals the successive K-complexes may become small and finally undetectable.   It should not necessarily be supposed that this *habituation* is necessarily cortical—similar effects have been detected at the cochlear nucleus.   (Figure after Davis *et al.*, 1939 *b*)

of abruptly, a technique that limits the spread of energy in the acoustic spectrum.   He found that high frequencies were represented at the anterior end of the auditory area and low frequencies posteriorly.   At any given frequency a band of the cortex was excited.   He found that it was possible to detect a change of $\frac{1}{10}$ octave at the cortex by this technique—a difference of the same order as the subjective threshold of frequency change.

In the monkey (Walker, 1937) the auditory area is small and is buried in the Sylvian fissure.   The precise position of the primary auditory area in man is unknown, but it too may be buried some distance from the surface (Campbell, 1905).   It is not entirely surprising, therefore, that normally it is impossible to detect any response to sounds in the human electro-encephalogram arising from the temporal regions.   Strangely enough, it is sometimes possible to pick up a discharge from the vertex of the skull in response to a noise (Davis, 1939).

In the sleeping subject large electrical changes may be elicited by auditory stimuli. These disturbances, known as *K-complexes*, consist of a mixture of two different sinusoidal rhythms, one slow (3 c/s) and the other faster (14 c/s) (Fig. 8.12). K-complexes vary a good deal in their duration but may last for some seconds. Although the subject is asleep not all noises are equally effective, nor does the relative efficacy of different sounds depend solely upon their physical intensity. Sounds which are meaningful are more effective than those which are not. The same sound repeated a number of times becomes progressively less efficacious unless an interval of rest is given. These responses were discovered by Davis, Davis, Loomis, Harvey & Hobart (1939 *b*) and they were emphatic that the waves did not arise from the temporal lobes.

THE TEMPORAL LOBES

In some respects the term *association cortex* has become confused. The name dates back to the associationist psychologists of the nineteenth century. It was supposed that various parts of the forebrain were concerned with the 'association of ideas'. This approach might, from a neurological point of view, lead to either of two viewpoints concerning the definition of 'association cortex'. First the name might be applied to any region to which more than one category of sensory information could be traced. Mickle & Adess (1952) have shown, for instance, that within the Sylvian fissure there is a 'polysensory area' that receives discharges from the auditory, vestibular and somaesthetic nerves. Alternatively the term might be restricted to the parts of the cerebral cortex which do not receive directly information from the sensory organs. These regions have, however, important connections with other parts of the cortex, and it seems likely that they deal with information which has already been 'sifted' or transformed to a considerable degree. The temporal lobes are remarkable for the paucity of their connections with the thalamus. It has long been observed that removal of a region of the cortex causes atrophy of the corresponding nucleus of the thalamus ('Gudden's atrophy'). These changes have been used extensively by Walker (1938 *a*) as a means of ascertaining the anatomical connections of different parts of the thalamus. Removal of the temporal lobes results in a retrograde degeneration of none of the main nuclei of the thalamus except for the medial geniculate body. Most of the temporal lobe is normally regarded as having no thalamic connections ; this view may have to be modified, but there seems little doubt that most of the lobe can be regarded essentially as association cortex. The representation of the labyrinth (p. 149) and of the cochlea have already been mentioned, but other parts of the lobe appear to be concerned with quite different functions.

The *uncus and hippocampus* have for long been regarded as being part of the olfactory system and this view, based upon anatomical studies in the first place, received some support from clinical observations of Hughlings Jackson. Tumours in the region of the uncus may, occasionally, give rise to a variety of epilepsy in which, amongst other disturbances, the patient suffers from a derangement of the sense of smell. One case report which is well known concerns a woman aged 53 (Hughlings Jackson, 1890) :

'The patient was a cook. In the paroxysm the first thing was tremor of the hands and arms ; she saw a little black woman who was always very actively engaged in cooking ; the spectre did not speak. The patient had a very horrible smell . . . which she could not describe. She had a feeling as if she were shut up in a box with a limited quantity of air. . . . She would stand with her eyes fixed and directed forwards for a few moments, and then say, "What a horrible smell !" The patient did not, so her sister reported, lose consciousness, but remembered everything that happened during the attack ; she turned of a leaden colour. The patient told us that she passed her urine in the seizures. There was no struggling, and the tongue was not bitten. She never believed the spectre to be a real person. After leaving her kitchen work she had paroxysms with the smell sensation but no spectre. She had had these paroxysms ever since, sometimes three a day, sometimes one in two days.' Postmortem examination revealed a small tumour at the tip of the right temporal lobe.

The view that the uncus and hippocampus are concerned principally with olfaction has recently been criticised. It has proved possible, during operations upon psychiatric patients, to stimulate electrically the exposed uncus (Liberson *et al.*, 1951). The stimulation stopped respiration, caused a loss of consciousness and gave rise to convulsions. There was no suggestion of an olfactory aura, and when the patients were unconscious there were no movements of the nostril or smacking of the lips as might be expected upon stimulation of a region concerned with smell. Papez (1937) has suggested that the hippocampus and uncus should be regarded as a part of the brain concerned with emotional reactions. Klüver & Bucy

(1939) in an important study on monkeys removed much of the temporal lobe including the uncus, amygdala and hippocampus on each side. Animals which previously had been bad-tempered and afraid of the attendants lost these traits and became sweet-tempered and easy to handle. These docile animals showed exaggerated sexual reactions and a most extraordinary tendency to lick, taste, mouth and smell every object with which they came into contact. Animals that have lost these parts of the brain appear to be fearless and may, for instance, learn to place lighted matches in the mouth.

Many *epileptic attacks* commence with abnormal discharges in the temporal region. A common cause of this type of disease is believed to be interference with the blood supply of this part of the brain at birth. The pathological changes vary between an atrophy or toughness of a single gyrus to atrophy of an entire temporal lobe and parts of the adjacent cortex (Earle, Baldwin & Penfield, 1953). Temporal lobe or psychomotor epilepsy, as it is called, is often characterised by bizarre and rather complicated stereotyped acts of behaviour rather than by frank convulsions. The patient may, for instance, turn round and look in a particular direction in an act which although fully co-ordinated is unconscious—he has no recollection of anything which happens during the period of the attack. More complicated behaviour patterns may be seen, although in any given patient the attacks usually follow similar courses. The patient may have an *aura* or warning of an attack, in which complex memories of some past event are activated. During operations upon the human brain Penfield (Penfield & Rasmussen, 1950) has found that electrical stimulation of the temporal region may 'unlock' these memories in epileptic patients. He finds that it is only in the temporal region that an epileptic discharge or electrical stimulation activates 'acquired neurone patterns' in this way. Electro-encephalographic studies of patients with psychomotor epilepsy have, however, shown that typical cases may be associated with discharges originating in other parts of the brain, although temporal foci are the most common. The relationship between the temporal lobe and memory is entirely in keeping with the belief that it is an area of association cortex. Lesions of the anterior part of the temporal lobe of the dominant hemisphere may give rise to much difficulty in the learning of new words even when there is no overt aphasia (Meyer & Yates, 1955).

The clinical manifestations of *tumours of the temporal lobes* are varied and depend upon the position of the lesion. One useful sign is a hemianopia, or a quadrantic defect of the visual fields, caused by interruption of the optic radiations. This sign is, however, only found in a minority of cases of this nature. Tumours of the right temporal lobe are notoriously difficult to diagnose in their early stages; on the other hand, the results of surgical intervention tend to be less satisfactory with left-sided tumours owing to the aphasia which is likely to result.

In conclusion it may be pointed out that knowledge of the properties of the ear and auditory apparatus have been gained by workers in many different disciplines and much progress has been made, for instance, by engineers working at the Bell Telephone Laboratories (Fletcher, 1953). Many of the techniques are specialised and cannot be comprehended by physicians unless they have received specialised scientific training. It is therefore understandable, although it must be regarded as highly regrettable, that the application of this knowledge to clinical problems has scarcely begun. It is evident that at present the statement that the hearing of a particular patient is normal should not be taken at its face value since more detailed investigations might be expected to reveal important differences.

CHAPTER 9

THE VISUAL SYSTEM

The elementary signs of language are only twenty-six letters and yet what wonderfully varied meanings can we communicate by their combination! Consider, in comparison with this, the enormous number of elementary signs with which the machinery of sight is provided. We may take the number of fibres in the optic nerves as two hundred and fifty thousand.[1] Each of these is capable of innumerable different degrees of sensation of one, two, or three primary colours. It follows that it is possible to construct an immeasurably greater number of combinations here than with the few letters which build up our words. Nor must we forget the extremely rapid changes of which the images of sight are capable. No wonder, then, if our senses speak to us in language which can express far more delicate distinctions and richer varieties than can be conveyed by words.—HELMHOLTZ (1893).

PHYSICAL NATURE OF LIGHT

ACCORDING to current physical theories light may be regarded either as consisting of particles of radiation, a view that is convenient when dealing with quantities of energy concerned in visual processes, or it may be looked upon as being a wave-motion. The wave theory of light is the viewpoint which is of the greater value when attempts are made to ascertain the performance of optical devices, such as the eye, which produce images. It is indeed the extreme shortness of the waves of visible light that enables small structures such as the eye to be used to produce a useful reproduction of the external world as represented by the distribution of light and shade. If the wavelength of light was of the same order as that of sound a structure many times the size of the body would be required for focusing the radiation satisfactorily. This is one

[1] A very conservative estimate. According to the enumeration of Bruesch & Arey (1942) there are 1 million fibres in each human optic nerve. By contrast there are only 31,400 in the cochlear division of the 8th nerve.

287

reason why the processes of evolution have restricted the sensitivity of eyes to the shorter end of the electro-magnetic spectrum. There are, it is true, sources of radiation which cannot be seen because the waves are of too short a wavelength, but this limitation is inevitable in a system such as the eye which contains water, for this compound absorbs such *ultra-violet* light. Part of the absorption is dependent upon the lens of the eye, and when this structure is removed (aphakic eye), as for the treatment of the disease known as cataract, the patient can use some rays which would be invisible to a normal observer (Goodeve, Lythgoe & Schneider, 1942).

The physical properties of light set a limit to the accuracy with which fine detail can be reproduced by even the most perfect optical instrument. The image of a straight line is inevitably blurred, and multiple images may be produced on either side of the primary one. These defects caused by diffraction are due to the wavelike properties of light, for the radiation does not strictly follow the laws of geometrical optics and can pass round obstructions when these are of a size comparable to the wavelengths concerned. The image of a geometrical point can never itself be a point, but consists of a circle of finite dimensions surrounded by a number of rings that become progressively weaker. These defects in images are, of course, only of importance when considering the fine grain of an image, just as the half-tone pictures in newspapers reproduce broad outlines satisfactorily whilst the minutiae are obscured by the distortions inevitable in the technique used for the reproduction. Diffraction and other defects in the image due to imperfections in the optical system of the eye clearly set a limit to the grain of the photo-sensitive surface that is likely to be useful.

RODS AND CONES

Histological examination of the human retina shows that two sorts of receptor cell are present, the rods and the cones. Some animals such as the snake and pigeon possess cones only, whilst the vision of the guinea-pig is mediated almost entirely by rods. The retinal receptors are of a size that seems to be matched to the imperfections of the retinal image ; the diameter of a cone for instance has been estimated at 3μ (*vide* Hartridge, 1950). The differentiation of rods from cones is not always easy, for cells having shapes which are intermediate in form between the classical varieties may be found. Nevertheless certain facts about the relative distribution of the two types of receptor appear to be clearly established. In the human eye (Fig. 9.1) the retina possesses a central depression, the fovea (fovea =pit) in which are present no rods, but only elongated cones. At this point the other layers of the retina are pushed aside as though it was functionally important for light to reach these receptors with

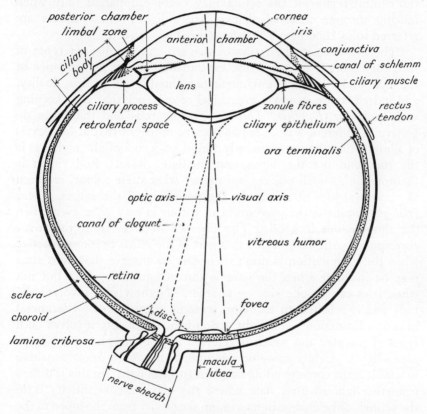

Fig. 9.1.—Diagrammatic cross-section of eye. The fovea does not lie on the optic axis of the eye. The yellow spot, 'macula lutea', is larger, and not as well defined as the fovea itself. (From Walls, 1942, after Salzmann)

a minimum of screening by the inner parts of the retina. As the region of the retina that is examined is removed farther and farther from the fovea so the proportion of rods increases, although even at the extreme periphery some cones may be found. The fovea lies at the centre of a yellow spot on the retina—the macula lutea, and the pigment that is present in this region enables an observer to be aware of his own macula for a short time if he looks at

U

a uniformly illuminated surface through a suitable coloured filter (*vide* Miles, 1954). Appearances such as this, caused by the features of the observer's own eye, are referred to as *entoptic* phenomena; it is as well to be aware of such experiences when an anxious patient complains of seeing 'spots before the eyes'. Some features of the central region of the retina may become apparent only when looking through material that polarises light; these effects are referred to as Haidinger's Brushes (*vide* Ogle, 1951).

The existence in the retina of two structurally distinct types of receptor naturally suggests that examination of the performance of the eye under varying circumstances should reflect this duality, and indeed, there is now a great deal of evidence that is in keeping with the view (*Duplicity Theory*) that the rods and the cones do behave in different ways. It has become apparent that at low levels of illumination, levels commonly found on a moonlight night, it is the rods and not the cones that mediate vision. Rod vision is 'achromatic', for all objects, no matter what their colour, are seen as various shades of grey. At the periphery of the retina, where rods predominate, the perception of colour is very poor even when the illumination is good. The absence of rods from the fovea corresponds with the fact that this part of the retina becomes inactive when the illumination is dim; it is easy to observe that faint stars may be invisible when the gaze is directed towards them but not when it is cast to one side or another. Night vision involves the rods and is referred to as being scotopic (Greek *scotos* = darkness) in contradistinction to daylight vision which probably involves both types of receptor and which is referred to as being photopic (Greek *phos* = light). Under scotopic conditions the eye is most sensitive to wavelengths corresponding to green spectral light; in this it differs from the light-adapted state where the maximum sensitivity is in the yellow. The change in maximum sensitivity from the green to the yellow as the illumination is raised is known as the *Purkinje shift*. This change is found in the intermediate regions of the retina, but not at the fovea, where there are no rods, nor at the extreme periphery where cones are scanty.

Changes of vision related to the Purkinje shift may readily be observed without the use of special apparatus.

'As the shades of evening descend, the brilliant red fruit of an apple tree begins to get darker and darker until presently the apples themselves look like black spots against the background of the foliage, the colour of which has also changed from green to a brighter grey. In the day-time

perhaps little difference of brightness can be discerned between two
bunches of flowers, one of which is red and the other blue, but in the
late evening twilight the red flowers look almost if not perfectly black,
whereas the blue ones seem to glow with a kind of magical whitish lustre'
(Southall, 1937).

The sensitivity of the dark-adapted eye to light of different wavelengths corresponds closely to the absorption curve of a pigment
that is found in the retina : *visual purple*. This pigment absorbs
light most effectively in the green part of the spectrum at 502 mμ
(Dartnall, 1952). Rod vision appears to depend upon the absorption

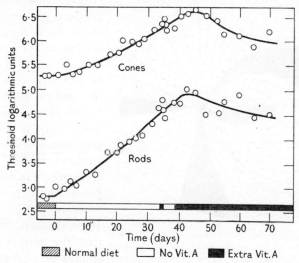

FIG. 9.2.—Changes in visual threshold caused by lack of Vitamin A. During
period subject was on deficient diet threshold for rods, and also for cones,
gradually increased. (From Hecht & Mandelbaum, 1939)

of light by this substance and when it is absent, or present in inadequate amounts, as may occur in Vitamin A deficiency, scotopic
vision is impaired, and there may also be some interference with
photopic vision as well (Fig. 9.2). The visual purple that is present
in the retina could not occupy more than about 10 per cent of the
volume of the distal portion of the rods, but it is not known whether
the molecules are restricted to certain sites such as the surface of
the receptors or are distributed throughout their substance (Granit,
Holmberg & Zewi, 1938). It seems certain that visual purple is rather
firmly attached to the structure of the rods, for fairly vigorous leaching,
with bile salts or alkalis, is needed to get the substance into solution.

DARK ADAPTATION

Under favourable conditions extremely little energy may be needed to stimulate the eye ; at night a lighted candle may be seen five miles away. In dealing with the sensitivity of the eye, it is instructive to consider the energy involved in terms of the units known as *quanta*. A quantum is a small 'packet' of energy and is indivisible ; according to current views one quantum represents the least amount of energy that can be regarded as existing. It has been shown by Hecht, Schlaer & Pirenne (1942) that the dark-adapted eye may respond to a flash containing as few as 60 quanta and yet only a fraction of these can be directly concerned in the events that lead up to the perception of light. Some light is reflected at the cornea, more at other surfaces within the eye, and of the remainder much passes through the retina without being absorbed. It is indeed remarkable that the retinal receptors should be so inefficient at trapping light ; in life the retina is a semi-transparent structure and the features

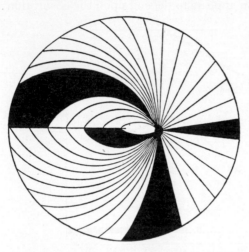

FIG. 9.3.—Diagrammatic representation of the projection of the nerve fibres of the right retina, showing four typical nerve fibre bundle defects. The arcuate scotoma show nasal steps. (Reproduced from Traquair, 1927)

of the various layers become apparent only upon treatment with histological stains or on examination by phase contrast microscopy. The relative transparency of the inner layers of the retina is essential, for otherwise the illumination of the receptors would be inadequate ; the light has to pass through the nervous elements of the retina before reaching the rods and cones.

The fibres of the optic nerve within the retina (Fig. 9.3) are un-myelinated and transparent ; on reaching the optic disc they gain myelin sheaths. Histological examination of the optic nerve reveals no unmyelinated axons but the diameter of the majority of the fibres is quite remarkably small—less than 2μ (Chacko, 1948). In keeping with the high spatial and low temporal resolving powers of the visual system (p. 320) the optic nerve is organised to provide a large number of independent 'channels' of information, but they conduct slowly. The slowness of conduction is one reason why it takes at least ¼ sec. to respond to a visual signal; much of the delay is, however, believed to be cortical.

In some otherwise normal people the fibres obtain their myelin sheaths whilst they are still in the retina and thus show as a white opacity spreading out from the normal limits of the blind spot. It is not surprising that defects in the visual fields are found that correspond to the position of the *opaque fibres*; these defects rarely give rise to much inconvenience.

Technically the relative transparency of the retina may be described by saying that the structure has low 'optical density' and it seems probable that of the 60 quanta referred to above as being necessary for the perception of a flash only about 6 are actually absorbed by the retina. Pirenne (1948) has given some statistical arguments in favour of the supposition that the 6 quanta are distributed over a corresponding number of receptors, and if this is so, it is clear that a flash may be perceived if 6 receptors become active at the same moment and that each is sensitive to only one quantum. It follows from this that excitation in a retinal receptor can probably be initiated by a change in one molecule only of the photo-sensitive substance (visual purple), for this is the most that can be accomplished by the energy represented by a single quantum. The retinal receptors appear to have reached a degree of sensitivity beyond which further improvement is physically impossible.

Although the receptors of the human retina themselves are extremely efficient detectors of light, the human eye taken as a whole is less sensitive than that of some other animals. The overall threshold of the eye of the cat has been measured by conditioned reflex techniques (Bridgman & Smith, 1942; Gunter, 1952) and is about ⅐ of the human value. This difference is due in part to the fact that the optical system of the cat's eye is more efficient at collecting light than is the human system and the cat has the additional advantage that behind the retina is placed a reflecting layer, or 'tapetum'. Tapetum is a Latin word that originally referred to a drapery or tapestry used for covering walls, floors, or couches. This reflecting surface ensures that light which has passed through the receptor layer on its way in is given another opportunity of being absorbed on its way out. The tapetum is responsible for the brilliant green reflection obtained from the eyes of a cat that is caught in the beam from the headlamps of a motor car.

The tapetum may not be an unmixed blessing, however, for there must inevitably be much more stray light in the eye of a cat than in that of a man. This reflecting surface is found in nocturnal animals and represents a development of the scotopic visual system at the expense of the perception of detail for there will be increased 'fogging' under photopic conditions. In the human eye the retina is backed with a pigment layer which must absorb much of the incident light. This backing varies greatly in different people, being much more prominent in negroes; it must be considered when evaluating the effects of glare, such as is caused by motor car headlights (Selling, 1939). Under normal conditions the

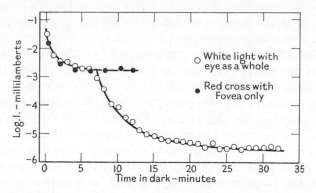

FIG. 9.4.—Changes in sensitivity of eye during dark adaptation. The changes with white light reveal the presence of a discontinuity that corresponds with the switch-over from photopic to scotopic visual systems. Red light on the contrary stimulates only the cones, and the increase in sensitivity that is shown is smaller and accomplished more rapidly. As red light does not affect the rods, the eye may be exposed to red light and then immediately be in its most sensitive state for other purposes. Radiologists often use red goggles for viewing X-ray films, for if they wish to enter the dark room they are already dark adapted (*vide* Miles, 1943). The range over which the sensitivity of the eye can be adjusted by the processes of dark adaptation is very great: 100,000-fold in this figure. (Reproduced from Fulton, 1946, after Murchison)

colour of the 'fundus oculi' is largely due to the pigment layer of the retina and the pigment in the choroid beyond. Careful measurement of the light reflected from the fundus oculi may, however, be used to study the changes in concentration of visual purple during dark adaptation (Weale, 1953 *c*).

It is easy to observe that the sensitivity of the eye during dark adaptation does not reach its optimum immediately, indeed the period involved may be greater than half an hour (*vide* Fig. 9.4). The gradual increase of sensitivity during this period is believed to be due to a regeneration of visual purple but attempts to explain the course of dark adaptation in mathematical terms [1] on this basis have not been entirely successful (*vide* Haig, 1941). In a very simple organism, the clam, that reacts to light by withdrawal of its siphon, Hecht (1919) was able to explain the changes during dark adaptation on the basis of the kinetics of a simple photo-chemical reaction. In the human retina dark adaptation is associated with an increase of the area over which effects summate (Craik & Vernon, 1941); this may be the functional counterpart of the greater convergence of the pathways for the rods (Polyak, 1941) as compared with those from the cones. Recent investigations (Arden & Weale, 1954) have shown that the changes in retinal sensitivity are much greater when 'large' (*e.g.* 1°) test spots are used than when the areas are small (*e.g.* 2·7′), and there are now grounds for believing, contrary to classical conceptions, that there is little to choose between the rods and the cones themselves as light detectors.

One striking change that occurs during dark adaptation concerns the relative sensitivity of the fovea and the surrounding parts of the retina. When light adapted the acuity of vision is greatest at the fovea, whilst after dark adaptation it is the surrounding ('parafoveal') regions that have the lowest threshold and which tend therefore to give the most information. Southall (1937) has pointed out that :—

'the disappearance and reappearance of objects as the eye turns past them and a curious lustre that pervades the brighter and more eccentric parts of the field invest vision on a dark evening with something unreal and ghostly; and doubtless the basis of reality of many weird tales of supernatural appearances in the dark—as, for instance, those "warlocks and witches in a dance" that so frightened Tam O'Shanter and his nag that stormy night as they rode past Kirk Alloway—is to be found in the simple fact, whether we are usually aware of it or not, that vision by night is not at all the same as vision by day'.

Additional evidence that the changes that occur during dark adaptation cannot be regarded as being a function solely of the receptors, without reference to the state of the nervous pathways, has been obtained by studying the relationships between the two eyes. Both Dunlap (1921) and Guildford (1927) showed that illumination of an area of the retina of one eye depressed the sensitivity of the corresponding region of the retina of the other eye. This interesting result was obtained using apparatus of ingenious

---

[1] Exposure of the eye to light that bleaches only 2 per cent of the visual purple may increase the visual threshold 50-fold.

simplicity. The changes that occur when the dark-adapted eye is exposed to light can take place much more rapidly than the changes in the reverse direction. The changes in the sensitivity that take place in one part of the retina when another region is exposed to light may be due to nervous interaction within the retina, or to glare : the diffusion of light in the eye (Schouten & Ornstein, 1939 ; Boynton, Bush & Enoch, 1954). Nervous factors may be responsible for the temporal summation of subliminal visual stimuli ; a brief flash which is not strong enough to reach threshold will summate with another similar flash if this arrives within $\frac{1}{10}$ sec. of the first (Granit & Davis, 1931).

CONTROL OF PUPIL SIZE

As has already been seen, the sensitivity of the retina is adjusted according to the degree of illumination falling on it. The range over which the retinal sensitivity may change is very large, a figure commonly quoted being 100,000 times. The sensitivity of the eye can also be changed by alterations in the diameter of the pupil ; it is probable that differences in sensitivity of up to perhaps 16 times can be accomplished in this way. The effects of pupillary changes, therefore, although much less than the effects of readjustments in the retina, are nevertheless sizeable ; they gain in significance when the speed with which they can be accomplished is considered. Observations have been made upon the size of the pupil during dark adaptation by an ingenious technique, using infra-red light to photograph the eye. In the rabbit the pupil dilates to half its maximal size in the first 20 seconds (Gullberg, Olmsted & Wagman, 1938) ; in man the pupillary changes may occasionally be complicated by a sharp constriction after being in the dark for about 5 minutes (Crawford, 1937).

Both rods and cones are involved in regulating the size of the pupil ; with dim illumination the energy needed to cause a given degree of pupillary constriction varies with the wavelength of the light in a way that corresponds with the sensitivity of the scotopic system (Wagman & Gullberg, 1942).

The pupillary reflex is dependent upon fibres that pass to the midbrain and probably end in the pretectal region lying just in front of the superior colliculus. The impulses from one eye affect not only the pupil of that eye, but also the pupil on the other side. The light reflex has therefore two components : 'direct' and 'consensual'.

The sympathetic system also plays a rôle in regulating the size of the pupil, and when the cervical chain is destroyed (Horner's syndrome, p. 447, Fig. 12.5) one of the symptoms is pupillo-constriction. When the third cranial nerve is severed the light reflex is unobtainable. Nevertheless, it has been claimed that the sympathetic system does play a rôle in the later stages of pupillary reaction (*vide* Lowenstein & Lowenfeld, 1950).

The constriction of the pupil in response to light is an example of a regulatory system and is a clear expression of a system employing negative feedback (p. 116). It is a characteristic of such devices that they have a tendency to oscillate under certain circumstances, and the pupillary regulatory system is no exception. If light is shone onto the edge of the pupil in a slit-like beam, it is clear that a given movement of the pupil will cause a greater change in the illumination than is customary and for which, so to speak, the regulatory system was 'built' (Campbell & White-side, 1950). When the light is applied the pupil contracts excessively, overshooting and cutting off the light. The constriction is followed by dilatation and a regular series of oscillations may result that are clearly visible to the naked eye ; these changes are referred to as 'hippus'. Even under normal conditions the pupil is never absolutely still and if it is observed with a magnifying glass it can be seen to be constantly executing small irregular movements. The loss of this 'pupillary unrest' is always pathological and may be one of the earliest signs of interference with the visual pathways.

When a subject looks at an object that is close to him he not only converges his eyes and accommodates his lens but, in addition, there is a constriction of the pupils. This pupillo-constriction increases the 'depth of focus' of the eye just as the use of a smaller aperture achieves the same end in the case of a camera. The change in the diameter of the pupil on changing the point of fixation is known as the 'reaction to convergence' and is a useful clinical test. [The pupillary changes appear to depend upon convergence of the visual axes rather than upon the state of accommodation of the lens (Renard & Massonnet-Naux, 1951).]

In syphilis of the central nervous system great diagnostic im-portance attaches to the recognition of a pupil that will not react by constricting when light is shone on the eye, but does change when the eyes are converged. This condition, the '*Argyll Robert-son pupil*', may be due, as Ingvar (1928 c) suggested, to the pupillo-constrictor fibres of the optic tract being particularly susceptible to damage. Another explanation is that there are two efferent pathways to the pupil, one concerned with reactions to light, the other with reactions associated with convergence. Removal of the ciliary ganglion has been reported to give rise to a pupil that does not react to light or darkness but does still react to convergence, and similar changes may be caused by injuries to the orbit (Nathan & Turner, 1942). It is difficult to decide which is the more satisfactory explanation of the Argyll Robertson pupil, but whatever explanation is finally adopted must take into consideration the facts that these pathological pupils are small in size and irregular in shape. It is not clear whether these changes are the direct result of ocular disease or whether they follow from the alterations in the behaviour of the iris.

A variety of disorders of the pupillary mechanism occur in otherwise healthy people and are grouped together as the 'Holmes-Adie' syndrome (p. 122); one characteristic feature of this condition is the slowness of the relaxation that the pupil shows after a period of constriction. In addition to this 'myotonic' pupillary phenomenon, these patients may have difficulty in adjusting the accommodation of the affected eye and, in association with this, they sometimes complain of headaches. For reasons that are quite unknown, it may be impossible to elicit the knee jerks from these people (Graveson, 1949).

COLOUR VISION

Many naturally occurring substances do not reflect, or transmit all of the wavelengths to which the eye is sensitive, to the same degree; they are therefore coloured. The properties of a coloured material are most satisfactorily described by means of a curve showing the proportion of light at different wavelengths that is transmitted or reflected. These spectral characteristics are determined in the laboratory by means of an instrument known as a spectro-photometer. To construct a satisfactory curve, it is necessary to make measurements at a number of different wavelengths and, in principle, a full description of the colour of an object would be obtained only by using an infinite variety of strictly monochromatic sources of light. The visual apparatus of many animals appears to be unable to distinguish in any way between the different wavelengths of the spectrum. The human eye appears to make use of a system of coding for colours which is simple and which yields a great deal of information.

The data that are of the greatest importance in understanding the mechanism of colour vision have been obtained in experiments in which observers have matched colours by *mixing light* obtained from different parts of the spectrum. It has been found that any part of the spectrum may be matched by adjusting the intensities of three coloured sources of illumination provided that these three sources are obtained from suitable regions of the spectrum. These facts have led to the conclusion that there must be three independent colour receptive mechanisms in the visual system, and of necessity in the receptors.

Some colours that are not found in the spectrum, such as brown and olive-green, cannot be produced in this way by the mixture of three spectral lights. The colour mixture experiments that have been referred to do not exclude the possibility that more than three types of colour mechanism are used by the eye, although they certainly suggest that under many circumstances any additional systems are of subsidiary importance.

That the same colour sensation may result from mixtures of light having totally different compositions is an expression of the ambiguity that arises in a system such as the eye that does not attempt to deal with the spectrum in the way that a spectro-photo-meter does (p. 298) but relies upon a simple system of coding. It is for these reasons that the medical student must learn to use a spectroscope when examining biological liquids, such as urine, for unidentified pigments. Coloured substances having quite different chemical compositions may appear similar to the unaided eye, but the use of a spectroscope will enable it to be established that the light involved has perhaps a very different spectral composition.

The view that sensations of colour are built up from the messages received from three types of cone is known as the trichromatic theory, and its foundations were laid by Thomas Young and Hermann von Helmholtz. These two men were scientists of dazzling brilliance; in their youth they received medical educations and their lives should be an inspiration to all interested in furthering medical science.

The substances which, it must be supposed, are associated with the cones and which are responsible for the way in which they respond to light of different wavelengths have not been isolated. There are, however, reasons for supposing that each of the three types of cone can respond to a wide region of the spectrum (Fig. 9.5). In this way monochromatic light may affect all three categories of receptor; this may help to explain why the acuity of vision in coloured light is as good, or nearly as good, as that in white light (cf. Hartridge, 1950). White light may be expected to stimulate the three types of cone to different degrees and any combination of coloured lights that also stimulates the three categories of receptors to corresponding degrees will also give rise to the sensation of white. Pairs of colours that behave in this way are known as *complementary*.

Additional evidence favouring the trichromatic theory has been obtained by Stiles (1939); his experiments are of outstanding interest for they provide evidence of three main types of colour mechanism obtained by a method quite different from the colour mixing experiments. He arranged to superimpose a coloured test flash of 1° diameter onto a field of

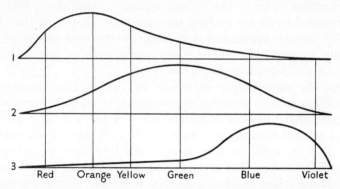

FIG. 9.5.—Trichromatic theory of colour vision. Each type of cone, it is supposed, is sensitive over a wide region of the spectrum—to some extent over the whole spectrum. Any light must, of necessity, stimulate more than one colour pathway. The colour sensation that would be aroused if, by artificial means, one of the three pathways alone could be stimulated is not known. These curves are entirely hypothetical but help to explain many facts of colour vision. The cones preferentially sensitive to the red end of the spectrum may have a secondary region of enhanced sensitivity at the blue end of the spectrum. The matching of one colour by a mixture of three primaries gives satisfaction as to hue, but the synthesised colour is often paler (less 'saturated') than the original; this pallor is explicable in terms of these response curves, for the spectral primaries will each stimulate all three mechanisms and inevitably the mixture will appear somewhat white

10° that was uniformly illuminated. The intensity of the test flash when this was just detectable was measured under a variety of conditions. Depending upon the wavelengths of the background illumination and of the test patch, so, close to threshold, only one of the colour mechanisms came into play at a time.

Colour vision is present in primates (*vide* de Haan, 1925), but perhaps not in the other mammalian orders. It is, however, found in fish, reptiles and birds as well as in insects and may have evolved independently in different divisions of the animal kingdom (*vide* Walls, 1942). Although there appear to be only three main colour mechanisms in man, the number of hues that can be distinguished has been estimated at 165 ; this considerable number indicates that the colour receptors are capable of being excited to different degrees. The mechanisms clearly do more than respond to a fixed extent when certain properties of the illumination rise above a critical value. Only a few of the main categories of subjective colour have names and it is pointless to argue as to whether there are, for instance, seven 'colours' when the number of distinguishable hues is so much greater. The artist presumably can make better use of the potentialities of his colour mechanisms than can the untrained observer.

At some point in the optic pathways hue must be evaluated, but the site at which this is performed is not definitely known. It has been shown, however, that at the lateral geniculate body there are present six layers which *might* correspond to the three systems from the two eyes (Clark, 1942 and 1949 ; cf. Walls, 1953). It is probable that the separate identity of the colour pathways is preserved as far as the cerebral cortex, for if hue as such was evaluated at a lower level there might be a need to increase the number of fibres in the visual pathways by 165-fold, corresponding to the number of distinguishable colour sensations. Further evidence pointing in the same direction comes from considering the facts of binocular colour mixture. Although this subject is not without controversy, there is no doubt that the colour of an image in one eye may profoundly influence the colour of another image of similar form but different hue presented to the other eye (Hurvich & Jameson, 1951).

At the level of the lateral geniculate bodies the pathways from the two eyes come together but have no opportunities for inter-action (p. 345). From the lateral geniculate body the fibres forming the optic radiations sweep into the medial surface of the occipital lobe. Those fibres concerned with the upper half of the retina, and therefore responsible for vision in the lower half of the visual field, proceed backwards to the cortex by a fairly direct route. On the other hand, the fibres which are concerned with the lower half of the retina and therefore convey information concerning the upper half of the visual field, travel by a more complicated pathway looping forwards around the ventricular system of the brain before travelling backwards to their destination (Fig. 9.6). This pathway, forwards and then backwards, carries these fibres through the white matter of the temporal lobes and is referred to as Meyer's loop (cf. Spalding, 1952 a). The types of visual field defect which arise with lesions at various points along the visual pathways are of great diagnostic importance, but will not be discussed further here since they are more properly dealt with in textbooks of anatomy and neurology.

It is, however, appropriate to consider something of the technique for *testing the visual fields*. The peripheral extent of the fields is most conveniently investigated by an instrument known as a perimeter. Small test objects are brought in from the periphery of the visual field until the subject can just see them. Throughout the test the subject should fixate a small spot at the centre of the instrument, and the examiner

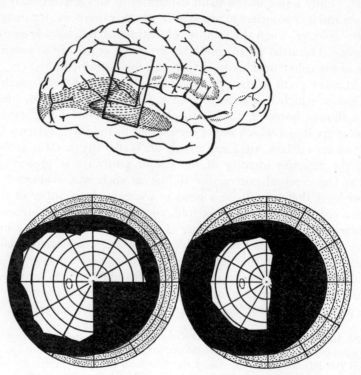

FIG. 9.6.—Effects on visual fields of two successive surgical resections involving increasing amounts of visual radiations. In upper diagram note relationship of radiations to ventricular system. Small and large rectangles indicate limits of first and second resections. First resection produced a quadrantic defect : note characteristic, although not invariable (Spalding, 1942 *a*) lower border. Extension of incision produced hemianopia. (From Fox & German, re-drawn as in Fulton, 1946)

observes during the test whether or not fixation is well maintained. In addition to white test objects, it is current clinical practice to employ also small coloured test papers ; it has been said that field defects may occasionally be found in this way that would otherwise be missed, but the question needs critical re-examination. In this sort of test there is commonly a zone in which objects may be seen but their colours cannot be recognised ('achromatic interval'). The position at which any given colour can first be perceived depends upon the intensity with which the coloured test object is illuminated. The size of the peripheral visual field mapped in this way has, therefore, no absolute significance, but the procedure may be of use in comparing patients with normal subjects.

The extent to which defects in the visual fields are detected in neurological patients does depend to a great extent upon the methods and care used in the examination. Small white test objects may show up defects that would not be apparent with larger ones. In addition some patients show an *attention defect* for one-half of the visual field. Although they may be able to identify normally objects on either nasal or temporal sides of the macula, when tested separately, they may fail if two objects are simultaneously presented, neglecting one-half of their visual field.

Colour vision is, as has been noted above, poor in the periphery and it is dichromatic, any spectral colour being matched by a mixture of two monochromatic lights. Blue can be appreciated even in the extreme periphery (Weale, 1953 *a*). One further anomaly of peripheral vision may be mentioned : during dark adaptation there is no shift in the sensitivity of the eye to shorter wavelengths (p. 290), but there is a small change in the opposite direction.

For testing for the presence of blind spots ('scotomata') towards the centre of the visual field the neurologist makes use of a *Bjerrum screen*, which consists of a vertical board covered with black cloth. The patient sits two metres from this board and fixates a small mark upon its surface. The examiner is clad in a black gown with black gloves to make himself inconspicuous and moves fine objects within the central region of the patient's visual field. One blind spot is always found and corresponds to the optic nerve head. As in perimetry, coloured test objects may be employed and the extent of the blind spot, or of a scotoma that is revealed, depends in part upon the nature of the stimulus that is used for mapping. In some animals the blind spot must be almost insignificant. In the mouse, for instance, the optic nerve is excessively fine, a fact related no doubt to the paucity of cones in the retina ; many rods commonly converge onto a single optic nerve fibre. The human blind spot is surprisingly large, however ; Helmholtz (1924) calculated that 11 full moons side by side can vanish in the blind spot, as may a human face at a distance of six feet.

COLOUR BLINDNESS (*vide* Wright, 1946)

Interesting defects of colour vision occur in otherwise entirely normal people, and the mechanism of these divergences have long intrigued scientists. John Dalton, the chemist, suffered from a defect of this type in which he had difficulty in detecting the presence of pink. Three incidents have been reported that show the sort of difficulty that may arise with this type of disturbance. On one occasion Dalton—

'presented his mother with a pair of stockings; she admired their texture but since their colour was vivid red they were quite unsuitable for attendance at the Quaker meeting. When preparing for his journey to Paris, Dalton selected what he took to be a drab material for a new suit only to be informed by his tailor that it was scarlet material intended for huntsmen's coats. It is also on record that the scarlet robe at the Oxford graduation ceremony did not conflict with his Quaker ideas as it appeared to him to be the colour of green leaves' (Barnes, 1944).

Another early report concerned a shoemaker investigated by J. Priestley in America. As a child this man had noted that other children could discern cherries 'by some pretended difference of colour'; they could see 'cherries at a greater distance than he, although he could see other objects at as great a distance as they, when the sight was not affected by the colour' (Houston, 1932).

Cases such as these may be caused by a loss of the normal red receptors, and this is demonstrated by the shortening of the long wavelength end of the spectrum in such subjects. The loss of the red, or first type, receptor is named *protanopia* (Greek *protos* = first). As was shown by Clerk Maxwell, the nineteenth-century physicist, subjects of this type are able to match any spectral colour by a mixture of not three, but only two, primaries. If a 'protanope' looks at a red and a green light through a red piece of glass, he notices, as does a normal subject, that the green appears darker whilst the red is but little changed, whilst if a green glass is used, the green light is unchanged, whilst the red light is fainter: 'In this way', Maxwell says, 'I have made colour-blind people distinguish the colours of a Turkey carpet'. If, therefore, he suggests, such a person had the courage to wear a pair of spectacles with one lens red and the other green, he might, in the course of time, come to form a judgement of red and green things intuitively.

In another type of colour blindness spectral colours may again be matched by a mixture of only two primary sources, but unlike the condition described above, the spectral sensitivity is normal even at the red end. It was first believed that this condition was due to an absence of the normal second category of receptors, those especially sensitive to green light; the condition was therefore called *deuteranopia* (Greek *deuteros* = second). It is now considered more likely that this defect arises because the pathways of the first and second categories (red and green) have fused together. A related but much rarer defect, *cone monochromatism* (Weale, 1953 *b*), shows its presence by complete colour blindness in the presence of good visual acuity. It seems that in this condition all three colour pathways have fused together. This fusion does not appear to occur in the retina for chromatic aberration; the production of coloured fringes around visual images may stimulate accommodation in a normal manner (Fincham, 1953). The midbrain in these subjects is presumably receiving information about colour which is not available to, or not utilised by, the cerebral cortex.

In *tritanopia* (Greek *tritos* = third) the sensitivity to blue light is reduced, presumably because of the absence of the third, blue sensitive, type of receptor. It is interesting to note that even normal subjects become tritanopic if the field of vision with which they are concerned is sufficiently small, at least if it falls on the fovea. It seems, therefore, that normally the blue receptors can summate their effects over a wider area of the retina than can the other types of cone. Occasionally some degree of tritanopia may be caused, not by any defect of the retina or visual pathways, but by yellowing of the ocular media as may occur in old age.

FIG. 9.7.—Benham's top. When rotated the black arcs change into coloured rings. This effect may be seen even when monochromatic light, as provided by a sodium lamp, is used; this fact is in keeping with the belief (Fig. 9.5) that even monochromatic light stimulates more than one of the colour pathways. The colours that are seen presumably depend upon the different colour pathways having different 'time constants'

Experimentally the drug santonin, which has long been used for the eradication of intestinal parasites, may cause a shortening of the blue end of the spectrum, a condition clearly allied to tritanopia. Under the action of this drug, bright objects appear a green-yellow colour whilst dark objects appear to be covered with violet (Helmholtz, 1924). Exposure of the eye to a bright coloured light also alters its colour sensitivity (Burch, 1898; Lythgoe, 1926), and may give rise to a condition which is temporary and which resembles one of the varieties of naturally occurring colour blindness. Thus exposure of the eye to a bright violet light makes the eye insensitive to the shorter wavelengths of the spectrum, a condition similar to tritanopia (Brindley, 1953).

In addition to the forms of colour defect in which only two colours are needed to match spectral hues, another class of colour

X

deficiency is known and is referred to as *anomalous trichromatism*. These subjects require, as the name suggests, three stimuli to make colour matches, but the proportions that they use differ from normal subjects. This type of disorder falls between normality and dichromatism in which two stimuli only are needed (protanopia or deuteranopia) : there seems to be no sharp dividing line between normal subjects and the colour blind (Nelson, 1938).

Electro-physiological techniques can scarcely be expected to give unequivocal evidence as to the mechanism of human colour vision unless they are applied to an animal with similar colour apparatus, a stringent requirement that has not clearly been met in any of the studies yet undertaken (cf. Granit, 1947). The trichromatic theory has never therefore been formulated in terms of present-day knowledge of the nature of nervous messages ; to state that the hue that is perceived depends on the proportional excitation of three separate pathways is inevitably loose. As has been seen, the area over which different colours may summate may differ (p. 305) ; furthermore, the temporal aspect must be taken into account. When the hue mechanism evaluates the intensity with which a given colour pathway has been excited, how long an interval of time is considered ? The colours that are seen when Benham's top is spun (Fig. 9.7) suggest that the times involved are different for the different colour mechanisms (*vide* Fry, 1933).

ELECTRO-RETINOGRAM AND RESTING OCULAR POTENTIAL

Of the events that lead up to excitation of the ganglion cells, and of the processes performed by the bipolar cells of the retina, there is little direct information. We know more of the overall performance of the retina than the way in which its accomplishments are achieved. It is possible that the receptor cells, rods and cones, induce activity in the nervous structures by generating slow electrical potentials ; such a procedure would be homologous with the generator potential systems found in some other sensory systems (p. 53).

It has long been known that slow potential swings, constituting the 'electro-retinogram', may be recorded from the eyes of both vertebrate and invertebrates in response to illumination (*vide* Granit, 1947). In the mammal there is evidence that these electrical changes are due to the activity of the bipolar cells, or of the receptors, or both, for it has been shown that the changes are still present and normal after section of the optic nerve, a procedure that induces a retrograde degeneration of the ganglion cell layer (Thompson, 1951). Evidence that is of a complementary nature has been obtained by the use of micro-electrodes inserted into the retina; it has been shown that part, at least, of the electro-retinogram arises in the receptor layers (Tomita & Funaishi, 1952 ; Ottosen & Svaetichin, 1953). The eye of the water-beetle, too, gives rise to slow changes of electrical potential on illumina-tion, and these changes also arise in the receptor layer (Bernhard, 1942).

The electro-retinogram (Fig. 9.8) consists of a sequence of fluctuations which classically show three peaks on illumination. The first or 'a' wave represents a change in which the front of the eye becomes negative with respect to the back, whilst the second and third ('b' and 'c') waves both have the opposite polarity. When the light is switched off another positive peak, the 'd' wave, may be seen. Of these changes the 'b' wave is usually the most prominent, whilst there is some doubt as to the extent to which the 'c' wave is generated by the retina

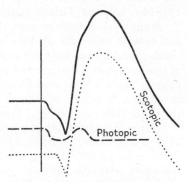

FIG. 9.8.—Analysis of electro-retino-gram of dark-adapted human eye into 'photopic' and 'scotopic' components. The small down-ward defections represent the 'a' wave, the upward excursions the 'b' wave. (From Armington, Johnson & Riggs, 1952)

and to what extent it is a muscular potential produced by the iris as it contracts. These waves may be further subdivided, for careful recording reveals that they are notched (Armington, Johnson & Riggs, 1952 ; Cobb & Morton, 1952).

Since the time of Einthoven & Jolly (1908) attempts have been made to analyse the electro-retinogram into a number of components of more simple form. The best known of these analyses is that of Granit (1947) and it was based on the changes that the electro-retinogram underwent when the retina was treated by different drugs (*vide* Therman, 1938). It is worth considering the grounds upon which any analysis of a complex curve of physiological origin may be based. It is clear that although any analysis must satisfy the mathematical criterion, that on recombination of the components the original form is reproduced, it is fallacious to assume that the components have physiological significance merely be-cause the mathematic demands are fulfilled. It is clear that independent evidence, preferably from more than one line of investigation, is needed before it can be assumed that the components of any analysis may be regarded as having biological importance. The use of drugs to analyse the electro-retinogram may be a powerful tool, but it is necessary to make sure that the responses that are recorded under the influence of pharmacological agents really do represent physiological components of the normal response and that these components have not themselves been disturbed. In certain respects, therefore, some of the analyses of the electro-retinogram that have been proposed are not entirely convincing (see, however, Granit, 1955).

Some workers have attempted to ascertain to what extent the scotopic, and to what extent the photopic system contributes to the human electro-retinogram (Adrian, 1945 and 1946 a; Armington, Johnson & Riggs, 1952). It has been shown that most of the waveform, and particularly the prominent 'b' wave is generated by the scotopic system (Fig. 9.9), a fact which is not entirely surprising since the rods are so much more numerous than the cones (Johnson & Riggs, 1951).

Karpe (1945) has investigated the electro-retinogram in a number of clinical conditions. A normal curve was obtained in 5 cases of glaucoma with optic atrophy giving a large peripheral loss of vision. Normal responses were also obtained from a case in which there was a loss of vision, without structural damage, in a squinting eye. In keeping with the origin of the greater part of the waves from the scotopic rather than the photopic system, Karpe found that the electro-retinogram was unobtainable in retinitis pigmentosa and hereditary night blindness whilst it was normal in diseases restricted to the region of the fovea. The presence of a foreign body composed of iron in the eye may damage the peripheral parts of the retina, a condition known as siderosis. In the early stages of this disease, before clinical manifestation become apparent, the electro-retinogram may be of enhanced amplitude, a fact that is said to be of some diagnostic importance.

The electro-retinogram may have some relationship to a curious appearance referred to as the 'blue arc' phenomenon. If an observer in a dark room allows a spot of light to fall on the retina, to the temporal side of the fovea he sees two horizontal blue arcs. These sensations are transient, fading in a second or so, and it has been suggested that they are the result of an excitation of the retina by the nervous discharges passing in the nerve fibre layer (Ellis, 1928).

In observations upon the electro-retinogram it is usual to employ electrical recording methods that respond to changes of potential rather than to steadily maintained differences. The fluctuations that have been described have been recorded, therefore, under conditions in which standing differences of potential have been cancelled out. There is indeed a large steady potential difference (*e.g.* 1 m.v.) between the front and the back of the eye, the cornea being positive with respect to the back of the globe (Fig. 9.9). This 'resting ocular' potential is believed to be dependent upon the integrity of the retina (Mowrer, Ruch & Miller, 1936); it appears to be generated at the junction between the choroid and the retina

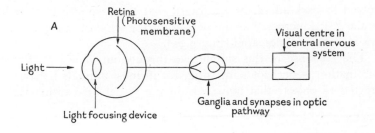

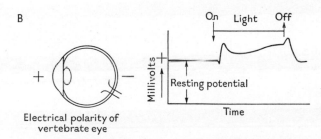

FIG. 9.9.—Resting ocular potential and electro-retinogram of vertebrate (Prosser, 1950)

(Noell, 1952). Records of this potential have been used to obtain an indication of the movements of the eyes, a method that has the advantage of simplicity if not of sensitivity (cf. Carmichael & Dearbourn, 1947; Marg, 1951). The resting potential, as such, does not appear to have been systematically investigated at a clinical level, although its existence has been known since 1849 (*vide* Bounds, 1953).

NERVOUS DISCHARGES INITIATED BY THE RETINA

Studies of the activity of single units in the optic system of a number of animals have now been reported and have provided a great deal of evidence that bears on the interpretation of visual form and movement. The simplest type of eye consists of a layer of receptor cells that themselves give rise to the axones constituting the optic nerve. Such an eye is found in the king crab (Limulus) and has been studied by Hartline (1941).[1] The units that he investigated were all found to have similar properties; a sequence of impulses was discharged in response to illumination and this train of action potentials continued with but little decrease of frequency throughout the period of stimulation (Fig. 9.10). If the eye was allowed to dark adapt, it was found that the response to a flash of standard size increased as the period during which the eye had been kept in darkness increased (Fig. 9.11).

The response of this simple eye throughout a period of steady illumination is perhaps surprising, for in most animals behaviour is directed to objects that move within the visual field rather than to

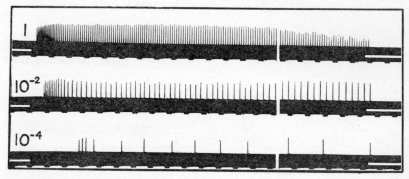

FIG. 9.10.—Discharge of very simple retina. King crab retina consists of receptor cells that give rise directly to optic nerve fibres. Record shows continued discharge in relation to illumination at three different intensities; relative values are shown on left of figure. Time tracing intervals: $\frac{1}{5}$ sec. (Reproduced from Hartline, 1941)

those that are stationary. Possibly, in the central nervous system of this creature neurones would be found that responded to a change, rather than to a steady level of illumination, for such information could rather easily be obtained from the optic nerve discharge.

The importance of movement in the visual field has been stressed by many observers. Herbert Spencer (1900, p. 380), the philosopher, wrote that :

'On following through ascending grades of creatures, the genesis of that vast structure of knowledge acquired by sight, we see that in the

[1] Later studies, reviewed by Hartline, Wagner & MacNichol (1952), have shown that the eye of Limulus is less simple than this statement would imply. and inhibition can be demonstrated between the effects of neighbouring ommatidia. The eye is nevertheless much simpler than that of a vertebrate.

first stage, where eye-specks suffice only for discriminating light from darkness, there can be no classifications of objects seen, save those based on the manner in which light is obstructed. . . . By such undeveloped visual organs, the shadows perceived would be merely distinguished into those of the stationary objects which the creature passed during its own movements, and those of the moving objects which came near while it was at rest; so that the extremely general classification of visible things into stationary and moving, would be the earliest formed.'

Considerable modifications in the nature of the nervous discharges seem to be introduced by the connections within the vertebrate retina itself (Fig. 9.12). There is a great deal of convergence, for whilst there are 6 million cones and 110 million rods in the human retina, the optic nerve possesses only one million nerve fibres (Lythgoe, 1938; Bruesch & Arey, 1942). Since some of the cones possess a pathway to the optic nerve which is dis-

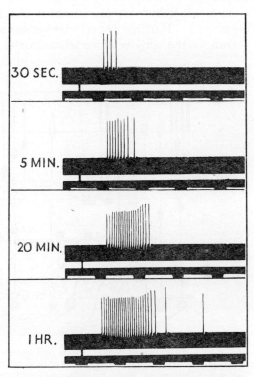

FIG. 9.11.—Effect of dark adaptation upon discharge of single visual cell. King crab eye, discharge recorded from single fibre in optic nerve. (Reproduced from Hartline, 1941)

tinct from other elements (Polyak, 1941), it is clear that many rods (*e.g.* 400) must connect, as a rule, with a single nerve fibre. In a sense, therefore, the optic nerve is a *bottle neck* for the transmission of visual information (Fig. 9.13); it is certain that many of the features of visual image must be lost before it reaches the visual cortex. We must assume that the function of the retina is to mitigate the loss of information as far as possible by coding the data derived from relatively numerous receptors for transmission along relatively few nerve fibres: the retina will tend to pick out

those features most likely to be of biological significance whilst
rejecting others.

The investigation of the discharge of the ganglion cell layer of
the retina and of the optic nerve fibres has shown that there are
in the optic nerve of vertebrates fibres that behave in different
ways when light is shone on a part of the retina to which they are
connected. Hartline (1941) has remarked that 'the most striking
feature of the activity of vertebrate optic nerve fibres wherein they

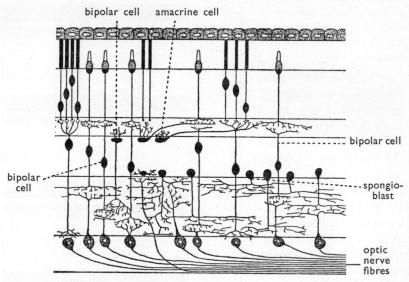

FIG. 9.12.—Structure of retina. Rods and cones are shown making contact with
bipolar cells which in turn connect with ganglion cells. Horizontal connections
across retina are made by amacrine cells; these connections are probable
anatomical basis, in part at least, of interactions that can be demonstrated
between different areas of retina. Disease processes may damage some
elements of the retina selectively; thus in juvenile amaurotic idiocy the brunt
of the damage falls upon the rods and cones (Greenfield & Holmes, 1925).
(Reproduced from Starling, 1941)

differ from simple sensory discharges is the wide diversity of the
responses of different fibres'. The investigation of the retina of
the frog has shown that some of the optic nerve fibres respond
with a burst of impulses when light is switched on, whilst other
fibres respond when the light is switched off. Another set of fibres
may be found that discharge both when the light is switched on
and when it is switched off, although there is no steady discharge
during prolonged illumination, or in darkness.

The retina of the vertebrate, of which the frog has been taken as an example, is therefore sensitive to fluctuations in the illumination rather than to steadily maintained levels, or maintained differences in the degree of illumination of different regions. In front of the photo-sensitive surface lie the blood vessels that radiate from, and towards, the blind spot ;

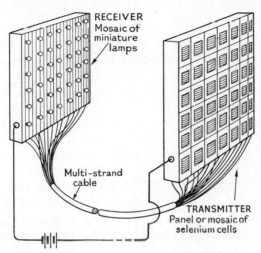

FIG. 9.13.—Attempts to see analogies between the visual system and television must bear in mind that television uses one 'high information' channel, whilst the visual system makes use of hundreds of thousands of 'low information' channels, optic nerve fibres. The engineer avoids a multiplicity of connections ; this type of system designed by Carley in the second half of the nineteenth century proved impracticable. With a million elements it might be possible to transmit a monochrome picture somewhat better than that provided by the current service ; the definition that would be obtained and the absence of colour would compare very poorly with the 'signal' that the visual centres in the brain receive. There are probably about a million nerve fibres in the human optic nerve, and the high level of acuity that is achieved, at least for the centre of the visual field, points to the advantages in having stationed close to the receptor cells a nervous network that can sift the information before it is transmitted backwards to the brain (cf. Thomson, 1953). It may be assumed that by picking out features, such as movement, most likely to be of biological significance, the fibres that are available in the optic pathways are used to greater advantage than might otherwise be the case. (From *Practical Television*, May 1951)

these vessels necessarily cast their shadows on the retina itself. Under normal conditions no trace of these shadows is perceived, presumably because they do not move but are cast fixedly upon the same regions of the retina.[1] If, however, the bulb of a small flashlamp is pressed close to

[1] By way of comparison the 'echo cancellation' employed by radar engineers may be mentioned. By additional circuits they rid the screen of unwanted, permanent, images such as those of mountains and thereby enhance the sensitivity of the system.

the lids of the eyes the observer may catch a momentary glimpse of tree-like branching vessels similar to the patterns seen on examination of an eye with an ophthalmoscope. If the bulb of the lamp is moved to and fro over the lid these images may be seen, moving in the opposite direction, for as long as the motion is continued. These appearances, *Purkinje's images*, are evidently due to the shadows of the blood vessels falling upon fresh parts of the retina.

A retina composed of a mosaic of receptive areas each of which is sensitive only to changes in its lighting would show the phenomenon of *successive contrast*. It has long been known that a white surface will appear whiter if it is looked at immediately after viewing a dark surface than after looking at one that is white or grey. The results of Hartline, that have been discussed, help to understand these phenomena, long considered the domain of the psychologist. Some of the remarkable illusions that may be seen on looking at striped patterns (cf. Erb & Dallenbach, 1939) may arise similarly, for as the eyes jump from one fixation point to another the images will be cast in different ways upon the retina. Enhanced brightness would be expected if as a result of changed fixation the images of a set of white stripes fell over regions that had hitherto been covered by the dark zones.

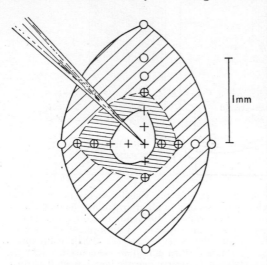

Fig. 9.14.—Receptive field of single fibre of frog's retina showing beam of light impinging on central zone. From this central region 'on' discharges were obtained, from the periphery 'off' discharges, whilst in the intermediate zone the response was of the 'on/off' type as shown in Fig. 9.15 c. (From Kuffler, 1952)

Further study of the responses of vertebrate optic nerve fibres has shown that the way in which they respond is not fixed but varies according to the conditions at the time of the observations. The classification of fibres according to whether they respond to a light stimulus at 'on', at 'off' or at 'on and off' is evidently not rigid ; if, for instance, the background level of illumination is altered, a fibre that responded in one way may change its behaviour and fall into one of the other two categories. Most interesting has been the finding that the responses may vary according to whether the illumination is restricted to the centre, or to the periphery of the receptive field (Fig. 9.14). Thus a fibre may respond at 'on' when a spot of light is thrown on the centre of the field, whilst it may discharge at 'off' when the periphery is illuminated (Fig. 9.15). It has been found that the illumination of 'on' areas may suppress the discharge from 'off' areas, and vice versa. Under natural conditions the discharges into the optic nerve fibres will represent a summation of effects resulting from the excitation of the various pathways leading to the ganglion cell (Kuffler, 1953).

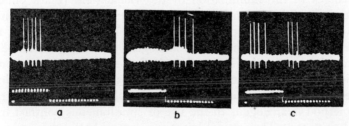

FIG. 9.15.—Change in response on illuminating different parts of the receptive field of retinal ganglion cell. Stimulus applied close to recording electrode : discharge when light switched on (a) ; periphery of area stimulated : discharge when light switched off (b). If, however, light is thrown on an intermediate part of field there is a discharge at both 'on' and at 'off' (c). See Fig. 9.14. (Reproduced from Kuffler, 1953)

These results, showing an antagonism between neighbouring regions, help in the understanding of another series of effects hitherto sometimes being regarded as being dependent upon the 'higher centres' and out of reach of physiological analysis. It is a matter of simple observation that a white surface appears whiter if it is surrounded by a dark field rather than by a grey field. Similarly a dark field appears blacker when surrounded by white rather than by grey ; it has indeed been said that black is only perceived by contrast with white. It is certainly true that total darkness does not give rise to the sensation of black but only to grey, for the observer is aware of a diffuse luminosity, the *idio-retinal light*. This sensation may be related to spontaneous discharges arising in the retina (Barlow, Fitzhugh & Kuffler, 1954). The influence of one part of the visual field upon the sensation aroused elsewhere is known as *simultaneous contrast*, and it is of interest that Asher (1950), by an ingenious series of experiments on man, has arrived at the conclusion that simultaneous contrast is retinal in origin.

The eye has obvious similarities to a camera and these resemblances have long been discussed and have a certain value. With the advent of television some scientists have been led to believe that useful analogies could be drawn between this technique and the visual system. Great caution is needed in making such comparisons (Walsh, 1952), for whilst the engineer transmits all the detail of a picture along a single channel, the visual system splits the information between a large number of different fibres. It is of interest, however, to note that some recent experimental television techniques have employed a method which depends only upon the transmission of changes in the illumination of the visual field (Plate 5). The advantage of this system is that very much less need be transmitted for, under most conditions, much of the image is unchanged from frame to frame : this method is analogous to the use of successive contrast in the visual system. In another experimental method the television signal that is transmitted depends upon differences in the degree of illumination of adjacent parts of the picture (Plate 6) ; this method is analogous to the use of simultaneous contrast in the visual system. The retinal apparatus uses both successive and simultaneous contrast ; it responds to moving contours (p. 311).

Simultaneous and successive contrast mechanisms play a rôle also in the perception of colour. As is well known, a colour is heightened by the close juxtaposition in the visual field of a complementary hue. Successive contrast is seen in the phenomena of after-images. After observing fixedly a coloured object it is found that white appears to be tinged with the complementary colour, a 'negative' after-image. Experiments with rotating discs have shown, strangely enough, that 'it is possible to arrange conditions so that the original stimulus never reaches consciousness, although it is constantly operating to maintain the after-image in the field of conscious perception. Thus, a red circle will appear green to the observer who is unable to see the original colour at any time' (Lehman, 1950).

It has become apparent that the retina performs quite complex transformations of the information with which it deals. It has long been known that a faint light is perceived more readily if the area concerned is large than if it is small, and studies of visual threshold in man have shown that within certain limits the product of intensity and area is a constant ; this relationship is known as *Ricco's law*. The reduction of

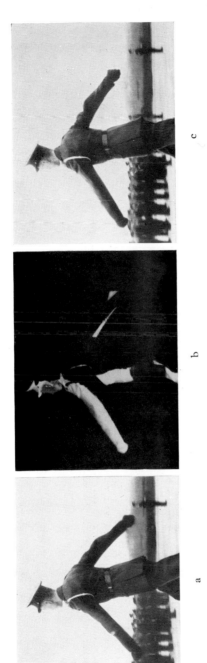

a

b

c

Use of 'successive contrast' in experimental television. Instead of transmitting the whole picture at each frame this system transmits the difference between successive frames. 'We are sending only our mistakes—the amount by which the next picture element surprises us' (Harrison 1952). This system has the great advantage that much less information need normally be transmitted. Two successive frames of a soldier marching are shown (a and c) as is the difference between these (b). From *Bell System Technical Journal*

Plate 5

A   B   C

Use of 'simultaneous contrast' in experimental television. It is customary to transmit a signal corresponding to the intensity of the image at each point examined by the scanning beam. In the experimental system under consideration a signal is only transmitted where there is a change in the level of illumination. A, the original picture; B, the same picture subjected to this process in a horizontal direction; C, the same but with vertical examination. Note absence of horizontal contours in B and of vertical contours in C. The advantages of this system, as of the system shown in Plate 5, is that it is necessary to transmit very much less information. Somewhat analogous systems appear to be used by the retina. From *Bell System Technical Journal*

Plate 6

threshold with increasing area, up to a certain size, is apparently due to nervous interaction within the retina. Barlow (1953) has studied these relationships as revealed in the discharge of optic nerve fibres and finds that the law holds over a wide range of intensities. He remarks that 'It is very remarkable that a simple nervous structure, consisting of a single ganglion cell connecting through bipolar cells with a number of receptor cells, can perform an addition sum with tolerable accuracy. The smallest spots in the area/threshold experiments are illuminated at an intensity 1000 times higher than the largest spots, and it therefore appears that the effects contributed by the receptors can be graded over this very large range.'

FLICKER

Although, as has been seen, the fibres of the vertebrate optic nerve respond to changes in illumination rather than to the steady level of lighting, there is a limit to the speed with which the visual

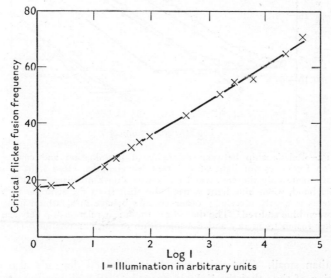

Fig. 9.16.—Relationship between intensity of illumination and flicker fusion frequency. The discontinuity of the curve probably corresponds with the shift from the scotopic to the photopic visual system. The linear relationship, over a wide range, between the logarithm of the intensity of the illumination and the critical flicker fusion frequency was first established by Porter (1902), who was a schoolmaster at Eton. The data on which this figure is based appear in his paper

apparatus can respond to alterations within the field of view. In the case of a moving object, for instance, if the speed of motion is too great the appearance is not that of a sharply defined image but

of a blur. When the fluctuations of light intensity are restricted to
one part of the retina and are rapidly repeated, a frequency is soon
reached at which the impression becomes that of a steadily maintained illumination. This limit is known as the 'critical flicker fusion
frequency', or for those to whom life is short the 'c.f.f.f.'.

This frequency is found to depend upon a number of factors being,
for instance, higher when the illumination is intense than when it is dim
(Fig. 9.16), and being higher when the area of the flickering object is large

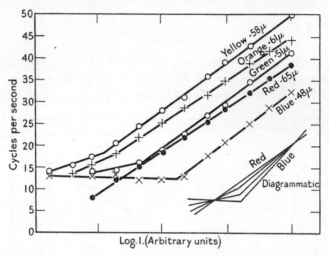

FIG. 9.17.—Relationship between intensity of illumination and critical flicker
fusion frequency for light of different wavelengths. Red light is believed
to stimulate only the cones and the curve shows no discontinuity. On the
other hand, when blue light is used the shift from the scotopic to photopic
systems is clearly revealed; other colours behave in a fashion intermediate
between blue and red. The data show the linear relationship between critical
flicker fusion frequency and the logarithm of the illumination. (From Ives,
1912)

rather than small. The value which is obtained depends also on the
proportion of time that the light is on compared with the time that it is
off : the light/dark ratio. In addition the frequency at which a flickering
light fuses to give a steady impression of brightness depends upon the part
of the retina which is involved; the scotopic system and the photopic
system behave differently (Fig. 9.17). In general it may be said that at some
frequency between 5 and 50 c/s, depending upon the conditions of observation, a flickering light appears to be steady and of a brightness that
would correspond to the light being delivered in periodic bursts. Electrical
stimulation of the retina, by passing an alternating current through the
head, or stimulation of the retina by placing the head in a powerful

fluctuating magnetic field, likewise demonstrates that the visual pathways can respond to frequencies up to, and somewhat higher than, 50 c/s (Barlow, Kohn & Walsh, 1947).

Studies of flicker fusion have been used extensively in the hope of obtaining quantitative data about, for instance, fatigue and the action of drugs (Simonsen & Brozek, 1952). It seems, therefore, important to consider the physiological mechanisms that may be concerned in the fusion of light to give a steady impression. When the rate of flickering is very slow, bursts of impulses will be present both when the flash starts and when it ceases. The 'on' and 'off' effects in the optic nerve have, however, latencies that may vary independently of one another according to the conditions of illumination. It is easy, therefore, to understand how, as the rate of flickering increases, the 'on' and 'off' bursts may run into one another. As the frequency of the flashes goes up so the relationship of the discharges to the stimuli vanishes. Different fibres respond in different ways; some, for instance, continue with an irregular discharge, whilst others cease their activity. Enroth (1952), who has studied these relationships, states that 'the discharge patterns obtained by repetitive stimulation with a flashing light are very varied and, on occasions, complex to the point that they cannot be deciphered'.

To perceive flicker it must be assumed that the discharge of some at least of the optic nerve fibres corresponds in some measure with the rate of flashing. At low rates of flicker bursts of impulses synchronised in many fibres will clearly indicate the varying nature of the stimulus. As the rate of flashing is increased the number of fibres that discharge in time with the flashes will decrease, and in those that remain to be considered the relationship of the bursts to the stimuli may become uncertain. The evaluation by the C.N.S. as to the presence or absence of flicker may turn upon the identification, on a statistical basis, of small temporal discontinuities in the optic nerve discharges. If these considerations are valid it scarcely seems reasonable to enquire, as is sometimes done, whether it is the retina or the higher centres that is 'responsible' for flicker fusion, since both must surely be involved (cf. Sherrington, 1906; Ireland, 1950). Landis (1954) has reviewed these problems and comments that it is 'always correct to say that CFF phenomena depend on both the retina and the brain'.

Flickering light in the visual field may alter the discharges of the cerebral cortex so profoundly that a rhythm corresponding to the stimulus frequency may be detected on applying electrodes to the scalp (Adrian & Matthews, 1934). This 'flicker following' may take some cycles to build up to a maximum and, in favourable subjects, the rhythmic responses may outlast the period during which the flickering light is applied (Toman, 1941). Flicker following may occur even though the intensity of the flickering light is not great, and even a small flickering area in the visual field may affect electrical rhythms of the brain if presented towards the centre of the visual field. Weak stimuli are probably most effective if they are presented as rhythmically pulsating patterns. One figure that was used by Marshall & Harden (1952) in their investigation of this point consisted of a circle of expanding diameter which started as a dot and increased at constant speed to a maximum and then returned to the dot form on the start of the next cycle. Such moving forms bring into play the heightening effect of simultaneous as well as successive contrast. It is not surprising that they hold the subject's interest, a fact not unknown to the advertising magnates of Piccadilly Circus and Times Square.

Flicker fusion represents a limitation of the capacity of the eye to follow rapid changes of illumination ; it is arguable that whilst the spatial resolving power of the eye has become highly developed there has been no comparable improvement, during evolution, of its temporal resolving power. There are, as the sense of hearing testifies, on all sides of us objects which can, and do, vibrate at high frequencies, and if the persistence of vision was less these vibrations could be seen. The rustle of leaves in a gentle breeze signifies that the structures are vibrating for transient periods at frequencies of thousands of cycles per second, but the eye is totally insensitive to such changes and only signals the slowest of the movements.

VISUAL ACUITY

Vision is the sense by which the spatial arrangements of relatively distant objects can be investigated. Tests of vision, of which there are many, require the subject to differentiate the pattern with which he is presented from a number of other possibilities (*vide* Senders, 1948). Naturally the numerical value that is finally given for the visual acuity of a subject will depend upon the type of pattern to which he is exposed and the way in which his results are scored. Visual acuity is sometimes regarded as depending solely upon the eye itself, but this is clearly fallacious. Discrimination depends not only upon the messages that are sent to the brain but also upon the way in which the information is handled (cf. Stroud, 1950).

What is the 'best' of the tests of visual acuity ? This is not an easy question to answer for the criteria for judging the value of any test will vary ; from a pragmatic point of view it is probably important that the alternatives should be as equally matched as possible as to difficulty of discrimination. On this basis Snellen's test types are bad ; a better test is the Landolt ring. Landolt's ring consists of a circle with a gap ; the circle can be rotated about its centre and the patient is required to state where the gap is situated.

Measurements of acuity under conditions in which the intensity of the illumination can be changed have shown that there is a discontinuity in the functioning of the visual apparatus. This discontinuity is another expression of the duplicity theory (p. 290) and represents the change-over from the scotopic to the photopic apparatus. Although it is usual for the visual acuity to improve as the illumination is increased, this relationship is not invariable. Indeed when a subject is required to tell whether he is exposed to one or to two closely juxtaposed luminous dots his resolving power is found to decrease with increasing brightness (Berger, 1941). Under these conditions the brighter images will excite a wider region of the retina, and it is not surprising that greater separation will be required for the separate identity of the spots to be established.

One interesting test of visual acuity measures the ability to set two rulers so that a fine transverse line on one of the rulers is aligned with a similar marking on the other. Under favourable conditions, provided that the lines are not too short, this ability may show striking accuracy, the difference between the two lines corresponding to an angular separation at the eye of less than 2 seconds of arc. This is a visual resolution

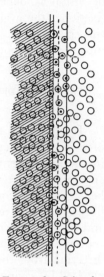

FIG. 9.18.—Stimulation of retinal mosaic by straight line. Fine movements of the eye may carry the edge of the image across a zone that is rather smaller than the one represented in this figure ; even so it is necessary to consider a process of excitation that not only has a spatial but also a temporal pattern (cf. Marshall & Talbot, 1942). (Reproduced from Andersen and Weymouth, 1923)

10-20 times better than would be expected on the basis of the size of the retinal receptors ; the brain can, it appears, use the data from a number of receptors to obtain an accurate estimate of the position of a line. The C.N.S., it seems, can average data where necessary ;

Y

indeed it has been said that 'the computer invariably integrates many sensory data into one single report' (Lorenz, 1951). It has sometimes (*e.g.* Marshall & Talbot, 1942) been supposed that the acuity of vision is dependent upon fine movements of the eye during fixation; the available evidence does not appear to be in favour of this possibility. Ratcliff (1952) has shown that the greater the movement the poorer the acuity (*vide* Fig. 9.18).

FACTORS UNDERLYING THE PERCEPTION OF VISUAL DIRECTION
(*vide* Walls, 1951 *a*)

It is believed that the first step in the evolutionary development of a vertebrate eye was represented by the development of a pit in the integumentum equipped with photo-sensitive cells. In such an eye the direction of movement of shadows across the body could be signalled according to the connections of the particular nerve fibres that were excited. With the development of a lens system and a formation of a clear image the excitation of a particular receptor would come to correspond with objects lying in a certain direction from the head of an animal; a fact that could be summarised by saying that the nerve fibres possessed 'local sign'.

In animals that do not move their eyes it is unnecessary to postulate any further mechanism for the perception of visual direction. Phylogenetically the ability to rotate the eyes has evolved *pari passu* with the development of a fovea in the retina. In human beings eye movements are particularly conspicuous, occurring over a wide range, and it is evident that the bearing of objects can only be established by the sense of sight if the central nervous system is provided with information dealing with the position of the globes in the orbits.

Some observers have suggested that information about the *position of the eyes* in the head is not available (Ludvigh, 1952). Helmholtz (1924, *vide* vol. 3, p. 279) was 'very emphatic as to how extremely uncertain we are about localising the entire field of view with reference to our body. . . . An idea of the degree of precision can be formed by comparing the optical localisation with the haptical (*haptische*) localisation, for instance, by trying to touch a visible object with the hand.' In testing the ability 'to put the finger on a visible point in an otherwise dark room, we find that our success is of a most imperfect kind'. Helmholtz gave, however, no figures and it is possible to investigate this problem using an apparatus which enables the experimenter to observe the movements of the hand of a subject pointing to a source of light in an otherwise entirely dark room (Fig. 9.19). Normal subjects can point, in this way,[1] with an accuracy that is usually better than 2°, and it follows that the knowledge that the brain has of the position of the eyes in their sockets must be at least as good as this.

There appear to be three mechanisms by which the position of the eyes in the orbit might be indicated to the C.N.S. As there is

FIG. 9.19.—'Projectionometer'—test of sense of visual direction. Subject cannot see his hand and attempts to place index finger in line with one of the marks. Observer can determine error by looking through the glass plate. A number of instruments based on similar principles have been described ; this version can be used in dark room. Inside of box is illuminated by blue light, whilst subject wears red goggles. A luminous target is used and is seen in an otherwise completely dark field of vision. There is thus no visual framework the position of which the subject might ascertain with respect to his body. Localisation depends, *inter alia*, upon the C.N.S. having information about the position of the eyes in their sockets. (Author—unpublished)

some evidence to support each of these possibilities, it may prove that all three may under suitable conditions be operative ; it is indeed to be expected that where there are three mechanisms for obtaining an important piece of information that all will be utilised. First it is conceivable that the movements of the globes might be estimated by monitoring the motor discharge to the eye muscles.

[1] This type of localisation is known as *egocentric*, and there is a voluminous continental literature on the subject. The estimation of verticality is an example of *absolute* localisation, whilst in *relative* localisation the person has to discriminate between the positions of two stimuli. These distinctions are often useful but sometimes rather artificial.

Following the nomenclature of Hughlings Jackson (Jackson & Paton, 1909), this view may be called the *outgoing theory* ; recurrent fibres branching from the outgoing axones are said to be present in all of the motor centres and could represent the anatomical features needed for this view. These recurrent fibres may constitute a feed-back mechanism controlling the discharge of motor cells (Holmgren & Merton, 1954). There is some evidence that the sensations of position in the limbs also may be determined, in part, by an evaluation of the motor discharge (Lashley, 1917) ; this point is discussed elsewhere (p. 424).

It has now been clearly established that the extra-ocular muscles of man contain *muscle spindles* (Cooper & Daniel, 1949) ; in the goat similar endings are found, and, as would be expected, they respond to stretch of the muscles by discharging a steady series of action potentials (Cooper, Daniel & Whitteridge, 1951). The cell stations of these afferent endings lie along the various nuclei of the 5th nerve (Cooper, Daniel & Whitteridge, 1953), a fact which is a little surprising in view of the motor innervation of the muscles from the 3rd, 4th and 6th cranial nerves. The perception of the position of the eyeball on the basis of the discharge of these endings (cf. Sherrington, 1918) would be in line with the proprioceptive system elsewhere. This view may be called the *inflow theory*.

The relationships between the perception of visual direction and the eye movements normally are often taken for granted since they are automatic, and it is only when these normal arrangements break down that attention is focussed on the processes that are involved. Paralyses of ocular muscles are not uncommon in adult life and give rise to double vision (p. 344). It is found that the attempt to look in a given direction, even though it may be entirely ineffective, is accompanied by a shift in the apparent position of the image. Thus if the external rectus is para-lysed on the right side and an attempt is made to look to the right, it is found that the images from the right eye swing to the right side. The perception of direction has been changed by the ineffective movement, the interpretation of the retinal images is that which would have been appro-priate if the eyeball had indeed moved obediently to the intended position. These symptoms are usually interpreted as being in favour of the 'outflow' theory and it is certainly the simplest explanation at present available. It must not, however, be forgotten that the eye muscles show reciprocal innervation, and when a powerful attempt is made to move a paralysed muscle, such as the external rectus, there may be a fuller relaxation of the opposing muscle, in this case, the internal rectus. It is probable, therefore, that in these cases the situation is rather complicated, for although the symptoms are explicable on the outflow theory there may be a change in the proprioceptive feed-back to the brain stem.

More conclusive evidence was obtained by Kornmüller (1930). This worker bravely submitted to an experiment upon himself, getting an ophthalmic surgeon to inject novocaine into his extra-ocular muscles ; thereby there was induced in one eye a temporary paralysis of movement (*ophthalmoplegia*) that was almost complete. At the time of the paralysis every attempt at an eye movement was accompanied by an apparent shift in the position of objects that he saw. Thus on looking to the left objects that lay on his right side appeared to move to the middle of his visual field or even appeared to cross the mid-line to the left side. These findings appear to afford strong support for the 'outflow' theory.

Neither the inflow nor the outflow theories, nor both together, can supply the whole answer to the problem of visual direction. This is shown by the fact that there is in the dark a greater degree of uncertainty as to the position of objects than under normal conditions. If a small light is fixated in an otherwise totally dark room, it often appears to move in an irregular course. These illusions of motion are referred to as *autokinetic sensations* and are probably related to slow movements of the eyes such as may be associated with varying degrees of convergence (cf. Skolnick, 1940). These sensations represent an imperfection of the visual apparatus, for if the central apparatus had available, and successfully dealt with, accurate data concerning the position of the eyes, arrangements could be made to 'cancel out' the effects of the shift of the image across the retina. As has already been seen (p. 310), Herbert Spencer rightly regarded it as most important that the visual system should be able to determine changes caused by movements in the external world from the changing visual impressions caused by the animal's own activity.

This is one aspect of a more general problem which concerns receptors stimulated in two ways—from the outside world (*ex-afference*), or from stimuli arising through the activity of the creature's own musculature (*re-afference*). These problems have recently been discussed (von Holst, 1954) and it has been pointed out that 'The *same* receptor can serve both the re- and the ex- afference. The CNS must, however, possess the ability to distinguish one from the other. This distinction is indispensable for every organism, since it must correctly perceive its environment at rest and in movement, and stimuli resulting from its own movements must not be interpreted as movements of the environment.'

In Herbert Spencer's simple creature (p. 310) it is possible to believe that retinal stimulation caused by movements of objects around the head could be differentiated from that caused by movements of the head itself in a fairly straightforward manner. It would be necessary for the visual centres to be supplied with information from the labyrinths. The differentiation of re-afference from ex-afference is unlikely to be as simple as this in all instances.

Finally, even if the C.N.S. had no direct information regarding the position of the eyes in the orbit, it is possible that the *sight of a limb* or of a part of the trunk or indeed of any object of known form that rested in contact with the surface of the body might enable the position of other objects in the field of vision to be determined. Once a part of the body gave an image that impinged on the retinal surface, this image could provide a bearing against which to align the position of objects giving rise to other images.

Carr (1935) has pointed out that under normal circumstances the retinal stimulus of any extraneous object is always a part of a larger retinal pattern in which the body is represented. He refers to the fact that the nose and the margins of the orbit normally obstruct the field of vision of the periphery of the retina. He believes that this obstruction may form a stable frame of reference by which the orientation of the eye may be judged. If arrangements are made to change the margins of this frame experimentally, the localisation of objects by vision may be disturbed, for the subject interprets his sensations in terms of their usual significance. He tacitly assumes that the edges of the restricted field stand in a standard relation to the head, and hence carries over his habitual mode of interpretation to the new conditions (Loemker, 1930).

The important rôle of visual data in evaluating the position of a part of the body may be illustrated by an account of an experiment of Tastevin (quoted by Piéron, 1950). 'On hiding one's hand behind a screen and being allowed to see a plaster finger such confusion can be produced that one mistakes the artificial finger for one's own at a distance which may be more than 15 cm. The direct perception of the finger is "captured" by the view of the false finger, and with the intention of displacing the latter, it is to the real finger that the desired movement is imparted.'

Similarly, by introducing a prism in front of one eye and closing the other, it is possible to create a conflict between the cues as to localisation, those depending upon the neuromuscular apparatus of the orbit and those that result from catching sight of a part of the body. Observations of this type may readily be made. Using a 12° prism, Paton reported that as soon as the finger came within the field of vision 'it also was subject to the same displacement as the object and was guided in (or out) towards the object' (Jackson &

Paton, 1909). When the hand is first brought into the displaced field of view to touch some object it fails to reach its target, for it is carried to a position that would be appropriate if the prism had not been interposed in the line of sight. Almost immediately, however, the relationship of the neuromuscular system of the body to the

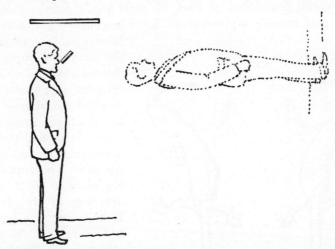

FIG. 9.20.—Experiment designed to test relationship between vision and proprioceptive sensation. Subject carried a light frame on which were fixed mirrors
so that he viewed himself as from above his own head. By means of screens
attached to the frame vision was confined as nearly as possible to the view
which the mirrors gave. The optical system reflected things not only out of
their proper direction, but gave them as well a false distance from the observer.
At first there was an utter discord in the spatial reports of the two senses ;
the whole body was seen in a different place from where it was felt. 'But the
constant sight of the feet and hands, for instance, tended to pull the feeling of
these members over into the place where they were seen.' This type of
experiment suggested that 'if we were to see a thing long enough in any given
place, we should, sooner or later, also feel it there. If the world had been
so constructed that we always saw our bodies a hundred yards away from
our point of view, our touch sensations would undoubtedly have taken this
same position.' This at least was the view of Stratton (1903) who performed
these experiments

retinal surface is readjusted and subsequent movements, even if rapidly performed, are as accurately executed as normal.

These readjustments that are so rapidly and effortlessly brought about indicate the dominance of the impressions of vision over the other cues as to the orientation of the optical axes. Under normal conditions it may be assumed that any image of a part of the body adds accuracy, and indeed determines, the direction of other objects in the visual field.

If the experimental arrangements are such, however, to introduce a more vigorous conflict between the various sources of information the subject experiences a great deal of discomfort.

One such experiment was performed by Stratton (1903) (cf. Fig. 9.20) who arranged a lens system that inverted his visual field. This worker found that, at first, his sight was a definite hindrance to the performance of movements, for if he caught sight of his limb

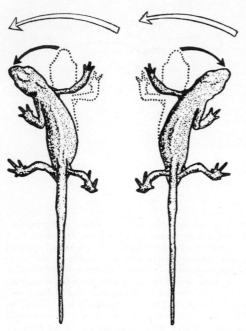

he was liable to move it in the direction opposite to the one that was intended. Stratton supposed that he would have become readjusted to these changed conditions if he had persisted in wearing the optical contrivance. This supposition has received striking confirmation by the work of Kohler who has repeated and extended Stratton's observations. By the tenth day Kohler could ski with inverted vision [see brief summary in Granit (1955); Stratton's work is discussed by Carr (1935)].

FIG. 9.21.—Optic pursuit reactions. On left, normal; on right, after rotation of eye through 180°. No adjustment of response to new circumstances; after rotation of eye, movement is mal-adaptive. (From Sperry in Stevens, 1951)

These experiments by Stratton in which the significance of stimulation of different parts of the retina were changed raise the problem of the origin of 'local sign'. The view that retinal local signs develop as a result of genetically determined nervous connections, *nativism*, appears to be well established in the case of certain vertebrates. Sperry (Stevens, 1951) found that it is possible by surgical means to rotate the eyes of newts through 180° without impairing vision, the optic nerves remaining intact. When this is done, the response to objects in the environment is incorrect and no compensation for the altered orientation of the globes ever appears to be established. The pursuit by the eyes of objects moving in the visual field proceeds in the wrong direction (Fig. 9.21). Even more surprising results were obtained when, in such animals, the optic nerve was severed. In the course of time the fibres regenerated, as they do in these creatures, and the optic pursuit reactions that eventually reappeared were still reversed; they would have been appropriate had the eye not been twisted through two right angles. It appears that there must be some attraction, possibly chemical, that draws the fibres from a particular part of the retina to form particular connections within the visual centres.

In the nineteenth century Douglas Spalding performed some experiments on chicks that, also, support the view that retinal local signs are dependent upon genetically determined nervous connections. The observations have been republished (Spalding, 1954). This worker covered the eyes of chicks just before they opened at hatching and then removed the covers after one to three days.

Describing his experiments, he says, 'Frequently the interesting little subject was unhooded on the centre of a table covered with a large sheet of white paper, on which a few small insects, dead and alive, had been placed. From that instant every movement with the data thereof, as shown by the watch, was put on record. Never in the columns of a court journal were the doings of the most royal personage noted with such faithful accuracy.'

Spalding found that within a few minutes the chicks were able to peck at the insects without hesitation in an accurate manner, and he concluded from his observations that the perceptions of distance and direction by the eye were not 'the result of experience of associations formed in the history of each individual life'.

It may well be wrong to assume that in man similar conclusions hold. The muscular movements of newts and of chicks are stereotyped when compared with the wide variety of which the human being is capable (p. 363). The much wider range of learnt muscular actions in the human might be expected to be dependent upon a very much greater degree of plasticity in the nervous system. It has indeed often been assumed that retinal local signs, in man, are dependent upon experiences built up in childhood. This view, *empiricism*, originated with the philosopher of the eighteenth century, Bishop Berkeley. The debate between the supporters of empiricism and of nativism (p. 328) is one aspect of the attempt to determine the relative rôles of heredity and environment in biological situations; clearly both sets of factors must be studied and the way in which they interact determined (*vide* Hebb, 1953).

Barnett (1954) discussing these problems has stated that : 'The nerve connections of a simple reflex, like the rest of the organism, develop as a result of the interaction of what is present in the organism with external effects. It is an axiom of embryology that development is epigenetic : it is not the mere unfolding of a pre-existing structure, but a process of continuous interaction between the organism and its environment. It seems, therefore, more reasonable to ask what factors determine a particular mode of behaviour rather than whether the cause is hereditary or environmental.' It is not surprising, therefore, that the arguments between the 'nativists' and the 'empiricists' still rage after centuries of debate and decades of investigation.

It has become apparent that behaviour must not be regarded as 'innate' or 'instinctive' merely because it is manifested by an animal under conditions in which the chance for learning has been brief. Learning may indeed occur quite rapidly : perhaps the most remarkable examples of rapid learning are those described under the name of 'imprinting' :

'Many young birds follow their parents about : the line of ducklings waddling or swimming after their mother is familiar enough, and it is easy to assume that such behaviour is wholly innate. However, O. Heinroth and later Lorenz have shown that this response depends on a learning process which takes place very rapidly during a short period just after hatching : the young birds will follow whatever living thing they see first during this period ; if it is a man, they will follow the man' (Barnett, 1954). The young animals are receptive to this type of learning for a short time only.

MECHANISMS UNDERLYING VISUAL FIXATION

When a subject fixates a stationary object with his eyes, the image can be held upon the same part of the retina rather accurately. Ditchburn & Ginsborg (1953) have measured the movements of the eyes during fixation and find that the eyeballs may show a very fine high-frequency (30-80 c/s) tremor, probably due to the incomplete tetanus of motor units in the extra-ocular muscles (p. 367). The extent of this tremor is such as to move the image across the retina by a distance approximately equal to the diameter of a cone ; the tremor may therefore be responsible for a small amount of blurring of the resultant perception. During a series of fixations the image of a small target is maintained within an area of the retina of about 100 μ diameter.

When a subject attempts to fixate a moving target his eyes cannot, at first, be expected to follow the movement with any accuracy (Fig. 9.22), for the delay in the visual system amounts to at least $\frac{1}{5}$ sec. If the motion of the target occurs regularly in a to-and-fro manner, however, the movements of the eyes come to anticipate the sensory signals and the performance, with practice, becomes much better. The brain is clearly predicting the future position of the moving object on the basis of its past experience. Visual fixation may be regarded as having achieved its aim if the image is kept towards the centre of the field of view, where visual acuity is at its highest, and if the 'slip' between the image and the retina is sufficiently slow for the brain to perceive the image without blurring. Satisfactory pursuit may be achieved as long as the angular velocity involved is below about 40° per sec. (Dodge, Travis & Fox, 1930).

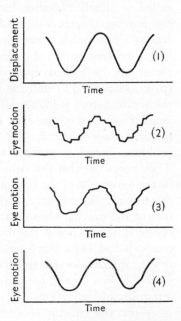

FIG. 9.22.—Motion of eyes in effort to fixate moving spot. Target oscillates to and fro smoothly as shown in (1); eye movement records are seen in (2), (3) and (4). Initially (2) the following is very poor with numerous discontinuities. Lowest record (4) indicates that C.N.S. has learnt to predict future position of spot since delay in neural apparatus makes continuous control of eye movements by visual information impossible. Similar discontinuities may be shown when limbs move under visual guidance. (From Stroud, 1950)

The ability to fixate upon a particular object in the environment might be thought to imply a fairly advanced degree of visual perception to enable the object as such to be differentiated from the background. Dogs are said not to fixate upon lines marked upon a rotating drum but may react if shown rabbits on a revolving platform (Rademaker & Ter Braak, 1948). Under suitable conditions man, apes, and dogs and cats, can follow a small object that moves in their visual environment, but the more humble guinea-pig will only react when the whole of its visual environment rotates (*vide* Smith & Bridgman, 1943), a condition to which the cat is reduced when its cerebral hemispheres have been removed.

If, in man, the eyes are exposed to a succession of objects moving in one direction they exhibit nystagmus with the quick phase to the opposite side. *Optokinetic* nystagmus, as these movements are called, is clearly of value, for during the slow phase the images of the moving objects will tend to be kept on the same area of the retina. The quick phase supervenes when a given object can no longer be kept within the central part of the visual field. The slow phase can be looked upon as being the result of a servo system (p. 112) designed to stabilise the position of an image on the retina ; the servo system is highly efficient and to a first approximation the angular velocity of the eyes is equal to the angular velocity of the image. Rademaker & Ter Braak (1948) have investigated this problem, using an optical system for recording eye movements. They point out that the stimulus to the movement of the eyes must be the movement of the retinal image—'it might therefore be expected that the angular velocity of the slow phase will always be less than that of the moving object. In reality, however, the angular velocity of the slow phase and the moving object is always equal.' If their methods had been more sensitive it is likely that small, but significant, differences in the velocities would have been revealed ; Dodge & Fox (1928), for instance, found that during the slow phase a number of 'refixations' occurred.

When the effector element of a servo system is prevented from functioning disturbances result analogous to reactions that may be seen in the mechanisms of visual fixation. If one eye is immobilised and is exposed to a series of stripes moving across the visual field, the nervous system makes vigorous, but of necessity ineffective, attempts to move the eye. If the opposite eye, which is free to move, is observed in such a way that it is screened from the visual stimuli, it is found to be in motion. The movements are those of nystagmus and the angular velocity of the slow phase may be many times greater than that of the contours moving across the immobilised retina (Rademaker & Ter Braak, 1948 ; cf. Dodge & Fox, 1928 ; Kornmüller, 1930).

Optokinetic responses may be seen on observing passengers in railway trains who are looking out of the windows ; they are sometimes referred to, therefore, as 'railway nystagmus'. It is not clear to what extent learnt reactions are involved in these movements in man, but they have been observed in apes that have been reared in total darkness (Riesen, 1947). In man this variety of nystagmus depends upon the integrity of the cerebral cortex although, *mirabile dictu*, it may be evoked in some types of coma. It is sometimes useful in clinical neurology to test for the responses by observing the patient's eyes whilst he sits before a rotating drum marked with vertical stripes. A failure of the movement when the drum is rotated to one side may indicate that there is a lesion of the ipsilateral cerebral hemisphere involving the angular gyrus (Fox & Holmes, 1926). Lesions in monkeys paradoxically abolish the response on rotation to the side opposite to the lesion (Henderson & Crosby, 1952) [cf. Fig. 5.20, p. 148].

Exaggeration of visual fixation as a result of cerebral damage is occasionally seen (Holmes, 1938). The patient may literally 'be unable to take his eyes off' whatever is in the centre of his visual field.

This disturbance is seen when there are bilateral lesions affecting the cerebrum and is probably dependent either upon destruction of the centres capable of controlling eye movement that lie anterior to the central sulcus (p. 379) or may be caused by interruption of the pathways from these centres. Such a patient 'cannot at will command the direction of his gaze'. This defect is not due to muscular paralysis for 'if asked to follow with his eyes a slowly moving object, his eyes do so. That is, though willed effort fails to produce the act, the eyes follow "of themselves" a moving point whose image is fixated by them. The eyes remain anchored to that object by the "fixation reflex". Those afflicted with this condition, when they want to look at something fresh, close the eyes for a moment, or toss the head, or place a hand between the eyes and the object fixing their gaze. By breaking the gaze a moment they free themselves from the fixation-reflex; though by willed effort they cannot break it.' The fixation-reflex is operated especially from the fovea. 'By means of reflex alone, the patient's gaze can still follow the printed lines across a page. The patient reads. "Each succeeding letter, dot, or segment of a line tends to excite a movement" swinging the eyes laterally towards it' (Sherrington, 1951).

The pathways that are concerned in the fixation-reflex and in optokinetic nystagmus have not definitely been established, but it has long been known that stimulation of the occipital lobe may give rise to movements of the eyes. It has been recorded that whilst stimulation in the lower half of the striate area in the monkey turned the eyes upwards and to the opposite side, stimulation in the upper half turned the eyes downwards and towards the opposite side (Crosby & Henderson, 1948).

The rôle of the cortex in controlling eye movements (see also p. 379) was investigated by Graham Brown (1922). He found that electrical stimulation of the occipital region of a monkey 'awakened' the orientation reflex, the reflex by which, when the head is moved, there is by way of the labyrinthine mechanisms a compensatory adjustment of the eyes (p. 143) so that the direction of the optical axes remains unchanged. Graham Brown also recorded the effects of stimulating the upper part of the frontal eye fields (p. 379); the head turned to the opposite side and the direction of sight was correspondingly altered. These events occurred whilst the orientation reflex was active, so that a comparable passive movement of the head elicited no change in the direction of vision. If during the stimulation of the frontal eye fields the head was restrained, the eyeballs now moved in their sockets instead of remaining in the same position and being carried passively into their new direction by the motion of the head. These experiments support the view that the frontal eye fields are concerned with directing vision to a new point in the environment, whilst the occipital regions regulate eye movements so as to keep the same objects in view.

It must not be supposed that the fixation of the eyes depends solely upon the cerebral cortex and its connections to the mid-brain. In some animals there is good evidence of the presence of a subcortical system which, also, appears capable of directing the eyes according to the conditions of excitation in different parts of the visual field. There is now evidence of a point-to-point representation of the retina upon the superior colliculus in some fish, birds and mammals (reviewed briefly by Hamdi & Whitteridge, 1954). In the cat the application of strychnine to a small part of the superior colliculus facilitates the fixation reflex, for the eyes will turn to the corresponding region of the visual field when a light appears in that region (Apter, 1946). The supposition that there are two alternative mechanisms, one cortical, the other subcortical, capable of moving the eyes according to the conditions within the visual field, should not be regarded as surprising. A multiplication of control systems may be expected where functions are involved that are of substantial importance. In the monkey eye movements are said to be normal after destruction of the superior colliculi (Ferrier & Turner, 1901), and if this is so, it would appear that the cortical control is not exerted through, or at least solely dependent upon, the pathways leading downwards to the colliculi.

Some interesting speculations by Pitts & McCulloch (1947) may help to understand the way in which a complex neural structure such as the colliculus may work.

'Consider the reflex-arc from the eyes through the tectum to the oculomotor nuclei and so to the muscles which direct the gaze. We propose that the superior colliculus computes by double integration the lateral and vertical coordinates of the "center of gravity of the distribution of brightness" referred to the point of fixation as origin, and supplies impulses at a rate proportional to these coordinates to the lateral and vertical eye-muscles in such a way that they turn the visual axis toward the center of gravity.' This interesting suggestion is a simplification, for visual fixation is by no means always directed towards the brightest part of the visual field.

It has been supposed that within the chain of nuclei supplying the muscles of the eye different patterns of control could be discerned according to the particular part under consideration. Some workers, for instance, have stated that stimulation of the upper part of the nuclear complex gives rise to an upward movement of the eyes, whilst stimulation in the lower part moves the eyes downwards. Teuber & Bender (1951) have reviewed this question and conclude that the problem is unsettled. The only localisation, therefore, of which it is at present possible to be certain, is that determined by the destination of the fibres from the motor cells themselves, the fibres of the 6th nerve, for instance, being concerned with lateral motion of the ipsilateral eye. Paralysis of conjugate movement may arise with lesions that interrupt the pathways from the cerebral cortex which are clearly above the level of the oculo-motor nuclei. These disturbances are referred to as supra-nuclear palsies (*vide* Collier, 1927). Inability to lower the eyes is a rare result of C.N.S. lesions, but one elegant case demonstrated that such a symptom could result from tegmental lesions. The areas of destruction were bilaterally symmetrical and lay just lateral to the oculomotor nuclei and dorsal to the red nuclei (André-Thomas, Schaeffer & Bertrand, 1933). See also p. 159.

FACTORS UNDERLYING THE ESTIMATION OF DISTANCE

Measurements of visual acuity show that the relative direction of different objects within the visual field may be determined with a high degree of precision (p. 320). The estimation of distance is also of the greatest importance, and it is now appropriate to consider how it is that the brain arrives at conclusions in this respect and the ways in which the mechanisms may break down in pathological conditions.

Depth perception is possible if one eye only is used, and indeed in many vertebrates the visual fields of the two eyes do not overlap.

Some idea of depth may be obtained *monocularly* by shading (Fig. 9.23), perspective and interposition, objects close to the observer obscuring those more distant.   The appearance of distant objects is changed by the presence of fine particles of dust and of moisture in the atmosphere.   These particles scatter light so that blacks are converted to bluish greys on distant landscapes in the country whilst in smoky cities the changes may be apparent at much shorter distances.   Finally an observer may estimate the distance of familiar objects according to the area of the retina that is stimulated by them ; a small image of a horse is interpreted as being a distant and not a miniature animal. All of these factors are used at different times ; they are all dependent upon learning processes and not one can be regarded as being an absolute indication of distance that will function under every circumstance (Fig. 9.24).

FIG. 9.23.—Shading of objects gives indication of solidity available in monocular vision. Back of donkey receives much more light than belly. (From Davson, 1949)

In bringing objects to a sharp focus on the retina, it is necessary to adjust the focus of the lens, and it might be found that by estimating the contraction of the ciliary muscle the C.N.S. could obtain an estimate of distance.   This method would be one way, indeed the only way, by which an absolute indication of distance could be obtained with monocular vision.   The available evidence suggests, however, that in man this system is not used, or, if it is available, is extremely inaccurate (Sisson, 1938 ; Woodworth, 1938).

In many respects the most satisfactory way of obtaining information about the position of objects depends upon getting more than one view of the environment for, by obtaining two or more bearings on a particular object, its position may be fixed unequivocally.   With monocular vision the images are received in succession ; if a hen is observed it may be seen to cock its head first in one direction and then in another before pecking at an object on the ground, as though it was determining position by taking more than one view.

In the hen it is likely that the information obtained from one angle has to be stored for a short time in order to be compared with data obtained when the head has changed in position. It might be possible to make a machine that would mimic the hen and being supplied with two somewhat different views estimate the position of objects in the environment. To give information about absolute distance, the instrument would have to be fed with measurements not only of the distance that the eye had moved, but also of any change in orientation. Monocular depth perception making use of *parallax* in this way must therefore, if it is accurate, involve a fairly complex computation by the central nervous system,

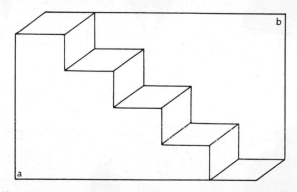

Fig. 9.24.—Schroeder's staircase. Figure is ambiguous and may be seen as though staircase is viewed from below (surface a behind surface b) or from above (surface a in front of surface b). Difficulties in the interpretation of depth arise in monocular vision which are of the same type as is found with this figure. Thus in looking with one eye at a gem carved in relief a cameo may easily be mistaken for an intaglio, or vice versa. (Southall, 1937)

for allowance must be made for the variable extent of the motion of the head between successive 'frames'.

In *binocular vision* similar information for the perception of depth becomes available without delay and the estimation must be a good deal simpler, for the images are recorded at a fixed distance from one another. It may be supposed that it is because of the greater speed with which information about depth can become available, and because the computation is more simple, that some species have adopted binocular vision. It may be no accident that binocular vision is found in the primates. Monkeys, jumping in trees, must obviously be able to estimate distance with speed and accuracy. These are the benefits which appear to be achieved ; the

z

price of binocular vision is high, for the visual fields are corre-spondingly restricted (Fig. 9.25).

The absolute perception of depth by means of binocular vision clearly depends upon the evaluation of two independent bearings of the same object. It is now necessary to consider the influence of the position of the eyes in the orbit on the perception of distance.

Helmholtz (1924) records that the influence of convergence is 'shown very definitely in the case of *wall-paper patterns*. Thus on looking at a paper on which the pattern recurs regularly, and converging the eyes to a

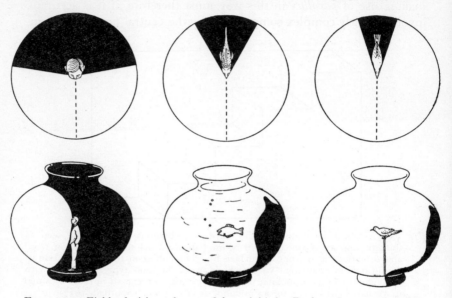

FIG. 9.25.—Field of vision of man, fish and bird. Dark regions are invisible. Creatures are represented inside bowls. Circular diagrams show angle of field of vision if observer is above the bowl. (From Mann & Pirie, 1946)

certain extent, it is possible to fuse corresponding parts of the pattern, either the first figure with the second one next to it, or the first with the third and fourth. The resultant effect will be the appearance of an image floating in air nearer the observer than it really is and also smaller, the extent of the illusion in this respect depending on the amount of conver-gence. If each portion of the pattern is fused in the same way with the corresponding portion next to it, the resultant figure will not be so small or so near as it would be if the first pattern were fused with the third or fourth one.'

These observations provide further evidence (p. 322) that the C.N.S. has available information concerning the position of the eyes in the orbit, and suggest that, contrary to the opinion held by Bishop Berkeley (1709), it is possible to 'judge of distance by the angle of the optic axes, just as one in the dark or a blind man by the angle comprehended by two sticks, one whereof he held in each hand' (*vide* Ogle, 1950).

Evidence that has already been considered (p. 322 and Fig. 9.19) suggests that the estimation of the position of the eyeballs by the C.N.S. is not highly accurate, and it follows, therefore, that the distance of an object from the observer can be estimated, on this basis, only with some error. Binocular vision would appear to be better suited to estimating the relative distance of different objects, rather than by itself forming the basis of an absolute judgement. In principle there would be enough data from the images in the two

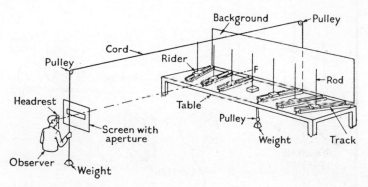

FIG. 9.26.—Apparatus used to test binocular vision. The subject fixates rod marked F and adjusts other rods until they appear to be in the same frontal plane. Only one rope shown in diagram for simplicity. Apparent frontal plane as indicated by this instrument does not necessarily correspond to true version and is called the 'horopter'. (From Ogle, 1950)

eyes to judge which of two objects was nearer the observer, even if there was no information about the orientation of the optical axes. Under all normal circumstances there will be available other cues as to distance (p. 336), and the presence of the observer's own hand in the field of vision may be expected to serve as a yardstick against which other distances can be compared.

The ability of the binocular apparatus to form an absolute judgement of position has rarely if ever been measured ; the methods of estimating stereoscopic acuity in common use depend upon the observer estimating whether or not an object lies closer to, or further from, himself than some visible reference point (Fig. 9.26).

Observations made in this way have shown how extremely sensitive is the apparatus of stereoscopic vision, for difference in the retinal images between the two eyes that are very small can be used for depth perception. These differences may correspond to less than the diameter of a retinal cone (Andersen & Weymouth, 1923 ; Langlans, 1929). High degrees of stereoscopic acuity may even be achieved when the test objects are illuminated only by a very brief flash.

Successful stereoscopic vision depends upon the various features of the images falling upon *corresponding points* of the two retinae.

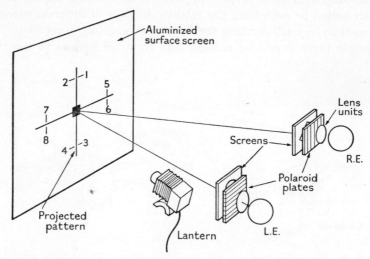

FIG. 9.27.—Apparatus for comparing the relative magnitudes of the images of the two eyes : an 'Eikonometer'. Lantern projects onto the screen pairs of marks, one of each pair being polarised in one direction, its twin polarised in the opposite direction. Polaroid plates in front of eyes of observer separate images ; if eyes are equally matched the members of each pair will appear in juxtaposition. (From Ogle, 1950)

Corresponding points may be defined in various ways (Ogle, 1950), but the meaning that will be used here concerns the sense of direction. A spot of light may be said to fall on corresponding points in the two eyes if it appears to come from the same direction when first one and then the other eye is closed. As follows from a consideration of geometrical optics, points on the temporal half of one eye correspond with points on the nasal half of the other retina. What is more surprising is that the points on the nasal half of one retina correspond to regions of the temporal half of the retina that lie at a smaller distance from the fovea.

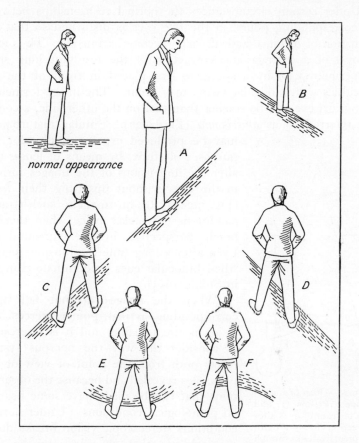

FIG. 9.28.—Changes in appearance of level grass lawn observed through different types of aniseikonic lenses. A, lenses rotate vertical meridian of each retina out by 1·14° at top. 'The ground appears to rise up in front at a severe angle of 45° or more and one has the feeling of being about 9 feet tall. Looking directly downward one sees the toes pointing upward with the sloping ground. All details on the ground appear increased in size.' B, same lenses but with opposite rotation. 'The ground slants in the opposite direction but with a less severe slope about 30°. One feels dwarf-like in stature, 3 or 3½ feet in height, and the toes are noticed pointed downward with the ground. All details in the ground appear reduced in size.' C, lens used that increases horizontal dimensions of image in left eye by 4 per cent. 'The ground appears to curve over and downward with slightly less steepness on the right. The left leg seems to be longer and the right leg to be shorter.' D, same as C but with lens placed in front of right instead of left eye. E, lenses used that cause an asymmetrical distortion of the images on the retinae with the temporal parts spread out relative to the nasal. 'The ground appears concave as if looking into a hollow.' F as E, but with the nasal parts spread out with respect to the temporal. 'The ground appears convex in all directions as if looking at a mound.' (Modified from Ames, 1946)

Under certain circumstances the normal relationships between the corresponding points in the two eyes is disturbed so that the estimation of distance and of shape become erroneous. Thus after removal of a cataract and correction of the resultant long sight ('hypermetropia') by a spectacle lens placed in front of the eye difficulties with binocular vision may occur. The image formed in the normal eye will be smaller than that on the other side, a condition referred to as *aniseikonia* (Fig. 9.27). Similar disturbances may be produced experimentally, for the purposes of study, by means of lenses that alter the dimensions of the images formed in the eyes without upsetting their focus (Fig. 9.28). Readjustment to such strange conditions only takes place when there is much perspective in the surroundings. Even after a long time the illusions persist when binocular cues predominate (Burrian in Stone, 1953).

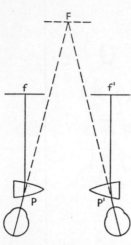

FIG. 9.29.—Plan of stereo-scope. Prisms (P and P¹) in front of eyes alter direction of rays of light. Subject fixates as though looking towards F, but images received by eyes originate instead at f and f¹. (From Woodworth (1938), after Bourdon)

When the images do not fall upon corresponding retinal points stereoscopic vision is unattainable, and it is interesting to consider the way the nervous system reacts both from the point of view of the principles revealed and because the observations that can be made have some bearing on pathological conditions. Under normal conditions stereoscopic vision breaks down with objects that are close to the face because there is a limit to the convergence that can be brought into play. In addition, as an object is brought close to the nose the disparity between the views received by the two eyes increases and may eventually become so great that it also hinders fusion. Indeed, under certain circumstances, the view that the two eyes receive is totally different.

The effect of varying the degree of difference between the images presented to the two eyes may be studied in a *stereoscope* (Fig. 9.29). When totally dissimilar pictures are placed in the two halves of this instrument, it is possible to learn something of the way in which the brain may react when it has to deal with incompatible data, impressions from the two eyes that cannot be meaningfully fused.

It is often found that the visual field is treated in a patchwork fashion ; the observer is aware in one region of a part of the image from one eye, whilst in a contiguous zone the other image may show through. The relationships are not static, for in any part of the field the image from one eye may suddenly and without warning be displaced by its fellow. These fluctuations are regarded as being an expression of *retinal rivalry* (Fig. 9.30).

Sometimes the appearance of the whole field may shift in this way, the image presented to one eye being seen at one moment, the image of the other side taking its place later on. When the image from one eye is suppressed, light stimuli thrown into that eye are relatively ineffective in eliciting pupillary constriction (Bárány & Halldén, 1948) ; this fact may indicate that retinal rivalry is a function of not only cortical regions but also of parts of the brain stem concerned in the light reflex.

Some subjects when tested in the stereoscope are said not to experience this retinal rivalry, seeing only the image from their *master eye*. Some degree of dominance of one eye over its fellow is nearly always present ; if the

LEFT EYE

RIGHT EYE

COMBINED IN STEREOSCOPE

FIG. 9.30.—Binocular combination of two dissimilar images produces a fluctuating image containing parts of them. The result is not static, the way in which the images are combined changes, first the image from one eye and then that from the other eye is seen at any given point : retinal rivalry. (From Starling, 1941)

control that the two eyes exerted was closely matched the result would be 'as clumsy as the attempt to rule the complexity that was Rome with two consuls having identical jurisdictions' (Walls, 1951 *b*). Dominance is shown in various ways ; one eye may be preferred in tasks such as sighting and in establishing direction, or it may be easier to close one eye than the other. It is sometimes inferred that the dominant eye is on the side of the dominant hand. Quinan (1930) investigated 1000 students and found that this relationship did not hold for left-handed subjects who might have either a right or a left master eye. It was true, however, that right-handed subjects *usually* showed dominance of the right eye.

In squints that have been present from early childhood double vision does not occur, for whilst the images do not fall on corresponding parts of the retinae, the visual acuity of the squinting eye is poor and its images do not compete effectively with those from the sound side. When, on the other hand, a squint develops for the first time in adult life the patient experiences, initially at least, troublesome double vision (*diplopia*); the images in the two eyes are referred to different positions in space.[1] Quite small degrees of squint, that may be scarcely noticeable even to a careful observer, can give rise to most disturbing diplopia; indeed it is often relatively small degrees of imbalance between the actions of the extra-ocular muscles on the two sides that causes the most distressing symptoms.

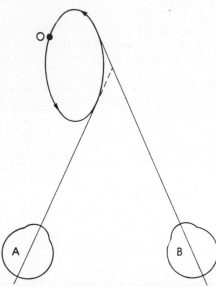

FIG. 9.31.—Differences between images reaching two eyes are not only static but dynamic. Events may occur at different times when viewed from different angles, as shown in this figure. Object O, swinging in elliptical orbit, is seen to reverse in direction at different moments by the two eyes (A and B). Brain interprets retinal time differences as movement in depth

The brain is sensitive to time differences arising at the two eyes when presented under suitable conditions, and this sensitivity appears to underlie what is known as the *Pulfrich phenomenon*. A swinging pendulum when viewed binocularly with a piece of dark glass in front of one eye appears to move in a pathway that is roughly elliptical. It is believed that the decrease of the light intensity reaching the eye behind the dark glass prolongs the time needed for retinal events underlying excitation to get under way so that the messages reaching the brain from that eye arrive later than those from the eye that has unobstructed vision of the pendulum. It will readily be seen (Fig. 9.31) that binocular temporal differences

[1] Abraham Lincoln related how disturbed he was when he discovered his double vision: 'my eyes fell upon the glass, and I saw distinctly two images of myself, exactly alike except that one was a little paler than the other' (Kempf, 1952).

of this type normally arise when some object moves in a pathway such as a horizontal ellipse which has a component of motion in the direction of sight of the observer. It is not surprising that a normal subject interprets the temporal difference in the excitation of his two eyes in terms of the phenomena which commonly set up similar differences. This subject has been reviewed by Ogle (1951 and 1952).

It is impossible to tell which of the eyes receives a stimulus unless there are available extraneous clues. If winking is not permitted, an observer cannot by introspection tell whether a flash of light has been delivered to his right or left eye (Helmoltz, 1924, vol. iii, p. 458). Nevertheless, the binocular phenomena which have been discussed are clear evidence that the C.N.S. has in fact 'knowledge' as to the contribution from each eye ; this information forms the basis of stereoscopic estimations of distance but cannot itself be directly linked to the speech mechanism. If the images reaching the two eyes are artificially transposed, as may be done with a system of mirrors ('pseudoscope'), objects which are solid may appear to be hollow, and vice versa. It is evidently dangerous to assume because a subject is unaware of some change in stimulus conditions that his C.N.S. cannot respond to these alterations. Thus because it is impossible with any accuracy to estimate the position of one's own optical axes, Ludvigh (1952) argued that the eye lacks position sense. This conclusion would appear to be erroneous (p. 322).

THE GENICULO-STRIATE SYSTEM

It has already been seen that in the retina the existence of cross connections between adjacent pathways enables particular features to be picked out. This sifting of information may continue at the level of the lateral geniculate body in most mammals. In the monkey any given optic nerve fibre forms synaptic connections with a number of the cells and each cell receives connections from a number of fibres. There is, however, little to suggest that information from the two eyes interacts at this level : 'crossed and uncrossed visual impressions remain isolated from each other in the lateral geniculate body' (Clark, 1942). In man the 'integrative' actions of the lateral geniculate body may have been lost ; the structure appears to serve merely as a simple relay station which does not present opportunities for lateral interaction between adjacent pathways (Walls, 1951 a).

Walls (1953) has likened the lateral geniculate body to a pile of maps of the retina, for in each of the sheets of cells of this laminated structure one-half of the field of view is represented in a point-to-point manner. In propounding his *Cartological Theory of Geniculate Lamination* he suggests that 'human laminae No. 1, No. 4 and No. 6 are related to each other as are three maps of the same country, one of which is geodetic, a second climatological, and the third agricultural. Just as three maps are required to keep such types of information apart and intelligible, so also a mammal with highly differentiated vision requires a multiplicity of genicular maps if the cortex is to be able to make full use of the classified information the retina sends. . . .' In the motor cortex (p. 379) and in the sensory cortex (p. 417) the body is represented in more than one way: Walls is suggesting that this also is the case with the geniculo-striate system (compare arrangements in the auditory system, p. 275).

As with other sensory systems there is at the level of the cortex a substantial increase in the number of neurones available to deal with the data. Sherrington (1906) made the following comparison :

'The retino-cerebral apparatus may be regarded as a structure of linked branching nerve-elements forming a system which expands as traced centrally from the retinal surface. It may be figured as a tree, with its stem at the retina and an arborization spreading into the brain, its ramifications there penetrating a vast cerebral field, interlacing with others in a cerebral forest composed of nervous arborizations. The simile fails, because in the nervous forest the arborizations make functional union one with another.'

There is indeed a 'multiplication of path of over one hundred times in the foveal area of the primary projection system' (Marshall & Talbot, 1942), but clearly in such a complicated structure activity may ramify and spread through the cortex in a manner and to an extent that defies definition. It is possible to map the striate area of experimental animals by physiological techniques. By shining a light into the visual field and recording the potentials that are evoked it is possible to define a topographical representation of different parts of the retina onto different parts of the cortex. In the primate the region given over to the representation of the macula is great, and clinical evidence (Spalding, 1952 b) suggests that in man also it is large, involving perhaps a third of the striate area. The macula is split so that one-half is represented in one hemisphere, the other half on the opposite side. Regarding the topographical arrangements, Spalding (1952 b) stated his conclusions in the following terms : 'serial concentric zones of the visual field from the fixation point to the periphery are represented in this order from behind forward'. The lower half field is represented in the upper half of the calcarine cortex, and vice versa.

When stimulated by a flash of light the visual system is liable to respond in a *rhythmical manner*. If electrodes are applied to

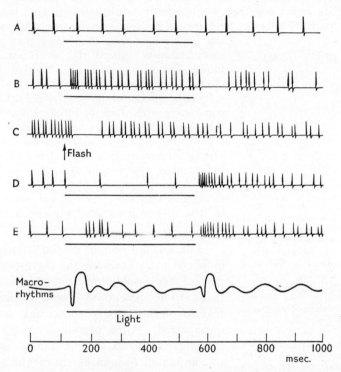

FIG. 9.32.—Varieties of neurone responses to light stimulation. Micro-electrodes in striate cortex of cat. Five types are shown. A, no response to light. B, activation by light with high-frequency initial discharge and sustained activation. Inhibition for short period when light is switched off. C, short inhibition of spontaneous fast discharge by short light flash. D, inhibition of spontaneous discharge by light and activation by dark. E, short primary inhibition by light, then late activation. Stronger activation by dark. (From Jung, 1953)

the surface of the cortex it is found that a complex sequence of waves is set up by a light (Fig. 9.32) and these disturbances have proved difficult to analyse. Occasionally in the human electro-encephalogram some disturbance may be detected when a light is first switched on (Brazier, 1953 ; Cruikshank, 1937). The sequence of waves that can be recorded directly from the striate cortex gradu-ally dies away as the illumination is maintained, only to recur when the light is switched off. Micro-electrode studies afford some hope that more may be learnt of the behaviour of the striate cortex, and already Jung (1953) has been able to differentiate 5 types of cortical neurone (Fig. 9.32).

The presence of 'on' and 'off' effects in the visual system including the striate cortex may help to understand a phenomenon that has long been known. Flashes of light are not necessarily more bright when they last for a longer time than when they are of short duration, indeed the reverse may be found (Fig. 9.33). It is possible that at the duration that gives the brightest flash the subjective effects of the 'on' discharges are summating with those of units responsive to cessation of illumination (cf. Howarth, 1954). One further suggestion may be made. Under certain circumstances a single flash gives rise to an image that recurs a number of times (*vide* Adams, 1929, p. 67). It is tempting to suggest that these recurrences are related to the rhythmicity that can be recorded electrically.

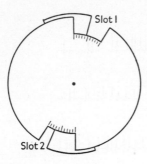

FIG. 9.33.—Action time. The disc was rotated one revolution in two seconds and intercepted a beam from a lantern which illuminated a disc of 8 mm. diameter on a piece of milk glass. Two adjustable slots allowed the duration of the flashes to be controlled. It was not always the wider aperture that gave the brighter flash. The duration needed to give the brightest flash at any given intensity is called the action time. (From McDougall, 1904)

The loss of one part of the striate area gives rise to a scotoma in the corresponding part of the visual field; it is of interest that vision depending upon contiguous regions of this part of the cortex may be unimpaired. After partial destruction of the calcarine cortex an animal may be able to compensate to some extent for the loss of vision in certain directions by moving the head and eyes. These considerations help to understand the interesting finding that the behaviour of a rat in response to visual stimuli was normal or nearly so when there were only 700 neurones left in the geniculo-striate system (Lashley, 1939).

In the condition known as *migraine* visual disturbances are common and usually affect one-half of the visual field only. These disturbances probably arise in the striate area on one side and a study of the symptomatology may throw some light on the normal functions of this area of the brain. During an attack a patient may experience strange illusions of geometrical shapes, *fortification spectra*, and towards the centre of the region a scotoma may slowly develop (Figs. 9.34 and 9.35). Under certain circumstances the brain may 'fill in' the missing part of the visual field so that the patient may be unaware of the defect.

Even with gross damage to the geniculo-striate system giving rise to a hemianopia the patient may be unaware that the visual field is restricted and perhaps only appreciates the deficit as a result of some bitter experience, such as being knocked over by a bicycle coming

FIG. 9.34.—Sketch showing development of scotoma in attack of migraine. Attack affected left field of vision, right side being free of symptoms. As is customary, first visual symptom was spot of light at, or close to, centre of field. As the attack progressed this spread towards the periphery and enlarged splitting to become a 'fortification' pattern, shown as zigzag on the sketch. Within the figure enlarging and travelling with the fortification pattern was the scotoma. (Reproduced from Gowers, 1904)

from the blind side. When the lesion interrupts the visual pathways below the level of the lateral geniculate body, however, the patient is usually aware of a blind area from the first.

As is the case with the 'completion' that occurs across scotomata caused by damage to the visual system the completion across the areas that are temporarily blind in migraine affects principally geometrical figures of simple shape. Lashley (1941) has given an interesting account of his own symptoms during an attack. A scotoma 'may completely escape attention, even when it is just off the macula, unless it obscures some object to which attention is directed. Talking with a friend, I glanced just to the right of his face, whereon his head disappeared. His shoulders and necktie were still visible, but the vertical stripes in the wall-paper behind him seemed to extend right down to the necktie. Quick mapping revealed an area of total blindness covering about 30 degrees, just off the macula. It was quite impossible to see this as a blank area when projected on the striped wall or other uniformly patterned surface, although any intervening object failed to be seen. On another occasion, with complete hemianopia, including the macula, it was possible to divide a complex object on any line of fixation. A human face was sharply

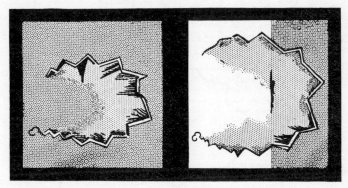

FIG. 9.35.—Visual symptoms in migraine affecting the right half of the visual field. In these figures the expanding spectrum has been sketched against a dark background (*left*) and also half against a light window (*right*). The luminosity within the spectrum is seen to be dark when viewed against the light; it corresponds to a scotoma. (Re-drawn from Gowers, 1904)

divided by fixating the tip of the nose, so that half, including one nostril only, was visible. At the same time it was impossible so to fixate a circular object that only half was seen. Fixating a chalk mark on the middle of a billiard ball failed to make any part of the ball invisible, although the ball was considerably larger than the readily divided nose.' Lashley remarks that : 'These observations are of interest as showing that filling in the blind spot and the completion of figures in scotomatous areas are not the result of habits of disregarding blind areas or identifying part figures. The phenomena appear immediately with new blind areas. They must, then, represent some intrinsic organizing function of the cortex. The figures completed are reduplicated patterns or very simple symmetrical figures. . . . Such phenomena can be made intelligible by the assumption that the integrative mechanism of the striate cortex tends to reproduce a pattern of excitation, aroused in one region, in any other region also if the latter is not dominated by different afferent patterns.'

The normal *blind spot* raises problems concerning visual perception similar to those concerning the scotomas of migraine. According to Ferree & Rand (1910) opposite sides of the blind spot are treated as being contiguous, although stimuli which fall on either side of the blind spot some distance from its margins have the same apparent separation that they would possess if they fell on any other part of the retina. The spatial qualities of the retina bordering closely on the blind spot are 'stretched out' by way of compensation. According to Brøns (1939) there is a ring 1° wide around the blind spot which has spatial qualities different from the rest of the retina. Images falling on this region appear to be distorted—'metamorphopsia'.

The fortification spectra of migraine suggest that the striate area may be concerned in the 'manipulation' of shapes or rather their neural equivalents. It would not be difficult to believe that a structure that can give rise to such regular angulated formations could detect and enumerate angles ocurring in the 'images' with which it is supplied by the eye. Some evidence from other directions also suggests that this is the sort of function with which the striate area is concerned. When the retina is stimulated in a rhythmic fashion the appearance of the visual field is not homogeneous but shows patterns of light and shade and of colour which tend to change in an unpredictable way (Walsh, 1952). Certain features of the sensations are common to various types of experiment. Thus *flickering lights* (*vide* Brown & Gebhard, 1948), *alternating magnetic fields* (Magnusson & Stevens, 1911) and *rhythmic electrical stimuli* (Ferree, 1906; Rohracher, 1935) may all give rise to the impression of geometrical form; one pattern that the visual system seems particularly liable to produce resembles a chess-board.

Tumours limited to the occipital lobes are relatively uncommon, but the visual symptoms that have been reported are of a relatively simple variety, for whilst the patient believes he sees lights flashing in the visual field he does not, in general, experience complex visual hallucinations (Horrax & Putnam, 1932). In keeping with these observations are the results obtained by *stimulating the occipital lobe* in the conscious human being. Penfield & Ramussen (1950) have reported that the patients saw flickering and dancing lights, colours, stars, wheels and discs rather than highly integrated visual forms. Intoxication with the drug *mescaline* also may bring out geometrical patterns. On looking at a white surface the subject may describe 'movement of grey and white lines apparently at different levels, horizontal and vertical, forming a lattice work, moving from left to right . . .' (Beringer quoted from Mayer-Gross, Slater & Roth, 1954).

IRRADIATION OF ACTIVITY FROM THE STRIATE AREA

From the striate area impulses concerned with vision reach out to other parts of the cortex and there are probably a number of different routes, perhaps very many, that may be concerned in this irradiation. It might be supposed that the two striate areas would be very closely linked, for the representation of the two halves of the visual field is quite separate on the two sides of the brain. The vertical line of subdivision is indeed believed to pass through the centre of the point of fixation (p. 346). Nevertheless, there is no good anatomical evidence for any direct connections between the striate areas on the two sides, and the physiological methods of demonstrating fibre connections have shown only indirect connections through other cortical regions. When, however, the corpus callosum is severed visual habits dependent upon one hemisphere cannot be transferred to the other side (Myers, 1956).

Short fibres connect the striate area with the neighbouring cortex ; they appear to ramify outwards into area 18 in a diffuse manner (Clark, 1941). Other pathways from the striate area lead to subcortical regions (Clark, 1942). These two routes from the striate area are of some clinical interest, for in many patients liable to epilepsy flickering light may provoke an attack. The visual system is, apparently, hyper-excitable (Cobb, 1947). This enhanced sensitivity may be of such a degree that attacks may be provoked under natural conditions by the flicker produced by driving along an avenue of trees or by the glare of sunlight on snow. The red end of the spectrum is particularly effective in provoking these attacks of *photic epilepsy* and spectacles that absorb red rays may have a place in the treatment of some of these patients (Carterette & Symmes, 1952 ; Marshall, Walker & Livingston, 1953).

Gastaut & Hunter (1950) have found that injection of small doses of *metrazol* into animals may produce, temporarily, a condition in which also flickering light may give rise to epileptic discharges. They obtained evidence that the activity in these animals spread from the striate area to subcortical regions and not through the cortex itself. It is tempting to suggest that this unphysiological procedure, the injection of metrazol, has brought to light a route that is in normal use and through which the visual system can exert a control on the somatic musculature. There is, however, another route by which such a control can be exerted. Wall, Rémond & Dobson (1953) have shown that when a flash of light is thrown into the eye of a cat anaesthetised with dial the threshold of the motor cortex to electrical stimulation is lowered. This facilitation persists even though the visual cortex or the two superior colliculi have been destroyed; the pathway involved probably takes its origin from the pretectal region.

There are reasons to believe (cf. p. 359) that the parts of the cortex that lie close to the striate area are concerned in vision. Nevertheless, clear-cut experimental evidence as to the rôle of these parts of the occipital lobe has not been forthcoming. Stimulation of areas 18 and 19 in the conscious human being produces visual sensations, of a simple form similar to those resulting from excitation of the striate area (p. 351). In the rabbit there is in the neighbourhood of the striate cortex a 'secondary' visual area; the region bears a point-to-point relationship with the retina similar to that found in the striate area itself (Thompson, Woolsey & Talbot, 1950), but the sequences are reversed so that the two zones bear a mirror image relationship.

Removal of the occipital cortex that borders upon the striate area in man 'produces no primary visual defect and no defect of which the patient is aware' (Penfield & Rasmussen, 1948), whilst in animals (Lashley, 1948; Evarts, 1952) destruction of the homologous regions does not appear to impair visual performance. Similarly destruction of the pulvinar, the thalamic nucleus connected with these regions, does not seem to disturb vision in the monkey (Chow, 1954).

By contrast there is a certain amount of evidence that suggests that visual memories may be stored in the temporal lobes. This at least is the interpretation that seems to fit the most facts. Electrical stimulation of the temporal lobes but not of other parts of the cerebrum may evoke complex visual hallucinations; the patient may 'see' events that occurred long ago. Bilateral destruction of the temporal lobes in monkeys produces a condition in which the animals appear to be unable to recognise objects that they have examined many times previously (Klüver & Bucy, 1939, vide p. 285). The defects tend to become less marked with practice, but there is little evidence or relearning if the pre-occipital regions also are removed (Ades & Raab, 1949).

Difficulties of this type in the recognition of objects that are seen [1] are referred to as *visual object agnosia*; the term agnosia was

[1] See Adler (1944) for good clinical description of this condition.

2 A

coined by the psychiatrist Sigmund Freud (1891) at a time at which he was interested in the study of neurology rather than of psychiatry. It is characteristic of agnosia that there is extreme difficulty in learning, or rather in relearning, the significance of objects that are in everyday use.

Visual object agnosia draws attention to the remarkable achievement of the healthy visual system in its ability to recognise objects irrespective of their position or orientation.

Lorenz (1951) was interested in this when he wrote that if he turned his pipe to and fro between his fingers, its image assumed an immense number of different contours yet its shape appeared to remain perfectly constant. Lorenz points out what a tremendous feat it is on the part of the 'computor' to 'deduce' the permanent form from the innumerable combinations of sensory data which represent the ever-changing contours of the moving pipe as it is depicted on the retina. The processes by which the changes in the retinal images are correctly 'understood' or 'interpreted' as movements of the whole object in space and not as changes in its shape must involve computations fully equivalent to complicated operations of projective geometry. Yet the perception of distance evidently does not play an important part in this performance as we can just as well interpret the movements of a solid body by watching its shadow. It is only the direction of turning of the movements which, in this case, becomes ambiguous.

This ability may, on rare occasions, be lost in patients with cerebral lesions. Holmes & Horrax (1919) described a patient with bilateral parieto-occipital lesions who when shown a cardboard box described it as a piece of flat cardboard no matter at what angle he saw it. He was surprised when it was placed in his hands to discover it was a box. It is also described how 'a glass tumbler appeared "a piece of flat glass" the shape of which varied according as it was presented to him'. The rarity with which these symptoms occur may well be related to the number of independent methods by which vision may give evidence as to solidity (p. 336); the cerebral lesions must interfere with all the alternative sources of information about relief.

The interpretation of visual sensations clearly depends upon extensive learning that takes place in infancy and childhood. Occasionally ophthalmic surgeons have removed cataracts from adult subjects that have been present since birth (Stratton, 1903). The patients have commonly been surprised how difficult it was to make use of their newly acquired sense and only the most industrious have made much headway, even in such apparently simple perceptions as differentiating a bottle from a horse or a circle from a triangle. Riesen (1947) reared two chimpanzees in total darkness and found that they too needed a long learning process before they were able to appreciate visual form, although from the first they would turn their eyes and heads towards a light. The interpretation of these findings is more complex than may at first appear. There is a good deal of evidence that suggests that in the absence of light the visual pathways do not develop normally and gross structural abnormalities occur.[1] Even when the visual apparatus has developed prolonged exclusion of light may result in an atrophy of the optic nerve (Walls, 1951 a).

Visual object agnosia raises the question of the mechanism by which patterns are normally recognised by the visual system. There would be little difficulty in drawing up a system of neurones that could respond to a particular distribution of excitation and to none other. Equally it would be simple to make such a system responsive to patterns which approached a particular grouping within certain limits. It is much more difficult to understand how it is that objects can be recognised even though their images may fall upon any part of the retinal surface. A triangle may be recognised, no matter where, within wide limits, it is located in the visual field, no matter what its orientation to the vertical and no matter what its size. The way in which patterns may be recognised, irrespective of the particular group of receptors involved, is known as 'stimulus equivalence', and is one of the main puzzles of sensory physiology at the present time (vide Lashley, 1942 ; Pitts & McCulloch, 1947 ; Hebb, 1949).

Whatever hypotheses are proposed for the recognition of patterns certain facts call for an explanation. It has become apparent that the appreciation of all but the simplest groupings require time. Instruments have been designed to afford the eye brief and controllable exposures of test objects ; it is usual to arrange that the background illumination before and after the exposure has the same value as that during stimulation (Woodworth, 1938). These devices are known as *tachistoscopes* and the extent to which patterns can be differentiated in one brief exposure is very limited. It may be supposed that this limitation is determined in part, but by no means wholly, by the fact that only a part of the pattern may fall on the fovea and much may fall upon parts of the retina where visual acuity is poor. Another reason for the limitation in tachistoscopic perception may be cerebral ; it is well known that more detail may be observed in an after-image when there is ample time for examination than in the original exposure of the eye to the test object.

[1] It is difficult to be dogmatic on this point. Goodman (1932) reared rabbits in complete darkness and could detect no anatomical change in the optic system.

The comprehension of a complex pattern such as a painting or a line of print is dependent upon *multiple visual fixations* (Fig. 9.36), and the result is somehow built up from this series of 'snapshots' (Vernon, 1930 ; Barlow, 1952). How are these different images welded together in the brain ? It would not be very difficult to devise a machine that would without human aid fit a number of snapshots together so as to give a full panoramic view, but whether in the brain such a topographical representation of the outside world is reconstructed can only be conjectural. In radar such a representation is achieved by displaying the information obtained when the aerial is pointing in a certain direction upon a corresponding region of the cathode-ray tube. As the aerial rotates to a fresh

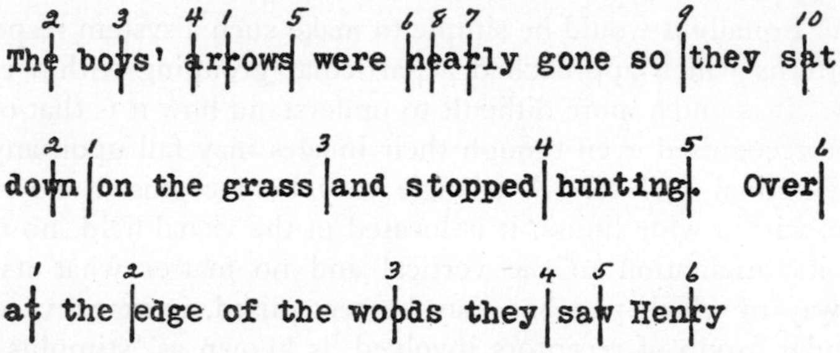

The boys' arrows were nearly gone so they sat

down on the grass and stopped hunting. Over

at the edge of the woods they saw Henry

FIG. 9.36.—Localisation of successive fixation points in three lines of reading. Vertical lines indicate fixations ; numbers above lines correspond to order in which the points were fixated. Note presence of regressive movements ; the number of regressions varies according to the nature of the material being read. When the subject attempts to read difficult passages regressions are relatively numerous. (After Buswell, reproduced from Woodworth, 1938)

position so the information which it receives is laid out upon the face of the tube. Any such arrangement within the brain would presuppose that information from the eye could be stored for short periods in appropriate regions of the C.N.S., presumably the cerebral cortex.

The distortions that might occur in such a display afford a model that may assist in the understanding of disorders of the visual system. Russell Brain (1941) described the following symptoms in a patient with a lesion of the right cerebral hemisphere :

'People coming towards him from the left appeared to move so fast that they seemed to glide rather than walk. Impairment of appreciation of relative distance of objects may lead to two objects appearing to be in the same place at the same time. To this patient people walking down the ward seemed to walk through the table. . . .' To patients with these disturbances vehicles approaching one another in the street may appear to be on the verge of colliding.

It is not surprising that patients with disturbances of this type have difficulty in drawing commonplace objects (Fig. 9.37) or maps (Fig. 9.38), for they have difficulty in appreciating spatial relation-

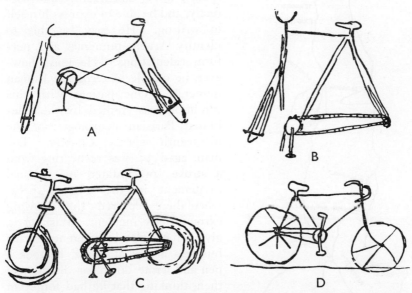

FIG. 9.37.—Drawing of bicycle by patient with injury to right angular gyrus. A series of attempts with progressive improvement (A, B, C and D). A, 'The salient parts of the machine are present but the spatial orientation is grossly disordered. Thus the frame is drawn in the frontal plane and the wheels in the horizontal.' B, much the same confusion of planes and the back wheel, except for the hub, is omitted. C, the articulation of component parts remains grossly upset. The mudguards are prolonged beneath the wheels and both pedals are placed side by side. D, probably falls within the lower range of normal free-hand performance. (Reproduced from Paterson & Zangwill, 1944)

ships. They similarly have difficulty in fitting together pieces of an object in their correct relations (Fig. 9.39). Whether defects of this type should be regarded as instances of *visual spatial agnosia* or of *constructional apraxia* is of less importance than that attempts should be made to ascertain the way in which the normal mechanisms have been deranged. Some constructional tasks are clearly dependent upon continuous visual control whilst others could be accomplished, although perhaps with more difficulty, in the dark.

In apraxia the patient is aware that his attempt is incorrect and the defect affects performances that do not, as well as those that do, depend upon visual inspection during the course of execution.

One remarkable disturbance that may occur with little or no other disability is *word blindness* or 'dyslexia'. A patient with this condition may comprehend the spoken word, talk fluently and correctly, and be able to express himself in writing. He may be able to identify Arabic numerals and perform calculations. He may, however, be unable to recognise Roman numerals. One patient with this condition was studied by the celebrated Parisian neurologist of the nineteenth century, Charcot. The man, aged 35, was recovering from a stroke 'precipitated by unusual excitement in the hunting field' when there occurred 'the following extraordinary incident. Wishing to give some order in reference to his business affairs at home, he took a pen and wrote down his directions; then, thinking that he had forgotten something, he asked to see the letter that he had just written, but he was unable to read it, thus exhibiting in all its originality the strange phenomenon *that he had been able to write, but was quite unable to read his own writing!* He was also unable to read printed matter' (Bateman, 1891).

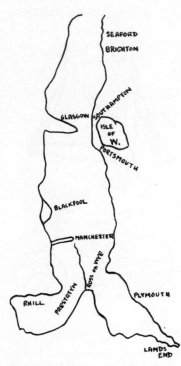

FIG. 9.38.—Map of Britain drawn by patient with marked disturbance of ability to construct figures dependent upon comprehending spatial relationships. Such disorders are found with especial frequency when there is a lesion of the right occipito-parietal region. (Reproduced from McFie, Piercy & Zangwill, 1950)

This type of disturbance may be illustrated by another case report (Holmes, 1945) that bears out many of the features noticed by earlier observers (Hinshelwood, 1895). 'A highly educated man under my observation became suddenly unable to read four years ago, following a slight stroke. The right halves of his visual fields are restricted, but central vision and vision to his left are unaffected. He is quite unable to identify by sight or name letters of the alphabet, and cannot learn to do so. . . . . He can recognise letters by tracing them and block letters by running his fingers over them. Only visual recognition is defective. The identification by sight of other objects, even of other visual symbols, as numerals, is undisturbed; he can use fingers in calculations and is able to keep his own accounts.' Holmes states that in other, similar, cases the lesions involved the lateral and inferior aspect of the occipital lobe close to the striate area. In some cases the damage was limited to the left side but in a few cases both sides were involved. The preservation of the ability to write in the face of dyslexia is interesting; writing, although learnt in childhood with the aid of vision, can, with a little

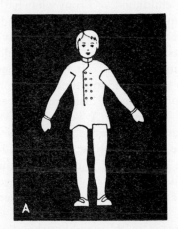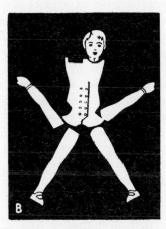

FIG. 9.39.—Assembly of 'Manikin' figure. A, correct. B, as put together by adult patient, the result indicates a gross disturbance in the execution of this constructional task under visual control. The level of performance might be normal for a 3-year-old child. (From McFie, Piercy & Zangwill, 1950)

difficulty, in the adult, be accomplished without visual control. The inability of some otherwise bright children to read, *congenital word blindness*, differs from the condition that has been described in that the brain itself is probably undamaged (Sinclair, 1948).

Many patients with lesions of the parieto-occipital region have abnormalities of their eye movements of the sort that might be expected if there was an interference with mechanisms of visual fixation (p. 330). The eyes wander more than is customary; visual fixation is more labile than is usual (Paterson & Zangwill, 1944). It is possible that these disturbances give rise to trouble with following a line of print, but it is difficult to believe that they do more than accentuate, or perhaps are only an expression of, the dyslexia that may be experienced. Patients who, for various reasons, have nystagmus, can usually still read, but they may complain of some blurring of vision which on analysis may turn out to be *oscillopsia*, apparent movement of objects in the visual field (Nathanson, Bergman & Bender, 1953).

DISORIENTATION

Bishop Berkeley in his *New Theory of Vision*, published in 1709, raises the question of the extent to which the perception of space depends upon experience acquired in childhood. 'From what hath been premised, it is a manifest consequence that a man born blind, being made to see, would, at first, have no idea of distance by sight ; the sun and stars, the remotest objects as well as the nearer, would all seem to be in his eye, or rather in his mind.' It is sometimes said that babies will attempt to grasp the moon, and the suggestion that learning is essential for the appreciation of distance receives support from a number of lines of evidence. A very primitive reaction depending upon the appreciation of distance is the *menace response* used by neurologists. In the adult an object coming suddenly and unexpectedly towards the face evokes a closure of the lids and an eversion of the head. This reaction cannot be obtained in monkeys from which the striate areas on each side have been removed.

In man, lesions of the cerebral cortex in the neighbourhood of the *angular gyrus* at the posterior end of the Sylvian fissure interfere with the perception of spatial relationships (Fig. 9.37) so that in them also the menace reaction may be abolished (Holmes, 1919). This region appears to link the visual and kinaesthetic systems. 'The transition from the visual perceptual to the motor level thus appears to be, primitively, the translation of one system of space coordinates into another' (Lashley, 1942). Patients with lesions in this part of the brain have trouble in estimating the relative positions of objects in the visual field and cannot appreciate spatial relationships within figures or estimate lengths. There may be an inability to localise objects by means of vision although, strangely enough, objects may still be readily recognised. Riddoch (1917 a), for instance, described a case in which the patient 'when told to take hold of a match-box which was held in front of him, though he saw it at once and kept looking at it, his hand groped around searching for it before it was finally grasped'. Holmes (1919) studied 8 similar cases ; the central vision was good but there was an inability to tell the position in space in relation to themselves of objects that they saw distinctly. Holmes makes the interesting comment that if the object 'touched any part of their own bodies they could always bring themselves to touch it immediately and correctly'. He refers to a patient who had trouble when eating soup with getting the spoon into the bowl, but could always bring it to his mouth. If, however, he was allowed to touch the bowl with his left hand he had no difficulty in placing the spoon into the vessel.

Instead of the appreciation of spatial relationships being lost there may be a change in the apparent size of the world. In the condition known as *micropsy* :

'All the objects within the visual field suddenly appear quite near before the subject's eye, simultaneously assuming tiny dimensions. The room in which the subject is standing seems to shrink to a doll's chamber enclosing his head while his chin (like Alice's) threatens to hit the floor.' An illusion of an opposite character, *macroscopy*, has also been described. 'If the subject . . . holds his thumb some inches before his eyes and tries to look into the distance, he perceives a gigantic thumb towering in that distance!' (Lorenz, 1951).

These visual illusions vary a great deal from patient to patient and are of brief duration. They have never been subjected to physiological investigation.

The visual system may be studied from a number of different viewpoints ; it is apparent that the scientific study of disorders of visual perception has hardly begun.

CHAPTER 10

THE CORTICAL CONTROL OF MOVEMENT: CORTICO-SPINAL AND EXTRA-PYRAMIDAL PATHWAYS

There is no need to dilate upon the myriad functions discharged by the mobile human digits. The lauding of these extremely primitive and basically simple anatomical structures has always been a mistaken enterprise of those who have a belief in human anatomical perfections. To imagine that the dexterity of the musician, the artist or the craftsman lies in the special anatomical perfection of the human hand is a delusion that is apparent in the writings of most of those who have given attention to the subject. Such elevating studies can only be undertaken by those who mistakenly ascribe to the primitive human hand those aptitudes conferred on it by the specialised human cerebral cortex. In abandoning this time-honoured point of view, we are in no way minimising the vast functional possibilities conferred upon a very primitive anatomical structure by a neuro-muscular mechanism evolved to a stage far in advance of anything displayed by any other mammal. The human hand is not a marvel of perfection ; but the human brain can command it and control it so that its functional role is immeasurably greater than that of even the most intelligent anthropoid ape.—WOOD JONES (1941).

GRAPHIC STUDY OF VOLUNTARY MOVEMENT

THE methods that have been used for the clinical study of voluntary movements have been extremely primitive. Marey (1874) was amongst the first to study movements by *graphic techniques*, but these simple methods (*e.g.* Figs. 10.1. and 10.2) have been employed only rarely for the investigation of the disorders produced by human disease. One should not be content with subjective impressions, where, with a little trouble, objective recordings can be obtained. Devices are now available for studying the velocity and acceleration of moving limbs (Taylor & Birmingham, 1948), but these methods have not, so far, been applied to disordered movements.

One striking feature which emerges from the graphic study of voluntary movement is the *variety of responses* which are seen when a person repeats the same task. The same end-result is achieved in an apparently infinite variety of ways and rarely, if ever, are the motor units of different muscles activated in the same spatio-temporal pattern. This problem has been put in more general terms by Lashley (1952) : 'Analysis of patterns of adaptive movement, repeated in the same situation, does not reveal a constant use of the same combination of muscles. The movements can only be described as constant with respect to a set of space or time coordinates.' A worker at a factory bench uses his muscles in different ways to achieve the same result time and time again, and it is interesting to speculate on the biological significance of this surprising fact. It has long been known that if someone is forced to repeat exactly the same movement with the same muscle (Fig. 10.3) *fatigue* rapidly sets in and he finds it at first difficult, and then impossible, to continue. It is often said that this fatigue is due to changes in the central nervous system, but Merton (1954 *b*) has shown that this is not the case. He found that, contrary to current belief, the muscle cannot be

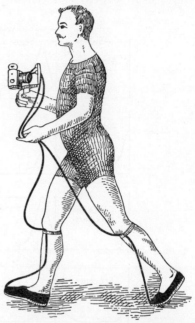

FIG. 10.1.—One of many ingenious devices used by Marey to study movement. The subject wears specially constructed shoes each containing an air-filled cushion. The pressures are transmitted by tubing to the apparatus that the subject holds in his hand and a graphic record of the change in pressure during walking is obtained. The Marey institute on the outskirts of Paris was built to enable Professor Marey to prosecute this type of investigation. The institute is now filled with electronic devices designed for physiological investigations. (After Luciani, 1915)

caused to contract by electrical stimuli delivered to the nerve after it has been fatigued by voluntary effort (Fig. 10.4). The failure does not appear to be at the neuromuscular junction because stimuli applied to the nerve still set up muscle action potentials. The muscle is, apparently, electrically excitable and the failure concerns the contractile mechanism itself.   This dissociation between electrical changes and the contractile process recalls a similar phenomenon which may occur in cardiac muscle.   Mines (1913) showed that a frog's heart deprived of calcium may fail to beat, and yet generate

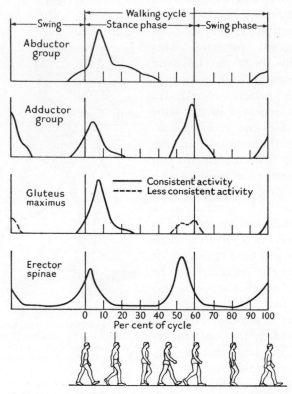

Fig. 10.2.—Activity of some muscles in walking. Whilst certain of the muscles contract once during each step others contract twice. The different muscles come into play at different times. ' "Co-ordination" is the principle according to which, from among a large number of units, *e.g.* muscles, certain fixed combinations are activated in definite associations and sequences ; in contra-distinction to the "unco-ordinated" operation of merely random selections' (Weiss, 1952). (Figure reproduced from Klopsteg, Wilson *et al.*, 1954)

a normal electro-cardiogram.   The fatigue of voluntary movements is due to the metabolic demands of the muscle outrunning its blood supply, and it is probable that the diversity with which muscles are engaged to perform the same tasks is a way in which fatigue is avoided by spreading the metabolic load over a greater mass of tissue.

Voluntary movements may seem to the eye to be smoothly executed, but graphic records show that they are often irregular and the impression of smoothness is an optical illusion depending on persistence of vision, a phenomenon which is used in the cinema. Schäfer (1886) was probably the first to observe that during the course of a voluntary movement there are *discontinuities* with a rhythm of between 8 and 13 cycles per second. These discontinuities are evidently related to the discharge of motor units, and the size of the irregularities depends upon the degree to which the different units are discharging synchronously (*vide* p. 118).

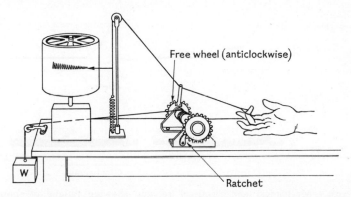

FIG. 10.3.—Simple ergograph. This apparatus provides a graphic record of the work done in flexing a finger. The movements are timed by a metronome and the work done may be calculated by measuring the distance that the weight, W, is raised. It is normal in this type of experiment to splint the arm so that the subject is forced to use the same set of muscles repeatedly. (Modified from McDowall, *Handbook of Physiology and Biochemistry*)

The simplest voluntary movements consist of brief flicks and in these the electromyogram may show only a few action potentials. A flick may even be associated with only a single discharge (Toman & Oster, 1942) and, in this case, the extent of the movement will depend only upon the number of motor units that are recruited. A movement of this type is *ballistic*; a brief and predetermined force is exerted on the limb which moves for a time, often greatly exceeding the duration of muscular contraction. The term 'ballistic' originally referred to the Roman weapon, 'ballista', which was a large catapult for hurling stones. Obviously, in such a device, a powerful force acting for a short time gives rise to motion which long outlasts the duration of application of the force. Movements that fall into this category cannot themselves be modified, but if for one reason or another this intended goal is not reached, a secondary corrective movement may be employed (Craik, 1947 and 1948). Vince (1948) studied brief movements in which the subject moved a lever to a fresh position as quickly as possible, and found that, if the subject encountered unexpectedly great resistance, a fresh start was made after the first movement had been completed. The delay before a second corrective movement could be initiated may be regarded as the kinaesthetic reaction time and amounted to 160 msec.

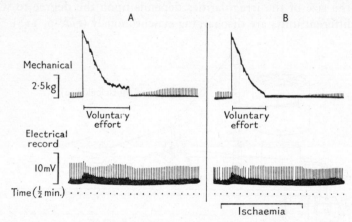

FIG. 10.4.—Mechanical and electrical records showing fatigue of maximum voluntary effort, A. Throughout the experiment electrical stimuli were delivered to the motor nerve at regular intervals and gave rise to the muscle action potentials seen in the electrical record. After the muscle had been fatigued to voluntary effort the stimuli failed to produce mechanical changes although the action potentials were still present. Ischaemia, B, produced by inflated blood pressure cuff prevented recovery from fatigue. The maximum tension that could be exerted equalled that produced by a motor nerve tetanus ; it is therefore perhaps unlikely that madmen can, in fact, develop any greater force than the sane. (After Merton, 1954 b)

Similar considerations apply when the rôle of vision in guiding movement is considered. The visual reaction time even under the most favourable conditions is too long (e.g. $\frac{1}{4}$-$\frac{1}{2}$ sec.) to allow a rapid movement to be performed under continuous visual supervision ; it must be supposed that if a movement is inaccurately executed it runs its course and then another response is organised and discharged. Craik (1947) has pointed out that 'in playing musical instruments, typewriting, sending morse, etc., complicated patterns of movement are executed at a rate which would be impossible if they were continuously guided by the value of the misalignment with the inevitable time delay'.

Movements of the eyes also must be regarded as being ballistic ; 'there is general agreement that the most usual type of movement is a rapid jerk, followed by a period of 0·1-0·3 sec. during which the eye is relatively stationary, and terminated by another quick movement bringing the eye to a new fixation position' (Barlow, 1952). The rapid jerks are known as 'saccadic' movements and are too brief (*e.g.* 25 msec.) to be modified by afferent impulses either from the retina or from the sensory endings that are known to exist in the extra-ocular muscles (Cooper & Daniel, 1949 ; Cooper, Daniel & Whitteridge, 1951). The mechanism by which these rapid movements are achieved may differ, however, from that concerned in brief movements of the limbs, for the extra-ocular muscles show tonic activity in all positions. Movement of the eyes appears to be associated with an increase in the frequency of discharge in the active fibres of the appropriate muscles together with a rapid recruitment of fresh motor units (Björk & Kügelberg, 1953 *a* and *b*). The rate of discharge (*e.g.* 50-100/sec.) is higher than that found on other voluntary muscles, but even so a mechanical tremor may be found during the fixation pauses which is probably due to incompletely fused tetanic contractions (Ditchburn & Ginsborg, 1953).

With *movements of longer duration* the situation is rather different. During sustained voluntary contractions of muscles Merton (1951) has obtained evidence that the stretch reflex is active. This indicates that if additional resistance is encountered there will be a rapid increase of the force available to overcome the resistance, and, conversely, if the movement proves easier than was anticipated the force supplied by the muscles becomes less. These differences between rapidly and slowly executed movements may explain why it is that rapidly performed movements are relatively inaccurately performed as compared with slow movements.

It is commonly believed that voluntary movements are mediated by activity in pathways that descend from the brain and control the activity of the motor neurones supplying the muscle fibres. Merton (1953) has suggested, however, that there is in addition an alternative and perhaps more important control system acting through the small motor fibres (Fig. 10.5). This system can alter the discharge from the muscle spindles and so, *reflexly*, cause a contraction. The mechanism would enable the sensitivity of the stretch reflex to be maintained throughout the movement and thus motion would blend into posture. This system would add a certain delay (about 30 msec.) to the initiation of the movement, but would have the great advantage that the important self-regulating properties of the stretch reflex would be preserved during the movement.   It has been shown (Granit & Kaada, 1953) that stimulation of a number of structures in the forebrain, including the motor cortex (p. 376), may alter the discharge from muscle spindles without necessarily evoking a response.   This finding, that descending impulses may alter the sensitivity of the muscle spindles, supports

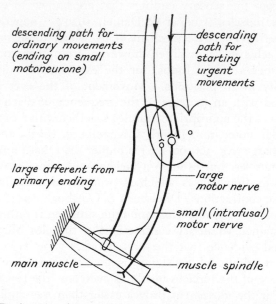

descending path for ordinary movements (ending on small motoneurone)

descending path for starting urgent movements

large afferent from primary ending

large motor nerve

small (intrafusal) motor nerve

main muscle

muscle spindle

FIG. 10.5.—Dual system that may be concerned in voluntary movements.   Fibres that activate the anterior horn cells supplying the muscle may be used for starting urgent movements, but a steadier pull would be achieved by changing the sensitivity of the muscle spindles.   (Merton, 1953)

Merton's view, for it shows that structures exist which could provoke movement in the way that he suggests (*vide* Eldred, Granit & Merton, 1953).

It might be supposed that it would be those movements that must vary widely in force to achieve a given end that would depend most upon proprioceptive information.   This appears to be borne out, for the relatively slight disability seen by 'de-afferenting' the face may be compared with the uselessness of a de-afferented hand. Mott & Sherrington (1895) found that section of the dorsal roots supplying the arm of a monkey rendered the limb almost useless. Such an animal may appear to regard the arm as a foreign body, and pick at it so severely as to cause damage. The 'paralysis' is more incapacitating than that caused by destruction of the motor area. In man the loss of posterior root sensibility does not prevent the affected limb from being used, and rapid movements may be executed reasonably accurately : 'a given intensity of motor excitation is aroused explosively without further possibility of control' (Lashley, 1917). Slow movements are, however, poorly controlled and stable postures cannot be maintained (see also Foerster, 1936).

Section, or alcohol block, of the trigeminal nerve removes the pathway through which the stretch receptors of the facial musculature reach the brain stem. On the anaesthetic side of the face postural sensitivity of the face is lost and movements of the ala nasi, for instance, may be elicited (by faradisation) without the patient's knowledge. The face on the side of the damaged nerve does not, however, move entirely normally. Acts which require a symmetrical movement, such as whistling, are performed with difficulty. Nevertheless, the disability is slight in keeping with the fact that the exertion of a given degree of tension by the muscles is likely always to cause about the same result, a very different condition from that found in the limbs. The swimming movements of fish and of toads exerted against the constant resistance of water also depend but little upon proprioceptive information (*vide* von Holst, 1954).

THE CORTICO-SPINAL PATHWAY

There is more than one route that impulses may follow on their way from the cerebrum to the spinal cord. The pathway which is most clearly defined anatomically, and which has received the most intensive study, is the *cortico-spinal tract*, the fibres of which travel through the medullary pyramids at which point the majority decussate to travel in the lateral columns of the spinal cord on the opposite side. The cortico-spinal tract is defined on the basis of its origin from the cerebral cortex and its termination in the spinal cord, whilst it is an experimentally observed fact that the constituent fibres traverse the pyramids in the medulla. The cortico-spinal tract and the pyramidal tract are not identical, for the *pyramidal tract* comprises by definition all of the fibres that pass through the pyramids irrespective of their origins and terminations, which in the case of some of its components are obscure. The pyramidal tract was, indeed, named years before Flechsig demonstrated that its fibres had a connection with the cerebral cortex, a fact that he

2 B

established by studying the development of the myelinisation of
this pathway (Marshall, 1936).   The degeneration of the pyramids
following removal of the cerebral cortex in man may be complete

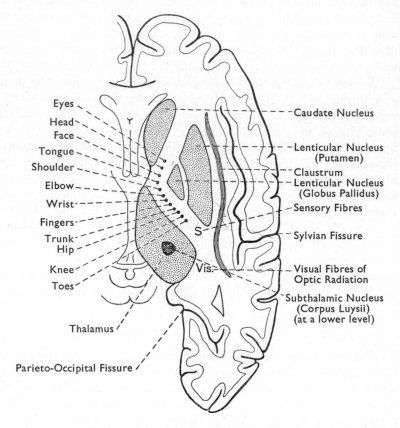

Eyes
Head
Face
Tongue
Shoulder
Elbow
Wrist
Fingers
Trunk
Hip
Knee
Toes
Thalamus
Parieto-Occipital Fissure

Caudate Nucleus
Lenticular Nucleus
(Putamen)
Claustrum
Lenticular Nucleus
(Globus Pallidus)
Sensory Fibres
Sylvian Fissure
Visual Fibres of
Optic Radiation
Subthalamic Nucleus
(Corpus Luysii)
(at a lower level)

FIG. 10.6.—Horizontal section through cerebrum at the level of the internal
   capsule.   Many cases of hemiplegia are caused by vascular lesions of the
   internal capsule where the condensation of fibres from the corona radiata into
   a small area makes the cortico-spinal system particularly vulnerable.   The
   spasticity that commonly accompanies the hemiplegia may be caused by concomitant damage to other (extra-pyramidal) descending pathways.   (Reproduced from Purves-Stewart, 1945)

(Lassek & Evans, 1946), or nearly so, a fact that emphasises the predominantly efferent nature of the pyramidal pathway.   Recently,
however, afferent fibres have been shown to run in the pyramids
(Brodal & Kaada, 1953).   This fact must be borne in mind when
interpreting attempts to ascertain the areas of the cerebrum that

contribute fibres to the cortico-spinal system by mapping the cortical responses evoked by the application of electrical shocks to the pyramids (Fig. 10.7).

There is now reason to believe that cortico-spinal fibres take their origin from a wide area of the cerebral cortex that lies both behind as well as in front of the central fissure (Lassek, 1948). This origin is much larger than was supposed until recently. From a part of the centre of this region movements may be evoked by the application of relatively weak electrical stimuli; the zone that responds in this manner is known as the *motor area*. It is damage to this motor region or to its contribution to the cortico-spinal pathway that gives rise to paralyses on the opposite side of the body. Those cortico-spinal fibres that arise in the motor area form only a part, indeed a minority, of the fibres that constitute the medullary pyramids. In hemiplegia (paralysis of the limbs on one side of the body) histological examination of the pyramids may, therefore, reveal no gross atrophy (Lassek, 1945).

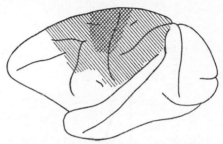

FIG. 10.7 —Probable origin of cortico-spinal fibres (monkey). A much greater area is involved than the region (motor cortex) from which muscular responses may readily be elicited by electrical stimulation. This map, prepared by recording the responses at the cortex caused by electrical stimulation of the pyramids, is in satisfactory agreement with the results of anatomical investigations (Lassek, 1948). (From Woolsey & Chang, 1948)

The cortico-spinal fibres of the motor area arise from the *large pyramidal cells* that are present in this region. Those fibres which reach to the sacral region arise from the areas that contain the largest of these cells; these very large neurones are sometimes called Betz cells, but they are not in a separate category from the other large pyramidal cells (Walshe, 1942 *b*). A small proportion of the cortico-spinal fibres are of large diameter and are capable of conveying information rapidly to the spinal cord (Fig. 10.8); Lloyd (1941) has measured the conduction velocity in the tract and has found rates as high as 60 metre/sec. There is substantial anatomical evidence that fibres of the cortico-spinal tract end upon internuncial neurones in the spinal cord, only a minority play, directly, on the anterior horn cells (Fig. 10.9). It is worth mentioning, in this connection, that the pathway in marsupials, ungulates and some rodents lies in the dorsal, and not in the lateral part of the white matter of the spinal cord. Lloyd (1941) has found that pyramidal stimulation may both excite and inhibit the discharge of internuncial neurones in the spinal cord.

Brouer (1933) has reached the conclusion that in most cases descending tracts do not end in motor nuclei but nearly always in co-ordinative centres, and he remarks that :—

'the descending tracts serving for pure reflex movements send their stimuli immediately to the motor cells ; the descending tracts, however,

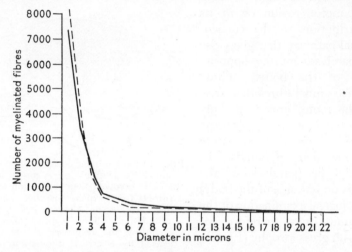

FIG. 10.8.—Diameter of fibres in medullary pyramid. Note that a few fibres are large but the majority are small. Histological and physiological observations often tend to emphasise importance of large fibres unduly since they are more readily investigated. The two graphs represent the result of counts on two human brains. (Lassek, 1942)

that stand under the direct influence of the extensive association mechanism of the cortex send their impulses chiefly to the sensory and association parts of the reflex arcs. They do not all immediately charge the motor cells but have an influence on the reflex arcs. . . .'

That the cortico-spinal fibres end principally on internuncial neurones suggests that there is no immutable relationship to specific muscles.

The cortico-spinal pathway is long and its function is disturbed in many diseases (*vide* Lassek, 1944) ; its fibres travel close to the lateral ventricles which frequently are affected by internal hydrocephalus, whilst in the brain stem they are again prone to injury.

It has long been held that the integrity of the pathway may be judged by studying certain reflexes that may be evoked by cutaneous stimulation. The most important of these *cutaneous reflexes* is that elicited by firmly stroking the outer edge of the sole of the foot ; the normal response in the adult is a plantar flexion of the big toe. The *Babinski response* consists of a dorsiflexion of the big toe with fanning of the small toes ; this reaction has been found after section of the cortico-spinal tract in the spinal cord in man (Hyndman, 1941) and after destruction of the medullary pyramid in the monkey (Tower, 1940). Nevertheless, to 'regard the Babinski response as a

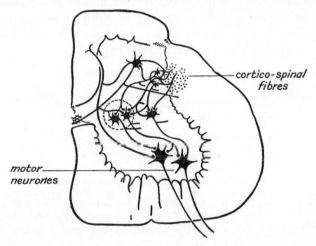

FIG. 10.9.—Section through one-half of the spinal cord. The majority of the fibres in the cortico-spinal tract activate internuncial neurones rather than the motor neurones themselves. (After Lloyd, 1941)

spinal reflex whose manifestation is prevented by the functioning of one and only one, descending tract, is an over-simple conception . . .' (Nathan & Smith, 1955). The reason for this reserve is that *at times division of the cortico-spinal tracts does not give rise to the sign* whilst it may be found as an accompaniment of lesions that do not involve these routes. Evidently the grey matter can be 'set' appropriately by more than one mechanism. The effective stimuli need not necessarily be painful, for under favourable conditions warmth, cold or touch may be effective. The afferent fibres for the Babinski reflex fall into two categories, A and C, both of which are slowly conducting (Kugelberg, 1948 ; see also Ashby, 1949). The disturbance of function giving this response may be of a purely temporary nature, as, for instance, with hypoglycaemic coma. In patients with periodic breathing the Babinski response may come and go, being found during the periods of apnoea, whilst a normal plantar response may be elicited at other times (Fig. 10.10).

Other cutaneous reflexes that are investigated in a neurological examination are those brought out by lightly stroking the skin of the abdomen. A failure of the abdominal wall to contract may be indicative of interference with the cortico-spinal tracts, but the sign is of less value than the Babinski response, for these reflexes may be unobtainable in some normal persons. Whilst they may be a useful lead in diagnosis, particularly if they are absent on one side only, it is essential to be aware that their relationship to the cortico-spinal pathways is indirect ; they may even reappear after the spinal cord has been completely severed (Riddoch, 1917 b).

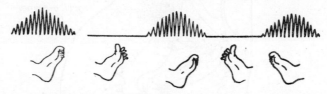

FIG. 10.10.—Change of cutaneous reflexes from the foot in periodic respiration. Babinski response during periods of apnoea, normal plantar response at other times. Other functions of the C.N.S., also, may show periodic fluctuations ; the level of consciousness and the size of the pupil may alter with the phases of the Cheyne-Stokes respiration. (After Tournay, reproduced from Fulton & Keller, 1932)

The *cortico-spinal control of movement* is very much more important in primates than in other mammals. A dog uses its legs to support its body, for walking and for scratching, whilst a cat can call upon a rather more extensive range of movements, for it may use its forepaws in playing and mousing. Nevertheless, the repertoire of limb movements in both of these animals and in other quadrupeds is small when compared with that of the monkey or the ape. These animals can climb trees, leap from branch to branch and feed themselves with their hands. In man the manual arts and crafts demand a degree of muscular control which in its turn dwarfs that required by other primates. Great precision is scarcely needed in movements of the foot, but there exist latent potentialities which are developed in ballet-dancers, and men who have lost their arms may learn to drive modified motor cars with their feet. A fine degree of control, both conscious and unconscious, is possible over the muscles of the face ; the expressions of the emotions were studied in detail by Charles Darwin (1872) ; facial expression is of particular significance for the physician.

Paralleling the differences of behaviour of the various mammals there exist corresponding variations in the central nervous system. The increased dependency upon the cerebrum as the evolutionary ladder is ascended is known as *encephalisation*, and it is important constantly to be aware of this process when comparing the effects of experimental lesions of the central nervous system in animals with the havoc wrought by disease in the brain of man.

In cats with bilateral destruction of the pyramids Liddell & Phillips (1943) could detect no disability in the ordinary acts of daily life. A surprising change in their behaviour was found, however, when they were placed on a horizontal ladder or upon a horizontal pipe. 'At once they become helplessly immobile, unable to take a step without slipping or falling.' This extra call on their skill revealed the magnitude of their clumsiness in performing any act which called for a degree of cortico-spinal co-ordination surpassing the mere rhythm of ordinary walking.

Encephalisation is nowhere better exemplified than in the control of movement, for whilst a rabbit, cat or dog may walk or even run after an operation that has removed the cerebral hemispheres, clinical observations show that, in man, interruption of the descending pathways from the cerebral cortex leads to a profound paralysis of the corresponding limbs.

The effects of sectioning the cortico-spinal tract are at present entirely controversial as far as the effects on *muscular tone* are concerned. The reasons for this difficulty arise in part from the fact that the tract has a different composition at different levels and in part from differences between different species. In the monkey (Tower, 1940) but not the cat (Liddell & Phillips, 1943), section of the pyramids at the level of the medulla gives rise to a flaccid paralysis on the contralateral side. These findings with the monkey have suggested that the intense spasticity that is so often seen in chronic lesions of the human cerebrum is determined by damage to extra-pyramidal (p. 390) descending fibres rather than by interference with the cortico-spinal tract itself. Most clinical lesions affecting descending pathways are liable to interrupt, to some extent, both cortico-spinal and extra-pyramidal fibres. It is usual, therefore, to speak of *upper motor neurone* lesions, a term that does not give a false sense of precision.

THE MOTOR CORTEX

The part of the cerebrum that appears to be most closely concerned with muscular control is known as the motor area; most of it lies in front of the central fissure. Walshe (1947) has given a careful description of the changes that may be observed in the arm on the side opposite to a lesion of this area. Different movements are affected to different degrees. Thus movements of the larger joints, and particularly the shoulder, are often retained when the hand has become useless. The first changes consist in a reduction of the number of movements that are possible. Whilst the patient may be able still to flex and extend his digits, he may be unable to exert separate control over them so as, for instance, to point with his index finger. It is often observed that with such lesions a muscle may be brought into play to accomplish one movement but cannot be contracted when it is required in another sequence. This is what the neurologist means when he says that it is 'movements and not the individual muscles which carry them out that are represented in the motor cortex' (Walshe, 1944).

A muscle may come into action when it is required as a synergist even though it cannot be used as a prime mover. Walshe (1944) points out that in many cases of residual hemiplegia the patient cannot extend the wrist but is able to clench the fist. 'If when he attempts to do the latter, we place a finger on the extensor tendons at the wrist we shall feel them tighten, fixing the hand in the midposition while the fingers flex. If now we ask the patient to extend the wrist and digits fully, we shall find no contraction of these extensors, for the movement in which they are now a component is paralysed.'

Something is now known as to the way in which the movements of the different parts of the body are represented in the cerebral cortex. Hughlings Jackson was the first to suggest that the movements of different parts of the body are represented in an orderly topographical manner. His surmise was a shrewd guess from a study of *epilepsy*. He was particularly interested in fits that start in one part of the musculature and spread to other parts of the body; fits of this type are now said to be 'Jacksonian'. Hughlings Jackson noted (*vide* Hitzig, 1900) that: 'The fits begin most often in those parts that suffer most in hemiplegia and these are always the muscles which are most concerned in arbitrary isolated movements. There are few cases in which the fits begin elsewhere than in the side of the face (usually in the cheek), in the hand or in the foot ; they very rarely begin in the upper arm or the calf.' He noticed that : 'Fits which begin in the foot have a different march from those which begin in the hand. When a fit begins in the hand it goes *up* the arm and *down* the leg. Now patients who have fits beginning in the foot tell me that the spasm goes *up* the leg and *down* the arm!'

Movements of different parts of the body are represented in the motor area in an *orderly sequence*, a fact that may be demonstrated

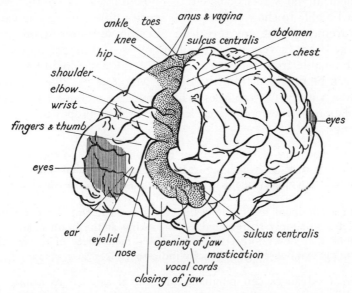

FIG. 10.11.—Motor cortex of chimpanzee. The area of the cortex given over to control of different parts of the body is not related to the anatomical size of the structure but to the diversity of movements that the part is called upon to perform. Thus the part concerned with the movements of the body is comparatively small. Note the separate region concerned with the movements of the eyes. (Grünbaum & Sherrington, 1901)

by the use of *electrical stimuli*. In these experiments it has been customary to use *repetitive shocks*, and to prevent the occurrence of a generalised epileptic attack the shocks used are the weakest that will provoke a response. One of the most important series of experiments was made by Grünbaum & Sherrington (1901) who worked on apes (Fig. 10.11). Their results were summarised in the following terms (Sherrington, 1906) : 'In the precentral gyrus, the sequence of representation of the musculature starting from below upward follows broadly that known for the lower apes. The sequence runs—tongue, jaw, mouth, nose, ear, eyelids, neck, hand, wrist, elbow, shoulder, chest, abdomen, hip, knee, ankle, toes and perineal muscles.'

The responses obtained from stimulating any given point were not fixed but were liable to change ('deviation of response') if a neighbouring point had been stimulated shortly beforehand. As the experiment proceeded, so more and more movements of different types were found, and it was felt that the results of any given experiment in no way exhausted the possibilities which the cortex might be able to show. There is a species difference in the variety of movements that are revealed; Leyton & Sherrington (1917) remarked that 'a very considerable number of different movements are obtainable from the motor cortex of the anthropoid,[1] far more than can be obtained from the dog or Macaque'.[2] The apparently limitless variety of responses which may be obtained by faradic stimulation of the motor area led Sherrington (1906) to issue this warning :

'The discovery of localisation of function in parts of the cortex has given the knowledge which now supplies to the student charts of the functional topography of the brain much as maps of continents are supplied in a geographical atlas. The student looking over the political map of a continent may little realise the complexity of the populations and states so simply represented. We looking at the brain chart of the text book may never forget the unspeakable complexity of the reactions thus rudely symbolised and spatially indicated.'

Great advances can be made in clinical science by those who are willing energetically to seek new knowledge and to equip themselves suitably by serving a rigorous apprenticeship in one of the basic sciences. Bacon remarked that 'we see voluptuous men turn friars, and ambitious princes turn melancholy, but of knowledge there is no satiety'. Penfield seized the opportunities presented by neurosurgery to learn more about the effect of stimulating various areas of the human brain. The investigations were performed after the brain had been exposed under local anaesthesia. The responses which Penfield obtained showed how large an area was concerned with movements of the hand and foot in comparison with the trunk and proximal segments of the limbs (Fig. 10.17). He found that motor responses could occasionally be obtained from behind the post-central sulcus (Penfield & Rasmussen, 1950).

[1] Ape.   [2] Monkey.

Penfield's work, in keeping with observations made on animals, shows that movements that are concerned with *feeding* may be elicited from the lower end of the precentral sulcus (Babkin & Buren, 1951).

In monkeys and apes the region that controls *movements of the eyes* is clearly separate from the main motor area, lying further forward in the frontal lobe (Fig. 10.11); it is possible to subdivide this frontal eye field, for stimulation of different parts produces movements of the eyes in different directions (Crosby, Yoss & Henderson, 1952). In man the eye fields have migrated backwards and form a part of the main motor area, although the region projects further forward than in the rest of the motor cortex; the points lie in the motor sequence at the junction of the hand and face areas (Penfield & Rasmussen, 1950).

Repetitive stimulation of the human or animal motor cortex, it has been seen, gives rise to a map of considerable complexity, and a map which is not static, for the details may change from trial to trial. It has, however, been shown that another and much simpler type of response may be obtained if *single electrical pulses* are used as stimuli. Liddell & Phillips (1950) explored the cortex of primates under light anaesthesia, and the precautions that they took to obtain reproducible conditions excelled those of most, and probably of all, of their predecessors in this type of investigation. The single electrical pulses set up muscular responses of the opposite side of the body after quite short latencies. The responses to faradic stimulation, on the other hand, only occur after a substantial delay, and, it may be supposed, involve a more complex system of excitation in the neuronal pathways. The responses produced by single pulses showed that the motor region may be divided into three regions (Fig. 10.12). Stimulation within the most lateral of these produced a movement of the angle of the mouth on the other side of the body, stimulation of the central area provoked a contralateral movement of the thumb, whilst stimulation of the most medial of the areas gave rise to a movement of the big toe. It is interesting that this approach has shown the same division of the motor cortex that was obtained from the study of focal fits.

The responses elicited by electrical stimulation of the motor cortex depend upon fibres that pass directly to the spinal cord. These cortico-spinal fibres arise in the deeper layers of the grey matter, a conclusion based on the findings of Dusser de Barenne (1934). He used the technique of thermo-coagulation; the cortex is warmed for a definite time, and it is possible to control the depth that is destroyed. Warming the cortex 'to 65 C. for two seconds destroys the nerve cells of the two outer layers' and 'heating to 70 C. for three or four seconds leads to a destruction of the three or four superficial layers, whereas application of a temperature of 80 C. for five seconds destroys all the nerve cells throughout the whole thickness of cortex'. This technique allowed it to be shown that the integrity of the layers containing the large pyramidal cells is essential for the responses to electrical stimulation, for the cortex lying superficial to this zone, but no more, may be destroyed. The fibres of the corona radiata themselves are, of course, excitable, and movements may be elicited after the grey matter has been destroyed, but the threshold

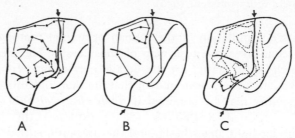

A   B   C

FIG. 10.12.—Map of motor cortex obtained by stimulating with single electrical pulses. The map is simple, for three zones only were found; it may be compared with the complicated systems revealed when the cortex is stimulated repetitively (Figs. 10.11 and 10.17). The size of each zone depended upon the strength of the current, and with strong shocks the zones were found to overlap 'so widely that each shock caused flick movements simultaneously in all three peripheries from the greater part of the motor area'. The zones controlled movements of the angle of the mouth (most lateral zone), of the thumb, index and little fingers (middle zone), and of the big and middle toes (medial zone). Baboon brain: A, thumb and finger area at strengths 1·2, 1·6 and 2·7 mA; B, toe area at strengths 2·05 and 4·7 mA; C, shows also area for mouth (solid line) at 2·35 mA. Arrows mark central fissure. (From Liddell & Phillips, 1950)

is substantially higher. The structures within the grey matter which are particularly liable to be stimulated by the electrical current are unknown. Electricity is 'a capricious agent. What exactly does it stimulate? Look at any histological section of cerebral tissue and consider how or where it strikes' (Liddell, 1953). Electrical stimulation cannot be expected to initiate, in the cortex, a pattern of activity which resembles the distribution that would occur under normal circumstances. Nevertheless, the responses which are obtained may be regarded as co-ordinated, for they do show reciprocal innervation of opposing muscle groups. This achievement must be due to activities of the spinal cord: an entirely abnormal type of discharge must descend through the cortico-spinal pathways.

Some observers have suggested, in spite of the data derived from clinical observation, that muscles are represented in the cerebral cortex, and it is certainly true that weak stimuli may, at times, cause a contraction of a *single muscle* only, or even of a part of a muscle. If the various parts of the motor cortex bore any rigid relationship to particular muscles it would, however, be expected that strong stimuli would excite a group of muscles including, inevitably, those that were excited by weak stimuli. Clark (1948) has shown that this is not always the case: 'At threshold stimulation of a fixed electrode the response was a fanning of the toes, while with a higher voltage there was only a violent flexion of the knee and hip without movement of the toes'. These observations were made on conscious cats and the animals appeared to suffer no discomfort from the presence, or the stimulation, of the implanted electrodes. Using this technique, it has also been shown (Ward, 1938) that the response to stimulation of the motor cortex varied with the *position of the limb*. Thus with the limb flexed initially it might partially extend, whilst with the limb extended initially it might flex; the movement elicited by stimulation if the cortex brought the limb always towards one definite position and so, depending upon the initial posture, either flexion or extension was elicited. These results are entirely incompatible with the 'muscle mosaic' theory, and they point to the extreme importance of afferent information from the limbs in determining the nature of the cortical response. It is interesting that the final position reached by a limb on stimulating a cortical point depends upon the position of the head (Ward, 1938), and it is probable that labyrinths are concerned in this effect. The powerful control that the labyrinth can exert upon cortically induced movement is shown by sectioning the 8th nerves. Electrical stimulation then only with difficulty elicits movement (Kempinsky & Ward, 1950).

The point at which information from the labyrinth and from proprioceptors modifies the effects of cortical excitation is uncertain. It would be wrong to assume that the locus of action is necessarily cortical : the interaction may, in part at least, occur at a spinal level. The same cortico-spinal discharge may be channelled in different ways according to the information coming in from other sources. The spinal cord is certainly capable of this sort of action. Thus in a spinal animal the effect of a tendon jerk upon the contralateral limb may vary according to the initial posture of that limb : flexion occurs if it is initially extended, extension if it is initially flexed (Magnus, 1924 ; Figs. 6 and 7, p. 31).

'It cannot be too much insisted upon that for every bodily movement of any complexity afferent impulses are as essential as the executive efferent impulses.' These words were written by Foster in 1879, and at that time experimental evidence as to the functions of the cerebrum was very scanty. Nevertheless, they have been repeatedly shown to be true. The part played by *sensory information of different types* in guiding voluntary movements is well exemplified in *grasping* an object. Normally vision guides the hand to the object, but the final clenching of the fingers is dependent upon contact, and it is probable that both tactile and deep-pressure receptors are concerned. Finally, if an attempt is made to remove the object from the hand, resistance may be encountered *pari passu* with the force exerted ; proprioceptive endings in the muscles are probably responsible for this reaction. In pathological conditions affecting the cortex grasping may be accentuated so that the patient may grasp any object that comes into contact with the hand. Just as, in normal grasping, information from several sources determines the movement, so the exaggeration caused by disease may take various forms. There may be an exaggeration of the response to visual stimuli so that the patient grasps at any object which moves into his field of view. In other patients it may be the response to tactile cues that is increased ; light contact with the thenar eminence may cause the hand to close (*vide* Walshe & Robertson, 1933). In yet others the dominant feature may be an exaggeration of the stretch reflex of the flexor musculature (Walshe & Hunt, 1936). The region of the cortex that is most commonly found to be damaged when there is pathological exaggeration of grasping is the anterior part of the motor cortex on the opposite side (Adie & Critchley, 1927). The work of Travis indicates that the important region is probably the supplementary motor area (p. 385) that lies largely on the medial surface of the hemisphere.

Removal of the motor cortex not only impoverishes or abolishes voluntary movements, but also affects the *tone of the limbs*. The changes which occur are, however, rather variable. Walker (1946) has summarised the results obtained by Bucy in the following terms :

'Removal of the arm or leg areas of the precentral motor cortex or both, in man results in a complete flaccid paralysis of the part or parts represented. The paralysis . . . begins to recede in four to sixteen days. The order of recovery is variable, but it progresses most rapidly in the proximal muscles. Some of the distal muscles may remain paralysed.

The final deficiency is less severe when either the arm or leg area is removed than when both are ablated. In the upper extremity the flexor muscles, and in the lower extremity the extensor muscles, show the greatest recovery. Spasticity appears within one or two weeks of the ablation. It is of the clasp-knife type and it is most marked in the stronger muscles, namely, the flexors of the arm and the extensors of the leg. It is not so severe as that seen in hemiplegias due to capsular lesions.' Occasionally chronic hemiplegia may be associated with hypotonia (Aring, 1940).

That either flaccidity or spasticity may result from a cortical lesion suggests that *more than one efferent system* may be present ; that the descending pathways may contain fibres which have different functions (*vide* Denny-Brown & Botterell, 1948). As has been seen, a study of histology and of the results of electrical stimulation also support this suggestion ; the cortex does not contain a layer of uniform cells the axones of which form a single and homogeneous final common path, and it is therefore not surprising that the organisation revealed by stimulation depends upon the type of stimulus (*e.g.* single or repetitive) that is used (*vide supra*).

It has been suggested that spasticity is more likely to arise when the destruction involves the anterior (area 6) rather than the posterior (area 4) half of the motor area, and some American workers (*vide* Fulton, 1943, and Bucy, 1944) have sought to show that the properties of these two zones can be sharply differentiated. This is a point of great practical, as well as theoretical, importance for therapeutic measures have been based upon these views. It may well be that regional differences do exist between different parts of the motor cortex but the differentiation that has been proposed has certainly not won universal support (*vide* Walshe, 1942 *b*).   Clark & Ward (1948) were particularly interested in these, suggested, differences, and concerning the results of stimulating the cortex in monkeys they said, 'We found no difference in the character of the responses obtained from the anterior as compared with those from the posterior portion of the motor cortex. Even with threshold strengths of stimulating current we were unable to confirm the repeated assertion that stimulation of the anterior portion of the motor cortex produces massive movements whilst isolated movements result from stimulation of the posterior portion. At all points in the motor cortex stimuli above threshold evoked responses of the entire limb and often of the other ipsilateral limb as well, frequently with after-discharge as shown by clonic activity.' This problem has interested another group of workers and their results differ somewhat from those that have just been considered (Woolsey, Settlage, Meyer, Spencer, Hamuy & Travis, 1952). They stimulated the motor cortex of monkeys during light pentothal anaesthesia. Using an alternating current stimulus they found that the proximal joints of the limbs were represented towards the front of the zone, the distal joints close to the central sulcus. The axes of the limbs were in fact represented rostrocaudally.

A further division of the motor cortex has been suggested. It has been supposed that a region (area 4 S) lying between area 4 and area 6 is particularly concerned with inhibiting the activity of area 4. The data which are at present available do not, however, give unqualified support to this conclusion (Druckman, 1952) and the question must be regarded

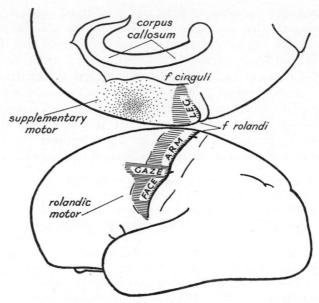

FIG. 10.13.—Supplementary motor area on medial surface of hemisphere. Travis (1955) suggests that spasticity is the result of damage to this area rather than to the main motor region. Within the supplementary area the body is represented somatotopically, the face anteriorly, the arm in the middle and the leg posteriorly. (After Penfield & Welch, 1951)

as being *sub judice*. It may be mentioned, however, that inhibitory effects on the motor area have clearly been demonstrated from the cingulate gyrus, the region that lies just above the corpus callosum on the medial surface of the hemisphere (pp. 464, 465).

In addition to the classical motor area, other neighbouring zones also play a rôle in the control of movement and should be regarded as *supplementary motor regions*. Thus stimulation of a region close to the lower end of the human motor cortex may, on occasion, give rise to responses, such as a movement of the hand, which are not compatible with the orthodox sequence (Penfield & Rasmussen, 1950).

Movement may also be obtained by stimulating the medial surface of the hemisphere in a region neighbouring on the upper end of the main motor cortex (Penfield & Welch, 1951; Bates, 1953 a). This supplementary area appears to be very important. The work of Travis (1955) suggests that many of the difficulties in understanding the results of cortical lesions can be resolved if care is taken to ascertain the extent to which this zone has been damaged. Travis relates hypertonia solely to damage to this region and accordingly would ascribe the differences that have been reported between areas 4 and 6 to incidental damage to this part of the cortex. Bilateral removal of the supplementary area results in no paralysis but in an immediate increase in tone. Grasp reflexes (p. 382) appear and the tendon jerks become hyperactive and clonic.

CONTROL OF THE MOTOR CORTEX BY SUBCORTICAL REGIONS

The motor cortex is an executive mechanism for performing movement but its destruction does not impair the ability to conceive the action needed to reach a certain goal. Ferrier (1890) said that :

'I hold that the centres of the sensations which accompany muscular action, and which form, in part, the basis of our ideas of movement, are distinct from the cortical centres, through and by which the particular movements are effected. The destruction of the cortical motor centres paralyses the power of execution, but not the ideal conception of the movement itself. A dog with its cortical centres destroyed has a distinct idea of the movements desired when asked to give a paw, but it makes only inefficient struggles and fails to comply. So, too, it not infrequently happens that a patient rendered hemiplegic by embolism of his Sylvian [1] artery only discovers his infirmity by his inability to execute the movements which he has distinctly conceived.'

It will be seen from the first sentence of this quotation that Ferrier had anticipated the demonstration of the functioning of a separate sensory centre, concerned with the position of the limbs ; this centre is now known to be the parietal lobe (Chapter 11). Leyton & Sherrington (1917), also, made some observations on the effect of removal of the motor cortex, and they state that :

'A point which impressed us repeatedly was the seeming entire ignorance on the part of the animal, on its awakening from an ablation-experiment, of any disability precluding its performance of its willed acts

[1] Middle cerebral artery.

as usual. Surprise at the failure of the limb to execute what it intended seemed the animal's mental attitude, and not merely for the first few minutes, but for many hours. It was often many hours before repeated and various failures to execute ordinary acts contributory to climbing, feeding, etc., seemed to impress gradually on the animal that the limb was no longer to be relied upon for its usual services. The impression given was that the fore-running idea of the action intended was present and as definitely and promptly developed as usual. All the other parts of the motor behaviour in the forms of action coming under observation seemed accurate and unimpeded except for the rôle, as executant, of the particular limb whose motor cortex was injured.'

FIG. 10.14.—Extent of lesion that did not abolish latch-box habits. The lesion is bounded caudally by the central fissure. The operation produced a temporary paralysis, but after recovery the monkey was capable of performing the necessary movements. During the recovery period the animal did not have access to the training boxes. When sufficiently recovered it opened the box without random exploratory movements. This experiment appears to rule out the motor cortex as playing an essential rôle in the conditioned reflex arc. (Reproduced from Lashley, 1924)

It has often been supposed that learning depends upon the *transcortical irradiation* of activity from the sensory to the motor areas (*vide* Pavlov, 1927). According to this theory destruction of the motor cortex on both sides of the brain should abolish conditioned reflexes. Lashley (1921) put the hypothesis to an experimental test by training rats to find their food by running into a lighted, illuminated alley and avoiding an unlit alley ; removal of the motor areas did not abolish this reaction. A number of experiments with the rat have shown indeed that habits based on visual discriminations survive destruction of any part of the cerebral cortex except the primary visual projection area (Lashley, 1950). In keeping with these findings removal of the motor cortex on both sides from a monkey did not abolish motor habits learnt before the operation (Fig. 10.14).

Transcortical conduction does not appear to be vitally important for muscular reactions depending upon the integrity of the motor area. Sperry (1947 *b*) made numerous incisions into the sensori-motor cortex of monkeys and could find no impairment of muscular co-ordination (Fig. 10.15). He states that with the 'foci in the cortex for movement of shoulder, elbow, wrist, and digits as well as corresponding sensory foci separated from each other by radial incisions in both hemispheres . . . and with the whole arm cortex separated from its neighbouring cortical fields, the coordination of the limb with respect to the trunk and of the various limb segments with respect to each other was nevertheless carried out in a normal manner. Well-organized motor function survived even in the case of refined "voluntary" manipulative movements of hand and digits which presumably are most highly dependent on cortical control.'

Electrical stimulation of the motor area sometimes gives rise to ipsilateral responses. For instance, Bates (1953 a) has shown that under certain circumstances the leg area may exert a control over the ipsilateral, as well as the contralateral, limb. He has suggested

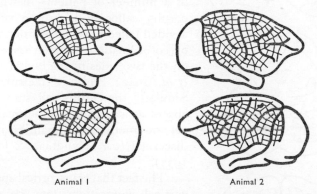

Animal 1   Animal 2

FIG. 10.15.—Incisions in sensori-motor cortex of monkeys that did not give rise to inco-ordination of the hand. Experiments of this type show that transcortical connections are not essential for the organisation of voluntary movements. (Reproduced from Sperry, 1947 b)

that the motor map should include, therefore, two legs. The greatest degree of *ipsilateral control* is probably achieved in patients suffering from hemiplegia dating from infancy ; in them the plasticity of the young brain has allowed the greatest possible compensation to be achieved. The diseased hemisphere is sometimes removed from these patients, for the damaged tissue may be the source of epileptic discharges. Patients who have undergone this operation of 'hemispherectomy' can walk, although not entirely normally, but there is little or no control over the contralateral hand. The anatomical basis for ipsilateral cortical control is well established, for some cortico-spinal fibres do not cross to the opposite side but descend in the anterior and lateral columns of the spinal cord on the same side (Fig. 10.16). Nevertheless, it is certainly true that the motor cortex is principally concerned with the contralateral half of the body, and it is therefore important to discover how the movements of the two halves are co-ordinated.

The *corpus callosum*, a large commissure of white matter, joins the two hemispheres and appears to connect each point of one hemisphere to the corresponding area of the opposite side. Curtis (1940 *a* and *b*) found that stimulation of a point of one hemisphere set up responses, sharply localised, at the corresponding position on the other side. Nevertheless, studies of a number of patients in whom the corpus callosum had been surgically divided failed to reveal any definite lack of co-ordination between the muscles on the two sides of the body (Akelaitis *et al.*, 1942; Smith & Akelaitis, 1942). Similarly the corpus callosum may be absent as a congenital abnormality and yet no motor abnormalities may be discerned (*vide* Hyndman & Penfield, 1937).

The fact that transcortical and intercortical connections may be divided without interfering seriously with the

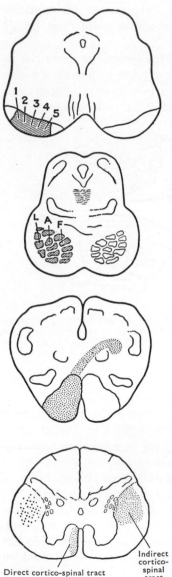

Fig. 10.16.—Diagram of cortico-spinal tracts as revealed by tracing degeneration (Marchi technique) following removal of right motor area. Stimulation of points 1, 2, 3, 4 and 5 in the midbrain gave rise to movements of the opposite foot, thigh, trunk, hand and face respectively. Stimulation of points F, A and L in pons produced movements of face, hand and foot respectively. Note presence of ipsilateral fibres in anterior and lateral columns of spinal cord. Similar studies, in which only a part of the motor area has been destroyed, have shown that the connections are more widespread than might be supposed; the arm area, for instance, sends fibres that reach to the lumbar region of the spinal cord. (From Leyton & Sherrington, 1917, as modified by Wright, 1945)

Direct cortico-spinal tract

Indirect cortico-spinal tract

execution of movements points to the possibility, or perhaps certainty, that the activity of different parts of the motor cortex, and the relationships between the two hemispheres, are dependent upon *subcortical connections.* Penfield (1954) has remarked that :

'When one considers the extraordinary dexterity of hand movement it is obvious that, if the precentral motor gyrus is to be utilised in the execution

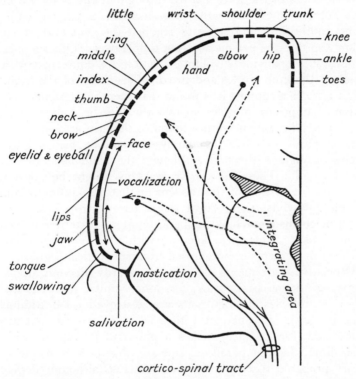

Fig. 10.17.—Control of movement by cortex. Note that the area given over to parts of the body is related to the variety of movements which they are called upon to perform. The two hemispheres are controlled by subcortical regions. (After Penfield, 1954)

of skilled acts, the nerve impulses that reach it must come in a pattern which is vastly varied in time of arrival, in rhythm and in the combination of ganglion cells selected for activation. One conclusion in regard to the origin of these patterned impulses may be established at once. They do not come directly across the neighbouring cerebral cortex to the precentral gyrus, for if the gyrus immediately in front of the precentral gyrus is excised, the skilled act may still be carried out, and if the postcentral gyrus immediately behind it is excised the act is not abolished either, although it may become awkward. Therefore, the controlling impulses flow upward to the precentral gyrus from some subcortical position. The impulses in this subcortico-cortical stream pass to the precentral gyrus and from there downward again to the bulbo-spinal grey matter on the way to the muscles' (Fig. 10.17).

In a simple action such as lifting a leg from the floor extensive rearrangements of the musculature throughout the body are necessary. Some of these *associative movements* are concerned with preserving equilibrium and serve to readjust the centre of gravity of the body so that the person does not topple over. Other associative reactions accompanying a voluntary action are concerned with the fixation of the limb girdles and proximal segments of the limb. In using a limb as a support it is found that there is simultaneous contraction of opposing muscles so that the limb is converted into a rigid pillar. If a patient with a lesion of the arm area of the motor cortex attempts to move the paralysed hand he brings into play muscles throughout the body, although the hand itself may move little, if at all. These associative reactions might be appropriate for a powerful version of the movement that was attempted and it is plain that whilst the cortical lesion has destroyed part of the effector mechanism much of the spatio-temporal pattern of movement remains intact. This is in keeping with the view that cortically controlled movements are organised from subcortical regions.

Associative movements do not necessarily depend upon the integrity of the cerebral cortex, for rather similar reactions may be seen when the descending tracts are destroyed (*vide* Riddoch & Buzzard, 1921). If a patient with a lesion of the internal capsule on one side, for instance, makes a powerful movement with the normal limb, then the paralysed side also may be seen to move. It appears probable that voluntary movements, although dependent for their execution upon the motor cortex, are organised from subcortical regions, and are associated with adjustments of posture that use, in part at least, descending pathways that are independent of the cortico-spinal system. It is uncertain to what extent the ipsilateral cortex is concerned with the associative reactions seen in capsular lesions.

EXTRA-PYRAMIDAL PATHWAYS

It has been seen that cortical lesions interfere with movements at an executive rather than an organisational level and there is evidence that subcortical pathways leading to the motor area are important in controlling its activity. It might therefore be supposed that suitably placed subcortical lesions would disrupt, in various ways, the general plan of muscular performances; this supposition is substantiated by a study of human diseases. The regions that must be considered in this connection are lumped together under the heading of the *extra-pyramidal motor system.* This term was introduced by Kinnier Wilson (1911) and may be taken to indicate those parts of the brain concerned with movement that do not discharge efferent impulses into fibres travelling through the medullary pyramids. 'Extra-pyramidal' is rather a loose word, but it is convenient : 'A cursory examination . . . of the neuro-anatomy of the "extra-pyramidal system" suffices to show that

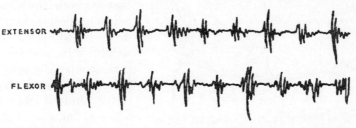

FIG. 19.18.—Electromyogram of tremor of Parkinsonism. this condition is sometimes called *paralysis agitans.* The tremor is rather remarkably regular in rate and affects opposing muscle groups alternately. This is not necessarily true of other varieties of tremor ; Brazier investigated a case of delirium tremens and found that opposing muscles became active at the same time. According to Hoefer & Putnam (1940) the tremor of paralysis agitans may be synchronised throughout the involved musculature. (Reproduced from Brazier, 1945)

"extra-pyramidal system" is a term of convenience not unlike the *terra incognita* of the early Renaissance map makers' (Ruch in S. S. Stevens, 1951).

Some diseases of the extra-pyramidal system produce a condition in which the mechanisms generating movements spring into action far too readily. In one disorder of this type, *chorea*, spontaneous movements occur which are rapidly executed and well co-ordinated ; the movements are purposeless, for they bear no relationship to the needs of the subject in the environment in which he finds himself.

The movements : 'It is especially to be observed . . . differ from the jerky movements of the arm occasionally seen in severe cases of locomotor ataxy. They are not mere spasms and cramps, but an aimless profusion of movements of considerable complexity, much nearer the purposive movements of health. They are not so much incoherences of muscles (like the "fist" we see in a partial fit of those convulsions which begin unilaterally where all the muscles of the hand are in action at once) as incoherences of *movements of muscles*. There is some method in their madness. They are not analogous to playing at once many keys of a piano in mere order of continuity, but to a random playing of harmonious chords' (Hughlings Jackson, 1868).

In addition it may be noticed that the associative movements are greatly exaggerated ; these additional, postural movements would be appropriate, perhaps, if the effort required was very much greater. A patient asked to lift a small object may use both hands and re-adjust his posture as though he was lifting a heavy weight. In walking, the patients may 'swagger' and swing their arms excess-ively ; indeed the word 'chorea' means a dance, and it is an apt term, for in dancing movements are made which are in excess of utilitarian require-ments. Locke (1689), the philosopher, remarked that in chorea the patient 'is perpetually dancing : he is not at liberty in this action, but under as much neces-sity of moving as a stone

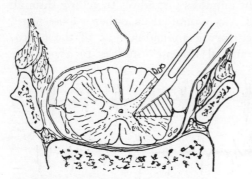

FIG. 10.19.—Surgical attack on lateral cortico-spinal tract for relief of tremor in Parkin-sonism. After apparently complete division of these fibres patients are hemiplegic, but this often passes away soon after the opera-tion. Although a poverty of movement may remain, they are rarely as incapacitated as is a patient with hemiplegia caused by a vascular lesion in the internal capsule. Interruption of the large bundle of fibres connecting the basal ganglia with lower regions—the ansa lenticularis—also may relieve Parkinsonian tremor (*vide* Spiegel & Wycis, 1954). (Reproduced from Putnam, 1940)

that falls or a tennis-ball struck with a racket'. Very rarely chorea may be restricted to a single limb ; that this may occur has been taken to indicate that there is a somatotopic representation in the basal ganglia (*vide* Davison & Goodhart, 1940 ; Jakob, 1925).

Occasionally with lesions of the small *subthalamic nucleus* a condition allied to chorea is seen in which the involuntary move-ments are of almost convulsive severity. 'The syndrome is a peculiar contralateral disturbance of movement which usually bears a similarity to choreiform movements of a stormy nature, but surpass by far the ordinary manifestations of chorea. It appears as irregular and inco-ordinated contorting movements of the muscle masses of an entire half of the body, with a pronounced tendency to attacks of twisting and turning. The symptom is called hemiballismus' (Jakob quoted by Whittier, 1947). The subthalamic nucleus is probably, therefore, of great importance in the organisation of movements, and Waller (1940) has shown that muscular reactions akin to walking may be elicited by electrical stimulation of a region lying close to this nucleus. The area concerned was sharply defined, and he concluded that it should be regarded as being a specific centre concerned with progression. The spontaneous movements of chorea, and of hemiballismus, are mediated by the motor cortex and the cortico-spinal pathway. This is a point of some

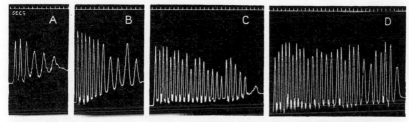

FIG. 10.20. Alternate voluntary flexion-extension of elbow in Parkinsonism. Local anaesthetic injected into muscle reduces rigidity and fatigue. A, before ; B, 10 min. after injection into biceps ; C, 15 min. after injection ; and D, 25 min. after injection into biceps and 6 min. after injection into triceps. P. B. C. Matthews & Rushworth (1956) studying cause of this effect concluded that the drug may preferentially block small motor nerve fibres supplying the muscle spindles. Rigidity may be abolished but voluntary power retained. (Reproduced from Walshe, 1929 *b*)

practical importance, for hemiballismus, if untreated, is usually, or invariably, fatal : accordingly, it may be rational to take the drastic therapeutic step of removing the motor cortex surgically (Meyers, Sweeney & Schwidde, 1950).

Chorea may be contrasted with *Parkinsonism*, a disease in which voluntary movements are difficult to initiate and associative and expressive movements are reduced or abolished. These patients do not 'give an observer the unqualified impression of being hypokinetic solely because they are endeavouring to move but find themselves incapable of it. Much of their immobility appears to be due to a lack of "will" to move and they seem afflicted not so much with a paralysis of movement as with a paralysis of volition' (Magoun, 1950). These patients have a mask-like expression which stands in marked contrast to the facial grimacing of chorea ; they blink but seldom, and in walking they do not swing their arms. The poverty of the associative reaction makes them rather unstable and they fall over rather readily.

Another prominent feature of Parkinsonism is *tremor* (Fig. 10.18). This is most prominent when the limbs are stationary but maintained in a posture that does not allow them to relax completely; during voluntary movement it is normally suppressed. The integrity of the cortico-spinal system is necessary for the production of the tremor; it has been observed that a stroke, causing hemiplegia, abolishes the tremor on the paralysed side. These considerations have led neurosurgeons to attempt to alleviate the tremor by resection of the motor cortex, or alternatively to attack the cortico-spinal pathways in the spinal cord (Fig. 10.19). In some cases the cure has been worse than the disease. No satisfactory explanation for the occurrence of the tremor advanced, but it is known that section of the posterior roots does not abolish the movements although they do then become irregular in rate and amplitude (Pollock & Davis, 1930 *b*). One is reminded in this connection of Sherrington's remarks about the scratch reflex in the spinal dog : 'It is not easy to say what tunes such a rhythm, since it is *not* timed by the periphery as in a *clonus*'.

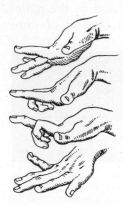

FIG. 10.21.—Movements of the hands in athetosis. The position changes slowly (cf. choreic movements). (From *The American Illustrated Medical Dictionary*, by Dorland)

One further striking feature of Parkinsonism is the great increase in muscular tone; it is known as *rigidity* (Fig. 10.20), and differs from spasticity (Chapter 5) in that on passive movement the resistance is maintained instead of suddenly collapsing (clasp-knife effect). In spite of this distinction rigidity resembles spasticity in that it is dependent upon the integrity of the reflex arc and is abolished by section of the posterior roots. The pathological lesions that are found in Parkinsonism are rather varied and it is probable that this clinical picture may be caused by disturbances at more than one site. The substantia nigra is the region most commonly affected (Heath, 1947 ; cf. Greenfield · & Bosanquet, 1953), and experimental lesions placed near by, in the tegmentum of the midbrain, may give rise to a similar condition in monkeys (Peterson *et al.*, 1949).

Another condition known as *athetosis* is a recognised syndrome of the basal ganglia; the word means 'without fixed position' and the disease is sometimes referred to as 'mobile spasm'. These are descriptive terms, for the limbs, especially their distal segments, are affected by slow writhing movements which give rise to strange postures (Fig. 10.21). Antagonistic muscles are simultaneously active, and the movements result from the differences in the power of the opposing groups (cf. Fig. 10.22). Athetosis would appear to be a caricature of a postural reaction but the stretch reflexes are not involved, for the condition persists, and may even be made worse, when the posterior roots are divided (Foerster, 1913). The disturbances may, however, be abolished by resection of the motor cortex of the opposite side (Horsley, 1909). The movements are caused by the activity of 'parapyramidal' pathways, for though the fibres arise in the motor cortex they do not pass through the pyramids, but are believed to relay in subcortical regions and to pass downwards in the anterior columns of the spinal cord. One must presume that the athetosis that sometimes follows the development of hemiplegia (Thomas, 1932) is due to activity in these subcortical regions. (For fine clinical studies of post-hemiplegic chorea see Weir Mitchell, 1874 *b*.)

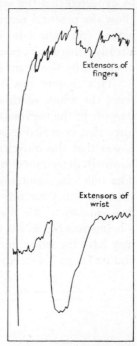

FIG. 10.22.—Sequence of changes when clenched fist is relaxed voluntarily. Normally as the finger extensors contract so, *pari passu*, the wrist extensors relax; in athetosis the normal reciprocal action may not be seen. The relaxation of the wrist extensors was late and was not maintained. Note irregularity of sustained contraction of extensors of the fingers. (Kinnier Wilson, 1925)

The mechanisms of postural fixation frequently cause a stiffening of the musculature that is most marked in the trunk and proximal joints of the extremities. It sometimes happens that this mechanism is 'released' in neurological disease so that curious contorting postures and movements are seen. This condition, *dystonia*, may be looked upon as being allied to athetosis (Herz, 1944).

It will have been seen that voluntary movements are initiated by the cortico-spinal tract that conveys orders directly to the spinal cord. The associative reactions that accompany the movement, however, are mediated by the extra-pyramidal system, and it may be expected that the synaptic relays that are found in the brain stem allow the postural reactions to be modified according to information gained from the labyrinths and other sources. As has been seen already (Chapter 5), postural reactions and righting reflexes are largely mediated by the brain stem.

This chapter has dealt with the control of movement, but in a sense the whole of this book deals with this subject, for this is the purpose of the nervous system. The appropriate use of the muscular force that is available is obviously more important than the absolute power that the muscles can exert ; and the control of the muscu- lature is determined by information obtained from many sources. The following quotation from the *Iliad* appears appropriate : 'Call your craft to your aid, my lad, and win the prize, for craft wins all. A woodman wields his axe better by craft than force, and by craft a helmsman steers his ship, and by craft a charioteer may win. He may have the worst horses to drive, but he keeps his eye on the post, and he keeps his steeds in hand.'

CHAPTER 11

THE SENSORY PATHWAY, THALAMUS AND PARIETAL LOBE, SPEECH

> The property in the hand of ascertaining the distance, the size, the weight, the form, the hardness or softness, the roughness or smoothness of objects, results from there being this combined perception—from the sensibility of the proper organ of touch being combined with the consciousness of the motion of the arm, hand, and fingers. But the motion of the fingers is especially necessary to the sense of touch. These blend, extend, or expand, moving in all directions like palpa, with the advantage of embracing the object, and feeling it on all its surfaces, sensible to its solidity and to its resistance when grasped, moving round it and gliding over its surfaces, and, therefore, feeling every asperity.—SIR CHARLES BELL (1833).

THE TYPE OF INFORMATION THAT IS PASSED UPWARDS ALONG THE SENSORY PATHWAYS

IN previous chapters some examples have been given of the way in which information about objects in the outside world is built up. Very frequently an object impinges upon more than one category of receptor element; data are available from a number of independent sources. It is to be expected that the information will carry the greatest weight if the evidence from the various sources combines harmoniously and in ways to which the organism is accustomed. It is not difficult to understand how it is that a number of *different qualities* may be ascribed to the objects that we touch, a number that clearly exceeds the number of independent sensory modalities available (p. 36). Just as it is probable that the large number of hues to which an observer may be sensitive depends upon the different levels of excitation of only three basic pathways, so the properties of objects which we can differentiate by contact alone is not inconsiderable.

As an example of the foregoing considerations, the sensation of wetness may be produced by a blend of pressure and of coldness

or warmth ; moisture is not an essential component of the stimulus
(Bentley, 1900).   Thus if a finger is dipped into cold water but
kept dry with lycopodium powder or with a thin rubber membrane
the feeling will be quite as characteristic as without such protection
(*vide* Geldard, 1953).   Similarly the property of hardness refers to
an even cold pressure with a good boundary, whilst softness requires
an uneven warm pressure of poor boundary.   The sensation of heat
also is compound, being due it appears to the simultaneous excitation of warm and cold spots.   Heat may be felt when warm spots
are subjected to moderate warmth and cold spots to cold (*vide*
Woodworth, 1938).

Pathological lesions of the nervous system of an irritative type
are likely to set off discharges in pathways concerned with more
than one modality.   The anatomical mixture of fibres in peripheral
nerve trunks is of such a type as to be especially liable to result in
activity in different categories of fibres when irritated.   This occurs
on banging the elbow when the ulnar nerve is concussed (p. 56).
Within the spinal cord some separation of sensory modalities occurs,
but this is probably always incomplete and irritation of a part of the
white matter will be liable to activate more than one type of afferent
pathway.   Patients with such lesions often experience great difficulty
in finding words adequate to describe their sensations.

Difficulties in describing 'paraesthesiae' are particularly likely
to arise when fibres are excited in unaccustomed combinations.
Some types of sensation set up by pathological lesions may bear a
specific relationship to the part of the sensory system in which the
lesion exists.   Thus according to Kinnier Wilson (1927) the sensation of wetness arises with lesions of the peripheral nerves and
sensory pathways in spinal cord and brain stem, but is exceptional
with lesions of the cortex or thalamus.

The size of the roots that together constitute the cauda equina
stands in striking contrast to the small diameter of the cord with
which they are connected.   The volume of the posterior roots is
far too great to allow all afferent fibres to turn in an oral direction
and proceed unchanged to the cerebrum.   In part, space may be
saved by the use of thinner axones in the ascending as compared
with the peripheral pathways (*vide* Lloyd & McIntyre, 1950), but
it is likely that economy is affected also by censoring the items of information that are transmitted forwards to the brain.   With an image
on the retina much information is neglected and pregnant features
only are retained to be transmitted to the optic nerve (p. 311):

similar arrangements may hold for somatic sensibility. Sigmund
Freud (1891) wrote :

'If one compares the total number of fibres entering the spinal cord from
the periphery with that of the fibre tracts leaving the cord to connect it
with the brain, the latter proves to be only a fraction of the former. . . .
Only in the spinal cord, and in analogous grey areas, do the prerequisites
for a complete projection for the body periphery exist. For each peripheral unit of innervation there exists a corresponding area of grey matter
in the spinal cord, and in the extreme case one single nervous element.
Owing to the reduction of the projection fibres through the grey matter
of the spinal cord, a unit of grey matter belonging to a higher level can no
longer correspond to one peripheral unit. . . .'

Little is known about the ways in which the data may be selected,
but it is surely significant that a number of visual illusions are
known to have tactile counterparts. It may be assumed that, as in
the case of the retina, it is to contours, angles and movement that
the system is especially reactive.

There is nothing new in considering that somatic afferent impulses are dealt with in the spinal cord, for the classical researches
of Sherrington pointed in this direction half a century ago. It is
not unreasonable to suppose that when the essential features of some
situation have been sifted from a mass of data by the cord that it is
this information that is especially likely to be passed to higher levels.
Movement across the skin may be of biological significance when
steady stimulation is not. Dealing with the scratch reflex, Sherrington (1906) stated that :

'A subliminal stimulus applied at a point A will render a subliminal
stimulus applied at a point B near A supraliminal if the second stimulus
follow within a short time, e.g. 500 γ (msec.). The space of receptive
surface across which this can be demonstrated amounts to 5-6 cm. . . .
the phenomenon is characteristically and simply illustrated by the difference between the potency as a stimulus of the edge of a card, say 6 in.
long, pressed simultaneously over its whole length against the receptive
skin-field, say for 5 sec., and on the other hand lightly drawing one corner
of the card along the same line in the skin-field also for 5 sec. The
former application simply evokes a reflex of a few beats, which then dies
out. The latter evokes a vigorous reflex that continues and outlasts the
application of the stimulus. A successive line is more effective as a
stimulus than a simultaneous line of equal length and duration.'

Even in the case of the dorsal columns some of the fibres that
ascend are secondary neurones the cells of which lie in the grey

substance of the spinal cord, and for these fibres, as well as for the other afferent pathways, there is the possibility of synaptic inter-action before impulses are discharged centrally (Hursh, 1940). In the medulla the fibres from the nuclei of the dorsal columns decussate almost completely (Berry, Karl & Hinsey, 1950 ; Bohm & Petersén, 1952) ; in this respect, therefore, one side of the body is connected with the opposite cerebral hemisphere. This arrangement is said to facilitate the handling of information coming from each side of the body, for somatic impulses on one side will reach the same hemisphere as visual impulses coming from the corresponding half of the visual field (Fig. 11.1). The im-portance of this crossing of somatic afferent impulses to the opposite side can be over-estimated, for in the rest of the spinal cord both crossed and uncrossed pathways are present (p. 57). In the cat the spino-thalamic tracts are vestigial and the im-pulses that ascend in the antero-lateral columns all relay in the lower brain stem. Fibres may cross to the opposite side at levels rostral to the spinal cord. Gardner & Haddad (1953) studied the central course of impulses from muscles, joints, inter-osseous membrane and skin in the cat. They stated that :

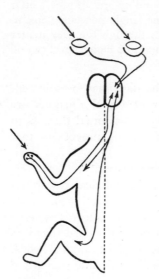

FIG. 11.1.—Crossing of sensory and motor fibres in relationship to visual system. Impulses dealing with the left side of the body and the left half of visual space are dealt with by the opposite hemi-sphere. (From Adrian, 1947 *a*)

'Aside from muscle nerves, which have few if any fibres ascending in dorsal funiculi, it appears that impulses from all nerves can reach the cerebral cortex by way of the dorsal funiculi. In addition there are crossed and uncrossed paths in each side of the rest of the spinal cord. Any nerve can project to any of the somatic areas (p. 404) by any one of these paths.'

Recently a good deal of interest has been taken in the possibility that afferent impulses may ascend by pathways other than the medial fillets or spino-thalamic tracts (p. 59). The route under consideration lies medially in the brain stem and the potentials evoked by afferent stimulation have long latencies and a wavelike configuration (Starzl, Taylor & Magoun, 1951). The transmission of these impulses in the central grey matter is said to be particularly susceptible to the action of certain general anaesthetics, and it is possible that this susceptibility has much to do with the action of these agents (French, Verzeano & Magoun, 1953).

THE TRANSMISSION OF SENSORY MESSAGES THROUGH THE THALAMUS
AND THE DETAILS OF THE CORTICAL REPRESENTATION OF THE
BODY, OF TASTE AND OF THE ALIMENTARY TRACT

Within the thalamus the different fibre tracts are regrouped and there is further opportunity for the interaction of different modalities. Walker (1938 *a*) remarked that 'from every part of the brain and spinal cord fibres converge to the thalamus to enter into synaptic relationships with neurones which project principally to

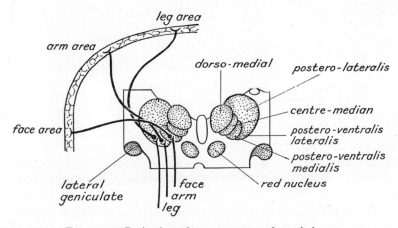

FIG. 11.2.—Projection of sensory system from thalamus
to post-central gyrus. (From Wright, 1952)

the cerebral cortex. This congregation of afferent tracts in the thalamus allows both intra- and inter-systemic integrations.'

In the thalamus itself the topographical plan of the body is reconstructed by resorting the fibres that enter the nucleus postero-ventralis lateralis. The representation of the leg lies most laterally, whilst that of the arm lies medially (Fig. 11.2), but there is overlap between the representation of different regions (Gaze & Gordon, 1954). The area for the face is found in the adjacent postero-ventralis medialis nucleus (Fig. 11.2). The activity of single neurones of these nuclei has been investigated by Adrian (1941). Brief afferent

2 D

volleys are sent to the cortex in response to a movement of hairs and more sustained responses can be produced by pressure. The impulses often appear in groups of two and three very closely spaced; furthermore, the afferent volley produced by a touch is often followed by a rhythmic after-discharge from the thalamus. This after-discharge has the same distribution to the cortex as the primary discharge and consists of a series of short volleys. As it persists in the fibres of the corona radiata after destruction of the cortex, it cannot depend upon a circuit from thalamus to cortex and back.

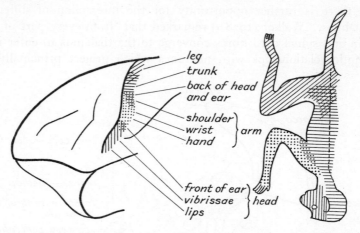

FIG. 11.3.—Sensory cortex of monkey. The face and occiput are represented some distance from one another, the arm area intervening. (From Adrian, 1941)

The cortical zone that is the chief receiving station for afferent impulses lies behind the central sulcus and stretches in a strip-like manner across the hemisphere (Fig. 11.3); it is the *post-central* gyrus (Marshall, Woolsey & Bard, 1941). Both anatomically and physiologically this area must be clearly separated from the remainder of the parietal lobe. The post-central gyrus has connections with the projection nuclei of the thalamus that have just been considered; the density of the projection from these nuclei is greatest towards the front of the gyrus (Clark & Powell, 1953) and especially to that part that is buried, forming the posterior lip of the central sulcus (Area 3). It is along the post-central sulcus, especially in its anterior part, that the arrival of afferent messages may be mapped by electrical techniques. For this work it is customary to use a fairly deep level of anaesthesia to prevent the responses from spreading widely through the cortex and obscuring the details of the sensory map (Fig. 11.4). The results that have been obtained correspond rather closely with those obtained for the motor cortex using faradic stimuli. The leg is represented most medially and then in sequence the trunk, arm and face, but a good deal remains to be learnt of the way in which the three dimensions of the body are represented in two dimensions

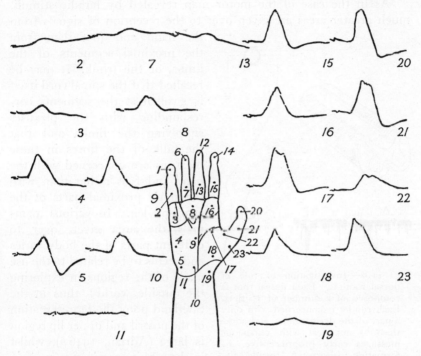

FIG. 11.4.—Electrical responses from a spot on the surface of the sensory cortex of the monkey caused by mechanical stimulation of different parts of the hand. A cat's whisker was used for the stimulation. (From Woolsey, Marshall & Bard, 1942)

on this sheet of the cortex, of the type of 'projection', in the carto-graphical sense, that is used.

According to Woolsey, Marshall & Bard (1942) the representa-tion in the sensory cortex follows the segmental pattern of the dermatomes, the representation of a part of a limb being dependent upon its relationship to the pre- and post-axial lines. Within each dermatome further subdivisions can be made out by examining the rootlets that make up the posterior roots (Fig. 11.5); it is not clear whether the finer grain of the cortical sensory map follows the pattern of these rootlets and whether the subdivisions of the face regions sometimes indicated by disease processes have any cerebral counterpart (Fig. 11.6). The opportunities presented by electro-corticography (p. 235) for the investigation of sensory areas in the human cortex have not been seized; there appears to exist but one brief report in the literature (Woolsey & Erickson, 1950).

As in the case of the motor map revealed by faradic stimuli, much greater areas are given over to the reception of signals from the hand and foot than from the proximal segments of the limbs, or the trunk. It may be recalled that the spinal cord itself is swollen at the segments corresponding with the plexuses supplying the limbs and that the bulk of the fibres in these plexuses are concerned with the hand and foot rather than with the more proximal parts of the arm and leg. In various mammals the area given over to different parts of the body varies and seems to be related to the use made of the regions in exploring the outside world; thus in the Shetland pony the representation of the nostril and upper lip region is large (Adrian, 1946 b), whilst in the rabbit prominence is given to the lips (Fig. 11.7).

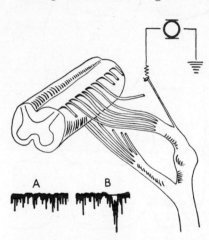

FIG. 11.5.—Investigation of rôle of dorsal rootlets. Each dorsal root is composed of a number of rootlets. Each rootlet is concerned with only a part of the dermatome; and some that do not deal with cutaneous messages carry proprioceptive information. Inserts: A, 'resting' discharge; B, a disturbance provoked by tactile stimulation. (From Kuhn, 1953)

The cortical representation that has been discussed was the first to be discovered and is therefore referred to as being primary. In addition it is now known that there is an additional or *secondary sensory area*. The secondary area lies in juxtaposition to the primary area; in man it is represented at the base of the post-central sulcus. Within the secondary area there may be the same divisions of the body that were met with in the primary area, but the map is much more cramped, for the area of the cortex concerned is much smaller. The face area in the secondary area lies close to the face area in the primary area, and in this neighbourhood there may be a zone that responds only to signals from the *ipsilateral* side of the face (Wool-sey & Fairman, 1946). Both sides of the body are represented in the secondary area, although the contralateral projection is the more prominent. The secondary area for the face receives its projections independently of those going to the primary area (Mountcastle & Henneman, 1949).

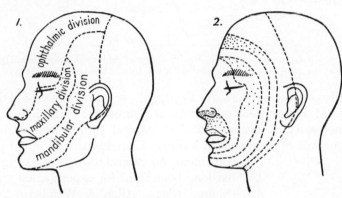

Fig. 11.6.—1. Distribution of divisions of Vth cranial nerve. 2. Progressively smaller concentric zones of pain and temperature sensibility in syringomyelia patients with progressively higher lesions in the descending nucleus of the Vth nerve. The area around the mouth where sensibility is preserved is the zone where it is lost in tabes. The segmentation revealed by syringomyelia may be developmentally more fundamental than that corresponding to the divisions of the Vth nerve. Some investigators have believed that pressure-pain is mediated by fibres that do not pass through the trigeminal ganglion but travel through the facial nerve or along sympathetic pathways (*vide* Davies, 1907; Maloney & Kennedy, 1911). More recent investigations (Carmichael & Woollard, 1933) have not supported these views but have suggested that *proprioceptive* information from the facial musculature is carried in the facial nerve. Following destruction of the Vth nerve 'such patients were unaware of the accumulation of food against the anaesthetic cheek, yet they recognised the displacement if this was brought about quickly by pushing against its inner and anaesthetic surface with a blunt instrument'. (From Richter & Woodruff, 1942)

The sense of *taste* is dependent upon four main modalities : 'salt', 'sweet', 'bitter' and 'acid' (Fig. 11.8). Most taste sensations can clearly be split into four components in this way, although the status of 'metallic' tastes is undecided and an alkaline taste is be-lieved to involve not only taste buds but also non-gustatory endings on the tongue (Kloehn & Brogden, 1948). Many of the subtleties 'of the palate' do not depend upon taste but upon the sense of smell. Taste may be investigated electro-physiologically ; Pfaffmann (1941) found three types of receptor in the cat—responsive to acid alone, to acid and to sodium chloride, and to acid and to quinine. There are reasons for believing that the gustatory impulses cross to the opposite side in the brain stem and that this decussation is

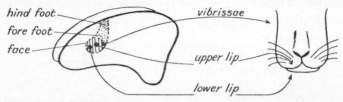

FIG. 11.7.—Representation within sensory cortex of rabbit. A considerable fraction of the total area is concerned with the lips. (From Adrian, 1941)

virtually complete (Fig. 11.9). Testing the sense of taste should therefore yield a great deal of important neurological information, but it is necessary to ensure that the chemical stimuli have access to only one side of the tongue at a time. Electrical stimuli might prove convenient for clinical testing; the technique has long been used for experimental studies (Shore, 1892; Allen & Weinberg, 1925). High-frequency (*e.g.* 1000 c/s) electrical currents applied to the tongue are said to give rise to a bitter sensation, whilst an acid taste is obtained with low frequencies (Bujas & Chweitzer, 1937). The sense of taste is represented at the foot of the post-central sulcus or in the upper lip of the Sylvian fissure; lesions in this region may give rise to heterolateral loss of taste.

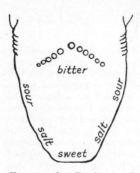

FIG. 11.8.—Regions of the tongue where the sensitivity to different tastes is highest. The four tastes can be appreciated in all of the regions to some extent. A useful discussion of the chemical aspects of taste will be found in Moncrieff (1944), the source of this figure

In spite of this it has been recorded that an anencephalic infant reacted differently according to the composition of the solutions placed in its mouth. Sucking movements followed the introduction of a sugary solution whilst the child attempted to spit out dilute acid (Monakow, 1926). Similarly, decorticate animals may show reactions to taste. The evidence that the new-born infant has taste sensitivity is reviewed by Pratt in Carmichael's monumental work on child psychology (Carmichael, 1954).

The eating of spicy foods sometimes gives rise to sweating of the face and head. In normal people such *Gustatory Sweating* is rarely prominent except in the tropics (*vide* Lee, 1954). In spite of the adjective 'gustatory', Lee's careful studies indicate that the sweating depends upon the stimulation of pain receptors rather than taste buds. Under pathological conditions the sweating may be greatly accentuated and then it may be

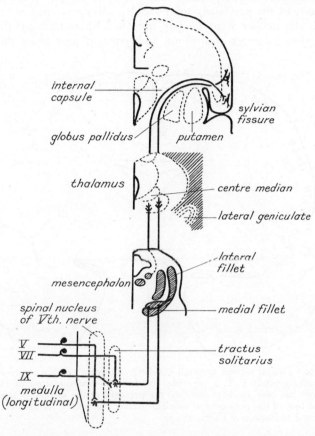

FIG. 11.9.—Taste pathways. The neurones decussate to travel on the opposite side in close association with the medial fillet (*vide* Patton, Ruch & Walker, 1944). Following hemispherectomy, taste is virtually abolished on the opposite side of the tongue. The course of the taste fibres in the cranial nerves has been a matter of dispute and they may run a different course in different people (*vide* Davies, 1907; Schwartz & Weddell, 1938). (From Pfaffman in Stevens, 1951)

provoked painlessly, as by eating chocolate. There have been several clinical studies of this condition and the evidence suggests that the essential lesion is an incomplete division of the cervical sympathetic pathways (Uprus, Gaylor & Carmichael, 1934; List & Peet, 1938; Haxton, 1948).

A similar type of disturbance has the curious title of the *syndrome of crocodile tears* (*vide* Chorobski, 1951). This condition is a complication of lesions of the facial nerve and appears to be due to impulses destined for the salivary glands reaching lachrymal apparatus. One case was that of 'a young girl who complained that whenever she ate or drank the eye on the side of the previously total facial paralysis overflowed with tears although she neither wept for joy nor shed bitter tears on that side'. The nervous messages controlling lachrymation pass along the nervus

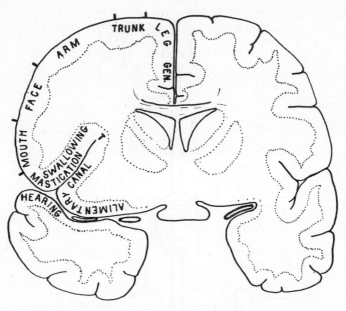

FIG. 11.10.—Frontal section through cerebrum showing sensory sequence. Gen. indicates genitalia; T, a possible site for the representation of taste. No attempt has been made to indicate the presence of the secondary sensory area at the foot of the post-central sulcus. (After Penfield & Rasmussen, 1950, as modified in Ranson & Clark, 1953)

intermedius and travel through the greater superficial petrosal nerve to the sphenopalatine ganglion. Thereafter they travel through the zygomatic and lachrymal nerves.

Within the insula the *alimentary canal* is represented (Fig. 11.10). In the case of epileptogenic foci in this region the patient may describe 'epigastric' aurae preceding his convulsions. The inaccessibility of this region and of the intestines themselves combine to make it difficult to obtain any detailed knowledge about the representation in this region (*vide* Penfield & Rasmussen, 1950). In the cat fast fibres from the viscera (Aβ) pass in the dorsal columns and reach the sensory cortex at a point between the areas for the arm and leg (Amassian, 1951), but it is not known whether in man the viscera are represented in the region for the trunk, as these findings might suggest.

Some idea of the magnitude of *ipsilateral representation* can be obtained by considering the extent to which the various modalities are retained after operations involving complete removal of all the sensory areas on one side. Thus after complete excision of one cerebral hemisphere, the sensitivity to light touch is abolished over the limbs on the opposite side and over the opposite side of the trunk, but is retained over the face. Painful stimuli are appreciated over the whole of the body, but are poorly localised on the side opposite to that from which the hemisphere has been removed. There is no response on the opposite side to differences of temperature unless these are so great as to activate the pain mechanisms. Passive movement of the opposite side of the body is poorly appreciated, but vibration sense is only moderately impaired (Dandy, 1933 ; Bell & Karnosh, 1949).

In view of these findings it is surprising that it is the loss of *postural sensibility* that so often stands out as the key disturbance in lesions of the parietal lobe. Naturally this defect is most readily detected in the limbs. For quantitative studies there is the apparatus of Slinger & Horsley (1906) (Fig. 11.11). It used to be believed that this type of sensibility depended upon the discharges of muscle spindles, but it now appears that joint receptors are the principal source of the information. In animal studies Mountcastle, Covian & Harrison (1952) could obtain no evidence that the discharge of muscle spindles reached the cerebral cortex ; the messages from the spindles are presumably used only at lower levels of the nervous system. In order to obtain information about the length of a muscle from the discharge of its spindles it would be necessary to have also data about the discharge of the small efferent nerves that regulate the contraction of the intrafusal fibres ; joint receptors are clearly more economical as to the number of pathways needed for the same information.

The loss of postural sensibility due to cortical lesions is said always to be most marked in the peripheral rather than the proximal joints (Bergmark, 1909). This is perhaps surprising, for in moving a limb the proximal joints have to be controlled more accurately than the peripheral ; indeed the sensitivity to angular movement is greater at the hip than elsewhere in the lower limb, whilst in the arm the shoulder is the most sensitive of the joints. Angular changes as small as o·2° at the hip joint may be appreciated, whilst the shoulder is forty times as sensitive as the joints of the finger. The proximal joints are also sensitive to slower rates of movement than are the distal. The physiology of joints is reviewed by Gardner (1950) [see also Piéron, 1952].

The sensitivity to *light touch*, also, may be reduced in patients with parietal lesions and, if attempts are made to measure the threshold by means of hairs of graded stiffness, difficulties are encountered

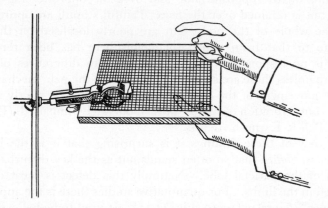

Fig. 11.11.—Measurement of proprioceptive sensitivity. A similar method was used by Head & Holmes (1911) in their classical studies on sensory disturbances following cerebral lesions. They used a sheet of stiff cardboard on one side of which a small depression was made to receive the tip of the index finger of the limb to be tested, while to the other side a sheet of white paper could be fastened. The cardboard was placed in any position and the patient was required to bring the normal index finger towards the tip of its fellow which lies on the opposite side ; the spot on which it impinged on the paper was marked by the observer. (From Slinger & Horsley, 1906)

owing to variability in the responses of the patient (Head & Holmes, 1911). After a series of stimuli the patient may, for instance, continue to respond despite the absence of peripheral stimulation. The area over which the sensory loss is greatest may take a number of forms, 'A segmental loss is frequently described, that is, an anaesthesia of some form limited to a hand or a foot, or a leg, but in cortical disease there is never a sharp or definite limit to the sensory defect . . .' The tactile loss may be more marked on one side of a limb than on the other, and it is rather common to find the mouth and radial border of the hand affected together (Holmes, 1927).

The tactile loss is usually, but not always, greatest at the periphery of the limb (Bergmark, 1909).

In addition to disturbances of threshold the sense of touch may be seen to be upset by other methods of investigation. Stimuli may be *incorrectly localised*, and to obviate fallacious results due to a loss of postural sensibility it may, in testing localisation, sometimes be desirable for the subject to indicate on a diagram the point at which he was stimulated. Another form of investigation that may be useful is the *compass test*; the patient is asked to state whether he is touched with one or with two of the points of the compass. The test may be varied in severity by adjusting the distance between the points. This procedure is analogous to the investigation of visual acuity (p. 320) by the use of two point sources of light, and just as visual acuity may be impaired by lesions of the optic nerve, so the performance on the compass test may fall off if the sensory pathways leading to the cortex are damaged. Performance is also impaired if the lesion is cortical; indeed the test is of the utmost importance in the investigation of cortical lesions : poor performance at it may be the only sensory sign that can be elicited. Holmes (1927) stated that 'Weber's compasses are not so regularly employed in clinical work as they deserve to be, for disturbance of the discrimination of one and of two simultaneous contacts is frequently the most striking effect of a lesion of the cortical sensory zone'.

The problem of the rôle of the cortex in the perception of pain is more involved. Lesions which are small and restricted to the post-central gyrus may give rise to areas of analgesia, whilst paradoxically this may not be the case with more extensive lesions spreading into the rest of the parietal lobe (Russell, 1945). Marshall (1951) has suggested that in the case of large lesions the opposite hemisphere takes over the handling of pain signals. Reports of the sensations aroused by electrical stimulation of the cortex mention unpleasant feelings such as 'pins and needles' but the word 'pain' is rarely used.

Patients with diverse neurological conditions may suffer from 'burning' pain that arises spontaneously. Sometimes pain that arises in the first instance as a result of a peripheral lesion is maintained solely by activity within the central nervous system, for it may persist after the nerve has been severed. In herpes zoster the virus attacks the posterior root ganglia but the pain may persist, in old people, long after the acute manifestations of the infection have subsided ; this pain may well be 'central'. In patients suffering from central pain stimulation of the post-central gyrus may provoke an attack, whilst excision of this area sometimes results in relief (Lewin & Phillips, 1952; Sugar & Bucy, 1951).

Temperature sensations also are represented in the cortex; Marshall (1951) has described two cases with small cortical wounds with loss of temperature sense but preservation of pain sensibility. That the various categories of sensation may be separately impaired by cortical lesions is of great theoretical interest, for it shows that, notwithstanding any interaction at a spinal, brain stem, or thalamic level, the pathways retain some degree of individuality to the cortex itself. It is surely in the cortex rather than at a lower anatomical level that afferent impulses are evaluated and linked to the speech mechanism.

There is electro-physiological evidence (Amassian, 1952) that fibres from cutaneous receptors may inhibit the discharge of thalamic units set up by stimulation of a visceral afferent nerve. There are therefore grounds for believing that the thalamus does much more than merely relay impulses to the cortex without modification. We have therefore to consider the implications of facts that point to an interaction of different modalities in the thalamus, and perhaps below in the sensory pathways, and, on the other hand, the evidence that different modalities may suffer to different degrees in cortical lesions. Clearly some compromise solution must be considered. For instance, some pathways may remain discrete whilst others may interact ; or perhaps some particular pathways preferentially carry one modality, but under certain circumstances the discharges may be modified by impulses from other sources. These questions are unanswered but, if they are not posed, there is little likelihood that an answer will be obtained (*vide* Gaze & Gordon, 1954).

THE THALAMIC SYNDROME.   THE EFFERENT FIBRES OF THE PARIETAL
   LOBE AND A HYPOTHESIS CONCERNING THEIR NORMAL FUNCTIONS

Spontaneous sensations occur not only with lesions in or close to the post-central gyrus (p. 402) but also, without evidence of epilepsy, when there is damage to the thalamus. Tumours within the thalamus itself give rise to mental rather than sensory symptoms (Smyth & Stern, 1938) ; it is vascular lesions and especially those tumours that invade the thalamus from its lateral side that most commonly give rise to the '*thalamic syndrome*' (Fig. 11.12).

Damage to the ventro-lateral nucleus of the thalamus interferes with sensation from the opposite side of the body. Light touch can no longer be appreciated over the limbs and trunk, although it may still be felt over both sides of the face. The temperature sensitivity of the affected limbs is reduced or abolished, whilst to pain the patient responds abnormally vigorously, even though the pain threshold (p. 61) may be increased.

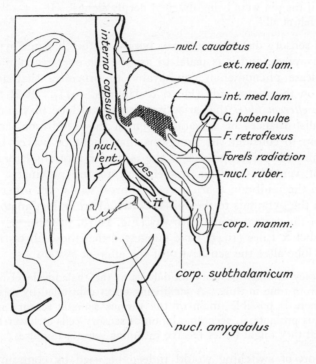

FIG. 11.12.—Coronal section through thalamus and neighbouring structures showing lesions (shaded) in a case of the thalamic syndrome. The destruction has involved the infero-lateral aspect of the thalamus. (From Holmes & Head, 1911)

As might be expected from the diversity of the sensory representation in the thalamus a wide variety of sensory disturbances may result. Kinnier Wilson (1927) has given the following account of the symptomatology in a patient who suffered from a stroke affecting the right thalamus :

'He complains of insufferable "*pins and needles*" all over the left side ; "I feel as if I were treading on tin tacks". At one time there is a pricking, *burning* sensation in the left face, trunk and limbs ; at another it is *icy cold*. Objectively, the characteristic hyperpathic response of an explosive nature is obtained, more especially with pain stimuli ; cotton-wool touch is diminished ; cold excitations fail to reach the sensorium, while heat or warmth is much better appreciated. There is no astereognosis (p. 418), loss of muscular sense, or defect of localisation, but the phenomenon of radiation is pronounced. In respect of pain, the "all-or-none" nature of the response prevails ; a single mild pin-prick becomes a "stab" and is felt "as if the pin were being dragged deeply along". If not a "stab" it is never felt at all.'

The sensory disturbances may persist in the thalamic syndrome for many years, and it is usual to ascribe the over-reaction to pain to a release phenomenon comparable to processes that are well known on the motor side (Head & Holmes, 1911). It is possible that the *efferent fibres* that arise in the parietal lobe play some part in the disturbances of sensation seen in this syndrome, and it is important to consider the functions that might be served by such a system. The fibres project to the posterior ventralis-lateralis and posterior ventralis-medialis nuclei, and to the pulvinar. Others reach to the midbrain (parieto-tectal fibres) whilst yet others travel through the pyramids to the spinal cord and are in fact anatomically a part of the cortico-spinal pathway (Fig. 10.16, p. 388).

Gobbel & Liles (1945) have suggested that these fibres from the parietal lobe alter the sensitivity of the afferent system :

'the efficacy of single sensory modalities at the thalamic level could be altered from time to time. A sensitising effect controlled by a region in which there is possible union of the various somatic sensory impulses could thus promote an accommodation of sensory cells at lower levels in order that they might better receive incoming sensory impulses.'

Some sort of switching would indeed be used by communication engineers faced with similar problems. There is available through the length of the spinal cord much more sensory data than can be transmitted centrally. It is almost to be expected that according to the conditions at any given time the fillet systems can be readjusted, by means of activity in the descending pathways, to 'listen in' to specific aspects of the information that is available.

This view is attractive and accounts for much that would otherwise be unexplained ; it is, moreover, not entirely without experimental support. Hagbarth & Kerr (1954) studied the volleys of impulses that were passed up the spinal cord and found that impulses that passed through synaptic junctions in the grey matter of the cord were subject to inhibitory influences descending from the brain stem and cerebrum. On electrical stimulation of a number of regions in the brain, including the motor and sensory areas of the cerebral cortex, the centripetal volleys were reduced in amplitude. It is uncertain to what extent this 'centrifugal control' is exerted on all the information relayed upwards by the spinal cord; certain synapses may escape this influence. Lloyd & McIntyre (1950) found that the cells of Clarke's column may relay upwards all of the impulses that reach them, but this is the case only when synchronous testing volleys are used (*vide* Barron & Matthews, 1935).

It is possible that the mechanisms that have been discussed afford the most satisfactory explanation of some experiments of Dusser de Barenne (1933 *a*) on the mode of action of strychnine on the spinal cord. This worker noted that when strychnine was applied to the dorsum of the spinal cord the animal behaved as though the corresponding part of the body was sore. There appeared to be 'paroxysmal, paraesthetic disturbances occurring without any appreciable stimulus'. The behaviour of the animal was the same even when the posterior roots of the poisoned segment and those of many adjacent segments had undergone Wallerian degeneration by section three weeks previous to the application of the poison. In an experimental fashion Dusser de Barenne had clearly mimicked the 'central pains' that are not uncommon in clinical practice (p. 411, and *vide* White & Sweet, 1955).

The application of strychnine to a wide area on the convexity of the cerebrum gives rise to hyperaesthesia, affecting principally the opposite side of the body. Dusser de Barenne (1924), using this technique, obtained evidence that there existed a sharp functional division between the regions dealing with the face, arm and leg (Fig. 11.13). The sensitive area extended well behind, and well in front of the central sulcus; there is at present no reason to believe that afferent impulses from the main sensory pathways are distributed over such an extensive zone. Dusser de Barenne found that hyperaesthesia followed the application of strychnine to the precentral region even after the whole of the parietal lobe behind the central sulcus had been removed. Removal of an extensive area of cortex behind and in front of the central sulcus on the opposite side also did not abolish the effect. These experiments can most simply be explained in terms of a descending influence sensitising the afferent system.

The sensations that are aroused by the application of *electrical currents* to the human cerebrum have been studied extensively by Penfield & Rasmussen (1950). The map which they have obtained corresponds closely with the sequences seen for the motor cortex (Fig. 10.17, p. 389, Chapter 10) ; it does not closely reflect the segmental order of the different parts of the body. The area from which these effects can be obtained is extensive and extends in front of, as well as behind, the central sulcus. Sensations aroused by stimulation of the precentral region do not necessarily stem from the effects of cortically induced movement, for they may be elicited when there is no evidence of this. Electrical stimulation is a procedure comparable to the application of strychnine ; much of the sensitive area may not itself receive afferent fibres from the sensory pathways. The relationship of much of the region to the mechanisms of sensation may be optional rather than obligatory. Similar considerations apply to the interpretation of sensory fits.

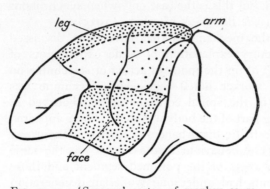

FIG. 11.13.—'Sensory' cortex of monkey as revealed by focal strychninisation. This technique 'blurs the finer functional differentiations' revealed in other ways and demonstrates the presence of a wide region both in front of and behind the central sulcus that is capable of modifying sensation. The changes caused by strychninisation of the precental region occur even when both post-central gyri have been removed. These effects presumably depend on cortico-fugal fibres : 'perhaps also the supposed condition of hyper-excitability and hyper-irritability occur not only in the cortex, but also in the sub-cortical centres and structures which are in close functional relationship with the poisoned cortical spot'. (From Dusser de Barenne, 1924)

It might be thought that the 'march' of a sensory seizure would follow a rigid pattern depending upon the sequence of representation in the cortex. In fact the march of epileptic seizures may vary widely. Sittig (1925) was interested in this point and found that, in different patients, sensory seizures proceeded in a number of different ways that were not easy to classify. He did, however, state that it was common for the thumb and corner of the mouth to be affected simultaneously. Some seizures involved a distribution that can be explained on functional but not on segmental grounds ; thus the tips of the fingers might be affected together. The march might follow the sequence : face, neck, shoulder, arm and fingers, or toes, leg, fingers, arm and face. Sometimes the march followed plainly a segmental pattern ; thus paraesthesiae might spread along the medial border of the arm or descend on one side and ascend on the other (for a discussion of Sittig's data see Woolsey, Marshall & Bard, 1942).

According to Critchley (1953) the hand is most commonly affected in sensory epilepsy, whilst the tongue and circum-oral region on one side are next most often implicated. 'Not infrequently several discrete regions (lips and thumb ; hand and mouth ; lips, tongue and fingers) are simultaneously the seat of a dysaesthesia so that the patient is unable to trace any kind of priority. When the hand is chiefly, or primarily, the seat of a sensory attack, the patient may at times specifically implicate a localised portion of this region. Thus the thumb, or thumb and forefinger, may be primarily affected. Other fingers are less often involved in isolation.'

In the motor cortex there is evidence that the body is topographically represented in more than one way (p. 379). The evidence suggests that this may also be the case with the sensory functions of the cortex.

THE RÔLE OF MOVEMENT IN TACTILE RECOGNITION

With the fingers as purely passive receptors much can be achieved. Hellen Keller was deaf and blind from infancy but obtained a college education with success largely through her ability to 'listen' to speech with her fingers. She placed her thumb on the larynx of her companion, her middle finger on the lip and her index finger on the ala of the nose (Tilney, 1929). The fingers in responding to vibration are able to distinguish differences of intensity fairly well, but are very poor at discriminating between different frequencies (vide Woodworth, 1938). Attempts to enable the deaf to interpret speech by electrical stimulation of the skin have not been entirely successful, as under these conditions also changes of frequency cannot readily be detected (Anderson & Munson, 1951). By her long practice Hellen Keller probably developed the highest discriminatory powers that are possible when the hand is used as a passive receptor of vibrations.

In recognising an article by feeling it with the hand a number of different sensory cues are used and combined together, the importance of different modalities varying according to the nature

2 E

of the material. As there often exist alternative ways of determining the identity of objects, tactile recognition may still be possible even though there is considerable interference with sensory mechanisms. Thus patients with severe postural loss may yet be able to identify objects placed in their hands (Holmes, 1927).

Tactile recognition probably depends not only on the post-central gyrus which receives the afferent messages but also upon the rest of the parietal lobe. With parietal lesions the ability to recognise objects by their feel may be lost even though other tests of sensibility reveal no gross defects (see, however, Campora, 1925). The failure may be referred to as *tactile agnosia* ; the term 'astereo-gnosis' is ambiguous, for it is sometimes taken to indicate instead a loss of postural sensibility.

In hemiplegia the patient cannot move his fingers and cannot, therefore, by himself recognise objects by the use of his hand. If the sensory pathways and parietal lobe are intact he may succeed when an observer closes his hand onto the article with which he is being tested. If, however, the hemiplegia has dated from infancy he is likely to fail even with this assistance ; there will have been no practice in the use of the hand as a palpatory organ (Critchley, 1953). Even under favourable circumstances, when the ability to make active exploratory movements is lost, the sensorium is likely to get into difficulties comparable to those that beset the six blind men of Indostan (Seashore, 1908) :

First blind man, falling against the elephant's side :

'God bless me ! but this elephant
Is very like a wall.'

Second blind man, feeling the tusk :

'This wonder of an elephant
Is very like a spear.'

Third blind man, grasping the squirming trunk :

'I see,' quoth he, 'the elephant
Is very like a snake.'

The fourth blind man, clasping the knee :

''Tis clear enough, the elephant
Is very like a tree.'

The fifth blind man, catching the ear :

'This marvel of an elephant
Is very like a fan.'

The sixth, seizing the swinging tail :

> 'I see,' quoth he, 'the elephant
> Is very like a rope.'

> And so these men of Indostan
> Disputed loud and long,
> Each in his own opinion
> Exceeding stiff and strong,
> Though each was partly in the right,
> And all were in the wrong.

If movement is prevented, even the most straightforward discriminations become difficult ; one disturbing factor will be the accommodation of end-organs. Bentley (1900) arranged to raise, slowly and very smoothly, a beaker containing an unknown liquid until the dependent and motionless finger of the experimental subject was immersed. 'Before the investigation had proceeded far, it became evident that the cutaneous processes, when isolated, function rather clumsily : differences in density, viscosity, etc., passed unnoticed when color, transparency, odor, sound and lateral or irregular movements were wanting. For example, molasses, benzine and even mercury passed under certain thermal conditions for water · an indication of how widely the organism is obliged to draw upon its resources for the completion of so simple a perception as that of a liquid.' It is apparent that motion of the finger-tip relative to the object under examination is essential for satisfactory tactile perceptions ; movement would appear to be as important for feeling as is successive contrast for vision (p. 314).

The parietal lobe should be regarded as a part of the brain concerned with actively gathering rather than passively receiving information. We may consider the analogy of the system used in a national newspaper. The press is linked with the outside world by means of correspondents. These correspondents register events in their neighbourhood and send reports, in summary form, by telegraph to the head office. The correspondents are, however, not merely passive receptors of information. Under instructions from the central control they may change their whereabouts, or orientate themselves to investigate some particular aspect of the situation with which they are in contact. They will send in reports of events that they consider important without being asked, but they are also subject to direction from the editor to cover some particular item.

Similarly the parietal lobe not only receives and evaluates sensory data but may order the collection of more information when the results of what is available are ambiguous.   The parietal lobe in this way controls the motor system, and indeed the distinction between a 'sensory' and a 'motor' system is somewhat blurred.

'The good player of a quick ball game, the surgeon conducting an operation, the physician arriving at a clinical decision—in each case there is a flow from signals interpreted to action carried out, back to further signals and on again to more action up to the culminating point of the achievement of the task' (Bartlett, 1947).

Under many circumstances afferent signals can only become meaningful if information about the effort put into moving the limb or digits is also available.   Ashby (1952) has pointed out that the interaction between organism and environment can be treated as a feed-back system.

'It is necessary to point to the existence of feedback in the relation between the free-living organism and its environment because most physiological experiments are deliberately arranged to avoid feedback. Thus, in an experiment with spinal reflexes, a stimulus is applied and the resulting movement recorded ; but the movement is not allowed to influence the nature or duration of the stimulus.   The action between stimulus and movement is therefore one-way.   A similar absence of feedback is enforced in the Pavlovian experiments with conditioned reflexes : the stimulus may evoke salivation, but the salivation has no effect on the nature or duration of the stimulus.
'Such an absence of feedback is, of course, useful or even essential in the analytic study of the behaviour of a mechanism, whether animate or inanimate.   But its usefulness in the laboratory should not obscure the fact that the free-living animal is not subject to these constraints.'

Some sensations can only be obtained when the hand moves over the object under examination.   Thus the discrimination of roughness from smoothness requires some degree of movement. Slight disturbances imparted to a sensitive skin send vibratory shock waves to a large number of pressure receptors.   If the fingers are coated with a thin layer of collodion, the discrimination can still be performed (Geldard, 1953).   The sensitivity of the fingers to vibration is of a surprisingly high order.   The finger-tips are sensitive to movements as small as $0\cdot02\,\mu$, a distance that is less than $1/200$ of the diameter of a red cell (Wilska, 1954).   The sensation of stickiness involves movement in association with varying traction, whilst for the perception of oiliness three factors have to be considered—movement, weak pressure and warmth.   Even more factors must be evaluated in some sensory discriminations such as those performed by expert cheese-makers :

'Cheese curd at the pitching stage is somewhat unusual material in that it consists of tiny particles from about 25 to 500 mm.[3] in volume, suspended in whey. When judging for firmness the experts both feel the impact of the particles while stirring in the whey and also squeeze a handful which has been removed from the whey' (Coppen, 1942).

In estimating the firmness of a substance such as cheese, the C.N.S. must keep a record of the force that is applied, for without this the sensory messages would be meaningless. As Coppen stated : 'the total deformation will depend upon the pressure applied as well as upon the time of its application. Moreover, the relationship between deformation, pressure and time will not be simple as is the case with true fluids and true solids, since such complex materials almost invariably get progressively softer the harder they are pressed (structural viscosity) and progressively harder the further they are pressed (work hardening). Thus the actual sensory data received by any subject will depend upon the way in which he handles the materials' (Coppen, 1942).

The limbs are equipped with receptors by which the force applied to an object in the external environment is registered ; the tendon endings may perhaps be the most reliable method of recording force put in by the muscles whilst joint receptors measure the extent to which movement is achieved. All the data are available to the C.N.S. that an engineer would need to construct a force/displacement/time diagram.

As Sherrington (1900) stated, the 'sense of resistance to muscular action may be based on compound sensation of joint movements and of changes of muscular tension with or without comparisons with sensations signifying changes of muscle form'. In this way substances may be classified according to their physical properties.

In stirring a spoon in a jar of treacle the cue to the viscous nature of the liquid lies in the fact that there is a disproportionately large amount of force needed in stirring rapidly compared with stirring slowly. This characteristic forms the basis of methods that the physicist uses to measure the viscosity of fluids. Pushing an object that is stationary until it moves may reveal the need for a decrease of force as soon as the movement starts. This indicates the presence of static friction. Not uncommonly the behaviour of an object when subjected to stress shows a 'step-function'. No deformation takes place until the force reaches a critical value at which the system ruptures. In this way chocolates that have soft centres may be differentiated from those that are hard before they have been tasted. Clearly, a number of laws of this type are evaluated by the parietal lobe in order to ascertain the nature, or more exactly the properties, of objects that can be grasped, bitten and kicked.

It is of interest that electronic instruments may be investigated by analogous methods. It is sometimes necessary to ascertain the electrical properties of an instrument or system when the structure is largely unknown. By applying pulses to the system and observing the way in which these pulses are handled, it may be possible to estimate the 'equivalent circuit', to design an apparatus that would behave similarly. There may be evidence that energy is stored, pulses delayed or reduced in size. These electrical properties all have mechanical analogies. Just as the hand may classify objects such as glass and steel together as 'hard' according to the way in which it responds to mechanical stress, so the electronic engineer may classify according to their common properties instruments that perform similarly, although they may be constructed in totally different ways.

We have in the sensory system a *feed-back mechanism* which is designed to give information about the properties of the feed-back loop which passes through the external environment and to which the hand may be coupled in different ways. Engineers are sometimes faced with the problem of designing a servo device with little or no *a priori* evidence as to the properties of the system involved. They may face this situation by using *informative feed-back*. In this method they apply a small fluctuating force and observe the size and phase of the waves which appear at the other end (Fig. 11.14). Under certain circumstances this method yields information that can be used in manipulations involving other and larger forces. Wiener (1948) has pointed out that informative feed-back may be used when driving a car on a slippery road. By imparting a to-and-fro motion to the steering-wheel, and observing the effects, the state of the road surface may be judged and speed adjusted accordingly to keep within safe limits. The use of rhythmic stimuli in this way is exceptional; it is much more common for the limb to push against an object, the force being exerted rapidly.

Little is known about the physiology of *after-contraction*, a phenomenon that is the basis of certain parlour tricks. As an example the effects of pushing outwards against a wall may be mentioned. If the arm is pressed in this way, against resistance for some time, at the end of the period of pressing there is often an involuntary raising of the arm. The limb feels light and seems to float upwards (*vide* Zigler, 1944). If the eyes are closed, the person may feel that someone is pushing his arm upwards. There is no alteration in the contractile properties of the muscle fibres (Forbes, Baird &

Hopkins, 1926), and what it is in the postural system that gets 'set' at a different level is uncertain. The disturbance could be at the muscle spindles or in the nervous system itself. After-contraction is normal in tabes and in cerebellar lesions, whilst it is diminished with lesions of the cortico-spinal tract and greatly prolonged in Parkinsonism (Sapirstein, Herman & Wechsler, 1938). It would be interesting to determine the effect of parietal lesions on after-contraction, for such disturbances often alter muscle tone on the

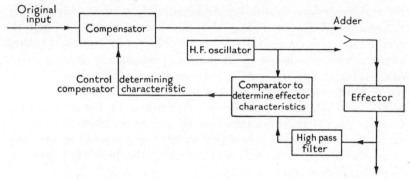

FIG. 11.14.—Control by informative feed-back. Under many conditions the load that a machine has to move to a certain position is somewhat indeterminate and liable to change. Thus the friction involved in rotating an anti-aircraft gun cannot be regarded as being constant; it will, for instance, depend upon the temperature of the grease in the bearings. Similarly limbs are often required to move loads of unknown physical properties with some precision. The system shown in this flow chart may be used to allow for changes in the characteristics of a load. To the original input is added a rapid vibration and the effector system reveals its properties by the way in which it handles this extra signal. Allowance can automatically be made, therefore, for relatively slow changes in the load. It is valuable to consider the ways that engineers overcome problems similar to those encountered by the body, but it is unlikely that any arrangement exists in the C.N.S. *closely* analogous to this particular mechanism. (From Wiener, 1948)

opposite side of the body (*vide* Peele, 1944). It is probably for this reason that in children parietal disease is liable to cause asymmetrical growth (Penfield & Robertson, 1943).

When the pathways that lead to the forebrain from the proprioceptors are interrupted the limbs may feel abnormally heavy, for in response to a given effort the sensory change is disproportionately small. In tabes dorsalis the proprioceptive sense is impaired and movements 'usually err on the side of exaggeration. This is well illustrated in the stamp of the heel which is so characteristic of the tabetic gait' (Brown, 1912). This disturbance is analogous to the excessively loud speech associated with nerve deafness. In estimating weight the sensorium appears to make use of more than one cue. The force exerted may be compared with the resulting movement, but weight discrimination is possible if objects are placed upon the supported hand. Under the latter conditions pressure receptors are doubtless involved.

There is evidence that more than one central pathway is concerned in the estimation of weight. Whilst lesions of the medial fillets cause a disturbance of this ability, recovery eventually occurs. By making lesions in the brains of suitably trained chimpanzees, Sjöqvist & Weinstein (1942) showed that pathways through the cerebellum were concerned in the restoration of function. Lesions of the cerebellum do not by themselves permanently disturb weight discrimination (p. 193). The estimation of weight may be upset not only by lesions of the afferent pathways but also by destruction of the parietal lobes themselves. According to Ruch, Fulton & German (1938) the discrimination of weight in parietal lesions is more severely affected when the weights are rested on the hand than when they are actively supported by the limb (see, however, Head & Holmes, 1911, p. 169).

THE POSSIBILITY THAT THE C.N.S. KEEPS A TALLY OF THE DISCHARGES
    OF THE MOTOR CENTRES AND THAT THIS RECORD IS FED TO THE
    PARIETAL LOBES

The sense of movement does not depend solely upon afferent impulses returning from the joints (p. 55), although in the absence of such information postures are poorly sustained. Weir Mitchell (1829–1914), the distinguished American physician and physiologist, described a case of the thalamic syndrome (p. 412) due to a vascular lesion. The patient suffered at the onset of the illness from hemiplegia that gradually passed away but left him with involuntary movements on the affected side. Mitchell made the following observations : 'If he willed a movement, as of the fingers, he could tell where the motion placed them, but if I bent the wrist and crossed the fingers he was absolutely unable to say where the parts were, or in what relation, but he walked or moved his hands as well with his eyes *closed* as with them open' (Mitchell, 1874 *b*).

When a limb is amputated many, indeed most, patients feel that it is still present and the description of such 'phantom limbs' makes fascinating reading. Weir Mitchell wrote the following lines about the sense of movement that may be experienced in phantom limbs :

'The physiology of the day accepts the belief that all of our accurate notions as to the amount of power put forth, and as to the parts thus stirred, reach the sensorium from the muscles acted on and the parts moved. It would appear, however, from the statements here made as if coevally with the willing of a motion, there came to consciousness perhaps from the spinal ganglia acted upon, some information as to these points. If, in reply to this, I be told that the constancy of long habit may have associated memorially with certain ganglionic activities the ideas of local movements, I should hardly feel that this was an answer, because in some of my cases the amputations took place so early in life that there was no remembrance of the lost limb, and yet, twenty years after, a volition directed to the hand seemed to cause movement, which appeared to be as capable of definite regulation, and was as plainly felt to occur as if it had been the other arm which was moved. Probably, then, a part of those ideas which are presumed to obtain through the muscular sense are really coincident with, and instituted by, the originative act of will, or else are messages sent to the sensorium from the spinal ganglia which every act of motor volition incites' (quoted from Livingston, 1943).

Even patients who have suffered lesions of the spinal cord with complete transverse sections may feel that they still possess the power to move the limbs (Bors, 1951). In such patients a strong attempt to move the phantom limbs gives rise to changes in the tone in the rest of the musculature, associative reactions that might have been appropriate had the intended movement taken place. Movements of phantom limbs may appear to be misleadingly natural. One of Riddoch's (1941) patients with an amputation of one leg had difficulty for this reason :—

'If he had occasion to get up suddenly from his chair, he often stepped off with his phantom foot, so natural did it appear to him.' William James (1887) recorded that, 'It is a common experience, during the first weeks after amputation, for the patient to forget that his leg is gone. Many patients tell how they met with accidents, by rising suddenly and starting to walk as if their leg were still there, or by getting out of bed in the same way ' (cf. Henderson & Smyth, 1948).

In many patients, perhaps in most, who have suffered amputation of a limb apparent movements of this type are inconspicuous or absent. Phantom fingers may even feel as though they have become fixed in the position in which they were placed just before the operation. The absence of normal proprioceptive response to exertion is doubtless responsible for the fixity.

The vividness with which absent limbs may be felt can be illustrated by a case recorded by William James (1887) of the man who having suffered an amputation of the leg and having a phantom foot 'found himself preparing with scissors to cut its nails, so distinctly did he feel them'. There are accounts which speak of patients who are liable to bring a phantom hand to the aid of the good when this is in difficulties. These remarkable hallucinations, occurring in people sound mentally, are important for understanding a condition not uncommon in cerebral disease, 'denial of disability' or *anosognosia*. The patient may believe that he is able to move a paralysed limb, and he is no doubt fortified in this belief because his sense of effort is relatively normal. Before long the patient learns to believe his eyes and not his feelings, at least if the intellect is well preserved (*vide* Weinstein & Kahn, 1950).

The tally that the C.N.S. appears to keep of motor impulses may be called the *motor discharge reflux*.

The observations on spinal patients that have been quoted above suggest that some of the reflux has its origin in the motor centres of the cerebrum, but it is to be expected that the discharge of the motor neurones also may be registered. Reflux from the anterior horn cells would not give unequivocal evidence as to the tension exerted by a muscle, for this depends also on the length of the fibres; the tendon receptors might give a better indication. In stabilising a limb, reflux from the anterior horn cells could be of value, for it might indicate when a servo mechanism was operating so close to its effective limits that small fluctuations might render the stabilisation ineffectual. It is a matter of common observation that when maximum voluntary effort is exerted the pull is markedly erratic; this instability is the cost of running the system with no reserve. Probably the C.N.S. 'keeps an eye on' the behaviour of any stretch reflexes that are in action. In supporting a weight by an arm nearly the whole of the contractile mechanism may come into play and stability will accordingly be liable to suffer. Under these circumstances there may have to be a 'decision' as to whether to carry on with the task by, for instance, bringing the other hand to assist, or whether to give up and jettison the load. These are obviously 'top level' decisions in which the parietal lobe plays an important part.

Cerebral lesions may no doubt interfere with the fate of the motor discharge reflux, and it is known that pathological processes may abolish phantom sensations. Head & Holmes (1911, p. 187) have recorded the case of a patient who had lost his left leg some time before he suffered a stroke. 'After the amputation, as in so many similar cases, he experienced movements in a phantom foot and leg. But these ceased immediately on the occurrence of the cerebral lesion.' This case was complicated by the fact that the cerebral lesion destroyed postural sensitivity. It is therefore interesting to be able to point to related observations on patients in whom sensibility was spared :

'Dr. Jefferson Browder, by sectioning the anterior limb of the internal capsule in cases of Parkinsonism, abolished tremor. In studying some of these cases, we noted that after operation the patient seemed unaware of the extremity which had been the site of tremor. For instance, he would sit on it ; if he was asked to elevate his arms, he would lift the other arm, and not the affected extremity. When he was told to lift the arm affected, he did so. He had no disturbance of any types of sensation' (Rabiner, p. 197, in discussion of paper by Penfield, 1952).

In earlier chapters it was seen that the discharge of anterior horn cells is controlled by many influences. Under certain circumstances the level of excitation will be high and the rate of discharge of the neurones will tend to outstrip the ability of the muscle fibres to respond to a corresponding degree ; there is little mechanical gain for frequencies of discharge of more than (e.g.) 20/sec. If too much is being asked of a muscle group, arrangements have to be made by the C.N.S. to deploy its resources in another way. Clearly, to wait for end-results as judged by joint endings, or by the eye, may be too late. It may be suggested that the motor discharge reflux is concerned with this aspect of motor control.

The reaction of *hopping* has been studied by Bard (1937) and by Brooks & Peck (1940). When an animal is stood on one leg and pushed sideways at some point the limb hops to take up a fresh position. It is not entirely clear to what extent this sudden resetting of the postural system is dependent upon proprioceptive and to what extent upon motor reflux discharge. Hopping in the monkey is dependent upon the precentral region, but upon no other part of the cortex. It would be expected that the parietal cortex would be involved in man.

It is likely that certain disease processes will selectively destroy the pathways carrying the motor discharge reflux. Under these circumstances the tone of the musculature might increase and there would be a decrease in associative muscular reactions. Other disease processes might heighten the excitability of the system, lead to a decrease in muscular tone and voluntary power and to an exaggeration of normal associative reactions. Little is known of the pathological physiology of Parkinsonism on the one hand and of chorea on the other (p. 391), but could it be that these syndromes represent the disturbances that are being sought ? Pritchard (1929) was principally interested in the mechanism of the tremor in Parkinsonism, but his conclusions from a study of electromyograms are relevant to this question : 'discharges of low frequency and regularity both as regards amplitude and spacing are comparatively rare. Either such responses at minimal active muscle tension are uncommon or else such patients show a greater difficulty in achieving and in maintaining such slight degrees of activation of their muscles.'

NEGLECT OF ONE SIDE OF THE BODY AS A RESULT OF A PARIETAL LESION

The parietal lobe appears to be concerned with evaluating sensations, principally those of the opposite side of the body. When this part of the cortex is damaged the mechanism that normally orders the collection of information from the corresponding regions, and impels appropriate action, is no longer available. Proprioceptive impulses cannot be used, and in addition it would appear that there is no appreciation of the motor discharge reflux. The patient is liable, therefore, to 'neglect' the opposite side of his body. After taking a bath, for instance, he may forget to dry the affected side, and similarly in dressing he is likely to be careless about those parts of his apparel that fit over the disturbed areas (see quotation from Nielson in Livingston, 1943). Clearly it is necessary for him to exercise continuous visual control over such matters. This may be difficult, for he is likely also to be poor at comprehending spatial relationships by means of vision (p. 357).

Elsewhere (p. 328) experiments are described in which, by placing lenses or mirrors in front of the eyes, the relationships between proprioceptive and visual information as to the position of various parts of the body were disturbed. Similar disturbances may be expected with parietal lesions ; the person may catch sight of a hand and deny at first that it is his own, for it may *feel* as though it is elsewhere.

In patients with unilateral parietal lesions some afferent impulses do reach the cerebral cortex, by travelling upwards on the same side or perhaps by reaching the secondary sensory area. Pain impulses, as have been seen, may often still be appreciated with lesions of the parietal lobe (p. 411), and it is interesting to consider the interpretation that a patient may put upon such signals, and the way in which he may react when he disowns the part of the body from which they originate. One way in which these messages may be handled is by referring them to another region ; they may, for instance, be regarded as originating from a corresponding point on the opposite side of the body : *alloaesthesia*. Alloaesthesia is derived from *allos* meaning 'other' and *aesthesia* 'feeling'.

Sometimes the patient may deny feeling the stimulus and yet show physical signs of suffering pain (*vide* Sandifer, 1946). Gilliatt & Pratt (1952) have studied this phenomenon very carefully in a patient with a lesion of the right side of the cerebrum. She was unable to tell when the stimuli were applied, but nevertheless they gave rise to restlessness, tachycardia, a rise of blood pressure, dilatation of the pupil and deepening of respiration, signs that would normally indicate that pain was felt. The woman did not associate her restlessness with the stimulation and when asked why she moved she was liable to rationalise her actions, saying, for instance, 'to make me more comfortable'.

Sensory impulses of various different types are under normal conditions brought together and evaluated in the parietal lobes. The interplay of different types of sensory information will usually enable more accurate perceptions to be formed, and more satisfactory responses to be made, than if one or the other category is non-existent. Clearly, in disease the dissociation of different modalities leads to difficulties that are broadly comparable to the problems with which the visual system must grapple when it receives discordant data from the two eyes (p. 343). This is the background against which the disordered perceptions seen in parietal lesions may be judged ; the sensorium may be faced with the necessity of accepting only one set of the available data as being reliable. The clinical evidence suggests that from time to time the wrong choice may be made and incorrect data handled as reliable signals, whilst those that indicate the true course of events are treated as fallacious and disregarded.

As has already been seen, the sense of movement may be convincing in some phantom limbs, and it is probable that the motor discharge reflux reaches the parietal lobe. Clearly, under normal circumstances the sense of movement may depend both upon the motor reflux and upon the return of proprioceptive messages from the moving member. In parietal lesions both sets of cues may be destroyed. Russell Brain (1941) has described the symptomatology of a 36-year-old woman who suffered a destruction of part of the left parietal lobe ; she stated that : 'All the right side feels as if it doesn't belong to me. When I move my right hand I don't feel I'm moving my hand myself, although it goes.' Conversely in sensory fits the person may feel that a limb is moving although it is actually stationary (*vide* Critchley, 1953).

It is necessary to assume that the information pouring into the parietal lobe is interpreted in terms of past experience of the shape and positions of the body. In the adult the rules are rather rigid, and if the body alters misleading results follow ; a phantom limb may persist for many years. Nevertheless, changes do occur and the phantom may eventually fade, the distal segments being the most persistent. Even when the experience has largely vanished it may, however, be reawakened artificially. Thus if hypertonic saline is injected into the interspinous tissues the 'amputee is usually startled by the sudden totality of the phantom' (Klopsteg, Wilson *et al.*, 1954). The rules used by the parietal lobe must change during growth, for as the proportions and size of the body alter and the peripheral nerves lengthen, so the way in which sensory signals are handled must change also. It is to data such as this that the term *body schema* is applied (*vide* Oldfield & Zangwill, 1942 ; Critchley, 1950). Sir Henry Head, who introduced this term, believed that the position of the various parts of the body was registered as though by dead-reckoning. At that time little was known about the behaviour of nerve endings. The receptors from joints adapt ; the rate of discharge depends both upon the position of the limb and also upon the length of time the limb has been in that posture. This interesting finding indicates that much of the clinical data relating to the body schema needs re-interpretation. (For further discussion of the behaviour of proprioceptive endings see p. 55, and Andrew, 1954.)

GERSTMANN'S SYNDROME. APRAXIA

Whilst lesions of the right hemisphere give rise to a failure to recognise the left side of the body, lesions of the left parietal lobe sometimes give rise to symptoms that are bilateral. Left-sided lesions sometimes give rise to *Gerstmann's syndrome*. The patient is unable to recognise either his own hands or those belonging to other people, and he cannot tell left from right (Gerstmann, 1940). He has great difficulty in dealing with numbers. It is interesting that arithmetical concepts, built up in association with knowledge of the fingers, should be so commonly lost when the ability to recognise the fingers is upset. It may be recalled that the word 'digit' means both 'finger' and any one of the Arabic numerals.

Some races do not have symbols for numbers and can only count with the hand ; Locke's (1689) comments upon this question are quaint to read :

'Some Americans I have spoken with (who were otherwise of quick and rational parts enough) could not, as we do, by any means count to one thousand, nor had any distinct idea of that number, though they could reckon very well to twenty ; because their language being scanty, and accommodated only to the few necessities of a needy, simple life, unacquainted either with trade or mathematics, had no words in it to stand for one thousand ; so that when they are discoursed with of those great numbers, they would show the hairs of their head, to express a great multitude which they could not number : which inability, I suppose, proceeded from their want of names. The Tououpinambos had no names for numbers above five ; any numbers beyond that they made out by showing their fingers and the fingers of others who were present.'

Hands that are not recognised are, naturally, of little use for purposive acts. That they are not paralysed may be clear for, without taking thought, they may yet be moved. Patients with Gerstmann's syndrome suffer from an inability to write, *agraphia*. This is one example of a more general type of disturbance known as 'apraxia'.

In *apraxia* a part of the body may be used for acts which are semi-automatic and yet the person may be unable to repeat at will movements that he has readily performed spontaneously. Patients with lesions affecting the internal capsule rather commonly show an apraxia for facial movements. They may be unable to smile when asked, but may do so a moment later in response to a joke. The emotional movements may even be exaggerated on the affected side, a condition that Monrad-Krohn calls 'facial hyper-mimia'. With cortical lesions apraxia is found most commonly in association with disturbances of the left parietal lobe (*vide* Kinnier Wilson, 1908).

Characteristically, then, the patient comprehends what is needed but, although there is no paralysis in the ordinary use of the term, is unable to translate his desires into action. Wilson (1908) quotes the case of a French patient. She 'was asked to lift her right arm, but after crossing it over her body, putting her hand in her left axilla, and making various energetic but hopeless efforts, she said

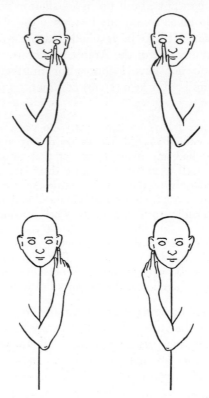

FIG. 11.15.—Tests for patients with apraxia or aphasia. The commands may be verbal or written or the patient may be shown the pictures. To execute the tests the receptive mechanisms must be intact and a fair intellectual capacity is demanded. In receptive varieties of aphasia the patient fails for want of understanding of what is required, whilst in apraxia he may understand perfectly and yet be unable to translate his ideas into the appropriate actions. Tests such as these are of particular value with mute patients, for they give evidence as to the state of the receptive and 'intellectual' mechanisms. (From Head, 1926)

plaintively, "Je comprends bien ce que vous voulez, mais je ne parviens pas à le faire," and there lies the whole situation in a nutshell'.

The substitution of one act for another is known as *parapraxia*. Parapraxia was a striking feature of a case described by Liepmann:

Liepmann's patient had 'bilateral motor apraxia for face and neck and head movements, and unilateral apraxia of the right arm and right leg. Asked to put his right forefinger on his nose, he said "yes", and with his stretched forefinger executed wide circling movements in the air. He made the correct movement at once with his left hand. Asked to close his right hand into a fist, he performed various absurd movements of his arm and body, but attained the required goal at once with his left hand.' This translation from the German is part of a classical contribution to the study of apraxia (Kinnier Wilson, 1908). A more recent account of the complex problems of apraxia is given by Nielsen (1947).

APHASIA AND RELATED DISORDERS

In studying disturbances of language little help can be obtained from animal experimentation. As Tinbergen (1953) says : 'Except perhaps in the highest mammals, all signalling behaviour is immediate reaction to internal and external stimuli. In this respect there is a great difference between animals and man. The signalling behaviour of animals can be compared with the crying of the human baby, or with involuntary expressions of anger or fear in humans of all ages.' It is no accident that in this particular field where complementary animal studies are not possible that progress should be slow and nomenclature muddled.

As has been seen in the condition known as apraxia a movement may be conceived but not executed ; similarly patients may be found who can conceive words and yet cannot write them down, although there is no paralysis of the hands—agraphia (p. 431).

Agraphia may result not only from lesions of the parietal lobe in association with Gerstmann's syndrome but it may also be caused by lesions lying in front of the motor area concerned with finger movements. The patient may have little difficulty with intellectual functions and in rare cases he may be able to talk fluently (Gardinier, 1899). Nearly always, however, he also suffers from motor aphasia, being unable to speak at all or he can perhaps use but a few words such as 'yes' or 'no'. Swear words seem to be particularly resistant to the effects of cortical disease. Motor aphasia may sometimes occur whilst the ability to write is retained. This was the case with Dr. Johnson.

On June 19th, 1783, he wrote to Mrs. Thrale : 'On Monday, the 16th . . . I went to bed, and in a short time waked and sat up, as has long been my custom, when I felt a confusion and indistinctness in my head, which lasted, I suppose, about half a minute. I was alarmed, and

2 F

prayed to God, that however he might afflict my body, he would spare my understanding. This prayer, that I might try the integrity of my faculties, I made in Latin verse. The lines were not very good : I made them easily, and concluded myself to be unimpaired in my faculties.

'Soon after, I perceived that I had suffered a paralytic stroke, and that my speech was taken from me. . . . When (next morning) I saw light, it was time to contrive what I should do. Though God stopped my speech, he left me my hand. . . . My first note was necessarily to my servant, who came in talking, and could not immediately comprehend why he should read what I put into his hands.

' I then wrote a card to Mr. Allen. . . . In penning this note, I had some difficulty, my hand, I knew not how nor why, made wrong letters. . . .' (quoted from Wilkie, 1953).

It is evident that Dr. Johnson's mind was clear in spite of the motor aphasia. Another similar example may be quoted ; it is that of a woman who suffered from complete mutism that was caused by a lesion of the left hemisphere. That her intellect was not seriously impaired was shown by the fact that she retained the ability both to read and to write in no less than four languages : English, French, Flemish and German (Kinnier Wilson quoted by Wilkie, 1953).

Motor aphasia is an interference with speech at an expressive level. The functions concerned with language may be interrupted also at the point of the reception and interpretation of writing and speech. *Word blindness* and particularly *word deafness* in their 'pure' forms are rare ; nevertheless, these conditions are of great theoretical interest (*vide* Henschen & Schaller, 1925).

It is worth considering to what extent the receptive functions of the cerebrum may be mimicked by machines. Instruments can be made that are capable of 'recognising' printed words, although it is true that their versatility is at present extremely limited and that they are of little practical value to the blind. These instruments depend upon the conversion of the printed forms into electrical signals and upon the recognition of certain inter-relationships between these signals. The heart of the letter recognition machine is the device known in electronic computer circles as a 'function matrix'. This consists of a network with a plurality of input circuits and a plurality of output circuits. The input circuits are individually activated by the application of potentials (Zworykin, Flory & Pike, 1950). The physiological aspects of word blindness have been discussed elsewhere (p. 358). Machines have also been made that can 'recognise' speech sounds by identifying certain aspects of the waveforms that are supplied ; depending upon their design, these instruments will respond satisfactorily to some syllables but may be insensitive to others

(Smith, C. P., 1952; and see also papers from a conference on speech analysis published in *J. Acoust. Soc. Amer.*, Nov. 1952).

In human beings pure word deafness has occasionally been recognised as a result of pathological lesions (Ziegler, 1952). One case that was studied in detail concerned a man aged 34 (Hemphill & Stengel, 1940); this patient was not deaf but could not interpret the significance of the sounds that he heard. He often complained that what he heard sounded like a foreign language. Part of one interview ran as follows :

'(What is your name?) "Voice comes but no words. I can hear, sound comes, but words don't separate."—(How are you?) "That is letters what you are saying."—(Show your tongue.) "I can't get it. I can hear your voice coming, but it does not finish. Your voice is dead plain."' Walking along the main road of the hospital one day he held up a lorry that was behind him, for although he heard the horn he did not recognise its significance (cf. p. 280).

Varieties of aphasia do therefore occur in which only one aspect of the language mechanism is destroyed, but it is usual for all of the functions to be disturbed to some extent and for there to be also an impairment of the intellect. Head laid particular stress on the difficulty in 'symbolic formulation' which is experienced by patients suffering from aphasia.

The close relationship between perception and speaking is illustrated by the effects of supplying to the speaker a record of his own voice taken a fraction of a second previously. He may become speechless (cf. motor aphasia) or develop a stutter. The responses vary a good deal between different subjects and are related also to the delay interval that is used (*vide* Lee, 1950). It is tempting to think that certain difficulties of *speaking* are, similarly, due to *perceptual* disturbances.

Head pointed out that patients might succeed in comprehending simple but not complex sentences ('semantic' aphasia) and that grammatical errors were common ('syntactical' aphasia). The commonest of the disorders of language that is seen is an inability to find the names of well-known objects, although the nature and properties of the article are well comprehended ('nominal' aphasia). Head's writings (1923 and 1926) are a mine of information about aphasia and his work drew attention to the need to understand what may be called the central mechanisms of speech. His conclusions have, however, not proved to be of great practical value. (For criticisms of Head's viewpoint see Kinnier Wilson, 1920 *b*, and Symonds, 1953.)

Speech is a cheap form of communication, for the energy expended is trifling. The energy radiated is even smaller, one estimate being 10^{-5} watt for an average conversational voice, 10^{-3} for loud talking and 10^{-7} watt for very soft speech. During a whisper the energy radiated may be as little as 10^{-9} watt; there is thus an overall range of 60 db. (see p. 266, and Licklider & Miller in Stevens, 1951).

There is a great deal of redundancy in speech; it is a form of

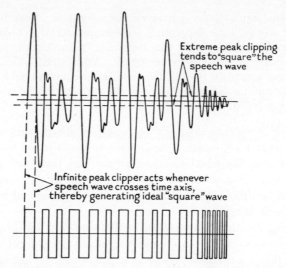

FIG. 11.16.—Owing to redundancy in speech gross distortion may interfere with intelligibility less than might be anticipated. Infinite speech clipping as shown in this figure does not reduce speech to a meaningless jargon, 70 per cent of words may still be understood. (From S. S. Stevens, 1951)

communication that developed in peasant communities and was not designed by Professors of Mathematics. The redundancy is shown in various ways. Physically the waveform may be grossly distorted by squaring each wave, and yet the meaning may often be made out (Fig. 11.16). Secondly, the energy in the speech may be split according to its pitch into high- and low-frequency components; much can still be made out when the listener is supplied with only the upper or lower halves of the spectrum (Fig. 11.17). It is interesting that the intelligibility is restored towards normal when the two halves of the speech are led to opposite ears. Finally, it is commonplace that words can follow one another only in certain sequences;

many combinations are barred. In reducing the number of possibilities in this way redundancy is introduced.

Redundancy has advantages; it enables speech of strange dialects to be made out, for if only certain of the words can be distinguished the whole meaning may be clear. Redundancy is an insurance against error. 'By using only a small fraction of the available symbol patterns we make it likely that an error will transform the pattern into some highly improbable pattern and thus enable us to detect the mistake. If all possible sequences were used, an error would transform the message into another meaningful pattern, and the mistake would be hard to discover' (Miller in Stevens, 1951).

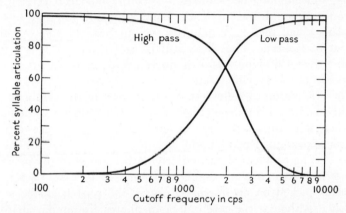

F<small>IG</small>. 11.17.—Intelligibility of filtered speech. Effect of rejecting the high or low frequencies. Graphs indicate that frequencies above 1900 c/s may convey as much information as those below. Most of the energy in speech is concentrated in the lower frequencies. (Data of French & Steinberg as re-drawn in S. S. Stevens, 1951)

Would it be possible to construct a machine that could speak or write? Miller (*loc. cit.*) has considered the implications of this problem. A good deal could be achieved by the use of statistical rules of verbal behaviour.

'Suppose that we had no knowledge of English, and that we were presented with a list of all the words in the language and told to compose statements or messages. The best we could do would be to draw words at random from the list. The zero-order approximation to English might run something like this: "nautical pillory alas prolix temporal depraved migrates irritability callous oil cent," etc.' If, however, information was available about the order in which words commonly occurred 'we might start with "we are going to," then draw from the set starting with "are going to" and obtain "are going to see," and so proceed to construct "we are going to see him is not correct to chuckle loudly and depart quietly for home," etc. Higher-order approximations to English do not qualify as great literature, but they come close to something somebody might say, given the proper situation. It would be interesting to compare these higher-order approximations with the speech of aphasics or psychotics' (Miller in Stevens, 1951).

Certainly on occasion speech may appear to consist of little more than a string of words obeying certain laws as to their order. 'Here is what I got down from the mild delirium of a middle-aged woman in the Royal Edinburgh Asylum, who sat talking to herself quietly, and laughing occasionally : "You're not dead yet. I'll not get you. When I was in York Lane why did you not take the candidate I had then ? When you was in Seafield you would not say that to Robert. That beautiful face of thine. When I forget Spittal Street I'll shine. If I'm no religious, can you lift it up in Spittal Street ?"' (Wyllie, 1894).

There is reason to believe that a large part of the cerebrum may be concerned with language (Fig. 11.18). It is difficult to define the limits of this area with any exactitude, partly because different patients appear to depend upon specific regions to widely varying degrees. The problem is particularly hard because of the bilaterally symmetrical structure of the cerebrum. It is easy to see why Descartes picked on an unpaired organ, the pineal, as the seat of the soul. Although the cerebral hemispheres are similar anatomically, from the point of view of function one or the other is usually *dominant*. Sometimes the dominance affects many functions and is stable, but we must also consider the possibility that the control that one hemisphere exerts over its fellow is precarious, just as with twin children one twin may be dominant, or there may be ceaseless wrestling for position.

In man both hemispheres are probably concerned with language, although the extent to which labour is divided between them varies a great deal. In strongly right-handed people the loss of speech following a lesion of the left (dominant) hemisphere may be very serious ; surgeons are reluctant to remove the speech areas of the left side even for the removal of tumours. Zollinger (1935) removed the whole of the left hemisphere from a right-handed person and his findings give some idea of the serious nature of the sequelae. The patient was a woman aged 43. Some hours after the operation she answered 'all right' to all questions. The following day she could say 'yes' and 'no', although their use was sometimes incorrect. Later she was taught to say 'thank you', 'please', 'goodbye' and 'sleep', but she died on the 17th post-operative day before further progress could be made.

The loss of the dominant hemisphere is less serious in children, and before the age of about 6 there is a very good chance of obtaining a satisfactory return of speech as the other hemisphere takes over from the damaged

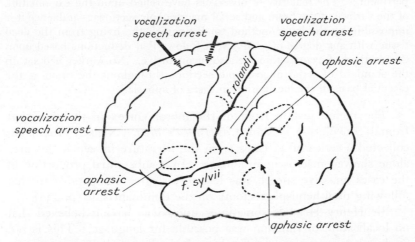

FIG. 11.18.—Regions in dominant hemisphere that may be concerned with speech. 'Aphasic arrest' signifies that on electrical stimulation of the region concerned speech could no longer be formulated, whilst 'speech arrest' signifies that whilst speech could be formulated no words could be uttered. One remarkable phenomenon has been reported on stimulating a zone (broken arrows) on the medial surface of the hemisphere, whilst the patient recited the alphabet. Each time the stimulus was applied 'the letter being uttered at the moment of application of the stimulus was repeated. The repetition continued throughout the period of stimulation, ceasing instantly upon termination of the stimulus when the ordinary recital of the alphabet continued' (Brickner, 1940). The patient said that she was aware of what had been happening but had been unable to check herself. (From Penfield & Rasmussen, 1950)

side. Even at an older age dominance may be shifted to the other side; this at least would appear to be the conclusion to be drawn from a case reported by Lovell, Waggoner & Kahn (1932). Their patient, a man of 31, had at the age of 10 suffered an injury to his right hand that necessitated its amputation. He soon learnt to write with his left hand although previously there had been no evidence of ambidexterity. At the age of 28 he suffered from a head injury that damaged the right parietal region, and for 3 years up to the time of surgical treatment he showed a mixed type of aphasia. With left-handed people the balance between the two hemispheres is much closer and they tend to develop aphasia when either of the hemispheres is damaged (*vide* Humphrey & Zangwill, 1952, and Brain, 1945).

Many of the reports concerning aphasic patients have represented attempts to *localise* specific disturbances to specific areas. This has proved much more difficult than at one time appeared likely (*vide* Fig. 11.19). Collier (1908) pointed out that in work of this type it is of little value to examine the brain by macroscopic methods only. His remarks are still pertinent: 'The majority of observers have relied upon the examination of the surface of the brain and serial macroscopic sections; and since it is impossible by the latter method to distinguish the living from the dead tissue with any degree of accuracy, it follows that deductions based upon this method of examination are also inconclusive. No worker had set up the standard of serial microscopic sections throughout the brain as the essential basis of the localisation in cases of aphasia.'

The region just in front of the motor cortex in the third left frontal convolution is known as *Broca's area*. Nielsen (1946) has collected a series of 43 cases from the literature in which this area alone showed macroscopic damage. In a substantial proportion of the cases emissive speech was lost to a degree comparable to that following total hemispherectomy on the dominant side (p. 438).

Sir Henry Head is sometimes quoted as having believed that no localisation of function was possible for language. This is not so, but he was aware of difficulties that others failed to appreciate. The following statement of his (Head, 1923, p. 429) would appear to go as far as can safely be done towards the correlation of the type of language disturbance with the cortical regions implicated :

'The form assumed by an aphasia may differ with the site of the lesion. The structural injury interrupts in various ways the sequence of complex processes necessary for orderly speech, and so produces diverse clinical manifestations. If it falls over the lower part of the central convolutions and the parts beneath them, the patient has difficulty in finding verbal forms in which to express his thoughts. Injury to the temporal lobe, on the other hand, leads to disordered rhythm and want of grammatical structure; speech tends to become true jargon. A lesion lying between the post-central fissure and the occipital lobule disturbs the appreciation of meaning, either verbal or general. In the first case, it is mainly the nominal value of words which suffers; in the latter, the patient finds difficulty in recognising the ultimate significance of logical conceptions evolved by himself, or placed before him orally, in print or in pictures.'

Schiller (1947) reached rather similar conclusions.

It is usual in neurology to classify speech disturbances according to whether there is a defect of articulation—dysarthria, or formula-

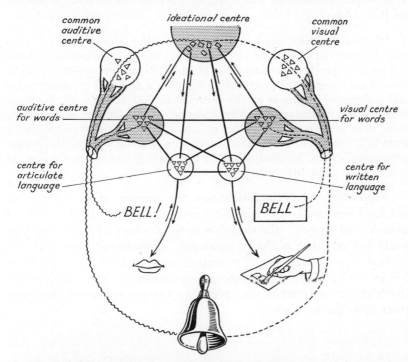

FIG. 11.19.—Charcot's diagram of the mechanisms of speech. The bell itself is seen (right-hand pathway) or heard (left-hand pathway.) Alternatively the word 'Bell' is observed on a card, or is heard. Patients may be able to repeat what they hear, or read aloud, without comprehending the meaning at all. Presumably for this reason Charcot has separated both the auditory and visual pathways into two parts, only one of each route being concerned with words. Although a gross simplification of an extremely complicated subject, diagrams such as this are a way of summarising a number of facts and may therefore have some value. It should not be supposed, however, that the 'centres' are necessarily entirely cortical. There is, for instance, some evidence that peripheral lesions of the auditory apparatus may interfere seriously with the understanding of speech, even though the audiogram (sensitivity to pure tones) is normal (see summary of evidence in *Year Book of Ear, Nose and Throat*, 1955/1956). On occasion highly specific psychic defects may arise. Pallis (1955) described a patient who, although otherwise highly intelligent, became unable to recognise faces ('prosopagnosia'), colours or places. (From Bateman, 1891)

tion—aphasia. Whilst aphasia is due to cortical lesions or perhaps to interference with cerebral association fibres, dysarthria is usually regarded as being subcortical in origin. Is this division always as sharp as we are led to suppose ? Scripture (1916, 1925) investigated by graphic techniques the disturbances of speech in a number of neurological conditions, and some of his conclusions have a bearing on this point :—

'General paralysis registers in its very earliest stages—even when no speech defect can be detected by the ear and when the diagnosis is doubtful —a specific speech defect known as asaphia. In normal speech the same sounds are repeated not exactly alike but with a degree of precision learnt and maintained as proper by the individual. For example, the intervals during which the lips are closed in repeating *pa-pa-pa* do not vary normally from their average by more than 5% to 15%. In paralytics they vary from 25% upward to 100%, 200% and more, without limit, as the disease progresses.' This, no doubt, is a cortical disturbance of speech and yet it is a defect of an articulatory type.

Since Scripture's investigations the science of phonetics has obtained new tools, but these have not been applied to the study of disorders of speech ; the descriptive terminology of neurology lags sadly behind what could be achieved. Discovered speech is described in lay metaphors : 'it sounds as though he has a plum in his mouth'. A more scientific approach would be to analyse the disturbances in terms of alterations in the resonances of the vocal tract (*vide* Stein, 1942).

CHAPTER 12

HYPOTHALAMUS, RHINENCEPHALON AND FRONTAL LOBES

The mechanisms that work wholly within the body and those that make extensive use of the environment are . . . only the extremes of a continuous series. Thus, a thirsty animal seeks water : if it is a fish it does no more than swallow, while if it is an antelope in the veldt it has to go through an elaborate process of search, of travel, and of finding a suitable way down to the river or pond. The homeostatic mechanisms thus extend from those that work wholly within the animal to those that involve its widest-ranging activities. . . .—ASHBY (1952).

HYPOTHALAMUS

IN previous chapters some of the ways by which the nervous system deals with sensory data, and some of the mechanisms underlying muscular control, have been considered. It is appropriate, therefore, now to pass to the hypothalamus, for this small centre plays a dominant rôle in determining the use that is made of the resources of the body and in directing somatic and vegetative reactions into channels likely to promote existence. It is difficult, indeed, to think of any function of the body that is not dependent, directly or indirectly, upon the hypothalamus. Anatomically a number of nuclei are found (Fig. 12.1), but the morphology of these groups of cells is extremely intricate, and the extent to which the smaller clusters of neurones should be regarded as constituting distinct subdivisions is debatable. The hypothalamus can control the activity of the cerebrum, the discharges of the autonomic nervous system and the production of hormones by the pituitary gland ; in addition it is capable of influencing directly the subcortical motor centres. These extensive executive functions are the striking feature of the physiology of the hypothalamus, and it is instructive to consider some of the ways by which these activities are controlled.

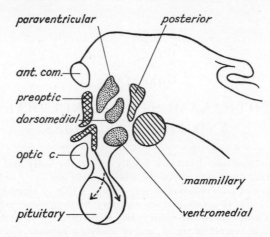

FIG. 12.1.—Nuclei of hypothalamus. In addition to the nervous connection with the posterior lobe, the hypothalamus exerts a control over the secretions of the anterior lobe of the gland.   This control appears to be by chemical means ; substances secreted in the hypothalamus are carried through vascular channels to the anterior lobe (dotted arrow).   The hypothalamus is extremely vascular ; some cells are even penetrated by capillaries. (From Cobb, 1950, slightly modified)

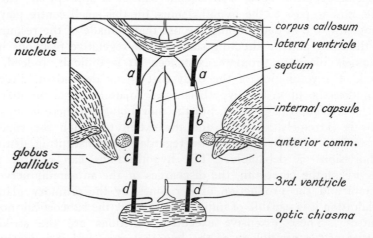

FIG. 12.2.—Frontal section through diencephalon showing region (b and c) responsive to local heating. (From Magoun, Harrison, Brobeck & Ranson, 1938)

TEMPERATURE REGULATION: SHIVERING AND SWEATING

In higher mammals the temperature of the blood is maintained within certain rather fine limits; this regulation ensures that chemical reactions and physical processes in the body will not be dependent as to their velocity upon extraneous factors. The evolution of this 'thermostatic' control has probably been of the greatest

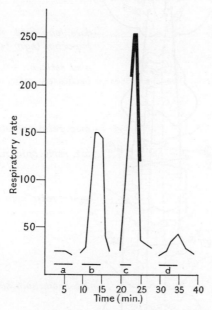

FIG. 12.3.—Changes in respiratory rate caused by heating regions shown in Fig. 12.2. The respiratory rate acceleration indicates that the heat loss mechanisms are being brought into action. Heavy line indicates panting. (From Magoun, Harrison, Brobeck & Ranson, 1938)

importance in allowing a complex nervous system to evolve; regulation of the body temperature is now a necessity (Barcroft, 1934).

The extensive operation of bilateral decortication (removal of the cerebral cortex on both sides) does not prevent an animal from stabilising its temperature, but this function is irretrievably lost if the hypothalamus is destroyed. In man, also, temperature regulation depends upon the hypothalamus, and damage to this region may give rise to either hyperpyrexia (Alpers, 1936) or hypothermia (Davison & Selby, 1935).

Charts of the region in the hypothalamic area that are sensitive to warmth have been prepared by observing the effects of heating small regions (Magoun, Harrison, Brobeck & Ranson, 1938); there

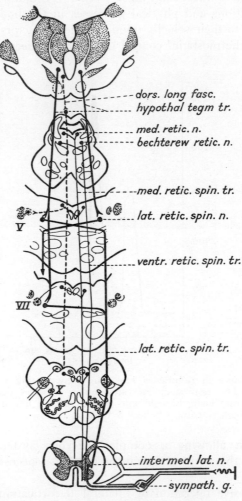

FIG. 12.4.—Efferent pathways from hypothalamus concerned with sweating. Only in the medulla and spinal cord will a unilateral loss of sweating be expected to arise from neurological lesions. (From List & Peet, 1939)

is reason to believe that there exist, in the sensitive zone, specialised *thermoceptors* comparable to the endings that exist in the skin (Figs. 12.2 and 12.3). When the hypothalamus is warmed it is possible (Euler, 1952) to record, from fine electrodes, slow changes of electrical potential which are probably produced by these sensitive structures and which are apparently analogous to the generator potentials which can be recorded from peripheral receptors (p. 53).

If the temperature of the body tends to rise, the hypothalamus responds by increasing the rate of heat loss, and one of the most effective ways of doing this is by sweating. Sweat cools the skin as it evaporates and the extent to which cooling is achieved depends upon the humidity of the atmosphere and the movement of air around the body. A knowledge of the pathways within the nervous system that control the sweating mechanism is of importance, for it may, on occasion, provide useful information about the site of a neurological lesion (Fig. 12.4). To test the sweating mechanism the patient is heated and is then sprinkled with a substance such as alizarin, which changes colour when it becomes moist. A failure of part of the body to respond to the heat may indicate that there is an interruption of the sympathetic pathways destined for that region (Fig. 12.5). When the sympathetic nerves are divided it is found that the vaso-dilatation in the corresponding area of the skin is maximal initially and gradually lessens as time elapses. There is much evidence that denervated vessels become hypersensitive

FIG. 12.5.—Paralysis of cervical sympathetic pathway on right side. In spite of heat the right side of face has not perspired and the powdered charcoal used in this case to demonstrate sweating has adhered only to the other side. The right pupil is smaller than the left and the upper lid droops (ptosis). Failure of sweating (anidrosis), ptosis and pupillary constriction, together with vaso-dilatation, constitute 'Horner's syndrome'. Horner's syndrome is a complication that may follow sympathectomy of the arm unless care is taken to leave the first thoracic sympathetic ganglion. Removal of the second, third and sometimes fourth ganglia on both sides stops all sweating from the lower neck (at about the level of the cricoid cartilage) to the upper chest. This operation may therefore be very effective as a treatment for hyperidrosis, for the axillae as well as the palms are denervated. (Redrawn from Purves-Stewart, 1945)

to certain chemical substances and it has often been assumed that it is this enhanced responsiveness that is responsible for the gradual alterations of calibre after sympathectomy. This question, which is of great importance from the viewpoint of the treatment of conditions such as Raynaud's disease, is discussed by Barcroft & Swan (1953).

Each side of the hypothalamus supplies the sympathetic system on both sides of the body (Fig. 12.6). This bilateral control applies not only to the sudomotor (sweating) system but also, for instance, to the fibres that regulate the size of the pupil, and to those

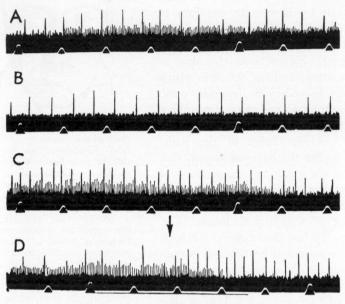

FIG. 12.6.—Control of cervical sympathetic by hypothalamus. Records show activity of single neurone of left cervical sympathetic during hypothalamic stimulation: A, left side of hypothalmus stimulated; B, right side of hypothalamus stimulated; C, both sides stimulated simultaneously; D, left side stimulated, and at arrow both sides stimulated. Both sides of the hypothalamus control activity of sympathetic pathways on both sides of the body. Time $\frac{1}{5}$ sec. (Reproduced from Pitts & Bronk, 1941)

controlling the calibre of blood vessels. As they descend the fibres from the hypothalamus gradually sort themselves out, so that at the level of the medulla they are travelling on the side to which they are destined. The loss of autonomic function caused by midbrain lesions cannot, for these reasons, be expected to be solely unilateral, as may be found when the area of destruction is in the medulla (Fig. 12.7).

Sweating, one of the ways by which the hypothalamus prevents the temperature of the body rising, may be contrasted with *shivering*, which increases heat production, for whilst sweating is mediated by the autonomic system shivering demonstrates that the heat-regulating centres may gain control of the somatic musculature. The operation of chordotomy (p. 58), which does not interfere with thermoregulatory sweating or the execution of voluntary acts, abolishes shivering on the ipsilateral side below the level of the lesion (Hyndman & Wolkin, 1943). Shivering, in cats, has been

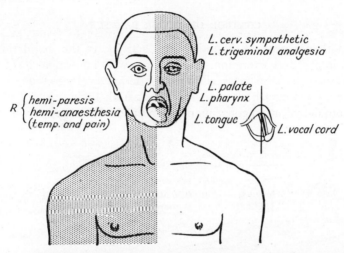

Fig. 12.7.—Bulbar syndrome. Neurological manifestations caused by a lesion on left side of medulla. Most of the sympathetic fibres destined to control the outflow into the cervical region on the left side have decussated above the level of the lesion; the patient therefore shows, *inter alia*, the effects of a left cervical sympathetic paralysis. Note the drooping eyelid and constricted pupil on the left side. (From Purves-Stewart, 1945)

shown to depend upon the integrity of the hypothalamus but not upon the integrity of the cerebral cortex, whilst, in man, shivering movements readily invade a hemiplegic limb (Pinkston, Bard & Rioch, 1934; Uprus, Gaylor & Carmichael, 1935). These facts indicate that extra-pyramidal rather than cortico-spinal fibres mediate shivering. When the movements first begin they may be shown to develop independently in different muscles; it must be supposed that under these conditions the descending pathways set the stage for the movements but that the details of execution are determined locally in the spinal cord. As the shivering grows in intensity the character of the movements alters, for the

2 G

rhythm 'becomes identical in almost the whole musculature'
(Denny-Brown, Gaylor & Uprus, 1935); this 'shuddering' suggests that the control of the details of timing of the contractions has
passed to the descending pathways. Shivering is one example,
others will be given later, of the ability of the hypothalamus to
control the motor system, and it is therefore not surprising to learn
that the hypothalamus may determine the blood supply to the
striated musculature (Eliasson, Folkow, Lindgren & Uvnäs, 1951).

CONTROL OF WATER BALANCE

Another aspect of hypothalamic activity is the regulation of
water intake and excretion. As is now well known, it is of vital
importance that the body should be adequately hydrated; in the
past many patients have succumbed not from their primary disease
but from dehydration consequent upon unconsciousness or vomiting.

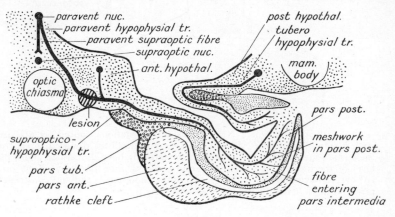

FIG. 12.8.—Connections between hypothalamus and posterior lobe of pituitary
    gland. Note particularly tract running from paraventricular and supraoptic
    nuclei into posterior lobe (Fisher, Ingram & Ranson, 1938, reproduced from
    Purves-Stewart, 1945)

In the unconscious patient water deficiency may be corrected by
judicious injection of fluids intravenously, but in the healthy person
the water balance is regulated by the hypothalamus, for this region
appears to be sensitive to the osmotic pressure of the blood (Verney,
1947). Fibres from the supraoptic and paraventricular nuclei
stream into the posterior lobe of the pituitary gland (Fig. 12.8) and
regulate the release of the antidiuretic hormone; there are now

some grounds for supposing that this hormone may even be manufactured in the hypothalamus to be passed down the nerve fibres to
the gland (Fig. 12.9).

Interruption of the nervous pathways leading to the posterior
pituitary gland gives rise to *diabetes insipidus*. In this disease very
large volumes of urine are excreted because, in the absence of the
antidiuretic hormone, the renal tubules can no longer re-absorb
water adequately. The increase in the quantity of urine (polyuria)
is followed by an in-
crease in the volume
of water that is drunk
(polydipsia) ; if this did
not occur the condition
would rapidly prove
fatal. It is evident that
although the lesion has
destroyed one of the
self-regulatory mechan-
isms concerned with the
body water, some
degree of compensation
has been achieved by
another regulatory
mechanism that remains
intact and involves a
response of the whole
organism—thirst. This
is an interesting example

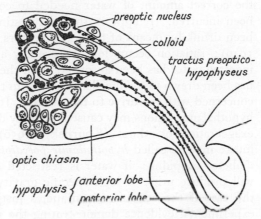

FIG. 12.9.—Supposed neurosecretory function of
hypothalamic cells. Diagrammatic representation of suggested mechanism whereby posterior
lobe hormone, formed in hypothalamus, is
passed down the nerve fibres to be liberated
into the blood stream from the posterior lobe.
(From Scharrer & Scharrer, 1944)

of the way in which the body may react to a destructive lesion ;
we witness a compensatory rebalancing of the injured system (cf.
Fig. 12.13).

Where water is in short supply it may dominate existence :—

'Because we may have it at almost any moment we are likely to overlook
its absolute necessity in our lives. Among inhabitants of desert regions,
however, water is the central nucleus of thought about which all other
ideas revolve ; it is an ultimate standard of things, incomparably more
stable and more exalted than the gold of civilised commerce, the constantly remembered basis of existence' (Cannon, 1917).

Thirst in diabetes insipidus may demand relief as imperatively as in
the desert. One patient of Trousseau's, who habitually drank 43

litres a day, when deprived of water 'seized the chamber pot and drank the contents to the last drop'. Another patient, after treatment with antidiuretic hormone, remarked that 'water tastes differently, it is flat and has no snap to it' (Bellows & Wagenen, 1939).

Sensations of *thirst* depend to some extent upon dryness of the mouth and throat (Cannon, 1917), whilst it is interesting to note that animals that have been deprived of water may drink rapidly the correct amount of water needed to correct the deficit that has been incurred. It appears that they estimate the volume that has been drunk by means of tension receptors in the stomach (Towbin, 1949); satiation occurs long before any appreciable volume of the ingested water has been absorbed from the gut. Recently, attention has been drawn to the mechanisms within the central nervous system concerned with the drive to take water. It now appears certain that hypothalamic lesions may cause a primary disturbance, a pathological exaggeration of, thirst (Kourilsky, 1950). The increased water intake may be called *hypothalamic polydipsia* to differentiate it from diabetes insipidus; if water is restricted a patient with polydipsia will produce urine of high specific gravity, whilst this will not be the case if the condition is diabetes insipidus. Most convincing experimental evidence demonstrating the rôle of the hypothalamus in the thirst mechanism of the goat has been obtained by Andersson (1953). He found that the injection of small volumes of hypertonic saline into this part of the brain could impel animals to swallow greedily large quantities of water. This effect could be demonstrated even if there had been a refusal to drink immediately before the injection. The latency of the response was as short as half a minute.

REGULATION OF APPETITE

Food intake, also, is regulated by the hypothalamus. Although *hunger* pangs are associated with contractions of the stomach (Fig. 12.10), it is evident that the desire to eat is influenced by many factors. In spite of this complex control of appetite the weight of adult human beings often remains almost constant over long periods, whilst Bruce & Kennedy (1951) have pointed out that :—'In the normal rat, the control of food intake appears to depend on calorie value only. Dilution of the diet with inert constituents causes a compensatory increase in the bulk eaten, whereas raising its calorie value is followed by reduced intake.' Richter (1943) also studied the feeding habits of rats and has demonstrated that these animals may themselves select food suited for their various nutritional requirements in a manner that may be remarkably accurate.

Lesions of the hypothalamus may disturb the balance between food intake and energy expenditure. Experimental lesions in, and close to, the ventro-medial nucleus may give rise to obesity, which Brobeck (1946) has shown is due to *excessive eating* (hyperphagia) rather than to a decrease of metabolism. Clinically, obesity is a recognised result of hypothalamic lesions, and the combination of

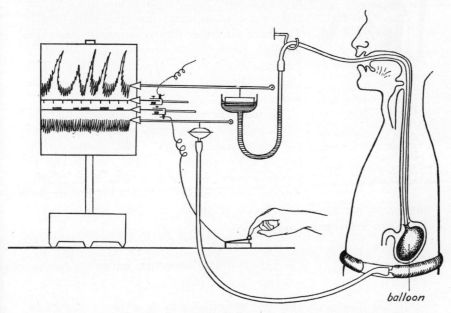

balloon

FIG. 12.10.—Investigation of relationship between hunger pangs and gastric contractions. The large contractions were found to coincide with the upsurge of epigastric discomfort typical of hunger. (From Cannon in Murchison, 1929)

obesity with a failure of the gonads to function adequately is known as Frohlich's syndrome (*vide* Bruch, 1939).

Hypothalamic lesions may not only increase food intake but may, if suitably placed, have the opposite effect. Annand & Brobeck (1951) found that rats with bilateral lesions at the extreme lateral margin of the hypothalamus refused food ; it seems possible that these findings may come to have some bearing upon the disease known as anorexia nervosa, a remarkable condition in which the patient may refuse to eat despite all entreaties (Fig. 12.11).

The hypothalamus therefore appears to be concerned in setting the food intake to a certain level, but the way in which this level is selected is uncertain. There are some grounds for believing that the central nervous system may be equipped with 'gluco-receptors' that signal the concentration of the circulating sugar and arrange that this should be stabilised (Mayer, 1953). The parts of the hypothalamus that control feeding are known to have biochemical properties different from those of adjacent regions. Forssberg & Larsson found that the areas rapidly absorbed labelled phosphorus presented in inorganic form to hungry rats (Larsson, 1954). The element became incorporated into organic molecules.

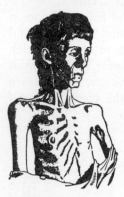

FIG. 12.11.—Anorexia nervosa—mysterious disease. Patient refuses food and despite constant efforts of attendants may die from starvation. (Reproduced from Gull, 1888)

In man there can be little doubt that the motor pathways concerned with eating involve the appropriate regions of the motor cortex, but in some animals, at least, an alternative motor centre for feeding has been found close to the olfactory tubercle on the under-surface of the cerebrum (Rioch & Brenner, 1938; Kaada, 1951; MacLean & Delgado, 1953).

SEXUAL ACTIVITY AND THE HYPOTHALAMUS
(*vide* Harris, 1955)

It has been seen that the hypothalamus is involved in certain homeostatic mechanisms, systems concerned with preserving the life of the individual. It is also concerned with the sexual functions, those activities directed towards perpetuating the species. The activity of the gonads and the behaviour of the animal are closely interrelated (Fig. 12.12), and it is important to consider the way in which sex hormones may influence the central nervous system. In the spinal cat some reflexes may be demonstrated that appear to be fragments of sexual behaviour, but attempts to influence these responses with oestrogens have failed. According to Bard (1940) 'it can be stated with some confidence that neither estrin, nor any bodily alteration produced by estrin can cause the spinal cord, after separation from the brain, to mediate any reflex

suggestive of normal estral behaviour which cannot also be evoked in
the anestral spinal animal'. Observations upon decerebrate animals
also have failed to demonstrate any difference between animals in
oestrus and those that have been anoestrus at the time of observation.

Writing of these results Bard (1940) remarked that 'it seems
clear that in the cat at least, estrin exerts its specific effect on the
nervous system at some point above the lower portion of the midbrain'. In the female the cerebral cortex itself is not essential for
the development of mating behaviour, for in the decorticate animal
'courtship activities even
occur spontaneously, the
male is readily accepted
and after reactions follow
intromission or any
mechanical stimulation of
the vagina'. It is clear
that there exists in the
hypothalamus, or close
by in the upper brain
stem, structures which
are sensitive to oestrogens
in the circulating blood.
In the case of sexual
behaviour, therefore, a
complex set of autonomic
and somatic responses are
liable to be 'triggered off'
if a chemical 'signal' is
reaching the hypothala-
mus. In the intact animal

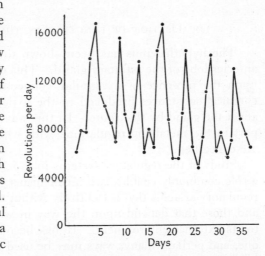

FIG. 12.12.—Relationship of activity to sexual
functions. Activity of rats recorded mechanically by specially designed cage. The peaks
of activity correspond to oestrus. (From
Brobeck in Fulton, 1946)

mating occurs only when the internal environment is in a propitious
phase of its cyclic fluctuations and when the conditions in the
external environment also are favourable. According to the composition of the blood so the hypothalamus appears to be capable of
furthering the organisation of particular patterns of behaviour.

There is evidence that the condition of the external environment
can modify the condition of the gonads as, for instance, by inducing
ovulation. These effects depend upon excitation that passes from
sense organs such as the eye to the hypothalamus. The hypothalamus, through its control of the secretion of gonadotrophic
hormones of the anterior pituitary, is the effector pathway. Clearly,

we have in the case of sexual activity a feed-back system, for not only do sex hormones influence the nervous system, but the nervous system regulates the production of sex hormones. The periodicity of menstrual changes may be looked upon as the rhythmic hunting of a servo system and is an indication that the effects take time to build up ; the main pathways concerned in the human being are purely hormonal, running between the gonads and the hypothalamus or anterior pituitary. The system can readily be upset by interjected nervous influences ; an emotional shock may abolish menstruation.

LOCALISATION OF FUNCTION IN THE HYPOTHALAMUS

The hypothalamus has been shown to exert a control over the anterior lobe of the pituitary gland. This control appears to depend upon the presence of a vascular connection ; it is supposed that chemical substances produced in the hypothalamus may reach and affect the gland by this route. In this way the diencephalon plays a part in the metabolic regulations with which the endocrine glands are concerned.

Study of the regulatory systems in which the hypothalamus plays a rôle commonly enables two mechanisms to be distinguished : the regulatory systems that act entirely within the compass of the body, and those that depend upon the way in which the organism reacts to its external environment. It has become clear that more than one, and perhaps many, ways may be used to stabilise a particularly important component of the internal environment ; it follows, therefore, that when a regulatory mechanism, such as the release of antidiuretic hormone in response to a rise of osmotic pressure, is uncovered by physiological experimentation, it must not, without further consideration, be taken to be a system that is in continuous operation.

If different 'feed-back loops' (p. 112) control one single variable, it is likely that the operational threshold of these different systems will not be identical and it follows, therefore, that minor alterations of the factor in question will bring into play only the most sensitive of the control pathways. If the fluctuations increase, then additional regulatory mechanisms will be recruited. It may be expected that if one of the more sensitive control systems is rendered ineffective, as often must be the case in disease, then the phenomena which are observed may disclose arrangements that normally lie latent. Wherever possible, it is likely that those regulatory pathways that act solely within the organism will come into action the most readily, for they will be innate, automatic, systems the functioning of which will not depend upon the vagaries of the external world. Furthermore, they are likely to be more economical systems than those that depend upon deflecting the whole behaviour towards some particular goal (cf. Fig. 12.13).

Those regulatory mechanisms that do act by directing the whole behaviour of the individual can only be effective if the details of direction and execution are delegated to the cerebral cortex, for only in this way can the detailed sensory data and the fine control of musculature become available. Externally directed behaviour is used to satisfy needs of the body, such as that for food that cannot

Fig. 12.13.—Externally directed behaviour used to compensate for inadequacy of internal mechanism. Rat builds nest of paper which is removed daily; amount of paper used can be read from cyclometer attached to reel at side of cage. Hypophysectomised rat, with resulting reduction of basal metabolic rate, builds larger nest than normal animal. (Reproduced from Richter, 1943)

be provided for by purely domestic arrangements. The metabolic requirements of the body are dealt with by eating, but this act is performed intermittently. It is the function of the internal metabolic regulatory systems that are in continuous operation to use the food in such a way as to provide a supply of nutriment to the tissues which is steadily maintained rather than discontinuous.

The results obtained by stimulating the hypothalamus electrically vary according to the precise region concerned; it is found, for instance, that stimulation towards the posterior of the hypothalamus tends to evoke discharges of the sympathetic system, whilst stimulation anteriorly produces parasympathetic activity. Although there are these regional differences, the responses to stimulation are commonly 'global'; no matter where in the hypothalamus the electrodes are applied, numerous effects are produced that involve the autonomic and to a lesser extent the somatic spheres.

The type of localisation that is revealed by stimulating the hypothalamus is one of *complex patterns of behaviour*, and no matter how small the electrodes that are used, the finely grained map typical of the sensory and motor areas of the cerebral cortex is not seen. Topographical relationships are not preserved in the hypothalamic nuclei, and it may be supposed that one of the main functions of this region is to determine the order of priority that should be accorded the various demands for homeostasis. As Barcroft (1934) has pointed out : 'the actual fight for the preservation of a constant internal environment is carried out in the brain'. The demands for the regulation of different variables must commonly show rivalry for the control of the efferent channels.

One anatomical point is worth considering at this point, the extremely rich blood supply to the hypothalamus. Neurones in this region may be literally bathed in blood, a fact that suggests that blood-borne stimuli, rather than signals brought in along neural channels, are of pre-eminent importance. The supraoptic nucleus is the most vascular region, but the paraventricular nucleus also is richly supplied with blood, as is also the locus caeruleus in the brain stem (Finley & Cobb, 1940).

THE HYPOTHALAMIC REGULATION OF SLEEP

One striking instance of the ability of the hypothalamus to control behaviour and dominate the activity of the cerebral cortex is in the imposition of sleep or of arousal. Even enormous lesions of fore- and inter-brain fail to interfere with the regulation of sleep if only a circumscribed area of the hypothalamus is left intact. This relationship between sleep and the hypothalamus was clearly established during an epidemic of *encephalitis lethargica*. Economo (1930) has stated that the most striking symptom of this virus disease is drowsiness 'of different degree varying from simple somnolence to the deepest sopor in which the patients may sleep for weeks or months but from which, in the majority of cases, it is possible to arouse them'.

Economo notes a number of other disturbances of sleep ; some patients, for example, showed a reversal of the normal periodicity of sleeping and waking, they slept by day and were awake at night. In others there was a 'dissociation of cerebral and body sleep', for at night their minds were asleep but their bodies were restless, whilst in the daytime they were 'mentally wide awake while their bodies were akinetic and drowsy as in sleep'. A related aberration of consciousness, 'akinetic mutism', may occur in patients with lesions near the third ventricle :—

One 14-year-old girl with a suprasellar cyst 'lay inert, except that her eyes followed the movement of objects or could be diverted by sound. As one approached her bedside her steady gaze seemed to promise speech, but no sound could be obtained from her by any form of stimulus' (Cairns, Oldfield, Pennybacker & Whitteridge, 1941 ; Cairns, 1952).

The brunt of the destructive process in encephalitis lethargica falls upon the grey matter towards the posterior of the hypothalamus, but in monkeys Ranson (1939) found that somnolence was more readily produced by lesions in the lateral hypothalamic areas. Economo (1930) noted that some patients with encephalitis lethargica suffered, paradoxically, from insomnia, and the work of Nauta (1946) has thrown some light on the mechanisms that may have been responsible for this symptom. He found that lesions placed in the preoptic region of rats prevented them from sleeping whilst, contrariwise, destruction of the posterior of the hypothalamus induced hypersomnolence. Nauta suggested that sleep is controlled by the balance between the activity of two centres—an anteriorly placed sleeping centre and a posteriorly situated waking centre. Hess has shown that electrical stimulation of the diencephalon in the cat may produce a state that appears to correspond to natural sleep, for the animal walks round, yawns and curls up in apparently normal slumber (Gloor, 1954). These results may perhaps be interpreted as being due to the current reaching the anterior sleeping centre or its connections.

The pathways by which the hypothalamus induces sleep or arousal have not been clearly defined anatomically, but a variety of clinical and experimental observations have suggested that there are involved not only ascending fibres that lead to the cerebral cortex but also descending tracts leading to the brain stem and influencing the activity of the spinal cord. During sleep there seems to be an active inhibition of postural mechanisms such as the righting reflexes, and at the spinal level responses such as the patella jerk may be unobtainable. Tarchanoff (1895) investigated the influence of the brain upon the spinal cord in sleeping puppies. When the animals were slumbering a current greater than normal was needed to elicit movement from the cerebral cortex ; on the other hand, sleep had no influence upon reflex excitability if the spinal cord had been isolated from higher control by a transverse lesion, 'the spinal cord never sleeps'. Tarchanoff concluded that the brain was not all inactive during sleep, but was the 'source of a depressor action propagating itself to all parts of the cord'.

Experimental lesions of the hypothalamus may interfere with the muscular relaxation that normally occurs with sleep. In the cat, destruction of an area close to the mammillary bodies leads to disturbances of posture as well as sleep (Ingram, Barris & Ranson, 1936). The cats 'can be aroused from sleep, and a limited amount of activity can be induced. This is chiefly confined to protective or righting movements : thus, when such a cat is pushed from the edge of a table it may gather itself together and leap so as to strike the floor right side up on its feet. Ordinarily, however, the animals remain in statuesque positions for hours and, because of the plasticity of their muscles, may be moulded into various poses, some of which are bizarre.' This state of *catalepsy* is of interest not only from the point of view of postural mechanisms, but because of the similarity to the human disease of catatonia, a condition in which the patient may remain immobile in odd postures for hours at a time. The various procedures that may produce catalepsy experimentally have been discussed by de Jong (1945).

Catalepsy caused by hypothalamic lesions may represent the effects of interference with a pathway from the hypothalamus to the brain stem that can exert an inhibitory influence over the activities of the extra-pyramidal system. The abrupt loss of muscular tone (akinetic attack) that may be caused by electrical stimulation of the diencephalon (Gloor, 1954) may be due to excitation of the same hypothetical inhibitory pathway, but clearly the relationships between the hypothalamus and the motor systems are in need of further study.

In sleep the electrical activity of the cerebrum changes, and when the sleep is moderately deep the normal alpha rhythm is replaced by waves of lower frequency (*vide* Blake, Gerard & Kleitman, 1939). These changes appear to be due to a cessation of the usual stream of impulses that reach the cortex from the hypothalamus and from the brain stem, for somewhat similar disturbances may be induced by lesions in these regions. It is quite clear that afferent volleys, reaching the cortex through the main sensory pathways of the brain stem, play an important rôle in determining whether sleep will occur. We do not readily fall asleep in a noisy environment. The evidence at present available does not suggest that sleep is due to a block in the conduction of impulses to the cerebral cortex ('de-afferentation theory of sleep'), at least of those messages that travel upwards along the 'classical' sensory pathways. Spike discharges may be generated in the temporal region of the cortex in certain epileptics in response to sound. Studying these responses Gastaut, Benoit, Vigoureux & Roger (1954) showed that sleep did not inter-fere with their size, alter their latency, or modify the refractory period of the system responsible for their production.

Recent work (Moruzzi & Magoun, 1949) has shown that sensory messages that pass into the reticular formation of the brain stem play an important rôle in determining the state of arousal. The influence that the hypothalamus exerts on the cortex is, it appears, mediated, via the thalamus, by the 'recruiting' system (p. 249).

RÔLE OF HYPOTHALAMUS IN EMOTION

Of the patterns of behaviour with which the hypothalamus is concerned the most dramatic is the expression of *rage*. A dog or cat that has lost both cerebral hemispheres is liable to show attacks which are, quite unmistakably, the motor expression in both its somatic and autonomic manifestations, of vitriolic temper. This reaction is called 'sham rage' because it has been regarded, rightly or wrongly, as representing the motor concomitants of an emotion that the animal cannot experience (Bard, 1928; Masserman, 1941).

An attack of sham rage may be set off by stimuli which ordinarily would cause no concern, *e.g.* a fly alighting on the nose, or gentle handling. Other attacks of sham rage may occur without any demonstrable external stimulus. In the episodes the animal may struggle, arch its back, bear a snarling expression and claw. The respirations become rapid, the pupil dilates and the nictitating membrane (*the third eyelid*) retracts, whilst the toe pads sweat and the blood pressure and pulse rise. In the decorticate cat these outbursts are not directed towards any object in the vicinity of the animal; indeed this scarcely could be expected because of the destruction of cortical areas concerned with the organs of special sense. The outbursts are yet another example of the downwardly directed control that the hypothalamus can exert on the motor mechanisms of the brain stem and on the autonomic system.

Rage may be produced by electrical stimulation of the hypothalamus, the cerebral cortex being intact. It is of considerable interest that under these circumstances the fury is directed effectively, being vented upon some object or person in the neighbourhood of the animal. It is clear that the hypothalamus can 'organise sensory, especially visual impulses into the affective behaviour pattern of rage' (Gloor, 1954). Bad temper may also result from lesions of the hypothalamus itself. In an important study, with careful histological controls, Wheatley (1944) has demonstrated that, in the cat, there is some especial relationship between rage and the *ventromedial nucleus* of the hypothalamus. Destruction of this region bilaterally turned placid cats into savage animals and their rage, unlike the sham rage of the decorticate preparation, was effectively directed outwards. They 'would attack the observer in a vicious, aggressive manner, biting and clawing, when attempts were made to pet them or when other innocuous stimuli were applied'.

The decorticate cat may also show unmistakable signs of fear, although this reaction is seen more rarely. Bard & Rioch (1937) noticed that a sudden alarming noise, the escape of steam from the valve of an autoclave, caused one of their cats to run away in alarm :

'The moment the loud noise of escaping steam was heard, the animal suddenly retracted and lowered her head, crouched, mewed and then dashed off, running rapidly in a slinking manner with head, chest, belly and tail close to the floor. After blindly colliding with several objects in her path she came to rest in a corner where she crouched, mewing plaintively. During this activity, and for some time afterwards the eyes were widely opened, the pupils were maximally dilated and there was some erection of hair on the back and tail.'

It would not be fitting to conclude this section without pointing out how difficult it is to define precisely an 'emotion' (*vide* Reid in Cobb, 1950). In a thoughtful review of this problem Hebb (1946) has pointed out that our belief that we can recognise emotional states more accurately subjectively rather than objectively may need qualification. As children 'we can only have learned what names to apply to our emotions if the emotions can be recognised objectively. Either adults must recognise the child's emotion from his behaviour and supply him with a name for it ; or he must first connect the name with something seen in others and then transfer this to his own behaviour.' (See also Leeper, 1948.)

The experimental findings suggest that emotional disturbances might be found in patients suffering from hypothalamic lesions ;

this supposition is supported by numerous clinical reports. Alpers (1937), for instance, recorded profound changes in personality as a result of a cyst in the third ventricle. The patient showed 'loss of memory especially for recent events, loss of inhibitions, with resulting coarseness in action and loss of the niceties of behaviour . . . suspiciousness and hypersensitivity . . . fits of rage provoked by apparently inadequate stimuli . . . and marked swings of mood from depression to elation'. It is interesting to note that whilst hypothalamic disease commonly gives rise to emotional disorders, such disturbances are relatively uncommon with lesions restricted to the cerebral cortex (Davison & Kelman, 1939). The changes that are found with hypothalamic lesions take various forms; there may, for instance, be attacks of weeping or of laughing, or the patient may become maniacal (Alpers, 1939).

RHINENCEPHALON

In lower mammals the part of the cortex that is developed in association with the sense of smell forms a prominent part of the cerebrum. The rhinencephalon (rhino = nose), as this part of the brain is called, is dwarfed in the primates by the great development of the neopallium, and the anatomical relations are changed, the smell brain being pushed so that its parts lie on the medial and inferior aspects of the cerebrum. In these relatively inaccessible sites experimental and clinical investigations are hampered, and it is only relatively recently that these regions have attracted much interest.

The hippocampus is one of the largest components of the rhinencephalon; it lies invaginated into the infero-medial aspect of the temporal lobe. It might be supposed from the evolutionary origin of this part of the brain, and from the name rhinencephalon, that this region would have some indubitable connection with the sense of smell. This has not, however, been established; it has been reported, for instance, that both hippocampi may be removed from dogs without interfering with conditioned responses depending upon olfactory discriminations (Allen, 1940). There is even considerable doubt as to whether olfactory impulses have ready access to this region of the cortex (Brodal, 1947); Kaada (1951), who stimulated the olfactory bulb in cats and monkeys, could find no evidence of evoked responses in the hippocampus.

Although the classical sensory pathways do not lead to the

hippocampus, information from the eye, ear and skin can modify the activity of the neurones of this region (Green & Machne, 1955). Some neurones respond to only one of these types of stimulation, but others respond to all three. The hippocampus can therefore legitimately be regarded as an association area. Its main efferent channel is the compact bundle known as the fornix which passes to the mammillary bodies of the hypothalamus.

If, however, the data carried by the two *fornices* are of great importance, it seems that there must be an alternative system by which the same information becomes available to the parts of the brain determining behaviour. This conclusion stems from the clinical observation that destruction of the fornices does not give rise to any permanent and insuperable barrier to satisfactory adjustment in society. Cairns noted that the fornices could be cut through without impairing consciousness (Cairns, Oldfield, Pennybacker & Whitteridge, 1941), and Dott has described two cases in which the fornices were sacrificed ; after stormy convalescence the personality appeared to be normal (Clark, Beattie, Riddoch & Dott, 1938). One of Dott's patients was an 8-year-old girl, and three months after the operation she was described as being 'bright, cheerful and intelligent'.

Whilst the fornix is the most prominent of the afferent pathways leading to the hypothalamus the mammillo-thalamic bundle (Column of Vic d'Azyr) is the most conspicuous efferent tract ; phylogenetically this bundle represents a condensation of the periventricular system of fibres, a neural pathway that is found running close to the lumen of the third ventricle linking the hypothalamus to the thalamus and brain stem. The mammillo-thalamic tract originates, as its name suggests, from the mammillary bodies and projects through the anterior nucleus of the thalamus to the anterior part (area 24) of the cingulate gyrus. This gyrus lies on the medial aspect of the hemisphere just above the corpus callosum, and it is known to be linked with the motor system through the caudate nucleus, one of the large nuclear masses of the basal ganglia (Fig. 12.14).

In contrast to the difficulty in ascertaining the rôle of the hippocampus the results of investigations of the *anterior cingulate gyrus* are in a sense embarrassing owing to the catholic nature of the effects that have been described. Stimulation with electrical currents has been reported to cause opening of the eyes, dilatation of the pupils, changes in facial expression, alterations of respiration,

cardio-vascular responses, vocalisation, pilo-erection, and an inhibition of muscular movements and tone (Smith, 1945). In addition
the motility of the stomach may be reduced (Babkin & Kite, 1950).
These widespread effects are reminiscent of the results obtained by
stimulating the hypothalamus, and they may suggest that the cingulate gyrus is concerned with the cerebral elaboration of behaviour
patterns commanded by the hypothalamus.

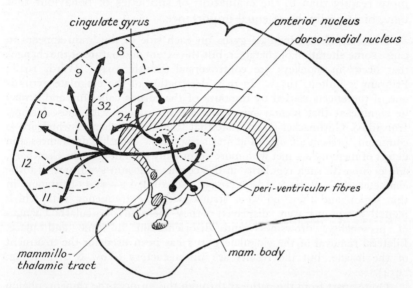

FIG. 12.14.—Connections of hypothalamus with frontal areas and cingulate gyrus.
Peri-ventricular fibres connect the hypothalamus to the dorso-medial nucleus
of the thalamus, a cell station which receives also fibres from other thalamic
nuclei. From the dorso-medial nucleus the projection to the frontal areas fans
out to the lateral, medial and inferior surfaces of the frontal areas. Another
important projection is to the anterior nucleus of the thalamus via the
mammillo-thalamic tract and thence to the cingulate gyrus which lies just
above the corpus callosum on the medial surface of the hemisphere. (Slightly
modified from Le Gros Clark, 1948)

It has been suggested that the rhinencephalon is concerned with
emotional reactions (Papez, 1937), and the results of stimulating the
cingulate gyrus lend some support to this suggestion. Nevertheless,
it is clear that emotions such as rage or fear normally depend upon
comprehending a complex external situation. These reactions are
the outcome of evaluating the significance of sensory data by cerebral
processes which must be common to other varieties of externally
directed behaviour. In placing the emphasis on emotional responses

2 H

as being especially linked with the hypothalamus and rhinencephalon there is a danger of being led to believe that the initiation of these dramatic reaction patterns depends upon quite separate pathways. There is no evidence that this is the case, and it seems highly improbable that such an arrangement would be found. Many physiological methods of investigation lend themselves to the recording of the autonomic and somatic manifestations of an emotion such as rage more readily than to the evaluation of subtleties of behaviour that may, biologically, be of equal importance.

Removal of the cingulate gyrus on each side of the brain appears to cause some alteration of character, but the extent and nature of the changes that occur in monkeys are controversial (Smith, 1945; Ward, 1948; Pribram & Fulton, 1954). In man destruction of the cingulate gyrus is one of the effects caused by tumours of the corpus callosum, and it may be significant that mental symptoms are prominent with these lesions. Ironside & Guttmacker (1929) state that 'the mental changes which are so commonly present are often the first symptoms. Apathy, drowsiness and defect of memory are met with more commonly than in growths elsewhere, and occur with such regularity in the corpus callosum syndrome as to be characteristic.' Voris & Adson (1935) also studied a series of tumours in this region and they too were struck with the frequency with which mental symptoms were displayed: they mention particularly changes of personality, drowsiness and disorientation in time and place. Bilateral removal of the cingulate gyrus has been used for the treatment of the insane, but the results are unsatisfactory (Tow & Armstrong, 1954).

Quite apart from the pathway through the fornices the rhinencephalon possesses another route by which it can influence the hypothalamus. From the *amygdaloid nucleus*, and to a lesser extent from the tip of the temporal lobe, fibres can be traced into the ventro-medial nucleus of the hypothalamus (Adey & Meyer, 1952). Since this nucleus appears to be concerned, *inter alia*, with the motor expression of rage (p. 461), it is interesting to enquire whether any disturbances of temperament result from destruction of the amygdaloid nuclei. There is no universal agreement about the effects of amygdaloidectomy (Spiegel, Miller & Oppenheimer, 1940; Bard & Mountcastle, 1948; Annand & Brobeck, 1952), but in one recent study, using cats, it has been found that the animals became hyperactive and showed an excessive tendency to sniffing and licking in the investigation of objects in their surroundings (Schreiner & Kling, 1953). The animals showed also an increase of sexual activity. These considerations make it probable that the amygdaloid region plays an important rôle in determining the activity of the hypothalamus. A trial has been made of amygdaloidectomy as a therapeutic procedure in hallucinated patients (Freeman & Wilkins, 1952).

THE FRONTAL AREAS [1]

These regions lying in front of the motor cortex are sometimes labelled on charts of the brain as 'silent' areas, for electrical stimuli provoke neither muscular movements nor, in the conscious patient,

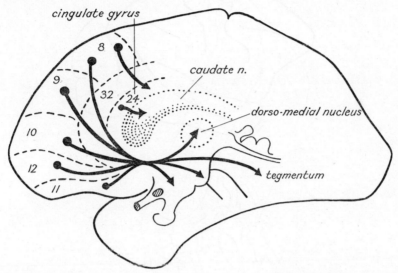

FIG. 12.15.—Efferent projections from frontal areas. Fibres project back to the dorso-medial nucleus (cf. Fig. 12.14), and also reach the hypothalamus and brain stem. The cingulate gyrus projects to the caudate nucleus. Area 8 is concerned with eye movements (Chapter 10, p. 379). (Slightly modified from Le Gros Clark, 1948)

induce sensations of any description. The removal of these areas produces neither paralysis nor any disturbance of sensibility. Ferrier destroyed these regions in monkeys and observed that:—'The sensory faculties, sight, hearing, touch, taste, and smell remain unimpaired.

[1] The frontal areas may be taken to include all parts of the frontal lobe that lie anterior to the motor cortex. On the medial aspect of the cerebrum the frontal areas extend back to the corpus callosum. Although the anterior cingulate gyrus is usually included in the frontal areas, it falls naturally into the rhinencephalon and has been dealt with earlier in the chapter. The term 'frontal lobe' includes also the motor cortex, or rather that part of it (the major portion) that lies anterior to the central sulcus. In measuring the size of the frontal lobe it is necessary to take into account the degree of convolution. Bonin (1948) has suggested that the frontal lobe is no better developed in the human being than would be warranted by the size of the brain. As compared with other primates this may well be true, but he arrived at this conclusion in a curious way. He plotted data of Brodmann concerning the area of the frontal lobes ('F') against the total area of the neocortex ('T') on *double logarithmic co-ordinates*. The straight line that he obtained merely implies a relationship of the form $F^n \propto T$.

The powers of voluntary motion are retained in their integrity'
(quotation from Jacobsen, 1936). Since the frontal areas do not
directly receive information from any of the organs of special sense,

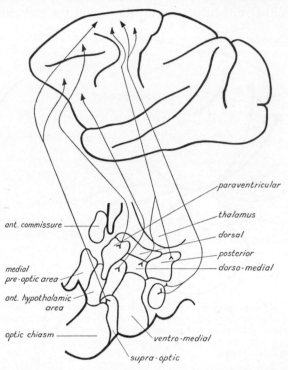

FIG. 12.16.—Projection of frontal areas to hypothalamus. Application of
strychnine to parts of frontal cortex sets up spike discharges that can be
identified in hypothalamus. These results, and similar data for under surface
of frontal lobe, point to rather complex relationship between different regions
and different nuclear groups in hypothalamus. (From Ward & McCulloch,
1947)

and do not appear to form part of the motor system, it may be expected that any behaviour with which these regions may be concerned
will be at a fairly complex level; indeed Ferrier noted that his
monkeys underwent 'a considerable psychological alteration'. It is
with the changes in the attitude to events in the external environment
consequent on injury that much of the work on the frontal areas has
been concerned.

The frontal region receives fibres which originate in other parts
of the cerebral cortex; most of these connections are short and

U-shaped, linking neighbouring gyri. The extent to which long association pathways reach into the frontal lobes is debatable. Le Gros Clark (1948) has remarked that—

'It is probably fair to say that the frontal cortex is commonly regarded as primarily an association area—*i.e.*, a cortical area predominantly concerned with the reception of impulses which pour into it from *other* regions of the cerebral cortex—and that it thus forms one of the highest functional levels for the intergration of cortical activities as a whole. But this conception has no sound anatomical basis, for there is no evidence for the existence of massive long association tracts streaming forward into the frontal lobe from all other regions of the cerebral cortex.'

Fibres from the hypothalamus project to the frontal areas by relaying through the dorso-medial nucleus of the thalamus ; there is, indeed, a point-to-point relationship between different parts of the frontal cortex and different regions of this thalamic nucleus (Meyer, Beck & McLardy, 1947). It has been said (Le Gros Clark, 1948) that 'the greater part of the cortex of the frontal lobe must be regarded as a projection area receiving the products of activity of the hypothalamus, in the same way that the visual cortex is the projection area for retinal activities' (*vide* Fig. 12.14). In turn the frontal cortex sends projections to the hypothalamic nuclei and into the brain stem (Figs. 12.15 and 12.16).

APPETITIVE BEHAVIOUR

The way in which human activities are directed by the hypothalamus is, in many respects, obscure, but there are probably important clues to be gleaned from the study of animal behaviour. The movements that are induced by a *particular internal state* are referred to as being *appetitive* and should be distinguished from *consummatory* acts that arise under appropriate combinations of *sensory stimuli*. Thus newts living under water have to ascend to the surface to breathe ; the ascent to the surface is appetitive behaviour, the filling of the lungs the consummatory act. The ascent to the surface is determined, in part at least, by the concentration of oxygen in the blood (Spurway & Haldane, 1953), whilst the filling of the lungs is probably determined by a change in the sensory messages received from the snout. Similarly, in other animals it has been shown that behaviour related to breeding and the care of young depends upon the internal condition of the animal as well as upon specific features of the environment.

'In spring, the lengthening hours of light or rising temperature cause endocrine changes in many birds and fishes : the animals, under the influence of increased secretion of certain hormones, leave their winter quarters and move around until a particular constellation of conditions releases the response of nest building or of territorial behaviour, or both' (Barnett, 1954).

Appetitive behaviour is recognised as a state which tends to persist until the consummatory act satisfies the intrinsic urge

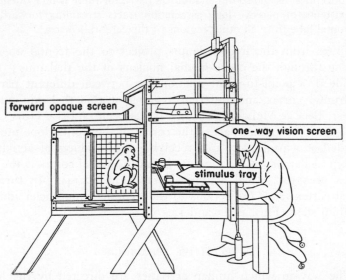

FIG. 12.17.—Apparatus used for testing monkeys with delayed reaction procedure. Monkey observes experimenter placing food under one of the two cups on the tray in front of the cage. The opaque screen is then lowered and the animal can no longer see the tray ; the purpose of the test is to ascertain whether the monkey can select the loaded cup when, after an interval, he is allowed access to the tray. (Reproduced from Harlow & Settlage, 1948)

involved. The pattern of the appetitive movements may vary somewhat according to the nature of the stimulus involved, but hyperactivity is characteristic (*vide* Craig, 1918) and may be looked upon as a quest. It is these aspects of behaviour which are disturbed by lesions of the frontal areas. This is not surprising for, as has been seen, the hypothalamus is sensitive to changes in the physical and chemical state of the blood that reaches that part of the brain. The factors that are known to affect the hypothalamus in this way are few in number, but they are of prime importance and clearly play a major rôle in determining behaviour patterns.

The frontal areas regulate the extent to which ideas may be pursued ; they determine distractibility. This problem was probed in an important investigation by Jacobsen (1936). This investigator studied the ability of chimpanzees to remember for a period of some seconds under which of two cups food had been concealed. This simple task is known as the *Delayed Response Test* (Fig. 12.17). Normal animals have no difficulty with this test if the period of delay is 20 seconds or even longer, whilst animals that have lost their frontal regions bilaterally (Fig. 12.18) cannot accomplish the task

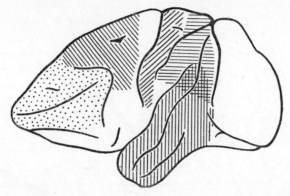

Fig. 12.18.—Area essential for 'delayed reaction test' (Fig. 12.17). Bilateral removal of dotted area destroys ability to choose correct cup after a short delay, whilst destruction of other regions does not (Chimpanzee). (From Jacobsen, 1936)

even though the delay before they have access to the cups is only a few seconds. It is as though 'out of sight, out of mind' was literally true. Jacobsen remarks that :—'The temporal organisation so characteristic of normal behaviour is greatly reduced if not entirely lacking . . . the operated animal seems more distractible in contrast to the sustained directed behaviour of the normal subject'. That distractibility has something to do with failure on this test has been shown by the observations of Malmo (1942), for if the animal is placed in darkness after he has observed the experimenter concealing the food he can, when light is readmitted, choose the correct cup.

LEUCOTOMY

These experiments on the delayed response test have had important repercussions in medicine, for they led to the development of an operation on the frontal regions that has been widely practised.

One of Jacobsen's chimpanzees was a sensitive creature; she was 'profoundly upset' if she made an error and was liable to display a temper tantrum, rolling on the floor defaecating and urinating. By the end of the pre-operative period of daily testing 'it was necessary to drag her from the living cage to the transfer cage, and in turn, force her into the experimental cage'. After the frontal lobes had been removed 'she repeatedly made errors, but the temper tantrums were noticeably absent'. The absence of these violent reactions was not due to an interference with the expressive mechanisms, for in

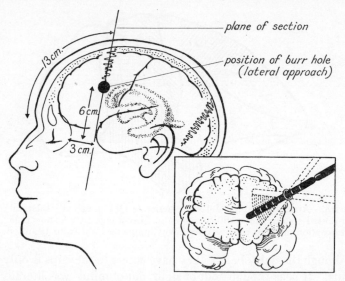

FIG. 12.19.—Technique of leucotomy as performed by Freeman & Watts. Leucotomy is guided by bony rather than by cerebral landmarks. (Elliott, Albert & Bremner, reproduced from Fulton, 1949)

other situations she showed a wide range of emotional behaviour. At no time whilst attempting the delayed response test did the violent reaction to frustration again develop (Crawford, Fulton, Jacobsen & Wolfe, 1948).

Professor Egas Moniz, a Portuguese neurosurgeon, learnt of the relief of this 'experimental neurosis' by frontal lobectomy and was stimulated to perform an operation which he had long been contemplating for the treatment of mental disease. By severing the white matter of the frontal regions the grey matter of the frontal areas was largely disconnected from the rest of the nervous system (Fig. 12.19); Moniz argued that this procedure, which is relatively simple surgically, should have similar effects in disrupting the 'morbid constellations' of neurones to the much more hazardous undertaking of a bilateral frontal lobotomy. The operation is known as *leucotomy*, which means 'a cutting of the white matter', or *lobotomy*, meaning an 'incision into the lobe'. The personality changes that result from the operation become more marked as the procedure is made more radical; Freeman & Watts (1942) have performed the operation under local anaesthesia and have stressed that dramatic alterations are seen only as the section of the white matter on the second side is completed.

Leucotomy is a blind procedure, for the extent of the lesion that is produced cannot be ascertained at the time of the operation (Fig. 12.20). It must not be assumed that in every patient submitted to this treatment there has been a severance of all, or even of any, of the thalamic connections with the frontal areas as the following case report of Meyer & Beck (1945) demonstrates. The patient, who suffered from a psychiatric condition known as paraphrenia, after the operation was much better in every way, he was less excited, and his hallucinations and delusions were far less obvious. He died later from carcinoma of the oesophagus, and it was evident that the leucotomy was placed too far posteriorly to interrupt the thalamic radiation; the section had passed

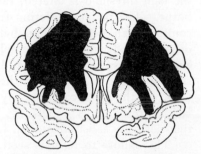

FIG. 12.20.—Destruction of tissue in leucotomy. Extent of destruction is inevitably uncertain. (Reproduced from Freeman & Watts, 1948)

through the operculum, insula, external capsule and claustrum. Owing to the anatomical uncertainties of leucotomy some surgeons have developed different approaches, attacking the cortex itself (Pool, 1949) or the nuclei of the thalamus (Spiegel & Freed, 1951).

Leucotomy seems to be of value in relieving the tension that may be associated with psychotic states; it may be successful in this respect whilst failing to relieve the basic disturbance. Freeman & Watts (1942) stated that 'without the frontal lobes there could be no functional psychosis', but McLardy & Davies (1949) examined this statement critically in the light of a series of patients who had relapsed after leucotomy. They stated that, 'Four of the present cases . . . can reasonably be described as having suffered practically complete bilateral isolation of the prefrontal cortex from its long fibre connections, gyrus rectus and posterior area 9 being the only regions consistently spared. The symptoms concerned in these four cases are fairly varied. Bilateral "isolation", therefore, does not prevent the remanifestation, after their relatively prolonged disappearance or striking amelioration, of many of the commoner psychotic symptoms. Hence, either the isolated cortex can in course of time become effectively reactivated through relays of subcortical U fibres, or through largely intra-cortical pathways and can redetermine abnormal behaviour, or else psychopathological symptoms can develop even without participation of the prefrontal regions.'

PSYCHOLOGICAL EFFECTS OF FRONTAL LESIONS

The relief of anxiety by leucotomy has found another application, for it may be used to relieve the distress of painful conditions, such as some inoperable cancers where other treatments are unavailing (Bonner, Cobb, Sweet & White, 1952); there is no evidence that the pain threshold is altered, rather the discomfort is more readily borne. The patient suffering from pain complains less of his discomfort than before. The hallucinated psychotic reacts less, as does the ape frustrated at the delayed response test. These different examples have in common a diminished reactivity; they do not show a failure to appreciate the situation but a failure to respond to it. In the instance of the psychotic and of the cancer patient the lack of response is a blessing, for in both instances mechanisms that normally assist adaptation have become a hindrance.

This failure to react is seen when stimuli that arise within the body itself are considered; but there may also be a diminished response to external situations. All the regulatory systems acting through the external environment operate at 'reduced gain'; the keynote of frontal lesions accordingly is *apathy*.

Loss of the frontal lobes often gives rise to a reduction in the number of 'spontaneous' movements. A patient with a frontal tumour :—

'becomes apathetic and lacking in initiative. The association and flow of ideas tend to fail. He sits about idly, lacks attention and becomes indifferent to cleanliness and other aspects of personal behaviour. He is apt to permit the unhindered passage of urine and even of faeces and to be totally insensitive to the embarrassments such conduct normally involves' (Purdon Martin & Elkington in Price, 1946).

In view of these clinical observations is it surprising that surgical damage of the frontal areas diminishes anxiety ?

The mechanisms concerned with anxiety and the mechanisms concerned with the ability to perform difficult and complicated tasks as well as possible are clearly related, if not identical. It is in this light that the changes in behaviour following frontal lesions may be considered. Such patients show defects in their goal-seeking activities of different degree.

The effects of destruction of small areas of the frontal regions are variable and are, in general, less pronounced than those caused by large bilateral lesions. In some patients practically the whole of the frontal areas of one hemisphere have been removed with consequences that have been relatively slight. One such case, with removal of the right frontal lobe, was described by Penfield & Evans (1935). The patient, Penfield's sister, was a housewife, and after the operation she was able to run her home and look after her children. She remembered how to cook and could deal with the preparation of individual parts of a meal, but was unable to organise her work so that the vegetables, meat and so forth were all cooked by the appointed hour. The defect was described as being a lack of capacity for planned administration, but could it not have been that she cared less about the results of her efforts?

Administration is poor when the administrators do not worry about their work. Intellectual work suffers if the student does not care about his academic prowess. Worry is not the prerogative of the neurotic; it is the psychological concomitant of efficient action. Rylander (1939) studied a series of patients from whom it had been necessary to remove a portion of the frontal areas on one side.

His investigation included a painstaking analysis of the post-operative personality assessed by visiting the patient in his home, by talking to relatives and by psychological tests. The work should be a model for clinical investigations of this type. Rylander found that the difficulties encountered by the patients varied according to their pre-operative intellectual capacity; the degree to which the 'deterioration was manifest undoubtedly did not depend solely on the disease and on the amount of brain tissue removed by operation, but to a great extent upon the intellectual training and type of occupation. . . . If a person whose life has been devoted to manual labour suffers a reduction in his capacity of abstract thinking, or in his power to survey a complicated state of matters and draw the correct conclusion therefrom, this change need not make itself known either to himself or to the people around him, as it affects functions for which he has never found any great amount of use in his daily life. A clergyman, a teacher or a businessman, on the other hand, is continually confronted in his social and working life with situations and tasks to which he will not be equal if there is any breakdown in this part of his mental machinery.' Rylander found that striking changes occurred in all of the domains of higher mental life, but no one symptom took a really dominant position (cf. Brickner, 1936).

As has been seen, the frontal areas are intimately connected with the hypothalamus, and there are therefore grounds for believing that damage to these regions will upset the relationships between the homeostatic mechanisms that operate wholly within the body and those that become effective through their control on overt activity (Fig. 12.13). Much effort is expended, by some at least, in the quest for food. 'I mind my belly very studiously, for I look upon it that he who does not mind his belly will hardly mind anything else' (Dr. Johnson).

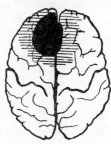

FIG. 12.21.—Crow bar case. Skull, preserved at Harvard, of Phineas Gage who survived, for some years, extensive brain damage caused by iron bar. Radical alteration of temperament but no disturbance of sensation, and no paralysis. (Reproduced from Cobb, 1946)

One symptom sometimes met with in patients with frontal lesions illustrates the type of disturbance that may result between the internal regulatory systems and externally directed behaviour. The regulation of appetite is clearly related to the metabolic needs of the body; with frontal lesions this relationship may break down, the patient eats excessively and becomes obese (Kirschbaum, 1951). Appetitive behaviour refers to the quest for a number of satisfactions such as sexual activities and drinking as well as eating. All of these quests may be upset in frontal lesions.

It is not surprising that activity may sometimes be increased and 'randomised' with frontal lesions. The symptoms that are seen when this occurs are dramatic and are therefore sometimes, incorrectly, regarded as the *sine qua non* of a frontal lesion. The patient may pace the floor like a caged lion. He may make puerile jokes, an activity referred to as 'Witzelsucht', a word derived from *witzeln,* 'to crack jokes', and *sucht,* 'a mania or passion'.

One famous case of injury to the frontal lobes concerned a man of 25, Phineas Gage; an iron bar $1\frac{1}{4}$ inches in diameter was driven by an explosion through the head and must have destroyed most of the frontal lobe

PROBABILITY OF FUNCTIONAL CORRECTION

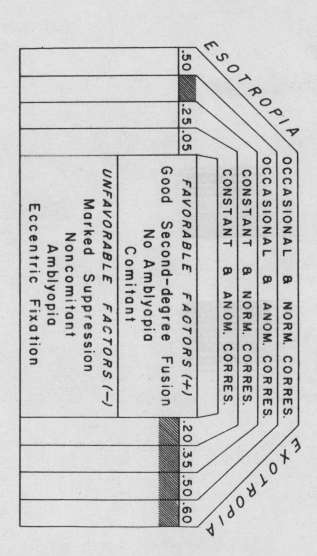

ESOTROPIA

EXOTROPIA

OCCASIONAL & NORM. CORRES.
OCCASIONAL & ANOM. CORRES.
CONSTANT & NORM. CORRES.
CONSTANT & ANOM. CORRES.

FAVORABLE FACTORS (+)
Good Second-degree Fusion
No Amblyopia
Comitant

UNFAVORABLE FACTORS (–)
Marked Suppression
Noncomitant
Amblyopia
Eccentric Fixation

.50   .25 .05   .20 .35 .50 .60

Starting with the probability associated with the frequency of the squint and the retinal correspondence, adjust the probability by 0.05 to 0.10 for each favorable (+) and each unfavorable (–) factor present. The resulting probability is a conservative estimate of the chances of obtaining functional correction of the squint using

on the left side and may well have damaged the right side also (Fig. 12.21). Before this injury Phineas Gage had been regarded by his employers as 'most efficient and capable', but afterwards his 'mind was radically changed'. He was described as 'fitful, irreverent, indulging at times in the grossest profanity (which was not previously his custom), manifesting but little deference for his fellows, impatient of restraint or advice when it conflicts with his desires, at times pertinaciously obstinate, yet capricious and

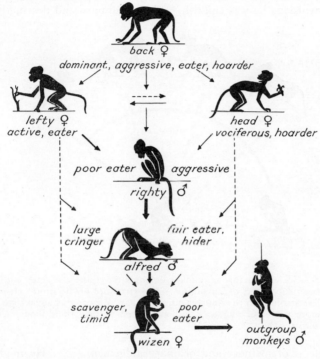

FIG. 12.22.—Social structure of a monkey colony before any of the animals had been leucotomised. 'Lefty' and 'Head' were rivals but otherwise aggression was directed downwards. (From Brody & Rosvold, 1952)

vacillating, devising many plans of future operation, which are no sooner arranged than they are abandoned in turn for others appearing more feasible'. The injury in this patient not only destroyed much tissue but set up discharging lesions and he suffered from numerous epileptic attacks. Jefferson (1937) believed that much of the change in behaviour in this case could be ascribed to the epilepsy rather than to the loss of tissue.

It has become apparent, as Jefferson (1937) supposed, that epileptogenic foci may greatly accentuate the abnormalities of conduct following damage to the cerebrum. Hebb (1945) has been particularly interested in this question and cites the case of a 16-year-old patient whose behaviour, following a severe injury to the frontal lobes, was reminiscent of that of Phineas Gage (*vide supra*). Removal of the damaged tissue restored his conduct to apparent normality.

Hebb states that :—'For ten years increasingly severe epileptic attacks made the patient an irresponsible charge to his parents. Between outright convulsions he was childish, violent, stubborn and destructive with

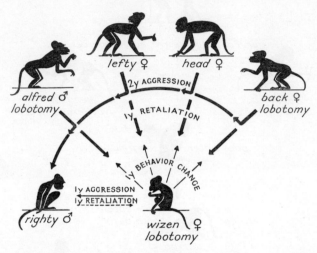

FIG. 12.23.—Social structure of monkey colony after 'Back', 'Alfred' and 'Wizen' had been submitted to leucotomy. The structure of the group changed and was less stable than previously; in particular 'Wizen' was aggressive towards the more powerful monkeys and attempted to take their food. (Brody & Rosvold, 1952)

gross defects of memory and ordinary judgement. . . . He might walk into any house he saw and destroy anything in his way. Since he was strong and big, the neighbors were terrified of him.' A partial, bilateral frontal lobectomy was performed to remove the tissue responsible for the fits and six years afterwards his behaviour was said to have been normal from the time that the operation was carried out. He had become 'one of the most popular persons in the village', being a 'strikingly easy-going, carefree fellow' who showed 'lack of concern for the distant future'.

Hyperactivity and aggression may result from frontal lesions when there is no evidence of epilepsy. Such changes have been observed in monkeys. The study of animals in colonies has the advantage that social interaction may be evaluated under controllable conditions.

Brody & Rosvold (1952) have studied the influence of leucotomy on the 'structure' of a small colony of monkeys and their results are summarised in Figs. 12.22 and 12.23. In a colony of monkeys 'each individual learns, by pleasant or bitter experience, which of its companions are stronger and must be avoided, and which are weaker and can be intimidated'. In this way there is a reduction of 'the amount of actual fighting. Individuals that do not learn quickly to avoid their "superiors" are at a disadvantage because they are an easier prey to predators during fights' (Tinbergen, 1953). In their experiments Brody & Rosvold found that when the operation of leucotomy was performed there was a tendency for the normal social relationships to break down. One of the monkeys (Wizen, Fig. 12.23) no longer 'accepted' his lowly position in the society. His aggression availed him little, merely inducing powerful retaliatory responses from the other monkeys. Speaking anthropomorphically we might say that the *anxiety* about the consequences of striking a 'superior' was reduced.

AUTONOMIC/SOMATIC INTER-RELATIONSHIPS

There are some grounds for believing that the *orbital surface* of the frontal lobe should be placed in a separate category from the other frontal areas. Beck (1950), for instance, has found that this region differs anatomically from other parts of the frontal regions in that it alone does not contribute fibres which pass into the brain stem (fronto-pontine tract). The part of the orbital surface that has been most intensively studied is area 13, lying just lateral to the olfactory tract (Fig. 12.24). The region must be regarded as an autonomic 'sensory' zone, for Bailey & Bremer (1938) found that stimulation of the central end of the vagus nerve gave rise to electrical disturbances in this part of the brain.

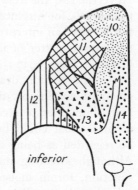

FIG. 12.24.—Orbital surface of frontal lobe of monkey. (From Walker, 1940)

As has already been noted, patients with frontal lesions are usually apathetic and inactive (p. 474), occasionally, however, they are restless. Similarly Ferrier noticed with his monkeys (p. 467) that though they were usually apathetic, they were at other times hyperactive and walked to and fro purposelessly.

Animals with frontal lesions may show so much ceaseless movement that they literally run themselves to death (Langworthy & Richter, 1939). It was therefore a step forward in experimental medicine when Ruch & Shenkin (1943) showed that removal of area 13 without destruction elsewhere gave rise to hyperactivity in monkeys. It is likely that the variability with which hyperactivity is seen after experimental lesions of the frontal areas, and in clinical cases, depends in part upon the extent to which the orbital surface of the frontal lobe is destroyed.

This part of the frontal lobe can discharge into the autonomic system, for stimulation by electrical currents had been reported to raise the blood pressure and alter the tonus in the gastric musculature (Bailey & Sweet, 1940; Kaada, 1951), and the region has some control over the respiratory movements (Smith, 1938). It is perhaps reasonable to relate this influence over vegetative functions to the control that the area may exert over somatic activity, to assume that the autonomic mechanisms are used to adjust the conditions of blood supply and so forth within the organism to the needs imposed by the externally directed activity. At present such a view must be regarded as being plausible, perhaps attractive, but certainly unproved. It is indeed found that autonomic and respiratory changes can be elicited from many parts of the central nervous system, the vegetative and the somatic functions appear to be intertwined. Nevertheless, the very diffuseness of the representation of some of the effects, for instance those concerning blood pressure and respirations, make an interpretation of their significance in terms of normal function a matter of no small difficulty (*vide* Hoff & Green, 1936; Green & Hoff, 1937 ; Kaada, 1951).

In the section dealing with the hypothalamus, examples were given of conditions under which the homeostatic demands of the body dominated behaviour. It is instructive to consider one example, of many that could be listed, of an autonomic response that may be regarded as being subordinated to the needs of somatic activity. Although sweating may be related to heat loss it serves another function, for in moistening the palm of the hand it increases the grip that the papillary ridges of the skin can exert upon objects held in the hand. After a dose of atropine, a drug that abolishes sweating, it may be noticed that some finely co-ordinated movements, such as dealing a hand of cards, can only be performed in a clumsy fashion.

Darrow (1936) has compared palmar sweating with 'the behaviour of the workman who spits upon his hands to obtain a better grip' and with the 'action of a clerk who more hygienically moistens his fingers with a sponge'. He also comments that 'where there is imminent demand for action, the mechanisms of palmar sweat secretion prepare automatically

for easy manipulative activity. Furthermore, the adhesiveness and plia-
bility of the palmar surfaces contribute materially to the keenness of
tactual acuity. A dry, stiff skin transmits but poorly the gradation in
pressure, in temperature and indeed traction on the skin by which we
make judgements regarding the things we touch.'

These considerations make clear the biological significance of
sweating that arises with stimuli that may signal the need for activity.

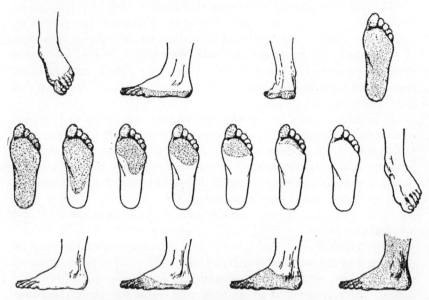

FIG. 12.25.—Regions of low electrical resistance in foot. Shaded areas have only
about $\frac{1}{4}$ of the resistance of skin elsewhere. The margins of these zones, at
any given time, are sharply defined, but may be altered by heating or cooling
the body. Low resistance indicates activity of sweat glands. Read each of
bottom two lines as a progressive series showing effect of change of temperature. Similar patterns were found on the palmar surface of the hands.
(Reproduced from Richter, Woodruff & Eaton, 1943)

Loud noises, threats and unexpected and painful stimuli alike are
effective in provoking sweating of the palms of the hands and soles
of the feet. Microscopic examination of the skin may reveal fine
droplets emerging from the orifices of the glands. The droplets
vanish as soon as they are formed by spreading onto the surrounding
skin or by evaporating, a process that is facilitated by their exceedingly small size (Darrow, 1932).

An indication of the activity of the sweat glands may be obtained
by measuring the electrical resistance of the skin (Richter, 1929).

21

Changes of electrical resistance provoked by external stimuli (*psycho-galvanic reflex*) probably depend upon the person being able to comprehend the significance of the stimulus that is used, and the largest alterations are seen when the subject becomes profoundly alarmed. Sweating is a common accompaniment of anxiety and this association is recognised in the expression 'a cold sweat'; patients suffering from anxiety states usually have cold, moist hands.

The fall of electrical resistance that occurs with sweating is, no doubt, due in part to the moistening of the surface of the skin (Fig. 12.25), but some of the electrical disturbances are a direct reflection of the activity of the secretory cells themselves, a type of action potential generated by the active tissue. Other glands, such as those responsible for salivation, are known to manifest their activity in this way (Langenskiöld, 1941).

In addition, some of the changes of skin resistance in response to stimuli are dependent upon alterations of vascularity (Carmichael, Honeyman, Kolb & Stewart, 1941). The central pathways that are involved in the psychogalvanic reflex have not been definitely established, but Schwartz (1937) found that ablation of the front portion (area 6) of the motor cortex abolished the responses. In the periphery the electrical changes are dependent upon the integrity of the sympathetic fibres.

The interaction of the autonomic and somatic systems may be illustrated by the actions of adrenaline. This compound is liberated into the blood stream during emotional states, the stimulus being neural. The compound in its turn acts upon the central nervous system; a person, after an injection of adrenaline, may feel apprehensive and develop a tremor. In an important series of experiments Dell and his colleagues have analysed the effects of adrenaline into those due to direct action on central neurones and those of carotid sinus stimulation. Their results may be summarised as follows :

Table 8

Mechanism	Effect on Cortex	Effect on Spinal Cord
Direct neural action	Activity accelerated	Facilitation
Carotid sinus distension	Activity slowed	Depression

(*Vide* Bonvallet, Dell & Hiebel, 1954, and Dell, Bonvallet & Hugelin, 1954.)

The changes wrought both at the spinal level and at the cerebral cortex are both mediated by neurones of the reticular formation.

In discussing the significance of these results Dell, Bonvallet & Hugelin (1954) point out that :

'(a) The excitatory action of adrenalin exerting its effects simultaneously upon the reticulo-cortical and the reticulo-spinal system heightens considerably the level of activity of the whole somatic system.

'(b) The counter-regulation exerted by the pressoreceptors acting by way of the inhibitory bulbar portion of the reticular formation keeps in check the output of the muscular apparatus and coordinates its activity with the capacities of the circulatory system at a given time.'

It is misleading to deal with autonomic demands that dominate the somatic system, and with somatic demands that dominate the autonomic system, for such divisions are arbitrary. The somatic and autonomic systems act upon one another; it is one of the functions of the physiologist to investigate these interactions. The function of the nervous system is to arrange to meet the demands that are made upon the body, to ascertain the urgency of these demands and to react accordingly with the resources that are available; this surely is what is meant by 'integration'.

BIBLIOGRAPHY

The page or pages in this volume that contain a reference to an original source are quoted in brackets after each entry. No distinction has been made between references to be found in the text and those referred to in footnotes or in captions of figures, but a page reference has not been quoted for certain figures taken from standard text-books.

ADAMS, D. (1929) 'Dark adaptation' (a review of the literature), *M.R.C. Special Report*, No. 127. [348]

ADAMS, R. D., DENNY-BROWN, D., & PEARSON, C. M. (1953) *Diseases of muscle*. Cassell. London. [17, 29, 31, 32, 33, 48]

ADES, H. W., & BROOKHART, J. M. (1950) 'The central auditory pathway', *J. Neurophysiol.*, **13**, 187-205. [278]

— & RAAB, D. H. (1949) 'Effect of pre-occipital and temporal decortication on learned visual discriminations in monkeys', *J. Neurophysiol.*, **12**, 101-108. [353]

ADEY, W. R., & MEYER, M. (1952) 'Hippocampal and hypothalamic connexions of the temporal lobe in the monkey', *Brain*, **75**, 358-383. [466]

ADIE, W. J., & CRITCHLEY, M. (1927) 'Forced grasping and groping', *Brain*, **50**, 142-170. [382]

— & GREENFIELD, J. G. (1923) 'Dystrophia myotonica (myotonia atrophica)', *Brain*, **46**, 73-127. [32]

ADLER, A. (1944) 'Disintegration and restoration of optic recognition in visual agnosia', *Arch. Neurol. Psych.*, **51**, 243-259. [353]

ADRIAN, E. D. (1916) 'The electrical reactions of muscles before and after nerve injury', *Brain*, **39**, 1-33. [19]

— (1926) 'The impulses produced by sensory nerve endings', *J. Physiol.*, **61**, 49-72. [48]

— (1928) *The basis of sensation. The action of the sense organs*. Christophers. London. Pp. 122. [49]

— (1936) 'The spread of activity in the cerebral cortex', *J. Physiol.*, **88**, 127-161. [238]

— (1941) 'Afferent discharges to the cerebral cortex from peripheral sense organs', *J. Physiol.*, **100**, 159-191. [401, 402, 406]

— (1943) 'Discharges from vestibular receptors in the cat', *J. Physiol.*, **101**, 389-407. [140, 141, 143]

— (1944 *a*) 'Afferent areas in the cerebellum connected with the limbs', *Brain*, **66**, 289-315. [180]

— (1944 *b*) 'Brain rhythms', *Nature*, **153**, 360-362. [236]

— (1945) 'The electric response of the human eye', *J. Physiol.*, **104**, 84-104. [308]

ADRIAN, E. D. (1946 a) 'Rod and cone components in the electric response of the eye', *J. Physiol.*, 105, 24-37. [308]

— (1946 b) 'The somatic receiving area in the brain of the Shetland pony', *Brain*, 69, 1-8. [404]

— (1947 a) *The physical background of perception*. Oxford Univ. Press. [400]

— (1947 b) 'General principles of nervous activity', *Brain*, 70, 1-17. [120]

— (1954) 'The basis of sensation. Some recent studies of olfaction', *Brit. med. J.*, I, 287-290. [110, 210]

— & BRONK, D. W. (1929) 'The discharge of impulses in motor nerve fibres. Part II : The frequency of discharge in reflex and voluntary contractions', *J. Physiol.*, 67, 119-151. [113]

— CATTELL, McK., & HOAGLAND, H. (1931) 'Sensory discharges in single cutaneous nerve fibres', *J. Physiol.*, 72, 392-404. [42]

— & MATTHEWS, B. H. C. (1934 a) 'The interpretation of potential waves in the cortex', *J. Physiol.*, 81, 440-471. [239, 243, 244, 320]

— — (1934 b) 'The Berger rhythm. Potential changes from the occipital lobes in man', *Brain*, 57, 355-385. [236, 237, 240]

— & MORUZZI, G. (1939) 'Impulses in the pyramidal tract', *J. Physiol.*, 97, 153-199. [250, 251]

— & UMRATH, K. (1929) 'The impulse discharge from the Pacinian corpuscle', *J. Physiol.*, 68, 139-154. [55]

— & YAMAGIWA, K. (1935) 'The origin of the Berger rhythm', *Brain*, 58, 323-351. [238]

— & ZOTTERMAN, Y. (1926 a) 'The impulses produced by sensory nerve endings. Part 2 : The response of a single end-organ', *J. Physiol.*, 61, 151-171. [48]

— — (1926 b) 'The impulses produced by sensory nerve endings'. Part 3 : Impulses set up by touch and pressure', *J. Physiol.*, 61, 465-483. [49]

AITKEN, R. S., ALLOTT, E. N., CASTLEDEN, L. I. M., & WALKER, M. (1937) 'Observations on a case of familial periodic paralysis', *Clin. Sci.*, 3, 47-57. [32]

AKELAITIS, A. J., RISTEEN, W. A., HERREN, R. Y., VAN WAGENER, W. P. (1942) 'Studies on the corpus callosum ; (3) a contribution to the study of dyspraxia and apraxia following partial and complete section of the corpus callosum', *Arch. Neurol. Psych.*, 47, 971-1008. [388]

ALANIS, J., & MATTHEWS, B. H. C. (1952) 'The mechano-receptor properties of central neurones', *J. Physiol.*, 117, 59P. [258]

ALEXANDER, E., GARVEY, F. K., & BOYLE, W. (1954) 'Congenital lumbo-sacral myelo-meningocoele with incontinence', *J. Neurosurg.*, 11, 183-192. [103]

ALEXANDER, G., & BÁRÁNY, R. (1905) 'Psychophysiologische Untersuchungen über die Bedeutung des Statolithenapparates für die Orientierung im Raume an Normalen und Taubstummen', *Z. f. Psychol.*, 37, 321-362 and 414-457. [132]

ALLEN, F., & WEINBERG, M. (1925) 'The gustatory sensory reflex', *Quart. J. Exp. Physiol.*, **15**, 385-420. [406]

ALLEN, W. F. (1937) 'Olfactory and trigeminal conditioned reflexes in dogs', *Amer. J. Physiol.*, **118**, 532-540. [211]

— (1940) 'Effect of ablating the frontal lobes, hippocampi, and occipito-parieto-temporal (excepting pyriform areas) lobes on positive and negative olfactory conditioned reflexes', *Amer. J. Physiol.*, **128**, 754-771. [463]

ALPERS, B. J. (1936) 'Hyperthermia due to lesions in the hypothalamus', *Arch. Neurol. Psych.*, **35**, 30-42. [445]

— (1937) 'Relation of the hypothalamus to disorders of personality', *Arch. Neurol. Psych.*, **38**, 291-303. [463]

— (1939) 'Personality and emotional disorders associated with hypothalamic lesions', *Res. Publ. Ass. nerv. ment. Dis.*, **20**, 725-752. [463]

ALVAREZ-BUYLLA, R., & RAMÍREZ DE ARELLANO, J. (1953) 'Local responses in Pacinian corpuscles', *Amer. J. Physiol.*, **172**, 237-244. [51]

AMASSIAN, V. E. (1951) 'Fiber groups and spinal pathways of cortically represented visceral afferents', *J. Neurophysiol.*, **14**, 445-468. [409]

— (1952) 'Interaction in the somato-visceral projection system', *Res. Publ. Ass. nerv. ment. Dis.*, **30**, 371-402. [412]

AMBACHE, N. (1949) 'The peripheral action of Cl. Botulinum toxin', *J. Physiol.*, **108**, 127-141. [31]

— MORGAN, R. S., & WRIGHT, G. P. (1948) 'The action of tetanus toxin on the rabbit's iris', *J. Physiol.*, **107**, 45-53. [31]

AMES, A. (1946) 'Binocular vision as affected by relations between uniocular stimulus patterns in commonplace environments', *Amer. J. Psychol.*, **59**, 333-357. [341]

ANDERSEN, E. E., & WEYMOUTH, F. W. (1923) 'Visual perception and the retinal mosaic. I. Retinal mean local sign—an explanation of the fineness of binocular perception of distance', *Amer. J. Physiol.*, **64**, 561-591. [321, 340]

ANDERSON, A. B., & MUNSON, W. A. (1951) 'Electric excitation of nerves in the skin at audiofrequencies', *J. Acoust. Soc. Amer.*, **23**, 155-159. [417]

ANDERSSON, B. (1953) 'The effect of injections of hypertonic NaCl solutions into different parts of the hypothalamus of goats', *Acta Physiol. Scand.*, **28**, 188-201. [452]

ANDRÉ-THOMAS (1910) 'Cerebellar functions'. Translated by W. C. Herring, *J. Nerv. ment. Dis.*, Monograph Series, No. 12. [133, 167, 170, 190, 196]

— (1924) 'La Paralysie horizontale du regard. Les voies oculomotrices. Le faisceau longitudinal postérieur', *Rev. d'oto-neuro-oculistique*, **2**, 16-207. [159]

— (1940) *Équilibre et équilibration*. Masson. Paris. [167, 169, 175, 177, 179]

— SCHAEFFER, H., & BERTRAND, I. (1933) 'Paralysie de l'abaissement du regard, paralysie des inférogyres, hypertonie des supérogyres et des releveurs des paupières', *Rev. Neurol.*, **40**, Tome 2, 535-542. [335]

ANDREW, A. M. (1953) 'Information theory', *Electronic Engineering*, **25**, 471-475. [11]

ANDREW, B. L. (1954) 'The sensory innervation of the medial ligament of the knee joint', *J. Physiol.*, **123**, 241-250. [430]

ANNAND, B. K., & BROBECK, J. P. (1951) 'Hypothalamic control of food intake in rats', *Yale J. Biol. Med.*, **24**, 123-140. [453]

— — (1952) 'Food intake and spontaneous activity of rats with lesions in the amygdaloid nuclei', *J. Neurophysiol.*, **15**, 421-430. [466]

APTER, J. T. (1946) 'Eye movements following strychninisation of the superior colliculus of cats', *J. Neurophysiol.*, **9**, 73-86. [334]

ARDEN, G. B., & WEALE, R. A. (1954) 'Nervous mechanisms and dark adaptation', *J. Physiol.*, **125**, 417-426. [295]

ARDUINI, A., & MORUZZI, G. (1953) 'Sensory and thalamic synchronisation in the olfactory bulb', *E.E.G. Clin. Neurophysiol.*, **5**, 235-242. [210]

ARING, C. D. (1940) 'Flaccid hemiplegia in man', *Arch. Neurol. Psych.*, **43**, 302-317. [383]

ARMINGTON, J. C., JOHNSON, E. P., & RIGGS, L. A. (1952) 'The scotopic A-wave in the electrical response of the human retina', *J. Physiol.*, **118**, 289-298. [307, 308]

ARVANITAKI, A. (1942) 'Effects evoked in an axon by the activity of a contiguous one', *J. Neurophysiol.*, **5**, 89-108. [27]

ASHBY, M. (1949) 'Delayed withdrawal reflex and perception of pain. Studies in a case of syphilitic meningomyelitis and tabes with extensor plantar responses of a type not previously described', *Brain*, **72**, 599-612. [65, 373]

ASHBY, W. R. (1952) *Design for a brain*. Chapman & Hall. London. [82, 420, 433]

ASHER, H. (1950) 'Contrast in eye and brain', *Brit. J. Psychol.*, **40**, 187-194. [316]

BABKIN, B. P., & VAN BUREN, J. M. (1951) 'Mechanism and cortical representation of the feeding pattern', *Arch. Neurol. Psych.*, **66**, 1-19. [379]

— DWORKIN, S., & SCHACHTER, M. (1946) 'Experimental motion-sickness and attempts at therapy', *Rev. Canad. Biol.*, **5**, 72-85. [125]

— & KITE, W. C. (1950) 'Central and reflex regulation of the activity of pyloric antrum', *J. Neurophysiol.*, **13**, 321-342. [465]

BAILEY, P. (1948) 'Concerning cytoarchitecture of the frontal lobe of chimpanzee (*Pan Satyrus*) and man (*Homo Sapiens*)', *Res. Publ. Ass. nerv. ment. Dis.*, **27**, 84-94. [26]

— BONIN, G. VON, GAROL, H. W., & McCULLOCH, W. C. (1943) 'Long association fibres in cerebral hemispheres of monkey and chimpanzee', *J. Neurophysiol.*, **6**, 129-134. [201]

— & BREMER, F. (1938) 'A sensory cortical representation of the vagus nerve', *J. Neurophysiol.*, **1**, 405-412. [479]

— & SWEET, W. H. (1940) 'Effects on respiration, blood pressure and gastric motility of stimulation of orbital surface of frontal lobe', *J. Neurophysiol.*, **3**, 276-281. [480]

BAKER, R. C., & GRAVES, G. O. (1931) 'Cerebellar agenesis', *Arch. Neurol. Psych.*, **25**, 548-555. [196]

BALDOCK, G. R., & WALTER, W. G. (1946) 'A new electronic analyser', *Electronic Engineering*, **18**, 339-345. [243]

BÁRÁNY, E. (1942) 'On the mechanical impedance of the human thorax', *Acta med. scand.*, **111**, 252-260. (263]

— & HALLDÉN, U. (1948) 'Phasic inhibition of the light reflex of the pupil during retinal rivalry', *J. Neurophysiol.*, **11**, 25-30. [343]

BÁRÁNY, R. (1921) 'Diagnosis of disease of the otolith apparatus', *J. Laryngol. Otol.*, **36**, 229-234. [141]

BARCROFT, H., & SWAN, H. J. C. (1953) *Sympathetic control of human blood vessels*. Arnold. London. [448]

BARCROFT, J. (1934) *Features in the architecture of physiological function*. Cambridge Univ. Press. [445, 458]

BARD, P. (1928) 'Diencephalic mechanisms for expression of rage with special reference to sympathetic nervous system', *Amer. J. Physiol.*, **84**, 490-515. [461]

— (1937) 'Studies on the cortical representation of somatic sensibility', *Harvey Lectures*, **33**, 143-169. [427]

— (1939) 'Central nervous mechanisms for emotional behaviour patterns in animals', *Res. Publ. Ass. nerv. ment. Dis.*, **19**, 190-218. [217]

— (1940) 'The hypothalamus and sexual behaviour', *Res. Publ. Ass. nerv. ment. Dis.*, **20**, 551-579. [454, 455]

— & MOUNTCASTLE, V. B. (1948) 'Some forebrain mechanisms involved in expression of rage with special reference to suppression of angry behaviour', *Res. Publ. Ass. nerv. ment. Dis.*, **27**, 362-405. [466]

— & RIOCH, D. M. (1937) 'A study of four cats deprived of neocortex and additional portions of the forebrain', *Johns Hopk. Hosp. Bull.*, **60**, 65-146. [277, 462]

BARENNE, J. G. DUSSER DE (1924) 'Experimental results on sensory localisation in cerebral cortex of the monkey (Macacus)', *Proc. Roy. Soc.*, B, **96**, 272-291. [415, 416]

— (1933 *a*) 'The mode and site of action of strychnine in the nervous system', *Physiol. Rev.*, **13**, 325-335. [415]

— (1933 *b*) 'Corticalisation of function and functional localisation in the cerebral cortex', *Arch. Neurol. Psych.*, **30**, 884-901. [277]

— (1934) 'Origin of motor reactions produced by electrical stimulation of the cerebral cortex', *Arch. Neurol. Psych.*, **31**, 1129-1138. [379]

— & McCULLOCH, W. S. (1938) 'Functional organisation in the sensory cortex of the monkey (*Macaca Mulatta*)', *J. Neurophysiol.*, **1**, 69-85. [200]

— — (1939) 'Factors for facilitation and extinction in the C.N.S.', *J. Neurophysiol.*, **2**, 319-355. [234]

BARLOW, H. B. (1952) 'Eye movements during fixation', *J. Physiol.*, **116**, 290-306. [356, 367]

— (1953) 'Summation and inhibition in the frog's retina', *J. Physiol.*, **119**, 69-88. [317]

BARLOW, H. B., FITZHUGH, R., & KUFFLER, S. W. (1954) 'Resting discharge and dark adaptation in the cat', *J. Physiol.*, **125**, 28P. [315]

— KOHN, H. I., & WALSH, E. G. (1947) 'Visual sensations aroused by magnetic fields', *Amer. J. Physiol.*, **148**, 372-375. [319]

BARNES, H. D. (1944) 'John Dalton', *Iscor News*, **9**, 493-496. [304]

BARNETT, A. (1938) 'The phase angle of normal human skin', *J. Physiol.*, **93**, 349-366. [20]

BARNETT, S. A. (1954) 'Instinct and learning', *Science News*, **33**, ed. by A. W. Haslett. Penguin Books. London. [330, 470]

BARRINGTON, F. J. F. (1915) 'The nervous mechanism of micturition', *Quart. J. Exp. Physiol.*, **8**, 33-71. [101]

BARRON, D. H., & MATTHEWS, B. H. C. (1935) 'Intermittent conduction in the spinal cord', *J. Physiol.*, **85**, 73-103. [7, 415]

— — (1938) 'The interpretation of potential changes in the spinal cord', *J. Physiol.*, **92**, 276-321. [23]

BARTLETT, F. C. (1947) 'The measurement of human skill', *Brit. med. J.*, I, 835-839. [420]

BATEMAN, F. (1891) *On aphasia or loss of speech and the localisation of the faculty of articulate language.* Churchill. London. [358, 441]

BATES, J. A. V. (1953 *a*) 'Stimulation of medial surface of human cerebral hemisphere', *Brain*, **76**, 405-447. [385, 386]

—. (1953 *b*) 'A technique for identifying changes in consciousness', *E.E.G. Clin. Neurophysiol.*, **5**, 445-446. [253]

BAZETT, H. C., & MCGLONE, B. (1932) 'Studies in sensation III. Chemical factor in the stimulation of end-organ giving temperature sensations', *Arch. Neurol. Psych.*, **28**, 71-91. [68]

— & PENFIELD, W. G. (1922) 'A study of the Sherrington decerebrate animal in the chronic as well as the acute condition', *Brain*, **45**, 185-265. [128, 277, 278]

BEATTY, R. T. (1932) *Hearing in man and animals.* Bell & Sons. London. [263, 266, 271]

BECK, E. (1950) 'The origin, course and termination of the pre-fronto-pontine tract in the human brain', *Brain*, **73**, 368-391. [479]

BECK, K. (1912) 'Untersuchungen über den statischen Apparat von Gesunden und Taubstummen', *Z. f. Psychol.*, Abt. 2. Sinnesphysiol., **46**, 362-378. [132]

BEIER, D. C. (1940) 'Conditioned cardiovascular responses and suggestions for the treatment of cardiac neuroses', *J. Exp. Psychol.*, **26**, 311-321. [220]

BÉKÉSY, G. (1949) 'The structure of the middle ear and the hearing of one's own voice by bone conduction' & 'On the resonance curve and decay period at various points on the cochlea partition', *J. Acoust. Soc. Amer.*, **21**, 217-232 and 245-254. [262, 269]

BELL, C. (1811) *Idea of a new anatomy of the brain submitted for the observation of his friends.* Strahan and Preston. London. Pp. 36. [35]

— (1833) *The hand—its mechanism and vital endowments as evincing design.* Wm. Pickering. London. [397]

BELL, E., & KARNOSH, L. J. (1949) 'Cerebral hemispherectomy ; report of a case 10 years after operation', *J. Neurosurg.*, **6**, 285-293. [409]

BELL, G. H., DAVIDSON, J. N., & SCARBOROUGH, H. (1950) *Textbook of physiology and biochemistry.* Livingstone. Edinburgh. [14, 150]

BELLOWS, R. T., & WAGENEN, W. P. VAN (1939) 'The relationship of polydipsia and polyuria in diabetes insipidus', *J. nerv. ment. Dis.*, **88**, 417-473. [452]

BENDER, M. B. (1952) *Disorders in perception.* Thomas. Springfield, Ill. [80]

— & FULTON, J. F. (1939) 'Factors in functional recovery following section of the oculomotor nerve in monkeys', *J. Neurol. Psychiat.*, **2**, 285-292. [225]

— NATHANSON, M., & GORDON, G. G. (1952) 'Myoclonus of muscles of the eye, face, and throat', *Arch. Neurol. Psych.*, **67**, 44-58. [189]

BENTLEY, I. M. (1900) 'The synthetic experiment', *Amer. J. Psychol.*, **11**, 405-425. [398, 419]

BERGER, C. (1941) 'The dependency of visual acuity on illumination and its relation to the size and function of the retinal units', *Amer. J. Psychol.*, **54**, 336-352. [321]

BERGMARK, G. (1909) 'Cerebral monoplegia, with special reference to sensation and to spastic phenomena', *Brain*, **32**, 342-477. [409, 411]

BERKELEY, BISHOP G. (1709) *A new theory of vision and other select philosophical writings.* Republished in Everyman's Library. Dent. London. [339, 360]

BERNHARD, C. G. (1942) 'Isolation of retinal and optic ganglion response in the eye of Dysticus', *J. Neurophysiol.*, **5**, 32-48. [307]

BERRY, C. M., HAGAMEN, W. D., & HINSEY, J. C. (1952) 'Distribution of potentials following stimulation of olfactory bulb in cat', *J. Neurophysiol.*, **15**, 139-148. [208]

— KARL, R. C., & HINSEY, J. C. (1950) 'Course of spinothalamic and medial lemniscus pathways in cat and rhesus monkey', *J. Neurophysiol.*, **13**, 149-156. [400]

BEST, C. H., & TAYLOR, N. B. (1939) *The physiological basis of medical practice.* Baillière, Tindall & Cox. London. [36, 146]

BIEBER, I., & FULTON, J. F. (1938) 'Relation of the cerebral cortex to the grasp reflex and to postural and righting reflexes', *Arch. Neurol. Psych.*, **39**, 433-454. [156]

BIGELOW, N., HARRISON, J., GOODELL, H., & WOLFF, H. G. (1945) 'Studies on pain. Quantitative measurements of two pain sensations of the skin, with reference to the nature of the "hyperalgesia of peripheral neuritis"', *J. Clin. Invest.*, **24**, 503-512. [64]

BING, H. I., & SKOUBY, A. P. (1949) 'The influence of skin temperature on the number of reacting cold spots', *Acta Physiol. Scand.*, **18**, 190-196. [36]

BISHOP, G. H. (1943) 'Responses to electrical stimulation of single sensory units of the skin', *J. Neurophysiol.*, **6**, 361-382. [43, 56, 66]

Bishop, G. H. (1946) 'Neural mechanisms of cutaneous sense', *Physiol. Rev.*, **26**, 77-102. [66]

Björk, A., & Kugelberg, E. (1953 a) 'Motor unit activity in the human extra-ocular muscles', *E.E.G. Clin. Neurophysiol.*, **5**, 271-278. [367]

— — (1953 b) 'Electrical activity of the muscles of the eye and eyelids in various positions and during movement', *E.E.G. Clin. Neurophysiol.*, **5**, 595-602. [367]

Blake, H., Gerard, R. W., & Kleitman, N. (1939) 'Factors influencing brain potentials during sleep', *J. Neurophysiol.*, **2**, 48-60. [460]

Blix, M. (1884) 'Experimentelle Beiträge zur Lösung der Frage über die specifische Energie der Hautnerven', *Z. Biol.*, **20**, 141-156. [35]

Blonder, E. J. (1937) 'Galvanic falling in clinical use', *Arch. Neurol. Psych.*, **37**, 137-141. [147]

Bloom, G., & Engström, H. (1952) 'The structure of the epithelial surface in the olfactory region', *Exp. Cell Res.*, **3**, 699-701. [210]

Bodian, D. (1947) 'Nucleic acid in nerve-cell regeneration', *S.E.B. Symposium*, **1**, 163-178. [14]

Bohm, E., & Petersén, I. (1952) 'Ipsilateral conduction in the medial lemniscus of the cat', *Acta Physiol. Scand.*, **29**, Suppl. 106, 138-142. [400]

Bonin, G. von (1948) 'The frontal lobe of primates : cyto-architectural studies', *Res. Publ. Ass. nerv. ment. Dis.*, **27**, 67-94. [467]

Bonner, F., Cobb, S., Sweet, W. H., & White, J. C. (1952) 'Frontal lobe surgery in the treatment of pain', *Psychosomatic Med.*, **14**, 383-405. [474]

Bonvallet, M., Dell, P., & Hiebel, G. (1954) 'Tonus sympathique et activité électrique corticale', *E.E.G. Clin. Neurophysiol.*, **6**, 119-144. [482]

Boring, E. G. (1932) 'The physiology of consciousness', *Science*, **75**, 32-39. [220]

— (1933) *The physical dimensions of consciousness*. Century Psychology Series. [230]

Borison, H. L., & Wang, S. C. (1949) 'Functional localisation of central co-ordinating mechanism for emesis in cat', *J. Neurophysiol.*, **12**, 305-313. [132]

Bors, E. (1951) 'Phantom limbs of patients with spinal cord injury', *Arch. Neurol. Psych.*, **66**, 610-631. [425]

Botelho, S. Y., Deaterly, C. F., Austin, S., & Comroe, J. H. (1952) 'Evaluation of electromyogram of patient with myasthenia gravis', *Arch. Neurol. Psych.*, **67**, 441-450. [29]

Bounds, G. W. (1953) 'The electroretinogram. A review of the literature', *A.M.A. Arch. Ophthal.*, **49**, 63-89. [309]

Boyd, I. A. (1954) 'The histological structure of the receptors in the knee-joint of the cat correlated with their physiological response', *J. Physiol.*, **124**, 476-488. [55]

Boyd, I. A., & Roberts, T. D. M. (1953) 'Proprioceptive discharges from stretch receptors in the knee-joint of the cat', *J. Physiol.*, **122**, 38-58. [55]

BOYNTON, R. M., BUSH, W. R., ENOCH, J. M. (1954) 'Rapid changes in foveal sensitivity resulting from direct and indirect adapting stimuli', *J. Opt. Soc. Amer.*, **44**, 56-60. [296]

BRAIN, R. (1927) 'On the significance of the flexor position of the upper limb in hemiplegia with an account of a quadripedal extensor reflex', *Brain*, **50**, 113-137. [155-156]

— (1941) 'Visual disorientation with special reference to lesions of the right cerebral hemisphere', *Brain*, **64**, 244-272. [356, 430]

BRAIN, W. R. (1945) 'Speech and handedness', *Lancet*, II, 837-842. [440]

BRAZIER, M. A. B. (1945) 'Tremors of combat neuroses', *Arch. Neurol. Psych.*, **54**, 175-180. [391]

— (1951) *The electrical activity of the nervous system.* Pitman. London. [254]

— (1953) 'A review of physiological mechanisms of the visual system in relation to activating techniques in electro-encephalography', *E.E.G. Clin. Neurophysiol.*, Suppl. **4**, 93-107. [347]

— & CASBY, J. U. (1952) 'Crosscorrelation and autocorrelation studies of electroencephalographic potentials', *E.E.G. Clin. Neurophysiol.*, **4**, 201-211. [250]

BREMER, F. (1932) 'Le Tonus musculaire', *Erg. de Physiol.*, **34**, 678-740. [176, 231]

— (1953) *Some problems in neurophysiology.* Univ. of London. Athlone Press. [253, 281]

BRICKNER, R. M. (1936) *The intellectual functions of the frontal lobes.* Macmillan. New York. [476]

— (1940) 'A human cortical area producing repetitive phenomena when stimulated', *J. Neurophysiol.*, **3**, 128-130. [439]

— (1948) 'Telencephalisation of survival characteristics', *Res. Publ. Ass. nerv. ment. Dis.*, **27**, 658-688. [79]

BRIDGMAN, C. S., & SMITH, K. U. (1942) 'The absolute threshold of vision in cat and man with observations on its relation to the optic cortex', *Amer. J. Physiol.*, **136**, 463-466. [293]

BRINDLEY, G. S. (1953) 'The effects on colour vision of adaptation to very bright lights', *J. Physiol.*, **122**, 332-350. [305]

BRINK, F. (1954) 'The rôle of calcium ions in neural processes', *Pharmacol. Rev.*, **6**, 243-298. [25]

BRITTON, S. W., & KLINE, R. F. (1943) 'The pseudaffective state and decerebrate rigidity in the sloth', *J. Neurophysiol.*, **6**, 65-69. [126]

BROBECK, J. R. (1946) 'Mechanism of the development of obesity in animals with hypothalamic lesions', *Physiol. Rev.*, **26**, 541-559. [453]

BRODAL, A. (1947) 'The hippocampus and the sense of smell', *Brain*, **70**, 179-222. [213, 463]

— (1948) *Neurological anatomy.* Clarendon Press. [192, 202]

BRODAL, A., & JANSEN, J. (1946) 'The ponto-cerebellar projections in the rabbit and cat', *J. Comp. Neurol.*, **84**, 31-118. [182]

BRODAL, A., & KAADA, B. R. (1953) 'Exteroceptive and proprioceptive ascending impulses in pyramidal tract of cat', *J. Neurophysiol.*, **16**, 567-586. [370]

BRODY, E. B., & ROSVOLD, H. E. (1952) 'Influence of prefrontal lobotomy on social interaction in a monkey group', *Psychosom. Med.*, **14**, 406-415. [477, 478, 479]

BRONK, D. W. (1939) 'Synaptic mechanisms in sympathetic ganglia', *J. Neurophysiol.*, **2**, 380-401. [25, 105]

— & FERGUSON, L. K. (1935) 'The nervous control of intercostal respiration', *Amer. J. Physiol.*, **110**, 700-707. [84]

— & STELLA, G. (1935) 'The response to steady pressures of single end organs in the isolated carotid sinus', *Amer. J. Physiol.*, **110**, 708-714. [85]

BRØNS, J. (1939) 'The blind spot of Mariotte', *Acta Ophthal.*, Suppl. 17. [351]

BROOKHART, J. M., MORUZZI, G., & SNIDER, R. S. (1951) 'Origin of cerebellar waves', *J. Neurophysiol.*, **14**, 181-190. [186]

BROOKS, C. M., & PECK, M. E. (1940) 'Effect of various cortical lesions on development of placing and hopping reactions in rats', *J. Neurophysiol.*, **3**, 66-73. [427]

BROUER, B. (1933) 'Corticofugal influence on centripetal systems in the brain', *Arch. Neurol. Psych.*, **30**, 456-460. [372]

BROWN, C. R., & GEBHARD, J. W. (1948) 'Visual field articulation in the absence of spatial stimulus gradients', *J. Exp. Psychol.*, **38**, 188-200. [351]

BROWN, G. L. (1937) 'The actions of acetyl choline on denervated mammalian and frog's muscle', *J. Physiol.*, **89**, 438-461. [18]

BROWN, J. J. G. (1912) 'Ataxia—a symptom', *Edin. med. J.*, New Series, **9**, 9-19. [191, 423]

BROWN, J. R. (1944) 'The anatomic basis of cerebellar symptoms', *Proc. Mayo Clinic*, **19**, 169-176. [164]

BROWN, T. G. (1915) 'On the effect of artificial stimulation of the red nucleus in the anthropoid ape', *J. Physiol.*, **48**, 185-194. [160]

— (1922) 'Reflex orientation of the optical axes and the influence upon it of the cerebral cortex', *Arch. Néer. de Physiol.*, **7**, 571-578. [333]

BRUCE, H. M., & KENNEDY, G. C. (1951) 'The central nervous control of food and water intake', *Proc. Roy. Soc.*, B, **138**, 528-544. [452]

BRUCH, H. (1939) 'The Fröhlich syndrome. Report of the original case', *Amer. J. Dis. Child.*, **58**, 1282-1289. [453]

BRUESCH, S. R., & AREY, L. B. (1942) 'The number of myelinated and unmyelinated fibers in the optic nerve of vertebrates', *J. Comp. Neurol.*, **77**, 631-665. [286, 311]

BUCHTHAL, F., & MADSEN, A. (1950) 'Synchronous activity in normal and atrophic muscle', *E.E.G. Clin. Neurophysiol.*, **2**, 425-444. [119]

BUCY, P. C. (1944) Editor. *The precentral motor cortex.* Univ. of Illinois Press. [383]

Bucy, P. C., & Buchanan, D. N. (1933) 'Studies in the human neuro-muscular mechanism. I. The theory of "subsidence of afferent flow" as an explanation of the "lengthening reaction" and other phenomena', *Amer. J. Physiol.*, **104**, 95-121. [121]

Bujas, Z., & Chweitzer, A. (1937) '"Goût électrique" par courants alternatifs chez l'homme', *C.-R. Soc. Biol.*, **126**, 1106-1109. [406]

Bülbring, E. (1954) 'Membrane potentials of smooth muscle fibres of the taenia coli of the guinea-pig', *J. Physiol.*, **125**, 302-315. [17]

Burch, G. J. (1898) 'On artificial temporary colour blindness with an examination of the colour sensations of 109 persons', *Phil. Trans.*, B, **191**, 1-34. [305]

Burns, B. D. (1951) 'Some properties of isolated cerebral cortex in the unanaesthetised cat', *J. Physiol.*, **112**, 156-175. [238, 248]

— (1953) 'Intracortical integration', *E.E.G. Clin. Neurophysiol.*, Suppl. **4**, 72-81. [248]

Cairns, H. (1952) 'Disturbances of consciousness with lesions of the brain stem and diencephalon', *Brain*, **75**, 109-146. [258, 459]

— & Brain, W. R. (1933) 'Aural vertigo. Treatment by division of the eighth nerve, *Lancet*, I, 946-952. [133]

— Oldfield, R. C., Pennybacker, J. B., & Whitteridge, D. (1941) 'Akinetic mutism with an epidermoid cyst of the 3rd ventricle', *Brain*, **64**, 273-290. [459, 464]

Callaghan, J. C., McQueen, D.A., Scott, J. W., & Bigelow, W. G. (1954) 'Cerebral effects of experimental hypothermia', *A.M.A. Arch. Surg.*, **68**, 208-215. [228]

Camis, M. (1930) *The physiology of the vestibular apparatus.* Translated by R. S. Creed. Clarendon Press. Oxford. [116]

Campbell, A. W. (1905) *Histological studies on the localisation of cerebral function.* Cambridge Univ. Press. (It is illuminating to read a contemporary review of this work—Bolton, *Brain*, 1906, **29**, 265-279. Bolton doubts, for instance, whether it is possible in the adult to differentiate by histological techniques the auditory area from other temporal regions.) [205, 282]

Campbell, F. W., & Whiteside, T. C. D. (1950) 'Induced pupillary oscillations', *Brit. J. Ophthalmol.*, **34**, 180-192. [297]

Campora, G. (1925) 'Astereognosis : its causes and mechanism', *Brain*, **48**, 65-71. [418]

Cannon, W. B. (1917) 'The physiological basis of thirst', *Proc. Roy. Soc.*, B, **90**, 283-301. [451, 452]

— Newton, H. F., Bright, E. M., Menkin, V., & Moore, R. M. (1929) 'Some aspects of the physiology of animals surviving complete exclusion of sympathetic nerve impulses', *Amer. J. Physiol.*, **89**, 84-107. [96]

— & Rosenblueth, A. (1949) *The supersensitivity of denervated structures.* Macmillan. New York. [87]

CARMICHAEL, E. A., DIX, M. R., & HALLPIKE, C. S. (1954) 'Lesions of the cerebral hemispheres and their effects upon optokinetic and caloric nystagmus', *Brain*, **77**, 345-372. [148, 149]
— HONEYMAN, W. M., KOLB, L. C., & STEWART, W. K. (1941) 'A physiological study of the skin resistance response in man', *J. Physiol.*, **99**, 329-337. [482]
— & WOOLLARD, H. H. (1933) 'Some observations on the fifth and seventh cranial nerves', *Brain*, **56**, 109-125. [405]
CARMICHAEL, L. (1954) *Manual of child psychology*. Chapman & Hall. London. [406]
— & DEARBOURN, W. F. (1947) *Reading and visual fatigue*. Houghton Mifflin. Boston. [309]
CARR, H. A. (1935) *An introduction to space perception*. Longmans. London. [326, 328]
CARRERA, R. M. E., & METTLER, F. A. (1947) 'Physiologic consequences following extensive removals of cerebellar cortex and deep cerebellar nuclei and effect of secondary cortical ablations in the primate', *J. Comp. Neurol.*, **87**, 169-288. [171]
CARTERETTE, E. C., & SYMMES, D. (1952) 'Color as an experimental variable in photic stimulation', *E.E.G. Clin. Neurophysiol.*, **4**, 289-296. [352]
CAVANAGH, J. B., & THOMPSON, R. H. S. (1954) 'Demyelinisation', *Brit. Med. Bull.*, **10**, 47-51. [12]
CAWTHORNE, T. (1954) 'Positional nystagmus', *Ann. Otol. Rhinol. Laryngol.*, **63**, 481-490. [141]
CHACKO, L. W. (1948) 'An analysis of fibre size in the human optic nerve', *Brit. J. Ophthalmol.*, **32**, 457-461. [292]
CHANCE, M. R. A. (1947) 'A peculiar form of social behaviour induced in mice by amphetamine', *Behaviour*, **1**, 64-70. [217]
CHATFIELD, P. O., & DEMPSEY, E. W. (1941) 'Some effects of prostigmine and acetyl choline on cortical potentials', *Amer. J. Physiol.*, **135**, 633-640. [200]
CHOROBSKI, J. (1951) 'The syndrome of crocodile tears', *Arch. Neurol. Psych.*, **65**, 299-318. [408]
CHOW, K. L. (1954) 'Lack of behavioural effects following destruction of some thalamic association nuclei in monkey', *Arch. Neurol. Psych.*, **71**, 762-771. [353]
CLARK, G. (1948) 'The mode of representation in the motor cortex', *Brain*, **71**, 320-331. [381]
— & WARD, J. W. (1948) 'Responses elicited from the cortex of monkeys by electrical stimulation through fixed electrodes', *Brain*, **71**, 332-342. [383]
CLARK, S. L. (1939) 'Responses following electrical stimulation of the cerebellar cortex in the normal cat', *J. Neurophysiol.*, **2**, 19-35. [174, 184]
CLARK, W. E. LE GROS (1941) 'Localised lesions in striate area of monkey traced to peristriate area (18)', *J. Anat.*, **75**, 225-235. [352]

CLARK, W. E. LE GROS (1942) 'The visual centres of the brain and their connections', *Physiol. Rev.*, **22**, 205-232. [301, 345, 352]
— (1948) 'The connections of the frontal lobes of the brain', *Lancet*, I, 353-356. [465, 467, 469]
— (1949) 'The laminar pattern of the lateral geniculate nucleus considered in relation to colour vision', *Doc. Ophthalmol.*, **3**, 57-64. [301]
— (1952) 'Note on cortical cyto-architectonics', *Brain*, **75**, 96-104. [206]
— BEATTIE, J., RIDDOCH, G., & DOTT, N. M. (1938) *The hypothalamus. Morphological, functional, clinical and surgical aspects.* Oliver & Boyd. Edinburgh. [464]
— & POWELL, T. P. S. (1953) 'On the thalamo-cortical connections of the general sensory cortex of Macaca', *Proc. Roy. Soc.*, B, **141**, 467-487. [402]
— & RUSSELL, W. R. (1938) 'Cortical deafness without aphasia', *Brain*, **61**, 375-383. [281]
COBB, S. (1919) 'Cutaneous sensibility in cases of peripheral nerve injury : epicritic and protopathic hypothesis of Head untenable', *Arch. Neurol. Psych.*, **2**, 505-517. [12]
— (1946) *Borderlands of psychiatry.* Harvard Univ. Press. [245, 476]
— (1947) 'Photic driving as a cause of clinical seizures in epileptic patients', *Arch. Neurol. Psych.*, **58**, 70-71. [352]
— (1948) *Foundations of neuropsychiatry.* 4th Ed. Williams & Wilkins. Baltimore. [204]
— (1950) *Emotions and clinical medicine.* Chapman & Hall. London. [444, 462]
COBB, W., & MORTON, H. B. (1952) 'The human retinogram in response to high-intensity flashes', *E.E.G. Clin. Neurophysiol.*, **4**, 547-556. [307]
COGHILL, G. E. (1929) *Anatomy and the problem of behaviour.* Cambridge Univ. Press. [81, 82, 83]
COHEN, L. A. (1953) 'Organisation of stretch reflex into two types of direct spinal arcs', *J. Neurophysiol.*, **16**, 272-285. [118]
COHEN, L. H., SEARS, R. R., LINDLEY, S. B., SHIPLEY, W. C., & SNEDDEN, P. K. (1936) 'Psychophysiological measurements during somnolence induced by phenobarbital (luminal)', *J. Gen. Psychol.*, **10**, 415-430. [222]
COLLIER, J. (1908) 'Recent work on aphasia', *Brain*, **31**, 523-549. [440]
— (1927) 'Nuclear ophthalmoplegia, with especial reference to retraction of the lids and ptosis and to lesions of the posterior commissure', *Brain*, **50**, 488-498. [335]
CONN, J. W., & LOUIS, L. H. (1956) 'Primary aldosteronism, a new clinical entity', *Ann. Int. Med.*, **44**, 1-15. [32]
COOK, H. F. (1952) 'The pain threshold for microwave and infra-red radiations', *J. Physiol.*, **118**, 1-11. [62]
COOPER, S., & DANIEL, P. M. (1949) 'Muscle spindles in human extrinsic eye muscles', *Brain*, **72**, 1-24. [324, 367]

2 K

COOPER, S., DANIEL, P. M., & WHITTERIDGE, D. (1951) 'Afferent impulses in the oculomotor nerve from the extrinsic eye muscles', *J. Physiol.*, **113**, 463-474. [324, 367]

— — — (1953) 'Nerve impulses in the brain stem of the goat. Short latency responses obtained by stretching the extrinsic eye muscles and the jaw muscles', *J. Physiol.*, **120**, 471-490. [324]

COPPEN, F. M. V. (1942) 'The differential threshold for the subjective judgement of the elastic and plastic properties of soft bodies', *Brit. J. Psychol.*, **32**, 231-247. [421]

COSH, J. A. (1953) 'Studies on the nature of vibration sense', *Clin. Sci.*, **12**, 131-151. [55]

CRAIG, W. (1918) 'Appetites and aversions as constituents of instincts', *Biol. Bull. Woods Hole*, **2**, 91-107. [470]

CRAIK, K. J. W. (1947) 'Theory of human operator in control systems, (1) The operator as an engineering system', *Brit. J. Psychol.*, **38**, 56-61. [366]

— (1948) 'Theory of human operator in control systems, (2) Man as an element in a control system', *Brit. J. Psychol.*, **38**, 142-148. [366]

— & VERNON, M. D. (1941) 'The nature of dark adaptation', *Brit. J. Psychol.*, **32**, 62-81. [295]

CRAWFORD, B. H. (1937) 'The dependence of pupil size upon external light stimulus under static and variable conditions', *Proc. Roy. Soc.*, B, **121**, 376-395. [296]

CRAWFORD, M. P., FULTON, J. F., JACOBSEN, C. F., & WOLFE, J. B. (1948) 'Frontal lobe ablation in chimpanzee : a résumé of "Beck" and "Lucy"', *Res. Publ. Ass. nerv. ment. Dis.*, **27**, 3-58. [472]

CREED, R. S., DENNY-BROWN, D., ECCLES, J. C., LIDDELL, E. G. T., & SHERRINGTON, C. S. (1932) *Reflex activity of the spinal cord.* Oxford Univ. Press. [104, 105, 111, 120]

CRITCHLEY, M. (1938) 'Spastic dysphonia (inspiratory speech)', *Brain*, **62**, 96-103. [231]

— (1950) 'The body-image in neurology', *Lancet*, I, 335-340. [430]

— (1953) *The parietal lobes.* Arnold. London. [417, 418, 430]

CROSBY, E. C., & HENDERSON, J. W. (1948) 'The mammalian midbrain and isthmus regions. (2) Fibre connections of the superior colliculus. B. Pathways concerned in automatic eye movements', *J. Comp. Neurol.*, **88**, 53-91. [333]

— YOSS, R. E., & HENDERSON, J. W. (1952) 'The mammalian midbrain and isthmus regions. Part II. The fiber connections. D. The pattern for eye movements on the frontal eye field and the discharge of specific portions of this field to and through midbrain levels', *J. Comp. Neurol.*, **97**, 357-382. [379]

CROSSLAND, H. R., MILLER, R. C., & BRADWAY, W. E. (1928) 'Oral perceptions in relation to anosmia', *J. Exp. Psychol.*, **11**, 161-166. [211]

CROWE, J. J., GUILD, S. R., & POLVOGT, L. A. (1934) 'Observations on the pathology of high tone deafness', *Johns Hopk. Hosp. Bull.*, **54**, 315-379. [270]

CRUIKSHANK, R. M. (1937) 'Human occipital brain potentials as affected by intensity-duration variables of visual stimulation', *J. Exp. Psychol.*, **21**, 625-641. [347]

CUAJUNCO, F. (1932) 'The plurisegmental innervation of neuromuscular spindles', *J. Comp. Neurol.*, **54**, 205-235. [48]

CURTIS, H. J. (1940 *a*) 'Intercortical connections of corpus callosum as indicated by evoked potentials', *J. Neurophysiol.*, **3**, 407-413. [388]

— (1940 *b*) 'An analysis of cortical potentials mediated by the corpus callosum', *J. Neurophysiol.*, **3**, 414-422. [388]

CUSHING, H. (1930) 'Experiences with cerebellar medulloblastomas. A critical review', *Acta path. microbiol. Scand.*, **7**, 1-86. [166]

DANDY, W. E. (1933) 'Physiological studies following extirpation of the right cerebral hemisphere in man', *Johns Hopk. Hosp. Bull.*, **53**, 31-51. [409]

— (1934) 'Effects on hearing after subtotal section of the cochlea branch of the auditory nerve', *Johns Hopk. Hosp. Bull.*, **55**, 240-243. [272]

DARROW, C. W. (1932) 'The relation of the galvanic skin reflex recovery curve to reactivity, resistance level and perspiration', *J. Gen. Psychol.*, **7**, 261-272. [481]

— (1936) 'The galvanic skin reflex (sweating) and blood-pressure as preparatory and facilitative functions', *Psychol. Bull.*, **33**, 73-94. [480]

DARTNALL, H. J. A. (1952) 'Visual pigment 467, a photosensitive pigment present in tench retinae', *J. Physiol.*, **116**, 257-289. [291]

DARWIN, C. (1872) *The expression of the emotions in man and animals.* Murray. London. [375]

DAVIES, H. M. (1907) 'The functions of the trigeminal nerve', *Brain*, **30**, 219-276. [405, 407]

DAVIS, H. (1950) 'Homeostasis of cerebral excitability', *E.E.G. Clin. Neurophysiol.*, **2**, 243-247. [116, 259]

— & DAVIS, P. A. (1939) 'The electrical activity of the brain : its relation to physiological states and to states of impaired consciousness', *Res. Publ. Ass. nerv. ment. Dis.*, **19**, 50-80. [255, 256]

— — LOOMIS, A. L., HARVEY, E. N., & HOBART, G. (1939 *a*) 'A search for changes in direct current potentials of the head during sleep', *J. Neurophysiol.*, **2**, 129-135. [234]

— — — — — (1939 *b*) 'Electrical reactions of the human brain to auditory stimulation during sleep', *J. Neurophysiol.*, **2**, 500-514. [283]

DAVIS, L. E. (1925) 'Decerebrate rigidity in man', *Arch. Neurol. Psych.*, **13**, 569-579. [127]

DAVIS, P. A. (1939) 'Effects of acoustic stimuli on the waking human brain', *J. Neurophysiol.*, **2**, 494-499. [283]

DAVISON, C., & GOODHART, S. P. (1940) 'Monochorea and somatotopic localisation', *Arch. Neurol. Psych.*, **43**, 792-803. [392]

— & KELMAN, H. (1939) 'Pathologic laughing and crying', *Arch. Neurol. Psych.*, **42**, 595-643. [463]

— & SELBY, N. E. (1935) 'Hypothermia in cases of hypothalamic lesions', *Arch. Neurol. Psych.*, **33**, 570-591. [445]

DAVSON, H. (1949) *The physiology of the eye*. Churchill. London. [336]

DAWSON, G. D. (1946) 'The relation between the electro-encephalogram and muscle action potentials in certain convulsive states', *J. Neurol. Neurosurg. Psychiat.*, **9**, 5-22. [248]

—— (1947 *a*) 'Cerebral responses to electrical stimulation of peripheral nerve in man', *J. Neurol. Neurosurg. Psychiat.*, **10**, 137-140. [250]

—— (1947 *b*) 'Investigations on a patient subject to myoclonic seizures after sensory stimulation', *J. Neurol. Neurosurg. Psychiat.*, **10**, 141-162. [250]

—— (1953) 'Autocorrelation and automatic integration', *E.E.G. Clin. Neurophysiol.*, Suppl. **4**, 26-37. [250]

DAWSON, R. E., WEBSTER, J. E., & GURDJIAN, E. S. (1951) 'Serial electro-encephalography in acute head injuries', *J. Neurosurg.*, **8**, 613-630. [253]

DEES, J. E., & LANGWORTHY, O. R. (1935) 'An experimental study of bladder disturbances analogous to those of tabes dorsalis', *J. Urol.*, **34**, 359-371. [101]

DEKAKAN, A. (1953) 'Human thalamus. An anatomical, developmental and pathological study. I. Division of human adult thalamus into nuclei by use of the cyto-myelo-architectonic method', *J. Comp. Neurol.*, **99**, 639-667. [245]

DELAFRESNAYE, J. F. (1954) Editor. *Brain mechanisms and consciousness*. Blackwell. Oxford. [183, 231, 247, 249, 253]

DELL, P., BONVALLET, M., & HUGELIN, A. (1954) 'Tonus sympathique, adrénaline et contrôle réticulaire de la motricité spinale', *E.E.G. Clin. Neurophysiol.*, **6**, 599-618. [482, 483]

DEMPSEY, E. W., & MORISON, R. S. (1941) 'The interaction of certain spontaneous and induced cortical potentials', *Amer. J. Physiol.*, **135**, 301-308. [250]

DENNY-BROWN, D. (1945) 'Cerebral concussion', *Brain*, **25**, 296-325. [257]

—— (1949) 'The interpretation of the electromyogram', *Arch. Neurol. Psych.*, **61**, 99-128. [120]

—— & BOTTERELL, E. H. (1948) 'The motor functions of the agranular frontal cortex', *Res. Publ. Ass. nerv. ment. Dis.*, **27**, 235-345. [383]

—— ECCLES, J. C., & LIDDELL, E. G. T. (1929) 'Observations on electrical stimulation of the cerebellar cortex', *Proc. Roy. Soc.*, B, **104**, 518-536. [173]

—— GAYLOR, J. B., & UPRUS, V. (1935) 'Note on the nature of the motor discharge in shivering', *Brain*, **58**, 233-237. [450]

—— & PENNYBACKER, J. B. (1938) 'Fibrillation and fasciculation in voluntary muscle', *Brain*, **61**, 311-334. [226]

—— & ROBERTSON, E. G. (1933 *a*) 'On the physiology of micturition', *Brain*, **56**, 149-190. [100, 101, 102]

—— —— (1933 *b*) 'The state of the bladder and its sphincters in complete transverse lesions of the spinal cord and cauda equina', *Brain*, **56**, 397-463. [97, 100]

DERBYSHIRE, A. J., & DAVIS, H. (1935) 'The action potentials of the auditory nerve', *Amer. J. Physiol.*, **113**, 476-504. [271]

DITCHBURN, R. W., & GINSBORG, B. L. (1953) 'Involuntary eye movements during fixation', *J. Physiol.*, **119**, 1-17. [330, 367]

DIX, M. R., HALLPIKE, C. S., & HARRISON, M. S. (1949) 'Some observations upon the otological effects of streptomycin', *Brain*, **72**, 241-245. [147]

DODGE, R., & FOX, J. C. (1928) 'Optic nystagmus. I. Technical introduction with observations in a case with central scotoma in the right eye and external rectus palsy in the left eye', *Arch. Neurol. Psych.*, **20**, 812-823. [332]

— TRAVIS, R. C., & FOX, J. C. (1930) 'Optic nystagmus. III. Characteristics of the slow phase', *Arch. Neurol. Psych.*, **24**, 21-34. [331]

DODT, E., & ZOTTERMAN, Y. (1952 *a*) 'Mode of action of warm receptors', *Acta Physiol. Scand.*, **26**, 345-357. [44]

— — (1952 *b*) 'The discharge of specific cold fibres at high temperatures. (The paradoxical cold)', *Acta Physiol. Scand.*, **26**, 358-365. [44, 45]

DOHLMAN, G. (1935) 'Some practical and theoretical points in labyrinthology', *Proc. Roy. Soc. Med.*, **28**, 1371-1380. [142]

DORAN, F. S. A., & RATCLIFFE, A. H. (1954) 'The physiological mechanism of referred shoulder tip pain', *Brain*, **77**, 427-434. [71]

DORCUS, R. M., & MOWRER, O. H. (1936) 'An experimental analysis of the vestibular pointing test', *Ann. Otol. Rhinol. Laryngol.*, **45**, 33-57. [150]

DOUGLAS, B., & LANIER, L. H. (1934) 'Changes in cutaneous localisation in a pedicle flap', *Arch. Neurol. Psych.*, **32**, 756-762. [223]

DOW, R. S. (1938 *a*) 'Effect of lesions in the vestibular part of the cerebellum in primates', *Arch. Neurol. Psych.*, **40**, 500-520. [166, 172, 173, 178]

— (1938 *b*) 'The electrical activity of the cerebellum and its functional significance', *J. Physiol.*, **94**, 67-86. [186]

— (1938 *c*) 'The effects of unilateral and bilateral labyrinthectomy in monkey, baboon and chimpanzee', *Amer. J. Physiol.*, **121**, 392-399. [133]

— (1939) 'Cerebellar action potentials in response to stimulation of various afferent connections', *J. Neurophysiol.*, **2**, 543-555. [165, 173]

— (1942) 'The evolution and anatomy of the cerebellum', *Biol. Rev.*, **17**, 179-220. [173]

DRUCKMAN, R. (1952) 'A critique of "suppression" with additional observations on the cat', *Brain*, **75**, 226-243. [384]

DUN, F. T. (1955) 'The delay and blockage of sensory impulses in the dorsal root ganglion', *J. Physiol.*, **127**, 252-264. [7]

DUNLAP, K. (1921) 'Light spot adaptation', *Amer. J. Physiol.*, **55**, 201-211. [295]

DUYFF, J. W., VAN GEMERT, A. G. M., & SCHMIDT, P. H. (1950) 'Binaural sound location in the horizontal plane', *Acta physiol. pharm. néerl.*, **1**, 540-561. [273]

DWORKIN, S., KATZMAN, J., HUTCHISON, G. A., & McCABE, J. R. (1940) 'Hearing acuity of animals as measured by conditioning methods', *J. Exp. Psychol.*, **26**, 281-298. [220, 221, 222]

EARLE, K. M., BALDWIN, M., PENFIELD, W. (1953) 'Incisural sclerosis and temporal lobe seizures produced by hippocampal herniation at birth', *Arch. Neurol. Psych.*, **69**, 27-42. [285]

EBBECKE, U. (1917) 'Über die Temperaturempfindungen in ihrer Abhängigkeit von der Hautdurchblütung und von den Reflexzentren', *Pflügers Arch. f. ges. Physiol.*, **169**, 395-462. [44]

ECCLES, J. C. (1953) *The neurophysiological basis of mind. The principles of neurophysiology.* Clarendon Press. Oxford. [27, 28, 88, 103, 104, 108, 109, 112, 229, 249]

— FATT, P., & KOKETSU, K. (1954) 'Cholinergic and inhibitory synapses in a pathway from motor-axon collaterals to motoneurones', *J. Physiol.*, **126**, 524-562. [119]

ECCLIN, F. A. (1944) 'The electroencephalogram associated with epilepsy', *Arch. Neurol. Psych.*, **52**, 270-289. [251]

ECONOMO, C. VON (1930) 'Sleep as a problem of localisation', *J. nerv. ment. Dis.*, **71**, 249-259. [458, 459]

EDINGER, L. (1906) 'A preliminary note on the comparative anatomy of the cerebellum', *Brain*, **29**, 483-486. [163]

— & FISCHER, B. (1913) 'Ein Mensch ohne Grosshirn', *Pflügers Arch. f. ges. Physiol.*, **152**, 535-561. [278, 279]

EGMOND, A. A. J. VON, GROEN, J. J., & JONGKEES, L. B. W. (1949) 'The mechanics of the semicircular canal', *J. Physiol.*, **110**, 1-17. [143, 146]

EINTHOVEN, W., & JOLLY, W. A. (1908) 'The form and magnitude of the electrical response of the eye to stimulation by light at various intensities', *Quart. J. Exp. Physiol.*, **1**, 373-416. [307]

ELDRED, E., GRANIT, R., & MERTON, P. A. (1953) 'Supra-spinal control of the muscle spindles and its significance', *J. Physiol.*, **122**, 498-523. [368]

ELFTMAN, H. (1940) 'The work done by muscles in running', *Amer. J. Physiol.*, **129**, 672-684. [127]

ELIASSON, S., FOLKOW, B., LINDGREN, P., & UVNÄS, B. (1951) 'Activation of sympathetic vasodilator nerves to the skeletal muscles of the cat by hypothalamic stimulation', *Acta Physiol. Scand.*, **23**, 333-351. [450]

ELLIOTT, F. A., & MCKISSOCK, W. (1954) 'Acoustic neuroma early diagnosis', *Lancet*, II, 1189-1193. [267]

ELLIS, F. W. (1928) 'The nature of the stimulus which excites the blue arcs of the retina and related phenomena', *Amer. J. Physiol.*, **84**, 485-489. [308]

ELSBERG, C. A. (1937) 'The newer aspects of olfactory physiology and their diagnostic applications', *Arch. Neurol. Psych.*, **37**, 223-236. [213]

ENGBAEK, L. (1951) 'Acetyl choline sensitivity in diseases of the motor system with special regard to myaesthenia gravis', *E.E.G. Clin. Neurophysiol.*, **3**, 155-161. [29]

ENGEL, G. L. (1950) *Fainting.* Thomas. Sprinfield, Ill. [85]

ENROTH, C. (1952) 'The mechanism of flicker and fusion studied on single retinal elements in the dark-adapted eye of the cat', *Acta Physiol. Scand.*, **27**, Suppl. 100. [319]

ERB, M. B., & DALLENBACH, K. M. (1939) 'Subjective colours from line patterns', *Amer. J. Psychol.*, **52**, 227-241. [314]

ERLANGER, J., & GASSER, H. S. (1930) 'The action potential in fibres of slow conduction in spinal roots and somatic nerves', *Amer. J. Physiol.*, **92**, 43-82. [56]

— — (1937) *Electrical signs of nervous activity.* Univ. Penn. Press. [14, 15]

EULER, C. VON (1952) 'Slow "temperature potentials" in the hypothalamus', *J. Cell. Comp. Physiol.*, **36**, 333-350. [447]

EVARTS, E. V. (1952) 'Effect of ablation of prestriate cortex on auditory-visual association in monkey', *J. Neurophysiol.*, **15**, 191-200. [353]

FATT, P., & KATZ, B. (1953) 'Chemo-receptor activity at the motor end-plate', *Acta Physiol. Scand.*, **29**, 117-125. [18, 27]

FELDBERG, W. (1951) 'The physiology of neuromuscular transmission and neuromuscular block', *Brit. med. J.*, I, 967-976. [2]

FERNÁNDEZ-MORÁN, H. (1954) 'The submicroscopic structure of nerve fibres', *Prog. in Biophysics*, **4**, 112-147. [8, 11]

FERRARD, A., & BARRERA, S. E. (1935) 'The effects of lesions of the dorsal spino-cerebellar tract and corpus restiforme in the Macacus Rhesus monkey', *Brain*, **58**, 174-202. [168, 189]

— — (1936) 'Effect of lesions of the juxta-restiform body (I.A.K. bundle) in Macacus Rhesus monkeys', *Arch. Neurol. Psych.*, **35**, 13-29. [172, 178]

— — & BLAKESLEE, G. A. (1936) 'Vestibular phenomena of central origin', *Brain*, **59**, 466-482. [158]

FERREE, C. E. (1906) 'An experimental examination of phenomena usually attributed to fluctuation of attention', *Amer. J. Psychol.*, **171**, 81-120. [351]

— & RAND, G. R. (1910) 'The spatial values of the visual field immediately surrounding the blind spot and the question of the associative filling in of the blind spot', *Amer. J. Physiol.*, **29**, 398-417. [351]

FERRIER, D. (1890) 'The Croonian Lectures (6) Motor centres', *Brit. med. J.*, II, 68-75. [385]

— & TURNER, W. A. (1894) 'A record of experiments illustrative of the symptomatology and degenerations following lesions of the cerebellum and its peduncles and related structures in monkeys', *Phil. Trans. Roy. Soc.*, B, Part 2, 719-778. [164, 187]

— — (1901) 'Experimental lesion of the corpora quadrigemina in monkeys', *Brain*, **24**, 27-46. [334]

FESSARD, A. (1952) 'Diversity of transmission processes as exemplified by specific synapses in electric organs', *Proc. Roy. Soc.*, B, **140**, 186-191. [2]

FINCHAM, E. F. (1953) 'Defects of the colour sense mechanism as indicated by the accommodation reflex', *J. Physiol.*, **121**, 570-580. [305]

FINLEY, K. H., & COBB, S. (1940) 'The capillary bed of the locus coeruleus', *J. Comp. Neurol.*, **73**, 49-58. [458]

FISCHER, M. H. (1928) 'Die Regulationsfunctionen des menschlichen Labyrinthes und die Zusammenhange mit verwandten Funktionen', *Erg. der Physiol.*, **27**, 209-379. [144]

FISHER, C., INGRAM, W. R., & RANSON, S. W. (1938) *Diabetes insipidus*. Edwards. Ann Arbor. [450]

FISHER, R. A. (1935) *The design of experiments*. Oliver & Boyd. Edinburgh. [216]

FITZGERALD, G., & HALLPIKE, C. S. (1942) 'Studies in human vestibular function : I. Observations on the directional preponderance ("Nystagmusbereitschaft") of caloric nystagmus resulting from cerebral lesions', *Brain*, **65**, 115-137. [148, 149]

FLETCHER, H. (1953) *Speech and hearing in communication*. Bell Laboratories Series. van Nostrand. New York. [286]

FLOTTORP, G. (1953) 'Effect of different types of electrodes in electrophonic hearing', *J. Acoust. Soc. Amer.*, **25**, 236-245. [268]

FOERSTER, H. VON (1949) Editor. *Cybernetics*. Trans. 6th. Josiah Macy. Conf. [24]

FOERSTER, O. (1913) 'On the indications and the results of the excision of posterior spinal nerve roots in men', *Surg. Gyn. Obst.*, **16**, 463-474. [115, 395]

— (1933) 'The dermatomes in man', *Brain*, **56**, 1-39. [57, 91]

— (1936) in BUMKE, O., & FOERSTER, O., *Handbuch der Neurologie*, Vol. V. [90, 94, 95, 369]

FORBES, A. (1950) 'A critique of frequency analysis in neurophysiology', *E.E.G. Clin. Neurophysiol.*, **2**, p. 204. [243]

— BAIRD, P. C., & HOPKINS, A. McH. (1926) 'The involuntary contraction following isometric contraction of skeletal muscle in man', *Amer. J. Physiol.*, **78**, 81-103. [423]

— & SHERRINGTON, C. S. (1914) 'Acoustic reflexes in the decerebrate cat', *Amer. J. Physiol.*, **35**, 367-376. [277]

FORD, F. R., & WALSH, F. B. (1936) 'Clinical observations upon the importance of the vestibular reflexes in ocular movements', *Johns Hopk. Hosp. Bull.*, **58**, 80-88. [144, 145]

FORSTER, F. M., ROSEMAN, E., & GIBBS, F. A. (1942) 'Electro-encephalogram accompanying hyperactive carotid sinus reflex and orthostatic syncope', *Arch. Neurol. Psych.*, **48**, 957-967. [253]

FORTUYN, J. DROOGLEEVER (1953) 'Anatomical basis of cortico-subcortical interrelationships', *E.E.G. Clin. Neurophysiol.*, Suppl. **4**, 149-162. [245]

FOSTER, D., SCOFIELD, J. E., & DALLENBACH, K. M. (1950) 'An olfactorium', *Amer. J. Psychol.*, **63**, 431-440. [212]

FOSTER, M. (1879) *A text-book of physiology*. Macmillan. London. [382]

FOWLER, E. P. (1939) 'Abnormal movements following injury to the facial nerve', *J.A.M.A.*, **113**, 1003-1008. [224, 225, 226, 227]

— (1942) 'A simple method of measuring percentage of capacity for hearing speech', *Arch. Otolaryngol.*, **36**, 874-890. [267]

BIBLIOGRAPHY

FOX, J. C., & HOLMES, G. (1926) 'Optic nystagmus and its value in the localisation of cerebral lesions', *Brain*, **49**, 333-371. [333]

— & KLEMPERER, W. W. (1942) 'Vibratory sensibility. A quantitative study of its thresholds in nervous disorders', *Arch. Neurol. Psych.*, **48**, 622-645. [56]

FRANKENHAEUSER, B. (1951) 'Limitations of strychnine neuronography', *J. Neurophysiol.*, **14**, 73-79. [200]

— (1952) 'The hypothesis of saltatory conduction', *Cold Spring Harb. Symp. Quant. Biol.*, **17**, 27-36. [23]

FRAZIER, C. H. (1910) 'The treatment of spasticity and athetosis by resection of the posterior roots of the spinal cord', *Surg. Gyn. Obst.*, **11**, 251-263. [115]

FREEMAN, W., & WATTS, J. W. (1942) *Psychosurgery: Intelligence, emotion and social behaviour following prefrontal lobotomy for mental disorders.* Thomas. Springfield, Ill. [473]

— — (1948) 'The thalamic projection to the frontal lobe', *Res. Publ. Ass. nerv. ment. Dis.*, **27**, 200-209. [473]

— & WILKINS, J. M. (1952) 'Human sonar: relationship of the amygdaloid nucleus to auditory hallucinations', *J. nerv. ment. Dis.*, **116**, 456-462. [466]

FRENCH, J. D., VERZEANO, M., & MAGOUN, H. W. (1953) 'A neural basis of the anesthetic state', *Arch. Neurol. Psych.*, **69**, 519-529. [401]

FREUD, S. (1891) *On aphasia: a critical study.* Translated by E. Stengel and republished 1954. Imago Publishing Co. London. [354, 399]

FREY, M. VON (1895) *Ber. sachs Ges. (Akad.) Wiss Lpz.*, **47**, 166. [35, 39]

FRISCH, K. VON (1954) *The dancing bees.* Translated by D. Ilse. Methuen. London. [213]

FROLOV, Y. P. (1937) *Pavlov and his school.* Kegan Paul. London. [218]

FRY, G. A. (1933) 'Colour phenomena from adjacent retinal areas for different temporal patterns of intermittent white light', *Amer. J. Psychol.*, **45**, 714-721. [306]

FULTON, J. F. (1936) 'Interrelation of cerebrum and cerebellum in the regulation of somatic and autonomic functions', *Medicine*, **15**, 247-306. [191]

— (1943) *Physiology of the nervous system.* 2nd Ed. Oxford Univ. Press. [127, 221, 383]

— (1946) Editor. *Howell's textbook of physiology.* Saunders. London. [455]

— (1949) *Functional localisation in the frontal lobes and cerebellum.* Oxford Univ. Press. [163, 472]

— & KELLER, A. D. (1932) *The sign of Babinski. A study of the evolution of cortical dominance in Primates.* Thomas. Baltimore. [374]

— LIDDELL, E. G. T., & RIOCH, D. McK. (1930) 'The influence of unilateral destruction of the vestibular nuclei upon posture and the knee jerk', *Brain*, **53**, 327-343. [129]

GALAMBOS, R. (1952) 'Microelectrode studies on medial geniculate body of cat. III. Response to pure tones', *J. Neurophysiol.*, **15**, 382-400. [277]

GALAMBOS, R. (1954) 'Neural mechanisms of audition', *Physiol. Rev.*, **34**, 497-528. [275]

— & DAVIS, H. (1943) 'The response of single auditory nerve fibres to acoustic stimulation', *J. Neurophysiol.*, **6**, 39-57. [275, 276]

— — (1944) 'Inhibition of activity in single auditory nerve fibres by acoustic stimulation', *J. Neurophysiol.*, **7**, 287-303. [275]

— — (1948) 'Action potentials from single auditory nerve fibres', *Science*, **108**, 513. [275, 276]

— ROSE, J. E., BROMILEY, R. B., & HUGHES, J. R. (1952) 'Microelectrode studies on medial geniculate body of cat. II. Response to clicks', *J. Neurophysiol.*, **15**, 359-380. [276, 277]

— ROSENBLITH, W. A., & ROSENZWEIG, M. R. (1950) 'Physiological evidence for a cochleo-cochlear pathway in the cat', *Experientia*, **6**, 438-440. [273]

GANTT, W. H. (1944) *Experimental basis for neurotic behaviour.* Hoeber. London. [220]

GARDINIER, H. C. (1899) 'A case of brain tumour at the base of the second left frontal convolution, with autopsy; the only positive localising symptom was agraphia uncombined with any form of aphasia', *Amer. J. Med. Sci.*, **117**, 526-535. [433]

GARDNER, E. (1950) 'Physiology of movable joints', *Physiol. Rev.*, **30**, 127-176. [410]

— & HADDAD, B. (1953) 'Pathways to the cerebral cortex for afferent fibres from the hind leg of the cat', *Amer. J. Physiol.*, **173**, 475-482. [400]

GASSER, H. S. (1935) 'Conduction in nerves in relation to fibre types', *Res. Publ. Ass. nerv. ment. Dis.*, **15**, 35-59. [56]

— (1950) 'Unmedullated fibres originating in dorsal root ganglia', *J. Gen. Physiol.*, **33**, 651-690. [15]

— (1955) 'Properties of dorsal root unmedullated fibres on the two sides of the ganglion', *J. Gen. Physiol.*, **38**, 709-728. [16]

GASTAUT, H. (1954) *The epilepsies: electro-clinical correlations.* Translated by M. A. B. Brazier. Thomas. Springfield, U.S.A. [251]

— BENOÎT, P. H., VIGOUREUX, M., & ROGER, A. (1954) 'Potentiels évoqués par des stimuli auditifs sur la région temporale de certains épileptiques', *E.E.G. Clin. Neurophysiol.*, **6**, 557-564. [461]

— & HUNTER, J. (1950) 'An experimental study of the mechanism of photic activation in idiopathic epilepsy', *E.E.G. Clin. Neurophysiol.*, **2**, 263-287. [352]

GAZE, R. M., & GORDON, G. (1954) 'The representation of cutaneous sense in the thalamus of the cat and monkey', *Quart. J. Exp. Physiol.*, **39**, 279-304. [401, 412]

— — (1955) 'Some observations on the central pathway for cutaneous impulses in the cat', *Quart. J. Exp. Physiol.*, **40**, 187-194. [57]

GELDARD, F. A. (1953) *The human senses.* Chapman & Hall. London. [209, 398, 420]

GEREBTZOFF, M. A. (1940) 'Recherches sur la projection corticale du labyrinthe. 1. Des effets de la stimulation labyrinthique sur l'activité électrique de l'écorce cérébrale', *Arch. Int. Physiol.*, **50**, 55-99. [149]

GERNANDT, B. (1950) 'Midbrain activity in response to vestibular stimulation', *Acta Physiol. Scand.*, **21**, 73-81. [149]

GERSTMANN, J. (1940) 'Syndrome of finger agnosia. Disorientation for right and left, agraphia and acalculia', *Arch. Neurol. Psych.*, **44**,398-408. [431]

GESELL, A., & AMATRUDA, C. S. (1947) *Developmental diagnosis.* 2nd Ed· Hoeber. London. [161]

— — (1945) *The embryology of behaviour. The beginnings of the human mind.* Hamish Hamilton. London. [152, 153, 154]

GILLIATT, R. W., & PRATT, R. T. C. (1952) 'Disorders of perception and performance in a case of right-sided cerebral thrombosis', *J. Neurol. Neurosurg. Psychiat.*, **15**, 264-271. [429]

GILMER, B. VON H., & HAYTHORN, S. R. (1941) 'Cutaneous pressure— vibration spots and their underlying tissues', *Arch. Neurol. Psych.*, **46**, 631-648. [40]

GLOOR, P. (1954) 'Autonomic functions of the diencephalon', *Arch. Neurol. Psych.*, **71**, 773-790. [459, 460, 462]

GOBBEL, W. G., & LILES, G. W. (1945) 'Efferent fibres of the parietal lobe of the cat (*Felis Domesticus*)', *J. Neurophysiol.*, **8**, 257-266. [414]

GOLDSCHEIDER, A. (1898) *Die Bedeutung der Reize für Pathologie und Therapie im Lichte der Neuronlehre.* Leipzig, Barth. Pp. 88. [35]

GOODEVE, C. F., LYTHGOE, R. J., & SCHNEIDER, E. E. (1942) 'The photosensitivity of visual purple solutions and the scotopic sensitivity of the eye in the ultra-violet', *Proc. Roy. Soc.*, B, **130**, 380-395. [288]

GOODHART, S. P., & DAVISON, C. (1936) 'Syndrome of the posterior inferior and anterior inferior cerebellar arteries and their branches', *Arch. Neurol. Psych.*, **35**, 501-524. [170]

GOODMAN, L. (1932) 'Effect of total absence of function on the optic system of rabbits', *Amer. J. Physiol.*, **100**, 46-63. [355]

GOODWIN, C. W., & STEIN, S. N. (1948) 'A brain wave "correlator"', *Science*, **108**, 507. [241]

GORDON, G. (1951) 'Observations upon the movements of the eyelids', *Brit. J. Ophthalmol.*, **35**, 339-351. [227]

— & WHITTERIDGE, D. (1943) 'Conduction-time for human pain sensations', *Lancet*, II, 700-701. [43]

GOWERS, W. R. (1886) *A manual of diseases of the nervous system.* Vol. I. Churchill. London. [91]

— (1904) *Lectures on disease of the nervous system.* 2nd Series. *Subjective sensations of sight and sound, abiotrophy and other lectures.* Churchill. London. [349, 350]

GRANIT, R. (1947) *Sensory mechanisms of the retina.* Oxford Univ. Press. [306, 307]

— (1955) *Receptors and sensory perception.* Yale Univ. Press. [48, 54, 308, 328]

GRANIT, R., & DAVIS, W. A. (1931) 'Comparative studies on the peripheral and central retina. IV. Temporal summation of subliminal visual stimuli and the time course of the excitatory after-effect', *Amer. J. Physiol.*, **98**, 644-653. [296]

— HOLMBERG, T., & ZEWI, M. (1938) 'On the mode of action of visual purple on the rod cell', *J. Physiol.*, **94**, 430-440. [291]

— HOLMGREN, B., & MERTON, P. A. (1955) 'The two routes for excitation of muscle and their subservience to the cerebellum', *J. Physiol.*, **130**, 213-224. [177]

— & KAADA, B. R. (1953) 'Influence of stimulation of central nervous structures on muscle spindles in cat', *Acta Physiol. Scand.*, **27**, 130-160. [368]

— LEKSELL, L., & SKOGLUND, C. R. (1944) 'Fibre interaction in injured or compressed region of nerve', *Brain*, **67**, 125-140. [24]

GRAVESON, G. S. (1949) 'The tonic pupil', *J. Neurol. Neurosurg. Psychiat.*, **12**, 219-230. [298]

GRAY, J. A. B., & MATTHEWS, P. B. C. (1951) 'Response of Pacinian corpuscles in the cat's toe', *J. Physiol.*, **113**, 475-482. [55]

— & SATO, M. (1953) 'Properties of the receptor potential in Pacinian corpuscles', *J. Physiol.*, **122**, 610-636. [50, 51]

GREEN, H. D., & HOFF, E. C. (1937) 'Effect of faradic stimulation of the cerebral cortex on limb and renal volumes in the cat and monkey', *Amer. J. Physiol.*, **118**, 641-658. [480]

GREEN, J. D. (1953) 'Hippocampal seizures and their propagation', *Arch. Neurol. Psych.*, **70**, 687-702. [232]

— & MACHNE, X. (1955) 'Unit activity of rabbit hippocampus', *Amer. J. Physiol.*, **181**, 219-224. [464]

GREENFIELD, J. G. (1954) *The spino-cerebellar degenerations.* Blackwell. Oxford. [189]

— & BOSANQUET, F. D. (1953) 'The brain stem lesions in Parkinsonism', *J. Neurol. Neurosurg. Psychiat.*, **16**, 213-226. [394]

— & HOLMES, G. (1925) 'The histology of juvenile amaurotic idiocy', *Brain*, **48**, 183-217. [312]

GREENWOOD, M. (1910) *Physiology of the special senses.* Arnold. London. [136]

GROAT, R. A., MAGOUN, H. W., DEY, F. L., & WINDLE, W. F. (1944) 'Functional alterations in motor and supranuclear mechanisms in experimental concussion', *Amer. J. Physiol.*, 117-127. [258]

GRODINS, F. S., OSBORNE, S. L., JOHNSON, F. R., ARANA, S., & IVY, A. C. (1944) 'The effect of appropriate electrical stimulation on atrophy of denervated skeletal muscle in the rat', *Amer. J. Physiol.*, **142**, 222-230. [21]

GRÜNBAUM, A. S. F., & SHERRINGTON, S. S. (1901) 'Observations on the physiology of the cerebral cortex of some of the higher apes', *Proc. Roy. Soc.*, B, **69**, 206-209. [377]

GRUNDFEST, H. (1939) 'The properties of mammalian B fibers', *Amer. J. Physiol.*, **127**, 252-262. [15]

GUILFORD, J. P. (1927) '"Fluctuations of attention" with weak visual stimuli', *Amer. J. Psychol.*, **38**, 534-583. [295]

GULL, W. (1888) 'Anorexia nervosa', *Lancet*, I, 516-517. [454]

GULLBERG, J. E., OLMSTED, J. M. D., & WAGMAN, I. H. (1938) 'Reciprocal innervation of the sphincter and dilator pupillae', *Amer. J. Physiol.*, **122**, 160-166. [296]

GUNTER, R. (1952) 'The spectral sensitivity of dark adapted cats', *J. Physiol.*, **118**, 395-404. [293]

GUTMANN, E., & GUTTMANN, L. (1944) 'The effect of galvanic exercise on denervated and re-innervated muscles', *J. Neurol. Neurosurg. Psychiat.*, **7**, 7-17. [21]

— & HOLUBÁR, J. (1950) 'The degeneration of peripheral nerve fibres', *J. Neurol. Neurosurg.*, **13**, 89-105. [13]

GUTTMANN, L. (1940) 'Topographic studies of disturbances of sweat secretion after complete lesions of peripheral nerves', *J. Neurol. Psychiat.*, **3**, 197-210. [96]

— (1953) In *History of the Second World War*, Surgery. Edited by Sir Z. Cope. Stationery Office. [93, 116]

— (1954) In *Peripheral circulation in man*. Ciba Symposium. Churchill. London. [98]

GUZMÁN, C. F., & POZO, E. C. DEL (1953) '"Jump reflex" in hypothalamic cat', *J. Neurophysiol.*, **16**, 376-380. [81]

HAAN, J. A. B. DE (1925) 'Experiments on vision in monkeys. I. The colour sense of the pig-tailed macaque (*Nemestrinus Nemestrinus L.*)', *J. Comp. Psychol.*, **5**, 417-453. [300]

HAGBARTH, K. E., & KERR, D. I. B. (1954) 'Central influences on spinal afferent conduction', *J. Neurophysiol.*, **17**, 295-307. [414]

HAGEN, E., KNOCHE, H., SINCLAIR, D. C., & WEDDELL, G. (1953) 'The role of specialised nerve terminals in cutaneous sensibility', *Proc. Roy. Soc.*, B, **141**, 279-287. [40]

HAIG, C. (1941) 'The course of rod dark adaptation as influenced by the intensity and duration of pre-adaptation to light', *J. Gen. Physiol.*, **24**, 735-751. [295]

HALLPIKE, C. S., HOOD, J. D., & BYFORD, G. H. (1952) 'The design, construction and performance of a new type of revolving chair', *Acta Oto-laryngol.*, **42**, 511-538. [145, 147]

HAMDI, F. A., & WHITTERIDGE, D. (1954) 'The representation of the retina on the optic tectum of the pigeon', *Quart. J. Exp. Physiol.*, **39**, 111-119. [334]

HAMPSON, J. L. (1949) 'Relationships between cat cerebral and cerebellar cortices', *J. Neurophysiol.*, **12**, 37-50. [182]

— HARRISON, C. R., & WOOLSEY, C. N. (1952) 'Cerebro-cerebellar projections and the somatotropic localisation of motor function in the cerebellum', *Res. Publ. Ass. nerv. ment. Dis.*, **30**, 299-316. [174, 175]

HARDY, J. D., WOLFF, H. G., & GOODELL, H. (1942) 'The pain threshold in man', *Res. Publ. Ass. nerv. ment. Dis.*, **23**, 1-15. [62]

HARE, W. K., MAGOUN, H. W., & RANSON, S. W. (1937) 'Localisation within the cerebellum of reactions to faradic cerebellar stimulation', *J. Comp. Neurol.*, **67**, 145-182. [174]

HARLOW, H. F., & SETTLAGE, P. H. (1938) 'Effect of extirpation of frontal areas upon learning performance of monkeys', *Res. Publ. Ass. nerv. ment. Dis.*, **27**, 446-456. [470]

HARRIS, G. W. (1955) *Neural control of the pituitary gland.* Arnold. London. [454]

HARRISON, C. W. (1952) 'Experiments with linear prediction in television', *Bell System Technical Journal*, **31**, 764-783. [5]

HARTLINE, H. K. (1941) 'The neural mechanisms of vision', *Harvey Lectures*, **37**, 39-68. [310, 311, 312]

— WAGNER, H. G., & MACNICHOL, E. F. (1952) 'The peripheral origin of nervous activity in the visual system', *Cold Spring Harb. Symp. Quant. Biol.*, **17**, 125-141. [310]

HARTRIDGE, H. (1950) *Recent advances in the physiology of vision.* Churchill. London. [288, 299]

HAXTON, H. A. (1948) 'Gustatory sweating', *Brain*, **71**, 16-25. [407]

HAYNE, R. A., BELINSON, L., & GIBBS, F. A. (1949) 'Electrical activity of subcortical areas in epilepsy', *E.E.G. Clin. Neurophysiol.*, **1**, 437-445. [247]

HEAD, H. (1920) *Studies in neurology.* 2 vols. Oxford Univ. Press. [57]
— (1923) 'Speech and cerebral localisation', *Brain*, **46**, 357-528. [435, 440]
— (1926) *Aphasia and kindred disorders of speech.* 2 vols. Cambridge Univ. Press. [432, 435]
— & HOLMES, G. (1911) 'Sensory disturbances from cerebral lesions', *Brain*, **34**, 102-254. [40, 410, 414, 424, 427]
— & RIDDOCH, G. (1917) 'The automatic bladder, excessive sweating and some other reflex conditions, in gross injuries of the spinal cord', *Brain*, **40**, 188-402. [98]

Hearing Aids and Audiometers. (1947.) *M.R.C. Special Report*, No. 261. [268]

HEATH, J. W. (1947) 'Clinico-pathologic aspects of Parkinsonian states', *Arch. Neurol. Psych.*, **58**, 484-497. [394]

HEBB, C. O. (1954) 'Acetyl choline metabolism of nervous tissue', *Pharmacol. Rev.*, **6**, 39-43. [200]
— SILVER, A., SWAN, A. A. B., & WALSH, E. G. (1953) 'A histochemical study of cholinesterases of rabbit retina and optic nerve', *Quart. J. Exp. Physiol.*, **38**, 185-191. [207]

HEBB, D. O. (1945) 'Man's frontal lobes : a critical review', *Arch. Neurol. Psych.*, **54**, 10-24. [478]
— (1946) 'Emotion in man and animal : an analysis of the intuitive processes of recognition', *Psychol. Rev.*, **53**, 88-106. [462]
— (1949) *The organisation of behaviour.* Chapman & Hall. London. [229, 355]

HEBB, D. O. (1953) 'Heredity and environment in mammalian behaviour', *Brit. J. Anim. Behav.*, **1**, 43-47. [329]

HECHT, S. (1919) 'Sensory equilibrium and dark adaptation in Mya Arenaria', *J. Gen. Physiol.*, **1**, 545-558. [295]

— & MANDELBAUM, J. (1939) 'The relation between vitamin A and dark adaptation', *J.A.M.A.*, **112**, 1910-1916. [291]

— SCHLAER, S., & PIRENNE, M. H. (1942) 'Energy, quanta, and vision', *J. Gen. Physiol.*, **25**, 819-840. [292]

HELMHOLTZ, H. VON (1893) *Popular Scientific Lectures.* Vol. I. Longmans. London. [1, 287]

— (1924) *Physiological optics.* 3 vols. Translated by J. P. C. Southall. Amer. Optical Soc. [303, 305, 322, 338, 345]

HEMPHILL, R. E., & STENGEL, E. (1940) 'A study on pure word-deafness', *J. Neurol. Neurosurg. Psychiat.*, **3**, 251-262. [435]

HENDERSON, J. W., & CROSBY, E. C. (1952) 'An experimental study of optico-kinetic responses', *A.M.A. Arch. Ophthal.*, **47**, 43-54. [333]

HENDERSON, W. R., & SMYTH, G. E. (1948) 'Phantom limbs', *J. Neurol. Neurosurg. Psychiat.*, **11**, 88-112. [425]

HENRY, C. E., & SCOVILLE, W. B. (1952) 'Suppression-Burst activity from isolated cerebral cortex in man', *E.E.G. Clin. Neurophysiol.*, **4**, 1-22. [254]

HENSCHEN, S. E., & SCHALLER, W. F. (1925) 'Clinical and anatomical contributions on brain pathology', *Arch. Neurol. Psych.*, **13**, 226-249. [434]

HENSEL, H., & ZOTTERMAN, Y. (1951 *a*) 'The response of the cold receptors to constant cooling', *Acta Physiol. Scand.*, **22**, 96-105. [44]

— — (1951 *b*) 'Action potentials of cold fibres and intracutaneous temperature gradient', *J. Neurophysiol.*, **14**, 377-385. [44]

— — (1951 *c*) 'Quantitative Beziehungen zwischen der Entladung einzelnen Kältefasern und der Temperatur', *Acta Physiol. Scand.*, **23**, 291-319. [44]

— — (1951 *d*) 'The persisting cold sensation', *Acta Physiol. Scand.*, **22**, 106-113. [44]

HERING, E. (1877) 'Grundzüge einer Theorie des Temperatursinns', *Sitzungsber. Wien. Akad.*, **75**, III, 101-103. [44]

HERRICK, C. J. (1915) *An introduction to neurology.* Saunders. London. [199]

— (1926) *Brains of rats and men. A survey of the origin and biological significance of the cerebral cortex.* Univ. of Chicago Press. [201]

HERZ, E. (1944) 'Dystonia', I and II, *Arch. Neurol. Psych.*, **51**, 305-355. [395]

HESS, A., & YOUNG, J. Z. (1952) 'The nodes of Ranvier', *Proc. Roy. Soc.*, B, 140-320. [8]

HILALI, S., & WHITFIELD, I. C. (1953) 'Responses of the trapezoid body to acoustic stimulation with pure tones', *J. Physiol.*, **122**, 158-171. [275]

HILGARD, E. R., & CAMPBELL, A. A. (1936) 'The course of acquisition and retention of conditioned responses in man', *J. Exp. Psychol.*, **19**, 227-247. [222]

HILL, D., & PARR, G. (1950) Editors. *Electroencephalography: A symposium on its various aspects.* MacDonald. London. [235]

HILTON, J. (1863) *On the influence of mechanical and physiological rest in the treatment of accidents and surgical diseases, and the diagnostic value of pain.* Edited by Walls, E. W., & Phillip, E. E. Republished 1950. Bell. London. [61, 92]

HINSHELWOOD, J. (1895) 'Word blindess and visual memory', *Lancet*, II, 1564-1570. [358]

HIRSH, I. J. (1948) 'Binaural summation—a century of investigation', *Psychol. Bull.*, **45**, 191-206. [261]

HITZIG, E. (1900) 'Hughlings Jackson and the cortical motor centres in the light of physiological research', *Brain*, **23**, 545-581. [376]

HODES, R. (1939) 'Exercise in the sympathectomised cat', *Amer. J. Physiol.*, **126**, 171-179. [96]

— (1953) 'Linear relationship between fibre diameter and velocity of conduction in giant axon of squid', *J. Neurophysiol.*, **16**, 145-154. [16]

— LARRABEE, M. G., & GERMAN, W. (1948) 'The human electromyogram in response to nerve stimulation and the conduction velocity of motor axons', *Arch. Neurol. Psych.*, **60**, 340-368. [16]

HODGKIN, A. L. (1951) 'The ionic basis of electrical activity in nerve and muscle', *Biol. Rev.*, **26**, 339-409. [5]

HODLER, J., STÄMPFLI, R., & TASAKI, I. (1952) 'Änderung der Reizschwelle und der Chronaxie längs einer einzelnen, markhaltigen Nervenfaser', *Helv. Physiol. Pharm. Acta*, **10**, C54-57. [20]

HOEFER, P. F. A., & PUTNAM, T. J. (1940 *a*) 'Action potentials of muscles in rigidity and tremor', *Arch. Neurol. Psych.*, **43**, 704-725. [120]

— — (1940 *b*) 'Action potentials of muscle in athetosis and Sydenham's chorea', *Arch. Neurol. Psych.*, **44**, 517-531. [120, 391]

HOFF, E. C., & GREEN, H. D. (1936) 'Cardiovascular reactions induced by electrical stimulation of cerebral cortex', *Amer. J. Physiol.*, **117**, 411-422. [480]

HOFF, H. E., & GRANT, R. S. (1944) 'The supernormal period in the recovery cycle of motoneurones', *J. Neurophysiol.*, **7**, 305-322. [108]

HOLBOURN, A. H. S. (1943) 'Mechanics of head injuries', *Lancet*, II, 438-441. [257]

HOLMES, G. (1917) 'The symptoms of acute cerebellar injuries due to gunshot injuries', *Brain*, **40**, 461-535. [176, 179, 193]

— (1919) 'Disturbances of visual space perception', *Brit. med. J.*, II, 230-233. [360]

— (1921) 'Palsies of the conjugate ocular movements', *Brit. J. Ophthalmol.*, **5**, 241-250. [159]

— (1922) 'Clinical symptoms of cerebellar disease and their interpretation', *Lancet*, II, 59-65. [191, 196]

— (1927) 'Disorders of sensation produced by cortical lesions', *Brain*, **50**, 413-427. [410, 411, 418]

HOLMES, G. (1933) 'Observations on the paralysed bladder', *Brain*, **56**, 383-396. [99]
— (1938) 'The cerebral integration of ocular movements', *Brit. med. J.*, II, 107-112. [333]
— (1945) 'The organisation of the visual cortex in man', *Proc. Roy. Soc.*, B, **132**, 348-361. [358]
— & HEAD, H. (1911) 'A case of lesion of the optic thalamus with autopsy', *Brain*, **34**, 255-271. [413]
— & HORRAX, G. (1919) 'Disturbances of spatial orientation and visual attention with loss of stereoscopic vision', *Arch. Neurol. Psych.*, **1**, 385-407. [354]
— & STEWART, T. G. (1908) 'On the connection of the inferior olives with the cerebellum in man', *Brain*, **31**, 125-137. [188]
HOLMGREN, B., & MERTON, P. A. (1954) 'Local feedback control of moto-neurones', *J. Physiol.*, **123**, 47P. [324]
HOLST, E. VON (1954) 'Relation between the central nervous system and the "peripheral organs"', *Brit. J. Anim. Behav.*, **2**, 89-94. [325, 369]
HORRAX, G., & PUTNAM, T. J. (1932) 'Distortions of the visual fields in cases of brain tumour', *Brain*, **55**, 499-523. [351]
HORSLEY, V. (1885) 'The Brown Lectures on Pathology', *Brit. med. J.*, I, 111-115. [26]
— (1906) 'On Dr. Hughlings Jackson's views of the functions of the cerebellum as illustrated by recent research', *Brain*, **29**, 446-466. [169]
(1909) 'The Linacre Lecture. The functions of the so-called motor area of the brain', *Brit. med. J.*, 11, 125-132. [395]
— & CLARKE, R. H. (1908) 'The structure and function of the cerebellum examined by a new method', *Brain*, **31**, 45-124. [182]
HOUSTON, R. A. (1932) *Vision and colour vision*. Longmans. London. [304]
HOWARTH, C. I. (1954) 'Strength duration curves for electrical stimulation of the human eye', *Quart. J. Exp. Psychol.*, **6**, 47-61. [348]
HUGHES, J. W. (1937) 'The monaural threshold : effect of a subliminal contralateral stimulus', *Proc. Roy. Soc.*, B, **124**, 406-420. [261]
— (1940) 'The monaural threshold : the effect of subliminal and audible contralateral and ipsilateral stimuli', *Proc. Roy. Soc.*, B, **128**, 144-152. [261]
HUGHES, R. A., & ROBINSON, F. (1951) 'Acetylcholine and the central nervous system', *Yale J. Biol. Med.*, **24**, 35-47. [200]
HUMPHREY, M. E., & ZANGWILL, O. L. (1952) 'Dysphasia in left-handed patients with unilateral brain lesions', *J. Neurol. Neurosurg. Psychiat.*, **15**, 184-193. [440]
HUNT, C. C., & KUFFLER, S. W. (1954) 'Motor innervation of skeletal muscle : multiple innervation of individual muscle fibres and motor unit function', *J. Physiol.*, **126**, 293-303. [17]
HUNT, J. R. (1921) 'Dyssynergia cerebellaris myoclonica—primary atrophy of the dentate system', *Brain*, **44**, 490-538. [196]

514 PHYSIOLOGY OF THE NERVOUS SYSTEM

HUNTER, J., & JASPER, H. H. (1949) 'Effects of thalamic stimulation in unanaesthetised animals', *E.E.G. Clin. Neurophysiol.*, **1**, 305-324. [255]

HURSH, J. B. (1939) 'Conduction velocity and diameter of nerve fibers', *Amer. J. Physiol.*, **127**, 131-139. [16]

— (1940) 'Relayed impulses in ascending branches of dorsal root fibers', *J. Neurophysiol.*, **3**, 166-174. [400]

HURST, A. F. (1911) *The sensibility of the alimentary canal.* Oxford Univ. Press. [70, 100]

HURVICH, L. M., & JAMESON, D. (1951) 'The binocular fusion of yellow in relation to color theories', *Science*, **114**, 199-202. [301]

HUXLEY, A. F., & STÄMPFLI, R. (1949) 'Evidence for saltatory conduction in peripheral myelinated nerve fibres', *J. Physiol.*, **108**, 321-339. [10]

HYDÉN, H. (1947) 'Protein and nucleotide metabolism in the nerve cell under different functional conditions', *S.E.B. Symposium*, **1**, 152-162. [14]

HYNDMAN, O. R. (1941) 'Physiology of the spinal cord, 1 : The role of the anterior column in hyperreflexia', *Arch. Neurol. Psych.*, **46**, 695-703. [129, 373]

— & PENFIELD, W. (1937) 'Agenesis of the corpus callosum', *Arch. Neurol. Psych.*, **37**, 1251-1270. [388]

— & WOLKIN, J. (1943) 'Anterior chordotomy', *Arch. Neurol. Psych.*, **50**, 129-148. [449]

IGGO, A. (1955) 'Tension receptors in the stomach and the urinary bladder', *J. Physiol.*, **128**, 593-607. [100]

INGRAM, W. R., BARRIS, R. W., & RANSON, S. W. (1936) 'Catalepsy. An experimental study', *Arch. Neurol. Psych.*, **35**, 1175-1197. [460]

— & RANSON, S. W. (1934) 'Bulbocapnine. Effect on animals with lesions of the central nervous system', *Arch. Neurol. Psych.*, **31**, 987-1006. [124]

— — HANNETT, F. I., ZEISS, F. R., & TERWILLIGER, E. H. (1932) 'Results of stimulation of the tegmentum with the Horsley-Clarke stereotaxic apparatus', *Arch. Neurol. Psych.*, **28**, 513-541. [160]

INGVAR, S. (1923) 'On cerebellar localisation', *Brain*, **46**, 301-335. [163, 164, 166, 172]

— (1928 a) 'Studies in neurology, I: The phylogenetic continuity of the central nervous system', *Johns Hopk. Hosp. Bull.*, **43**, 315-337. [173]

— (1928 b) 'Studies in neurology, II : On cerebellar function', *Johns Hopk. Hosp. Bull.*, **43**, 338-362. [164, 176]

— (1928 c) 'On the pathenogenesis of the Argyll-Robertson phenomenon', *Johns Hopk. Hosp. Bull.*, **43**, 363-396. [297]

IRELAND, F. H. (1950) 'A comparison of critical flicker frequencies under conditions of monocular and binocular stimulation', *J. Exp. Psychol.*, **40**, 282-286. [319]

IRONSIDE, R., & GUTTMACKER, M. (1929) 'The corpus callosum and its tumours', *Brain*, **52**, 442-483. [466]

IVES, H. E. (1912) 'Studies in the photometry of lights of different colours, II : Spectral luminosity curves by the method of critical frequency', *Phil. Mag.*, 6th Series, **24**, 352-370. [318]

JACKSON, J. HUGHLINGS (1868) 'Observations on the physiology and pathology of hemi-chorea', *Edin. med. J.*, **14**, 294-303. Reprinted in *Selected writings of John Hughlings Jackson*, edited by James Taylor. 1932. Hodder & Stoughton. London. [392]

— (1874) 'On the nature of the duality of the brain', *Medical Press & Circular*, **1**. Reprinted in *Brain* (1915), **38**, 80-103. [279]

— (1890) 'Case of tumour of the right temporo-sphenoidal lobe bearing on the localisation of the sense of smell and on the interpretation of a particular variety of epilepsy', *Brain*, **12**, 346-357. [284]

— (1906 *a*) 'Case of tumour of the middle lobe of the cerebellum— cerebellar paralysis with rigidity (cerebellar attitude)—occasional tetanus-like seizures', *Brain*, **29**, 425-440. [185]

— (1906 *b*) 'Case of tumour of the middle lobe of the cerebellum. Cerebellar attitude. No tetanus-like seizures. General remarks on the cerebellar attitude', *Brain*, **29**, 441-445. [127]

— & PATON, L. (1909) 'On some abnormalities of ocular movements', *Lancet*, 900-905. [324, 327]

JACKSON, S. (1945) 'The rôle of galvanism in the treatment of denervated voluntary muscle in man', *Brain*, **68**, 300-330. [21]

JACOBSEN, C. F. (1936) 'Studies of cerebral function in primates, 1 : The functions of the frontal association areas in monkeys', *Comp. Psychol. Monogr.*, **13**, 3-60. [168, 471]

JAKOB, A. (1925) 'The anatomy, clinical syndromes and physiology of the extra-pyramidal system', *Arch. Neurol. Psych.*, **13**, 596-620. [392]

JAMES, W. (1887) 'The consciousness of lost limbs', *Amer. Soc. Psychical Res.*, **1**, 249-258, reprinted in James, W. (1920) *Collected Essays and Reviews*. Longmans. London. [425, 426]

JANSEN, A., & BRODAL, A. (1954) *Aspects of cerebellar anatomy*. J. G. Tanum. Oslo. [172, 181, 182]

JANSEN, J. (1950) 'The morphogenesis of the cetacean cerebellum', *J. Comp. Neurol.*, **93**, 341-400. (203)

JARCHO, L. W., EYZAGUIRRE, C., BERMAN, B., & LILIENTHAL, J. L. (1952) 'Spread of excitation in skeletal muscle : some factors contributing to the form of the electromyogram', *Amer. J. Physiol.*, **168**, 446-457. [17]

JASPER, H. H. (1949) 'Electrical signs of epileptic discharge', *E.E.G. Clin. Neurophysiol.*, **1**, 11-18. [251]

— & ERICKSON, T. C. (1941) 'Cerebral blood flow and *p*H in excessive cortical discharge induced by metrazol and electrical stimulation', *J. Neurophysiol.*, **4**, 333-347. [234]

— & FORTUYN, J. D. (1947) 'Experimental studies on the functional anatomy of Petit Mal epilepsy', *Res. Publ. Ass. nerv. ment. Dis.*, **26**, 272-298. [255]

JEFFERSON, G. (1937) 'Removal of right or left frontal lobes in man', *Brit. med. J.*, II, 199-206. [477]

JIELOF, R., SPOOR, A., & DE VRIES, HL. (1952) 'The microphonic activity of the lateral line', *J. Physiol.*, 116, 137-157. [147]

JOHNSON, E. P., & RIGGS, L. A. (1951) 'Electroretinal and psychophysical dark adaptation curves', *J. Exp. Psychol.*, 41, 139-147. [308]

JOHNSON, H. C., WALKER, A. E., BROWNE, K. M., & MARKHAM, J. W. (1952) 'Experimental cerebellar seizures', *Arch. Neurol. Psych.*, 67, 473-482. [187]

JONES, F. WOOD (1941) *The principles of anatomy as seen in the hand.* Baillière, Tindall & Cox. London. [362]

JONG, H. H. DE (1945) *Experimental catatonia.* Williams & Wilkins. Baltimore. [460]

JONGKEES, L. B. W. (1950) 'On the function of the saccule', *Acta Oto-laryngol.*, 38, 18-26. [139]

— (1952) 'Some remarks on vestibular examinations', *Proc. Roy. Soc. Med.*, 45, 127-133. [146]

— & GROEN, J. J. (1946) 'The nature of the vestibular stimulus', *J. Laryngol. Otol.*, 61, 529-541. [137]

JUNG, R. (1953) 'Neuronal discharge', *E.E.G. Clin. Neurophysiol.*, Suppl. 4, 57-71. [347, 348]

KAADA, B. R. (1950) 'Site of action of myanesin (Mephenesin, Tolserol) in the central nervous system', *J. Neurophysiol.*, 13, 89-104. [115]

— (1951) 'Somato-motor, autonomic and electrocorticographic responses to electrical stimulation of "rhinencephalic" and other structures in primates, cat and dog', *Acta Physiol. Scand.*, 24, Suppl. 83. [454, 463, 480]

KABAT, H. (1952) 'Restoration of function through neuromuscular re-education in traumatic paraplegia', *Arch. Neurol. Psych.*, 67, 737-744. [92]

KAHR, S., & SHEEHAN, D. (1933) 'The presence of efferent fibres in posterior spinal roots', *Brain*, 56, 265-292. [4]

KARPE, G. (1945) 'The basis of the clinical electro-retinography', *Acta Ophthalmol.*, Suppl. 24. [308]

KARPLUS, J. P., & KREIDL, A. (1914) 'Über Totalexstirpationen einer und beider Grosshirnhemisphären an Affen (*Macacus rhesus*)', *Arch. f. Anat. und Physiol.*, Physiol. Abt., 155-212. [278]

KATZ, B. (1950) 'Depolarisation of sensory terminals and the initiation of impulses in the muscle spindle', *J. Physiol.*, 111, 261-282. [51]

— (1952) 'The properties of the nerve membrane and its relation to the conduction of impulses', *S.E.B. Symposium*, 6, 16-38. [7]

KEEGAN, J. J., & GARRETT, F. D. (1948) 'The segmental distribution of the cutaneous nerves in the limbs of man', *Anat. Rec.*, 102, 409-437. [96]

KELLER, A. D. (1945) 'Generalised atonia and profound dysreflexia following transection of the brain stem through the cephalic pons', *J. Neurophysiol.*, 8, 273-285. [128]

KELLER, A. D., & HARE, W. K. (1934) 'The rubro-spinal tracts in the monkey', *Arch. Neurol. Psych.*, **32**, 1253-1272. [160]

KELLGREN, J. H. (1938) 'Observations on referred pain arising from muscle', *Clin. Sci.*, **3**, 175-190. [72, 73]

— (1939) 'On the distribution of pain arising from deep somatic structures with charts of segmental pain areas', *Clin. Sci.*, **4**, 35-46. [73]

— McGOWAN, A. J., & HUGHES, E. S. R. (1948) 'On deep hyperalgesia and cold pain', *Clin. Sci.*, **7**, 13-27. [69]

KEMPF, E. J. (1952) 'Abraham Lincoln's organic and emotional neurosis', *Arch. Neurol. Psych.*, **67**, 419-433. [344]

KEMPINSKY, W. H., & WARD, A. A. (1950) 'Effect of section of vestibular nerve upon cortically induced movement in cat', *J. Neurophysiol.*, **13**, 295-304. [381]

KENNARD, M. A. (1940) 'Relation of age to motor impairment in man and in subhuman primates', *Arch. Neurol. Psych.*, **44**, 377-397. [129]

KILOH, L. G., & NEVIN, S. (1951) 'Progressive dystrophy of the external ocular muscles (ocular myopathy)', *Brain*, **74**, 115-143. [19]

KINSELLA, V. J. (1948) *The mechanism of abdominal pain*. Austral. Med. Publ. Co., Sydney. [72]

KIRSCHBAUM, W. R. (1951) 'Excessive hunger as a symptom of cerebral origin', *J. nerv. ment. Dis.*, **113**, 95-114. [476]

KLEIJN, A. DE (1921) 'Tonische Labyrinth- und Halsreflex auf die Augen', *Pflügers Arch. f. ges. Physiol.*, **186**, 82-97. [143]

— (1923) 'Experimental physiology of the labyrinth', *J. Laryngol. & Otol.*, **38**, 646-663. [133, 151]

— & VERSTEEGH, C. (1924) 'Labyrinthine compensatory eye positions in patients', *Proc. Roy. Soc. Med.*, **17**, Sect. of Laryngol., 17-20. [143]

KLEYN, A. P. H. A. DE, & DEINSE, J. B. VAN (1950) 'The influence of streptomycine on the vestibular system', *Acta Otolaryngol.*, **38**, 1-7. [145]

KLOEHN, N. W., & BROGDEN, W. J. (1948) 'The alkaline taste : a comparison of absolute thresholds for sodium hydroxide on the tip and mid-dorsal surfaces of the tongue', *Amer. J. Psychol.*, **61**, 90-93. [405]

KLOPSTEG, P. E., WILSON, P. D., et al. (1954) *Human limbs and their substitutes*. McGraw-Hill. New York. [364, 430]

KLÜVER, H., & BUCY, P. C. (1939) 'Preliminary analysis of functions of the temporal lobes in monkeys', *Arch. Neurol. Psych.*, **42**, 979-1000. [284, 353]

KORNMÜLLER, A. E. (1930) 'Eine experimentelle Anästhesie der äusseren Augenmuskeln am Menschen und ihre Auswirkungen', *J. f. Psychol. und Neurol.*, **41**, 354-366. [325, 332]

KOURILSKY, R. (1950) 'Diabetes insipidus', *Proc. Roy. Soc. Med.*, **43**, 842-844. [452]

KRAUS, W. M., & WEIL, A. (1926) 'The measurement of the human cerebellar surface', *Res. Pub. Ass. nerv. ment. Dis.*, **6**, 238-243. [181]

KREEZER, G. L. (1949) 'Derivation of transfer functions of homeostatic systems from experimental response curves', *J. Psychol.*, **28**, 487-493. [117]

KRISTIANSEN, K., & COURTOIS, G. (1949) 'Rhythmic electrical activity from isolated cerebral cortex', *E.E.G. Clin. Neurophysiol.*, **1**, 265-272. [249]

KRNJEVIC, K. (1954) 'Some observations on perfused frog sciatic nerves', *J. Physiol.*, **123**, 338-356. [20]

KUBIK, C. S., & ADAMS, R. D. (1946) 'Occlusion of the basilar artery—a clinical and pathological study', *Brain*, **69**, 73-121. [128]

KUFFLER, S. W. (1952) 'Neurons in the retina : organisation, inhibition and excitation problems', *Cold Spring Harb. Symp. Quant. Biol.*, **17**, 281-292. [314]

— (1953) 'Discharge patterns and functional organisation of mammalian retina', *J. Neurophysiol.*, **16**, 37-68. [315]

— HUNT, C. C., & QUILLIAM, J. P. (1951) 'Function of medullated small nerve fibers in mammalian ventral roots : efferent muscle spindle innervation', *J. Neurophysiol.*, **14**, 29-54. [54]

— & WILLIAMS, E. M. V. (1953) 'Small nerve junctional potentials. The distribution of small motor nerves to frog skeletal muscles and the membrane characteristics of the fibres they innervate', *J. Physiol.*, **121**, 289-317. [15, 16]

KUGELBERG, E. (1944) 'Accommodation in human nerves', *Acta Physiol. Scand.*, **8**, Suppl. 24. [23]

— (1946) '"Injury activity" and "trigger zones" in human nerves', *Brain*, **69**, 310-325. [24, 25]

— (1948) 'Demonstration of A and C fibre components in the Babinski plantar response and the pathological flexion reflex', *Brain*, **71**, 304-331. [373]

— (1952) 'Facial reflexes', *Brain*, **75**, 385-396. [114]

KUHN, R. A. (1953) 'Organisation of tactile dermatomes in cat and monkey', *J. Neurophysiol.*, **16**, 169-182. [404]

LAGET, P., & LUNDBERG, A. (1949) 'On the effect of K^+ and Ca^{++} on thermal stimulation and spontaneous activity of mammalian nerve fibres', *Acta Physiol. Scand.*, **18**, 128-138. [3]

LANDAU, W. M. (1951) 'Synchronisation of potentials and response to direct current stimulation in denervated mammalian muscle', *E.E.G. Clin. Neurophysiol.*, **3**, 169-182. [119]

LANDIS, C. (1954) 'Determinants of the critical flicker fusion threshold', *Physiol. Rev.*, **34**, 259-286. [319]

LANGENSKIÖLD, A. (1941) 'Component potentials of the sub-maxillary gland electrogram and their relation to innervation and secretion', *Acta Physiol. Scand.*, **2**, Suppl. 6. [482]

LANGLANS, N. M. S. (1929) 'Experiments on binocular vision', *M.R.C. Special Report Series*, No. 133. H.M. Stationery Office. [340]

LANGWORTHY, O. R. (1932 a) 'Development of behaviour patterns and myelinisation of tracts in the nervous system', *Arch. Neurol. Psych.*, **28**, 1365-1382. [199]

LANGWORTHY, O. R. (1932 *b*) 'A description of the central nervous system of the porpoise', *J. Comp. Neurol.*, **54**, 437-488. [205]

— LEWIS, L. G., DEES, J. E., & HESSER, F. H. (1936) 'A clinical study of the control of the bladder by the central nervous system', *Bull. Johns Hopk. Hosp.*, **58**, 89-108. [102]

— & RICHTER, C. P. (1939) 'Induced spontaneous activity produced by frontal lobe lesions in cats', *Amer. J. Physiol.*, **126**, 158-161. [479]

LARSELL, O. (1937) 'The cerebellum. A review and interpretation', *Arch. Neurol. Psych.*, **38**, 580-607. [182]

— & DOW, R. S. (1939) 'The cerebellum. A new interpretation', *Western J. Surg.*, **47**, 256-262. [163]

LARSSON, S. (1954) 'On the hypothalamic organisation of the nervous mechanism regulating food intake', *Acta Physiol. Scand.*, **32**, Suppl. 115. [454]

LASHLEY, K. S. (1917) 'The accuracy of movement in the absence of excitation from the moving organ', *Amer. J. Physiol.*, **43**, 169-194. [324, 369]

— (1921) 'Studies of cerebral function in learning, III : The motor area', *Brain*, **44**, 255-285. [386]

— (1924) 'Studies of cerebral function in learning, V : The retention of motor habits after destruction of the so-called motor areas in primates', *Arch. Neurol. Psych.*, **12**, 249-276. [386]

— (1929) *Brain mechanisms and intelligence: a quantitative study of injuries to the brain.* Univ. of Chicago Press. [105, 217, 229]

— (1937) 'Functional determinants of cerebral localisation', *Arch. Neurol. Psych.*, **38**, 371-387. [231]

— (1938) 'Factors limiting recovery after central nervous lesions', *J. nerv. ment. Dis.*, **88**, 733-755. [87, 214, 252]

— (1939) 'The mechanism of vision (16). The functioning of small remnants of the visual cortex', *J. Comp. Neurol.*, **70**, 45-67. [348]

— (1941) 'Patterns of cerebral integration indicated by the scotomas of migraine', *Arch. Neurol. Psych.*, **46**, 331-339. [349]

— (1942) 'The problem of cerebral organisation in vision', *Biol. Symp.*, **7**, 301-322. [355, 360]

— (1948) 'Effect of destroying the visual "associative areas" of the monkey', *Genet. Psychol. Mon.*, **37**, 107-166. [353]

— (1950) 'In search of the engram', *Symposia Soc. Exp. Biol.*, **4**, 454-482. [229, 386]

— (1952) 'Functional interpretation of anatomical patterns', *Res. Publ. Ass. nerv. ment. Dis.*, **30**, 529-547. [363]

— & CLARK, G. (1946) 'The cyto-architecture of the cerebral cortex of ateles : a critical examination of architectonic studies', *J. Comp. Neurol.*, **85**, 223-305. [207]

LASSEK, A. M. (1942) 'The human pyramidal tract (4). A study of the mature myelinated fibers of the pyramid', *J. Comp. Neurol.*, **76**, 217-225. [372]

LASSEK, A. M. (1944) 'The human pyramidal tract (10). The Babinski sign and destruction of the pyramidal tract', *Arch. Neurol. Psych.*, **52**, 484-494. [372]

— (1945) 'The human pyramidal tract (13). A study of the pyramids in cases of acute and chronic vascular lesions of the brain', *Arch. Neurol. Psych.*, **54**, 339-343. [371]

— (1948) 'The pyramidal tract : basic considerations of cortico-spinal neurones', *Res. Publ. Ass. nerv. ment. Dis.*, **27**, 106-128. [371]

— & EVANS, J. P. (1946) 'The human pyramidal tract (14). A study of the representation of the cortico-spinal components in the spinal cord', *J. Comp. Neurol.*, **84**, 11-16. [370]

LEARMONTH, J. R. (1931) 'A contribution to the neurophysiology of the urinary bladder in man', *Brain*, **54**, 147-176. [100, 103]

LEE, B. S. (1950) 'Effects of delayed speech feedback', *J. Acoust. Soc. Amer.*, **22**, 824-826. [407, 435]

LEE, T. S. (1954) 'Physiological gustatory sweating in a warm climate', *J. Physiol.*, **124**, 528-542. [407]

LEEPER, R. W. (1948) 'A motivational theory to replace "emotion as dis-organised response"', *Psychol. Rev.*, **55**, 5-21. [462]

LEHMANN, L. (1950) 'Preliminary report on a device for the objective measurement of the negative after-image phenomenon', *Science*, **112**, 199-201. [316]

LELE, P. P., & WEDDELL, O. (1954) 'The relationship between neuro-histology and corneal sensitivity', *Brain*, **79**, 119-154. [41]

LENNANDER, K. G. (1903) *Observations on the sensibility of the abdominal cavity.* Bale. London. [70]

LEWIN, W., & PHILLIPS, C. G. (1952) 'Observations on partial removal of the post-central gyrus for pain', *J. Neurol. Neurosurg. Psychiat.*, **15**, 143-147. [412]

LEWIS, T. (1936) 'Experiments relating to cutaneous hyperalgesia and its spread through somatic nerves', *Clin. Sci.*, **2**, 373-416. [63, 64]

— (1938) 'Suggestions relating to the study of somatic pain', *Brit. med. J.*, I, 321-325. [73]

— & POCHIN, E. E. (1937) 'The double pain response of the human skin to a single stimulus', *Clin. Sci.*, **3**, 67-76. [43]

LEYTON, A. S. F., & SHERRINGTON, C. S. S. (1917) 'Observations on the excitable cortex of the chimpanzee, orang-utan, and gorilla', *Quart. J. Exp. Physiol.*, **11**, 135-222. [378, 385, 388]

LIBERSON, W. T., SCOVILLE, W. B., & DUNSMORE, R. H. (1951) 'Stimulation studies of the prefrontal lobe and uncus in man', *E.E.G. Clin. Neuro-physiol.*, **3**, 1-8. [284]

LIBET, B., & GERARD, R. W. (1941) 'Steady potential fields and neurone activity', *J. Neurophysiol.*, **4**, 438-455. [240]

LIDDELL, E. G. T. (1934) 'Spinal shock and some features in isolation-alteration of the spinal cord in cats', *Brain*, **57**, 386-400. [87]

— (1953) 'The brain and muscle management', *Quart. J. Exp. Physiol.*, **38**, 125-137. [380]

LIDDELL, E. G. T., & PHILLIPS, C. G. (1943) 'Pyramidal section in the cat', *Brain*, **67**, 1-9. [375]

— — (1950) 'Thresholds of cortical representation', *Brain*, **73**, 125-140. [379, 380]

— & SHERRINGTON, C. (1924) 'Reflexes in response to stretch (Myotatic Reflexes)', *Proc. Roy. Soc.*, B, **96**, 212-242. [111]

LILLIE, R. S. (1925) 'Factors affecting transmission and recovery in the passive iron nerve model', *J. Gen. Physiol.*, **7**, 473-507. [8]

LILLY, J. C. (1953) 'Recent developments in electro-encephalographic techniques', *E.E.G. Clin. Neurophysiol.*, Suppl. 4, 38-50. [242]

LINDQVIST, T. (1941) 'Finger tremor and the α-waves of the electro-encephalogram', *Acta Med. Scand.*, **108**, 580-585. [118]

LINDSLEY, D. B. (1935) 'Myographic and electromyographic studies of myasthenia gravis', *Brain*, **58**, 470-482. [30]

— SCHREINER, L. H., & MAGOUN, H. W. (1949) 'An electro-myographic study of spasticity', *J. Neurophysiol.*, **12**, 197-205. [128]

LIST, C. F., & PEET, M. M. (1938) 'Sweat secretion in man, IV: Sweat secretion of the face and its disturbances', *Arch. Neurol. Psych.*, **40**, 443-470. [407]

— — (1939) 'Sweat secretion in man, V: Disturbances of sweat secretion with lesions of the pons, medulla and cervical portion of the cord', *Arch. Neurol. Psych.*, **42**, 1098-1127. [446]

— & PIMENTA, A. D. (1944) 'Sweat secretion in man, VI: Spinal reflex sweating', *Arch. Neurol. Psych.*, **51**, 501-507. [94]

LITTLER, T. S., KNIGHT, J. J., & STANGE, P. H. (1952) 'Hearing by bone conduction and the use of bone-conduction hearing aids', *Proc. Roy. Soc. Med.*, **45**, 783-790. [265]

LIVINGSTON, W. K. (1943) *Pain mechanisms. A physiological interpretation of causalgia and its related states*. Macmillan. New York. [425, 428]

LLOYD, D. P. C. (1941) 'The spinal mechanism of the pyramidal system in cats', *J. Neurophysiol.*, **4**, 525-546. [249, 371, 372, 373]

— (1943) 'Conduction and synaptic transmission of the reflex response to stretch in spinal cats', *J. Neurophysiol.*, **6**, 317-326. [117]

— & McINTYRE, A. K. (1950) 'Dorsal column conduction of group I muscle afferent impulses and their relay through Clarke's column', *J. Neurophysiol.*, **13**, 39-54. [398, 415]

LOCKE, J. (1689) *An essay on the human understanding.* [392, 431]

LOEMKER, K. K. (1930) 'Certain factors determining the accuracy of a response to the direction of a visual object', *J. Exp. Psychol.*, **13**, 500-518. [326]

LÖFGREN, B. (1951) 'The electrical impedance of a complex tissue', *Acta Physiol. Scand.*, **23**, Suppl. 81. [20]

LORENTE DE NÓ, R. (1933 a) 'Vestibulo-ocular reflex arc', *Arch. Neurol. Psych.*, **30**, 245-291. [159]

— (1933 b) 'The central projection of the nerve endings of the internal ear', *Laryngoscope*, **43**, 1-38. [158]

LORENTE DE NÓ, R. (1935) 'Facilitation of motoneurones', *Amer. J. Physiol.*, **113**, 505-523. [107]
— (1939 *a*) 'Transmission of impulses through cranial motor nuclei' *J. Neurophysiol.*, **2**, 402-472. [104, 106, 107]
— (1939 *b*) In a discussion published in *Res. Pub. Ass. nerv. ment. Dis.*, **20**, 771-772. [201]
LORENZ, K. Z. (1951) *The rôle of Gestalt perception in human and animal behaviour* in *Aspects of Form*, edited by L. L. Whyte. Humphries. London. [322, 354, 361]
LOVELL, H. W., WAGGONER, R. W., & KAHN, E. A. (1932) 'Critical study of a case of aphasia', *Arch. Neurol. Psych.*, **28**, 1178-1181. [439]
LÖWENSTEIN, O. (1955) 'The effect of galvanic polarisation on the impulse discharge from sense endings in the isolated labyrinth of the thornback ray (*Raja clavata*)', *J. Physiol.*, **127**, 104-117. (147]
— & LOWENFELD, I. E. (1950) 'Mutual rôle of sympathetic and para-sympathetic in shaping of the pupillary reflex to light', *Arch. Neurol. Psych.*, **64**, 341-377. [297]
— & ROBERTS, T. D. M. (1949) 'The equilibrium function of the otolith organs of the thornback ray (*Raja clavata*)', *J. Physiol.*, **110**, 392-415. [139]
— — (1951) 'The localization and analysis of the responses to vibration from the isolated elasmobranch labyrinth. A contribution to the problem of the evolution of hearing in vertebrates', *J. Physiol.*, **114**, 471-489. [137]
— & SAND, A. (1940) 'The individual and integrated activity of the semicircular canals of the elasmobranch labyrinth', *J. Physiol.*, **99**, 89-101. [143]
LUCIANI, L. (1915) *Human Physiology* in 5 vols. Translated by F. A. Welby. Macmillan. London. [167, 168, 363]
LUDVIGH, E. (1952) 'Possible rôle of proprioception in the extra-ocular muscles', *A.M.A. Arch. Ophth.*, **48**, 436-441. [322, 345]
LUHAN, J. A. (1932) 'Some postural reflexes in man', *Arch. Neurol. Psych.*, **28**, 649-660. [154]
LYONS, L. V., & BRICKNER, R. M. (1931) 'Physiologic differences between generic and individually acquired associated movements', *Arch. Neurol. Psych.*, **25**, 998-1002. [162]
LYTHGOE, R. J. (1926) 'Illumination and visual capacities (a review of recent literature)', *M.R.C. Special Report*, No. 104. [305]
— (1938) 'The structure of the retina and the rôle of its visual purple', *Proc. Physical Soc.*, **50**, 323-329. [311]
McALPINE, D. (1924) 'A clinical study of plastic tonus as observed in a rare sequela of epidemic encephalitis', *Brain*, **47**, 178-206. [124]
McCALLUM, D. M., & SMITH, J. B. (1951 *a*) 'Mechanised reasoning. Logical computors and their design', *Electronic Engineering*, **23**, 126-133. [198]
— — (1951 *b*) 'Feedback logical computors', *Electronic Engineering*, **23**, 458-461. [198]

McCouch, G. P., & Adler, F. H. (1932) 'Extraocular reflexes', *Amer. J. Physiol.*, **100**, 78-88. [114]

— Deering, I. D., & Ling, T. H. (1951) 'Location of receptors for tonic neck reflexes', *J. Neurophysiol.*, **14**, 191-195. [151, 152]

— — & Stewart, W. B. (1950) 'Inhibition of knee jerk from tendon spindle of crureus', *J. Neurophysiol.*, **13**, 343-350. [113, 123]

— Hughes, J., & Stewart, W. B. (1943) 'The monkey (*Macaca mulatta*) after hemisection and subsequent transection of the spinal cord', *J. Neurophysiol.*, **6**, 155-159. [89]

McCulloch, W. S. (1949) 'Mechanisms for the spread of epileptic activation of the brain', *E.E.G. Clin. Neurophysiol.*, **1**, 19-27. [200]

McDougall, W. (1904) 'The variation of the intensity of visual sensation with the duration of the stimulus', *Brit. J. Psychol.*, **1**, 151-189. [348]

McFie, J., Piercy, M. F., & Zangwill, O. L. (1950) 'Visual-spatial agnosia associated with lesions of the right cerebral hemisphere', *Brain*, **73**, 167-190. [358, 359]

Mach, E. (1875) *Grundlinien der Lehre von den Bewegungsempfindungen*. Engelmann. Leipzig. [137]

MacKay, D. M. (1953) 'Some experiments on the perception of patterns modulated at the alpha frequency', *E.E.G. Clin. Neurophysiol.*, **5**, 559-562. [236]

MacKenzie, J. (1913) *Disease of the heart*. 3rd Ed. Oxford Medical Publications. [70]

— (1920) *Symptoms and their interpretation*. 4th Ed. Shaw & Sons. London. [71]

McLardy, T., & Davies, D. L. (1949) 'Clinical and pathological observations on relapse after successful leucotomy', *J. Neurol. Neurosurg. Psychiat.*, **12**, 231-238. [473]

MacLean, P. D., & Delgado, J. M. R. (1953) 'Electrical and chemical stimulation of fronto-temporal portion of limbic system in the waking animal', *E.E.G. Clin. Neurophysiol.*, **5**, 91-100. [454]

McNally, W. J. (1953) 'Some remarks about dizziness—its diagnostic significance and treatment', *Ann. Otol. Rhinol. Laryngol.*, **62**, 607-629. [130]

Magladery, J. W., Park, A. M., Porter, W. E., & Teasdall, R. D. (1952) 'Spinal reflex patterns in man', *Res. Publ. Ass. nerv. ment. Dis.*, **30**, 118-151. [118]

Magnus, R. (1924) *Körperstellung*. Springer. Berlin. [381]

— (1925) 'Animal posture (Croonian Lecture)', *Proc. Roy. Soc.*, B, **98**, 339-353. [151, 152, 156]

Magnusson, C. E., & Stevens, H. C. (1911) 'Visual sensations caused by changes in the strength of a magnetic field', *Amer. J. Physiol.*, **29**, 124-136. [351]

Magoun, H. W. (1950) 'Caudal and cephalic influences of the brain stem reticular formation', *Physiol. Rev.*, **30**, 459-474. [393]

MAGOUN, H. W., HARE, W. K., & RANSON, S. W. (1937) 'Rôle of the cere-bellum in postural contractions', *Arch. Neurol. Psych.*, **37**, 1237-1250. [174]

— HARRISON, F., BROBECK, J. R., & RANSON, S. W. (1938) 'Activation of heat loss mechanisms by local heating of the brain', *J. Neurophysiol.*, **1**, 101-114. [444, 445, 446]

— & RHINES, R. (1946) 'An inhibitory mechanism in the bulbar reticular formation', *J. Neurophysiol.*, **9**, 165-171. [129]

MALCOLM, D. S. (1951) 'A method of measuring reflex times applied in sciatica and other conditions due to nerve root compression', *J. Neurol. Neurosurg. Psychiat.*, **14**, 15-24. [123]

MALING, H. M., & ACHESON, G. H. (1946) 'Righting and other postural activity in low decerebrate and in spinal cats after d-amphetamine', *J. Neurophysiol.*, **9**, 379-386. [157, 160, 161]

MALMO, R. B. (1942) 'Interference factors in delayed response in monkeys after removal of frontal lobes', *J. Neurophysiol.*, **5**, 295-308. [471]

MALONEY, W. J., & KENNEDY, R. F. (1911) 'The sense of pressure in the face, eye, and tongue', *Brain*, **34**, 1-28. [405]

MANN, I., & PIRIE, A. (1946) *The science of seeing.* Pelican Books. [338]

MAREY, E. J. (1874) *Animal mechanism. A treatise on terrestrial and aerial locomotion.* International Scientific Series. King. London. [362]

MARG, E. (1951) 'Development of electro-oculography', *A.M.A. Arch. Ophthal.*, **45**, 169-185. [309]

MARQUIS, D. G., & WILLIAMS, D. J. (1938) 'The central pathway in man of the vasomotor response to pain', *Brain*, **61**, 203-220. [215]

MARSAN, C. A., & STOLL, J. (1951) 'Subcortical connections of the temporal pole in relation to temporal lobe seizures', *Arch. Neurol. Psych.*, **66**, 669-686. [246]

MARSHALL, C. (1936) 'The functions of the pyramidal tracts', *Quart. Rev. Biol.*, **11**, 35-36. [370]

— & HARDEN, C. (1952) 'Use of rhythmically varying patterns for photic stimulation', *E.E.G. Clin. Neurophysiol.*, **4**, 283-287. [320]

— & WALKER, A. E. (1950) 'The electro-encephalographic changes after hemispherectomy in man', *E.E.G. Clin. Neurophysiol.*, **2**, 143-156. [238]

— — & LIVINGSTON, S. (1953) 'Photogenic epilepsy : parameters of activation', *Arch. Neurol. Psych.*, **69**, 760-765. [352]

MARSHALL, J. (1951) 'Sensory disturbances in cortical wounds with special reference to pain', *J. Neurol. Neurosurg. Psychiat.*, **14**, 187-204. [411, 412]

— (1953 *a*) 'The paraesthesiae induced by cold', *J. Neurol. Neurosurg. Psychiat.*, **16**, 19-24. [69]

— (1953 *b*) 'The pain threshold in nerve blocks', *Clin. Sci.*, **12**, 247-254. [62, 66]

— & WALSH, E. G. (1956) 'Physiological tremor', *J. Neurol. Neurosurg. Psychiat.*, **19**, 260-267. [109, 118]

MARSHALL, W. H. (1950) 'The relation of dehydration of the brain to the spreading depression of Leao', *E.E.G. Clin. Neurophysiol.*, **2**, 177-185. [232]

— & TALBOT, S. A. (1942) 'Recent evidence for neural machanisms in vision leading to a general theory of sensory acuity', *Biol. Symp.*, **7**, 117-164. [321, 322, 346]

— WOOLSEY, C. N., & BARD, P. (1941) 'Observations on cortical somatic sensory mechanisms of cat and monkey', *J. Neurophysiol.*, **4**, 1-24. [402]

MASON, E. F. (1949) 'Some aspects of electro-diagnosis and electro-therapy in the Royal Air Force', *Proc. Roy. Soc. Med.*, **42**, 582-586. [22]

MASSERMAN, J. H. (1941) 'Is the hypothalamus a centre of emotion?', *Psychosom. Med.*, **3**, 1-25. [461]

MATTHEWS, B. H. C. (1933) 'Nerve endings in mammalian muscle', *J. Physiol.*, **78**, 1-53. [54]

MATTHEWS, P. B. C., & RUSHWORTH, G. (1956) 'Differential nerve narcosis with procaine', *J. Physiol.*, **131**, 30-31P. [393]

MAXWELL, J. C. (1868) 'On governors', *Proc. Roy. Soc.*, **16**, 270-283. [113]

MAXWELL, S. S. (1923) *Labyrinth and equilibrium.* Lippincott. London. [157]

MAYER, J. (1953) 'Genetic, traumatic and environmental factors in the etiology of obesity', *Physiol. Rev.*, **33**, 472-508. [454]

MAYER-GROSS, W., SLATER, E., & ROTH, M. (1954) *Clinical Psychiatry.* Cassell & Co., Ltd. London. [352]

MERRINGTON, W. R., & NATHAN, P. W. (1949) 'A study of post-ischaemic paraesthesiae', *J. Neurol. Neurosurg. Psychiat.*, **12**, 1-18. [68]

MERRITT, H. H. (1951) Editor. *Nerve impulse.* Trans. 2nd Conf. Macy Foundation. [5]

— (1952) Editor. *Nerve impulse.* Trans. 3rd Conf. Macy Foundation. [6, 11]

MERTON, P. A. (1951) 'The silent period in a muscle in the human hand', *J. Physiol.*, **114**, 183-198. [121, 367]

— (1953) '*Speculations on the servo-control of movement*' in '*The Spinal Cord*'. Ciba Symposium Churchill. London. [189, 367, 368]

— (1954 a) 'Interaction between muscle fibres in a twitch', *J. Physiol.*, **124**, 311-324. [119]

— (1954 b) 'Voluntary strength and fatigue', *J. Physiol.*, **123**, 553-564. [364, 366]

METZ, O. (1951) 'Studies on the contraction of the tympanic muscles as indicated by changes in the impedance of the ear', *Acta Oto-laryngol.*, **39**, 397-405. [264]

MEYER, A., & BECK, E. (1945) 'Neuropathological problems arising from prefrontal leucotomy', *J. Ment. Sci.*, **91**, 411-422. [473]

— — & McLARDY, T. (1947) 'Prefrontal leucotomy: a neuro-anatomical report', *Brain*, **70**, 18-49. [469]

MEYER, V., & YATES, A. J. (1955) 'Intellectual changes following temporal lobectomy for psychomotor epilepsy', *J. Neurol. Neurosurg. Psychiat.*, **18**, 44-52. [285]

MEYERS, I. L. (1919) 'The cerebellar gait. A pedegraphic study', *J. nerv. ment. Dis.*, **49**, 14-34. [187]

MEYERS, R., SWEENEY, D. B., & SCHWIDDE, J. T. (1950) 'Hemiballismus : aetiology and surgical treatment', *J. Neurol. Neurosurg. Psychiat.*, **13**, 115-126. [393]

MICKLE, W. A., & ADES, H. W. (1952) 'A composite sensory projection area in the cerebral cortex of the cat', *Amer. J. Physiol.*, **170**, 682-689. [283]

MILES, W. R. (1929) 'Horizontal eye movements at the onset of sleep', *Psychol. Rev.*, **36**, 122-141. [133]

— (1943) 'Red goggles for producing dark adaptation', *Fed. Proc.*, **2**, 109-115. [294]

— (1954) 'Comparison of functional and structural areas in human fovea, I : Method of entoptic plotting', *J. Neurophysiol.*, **17**, 22-38. [290]

MILLER, F. R. (1926) 'The physiology of the cerebellum', *Res. Publ. Ass. nerv. ment. Dis.*, **6**, 361-380. [175]

MILLS, C. K. (1891) 'On the localisation of the auditory centre', *Brain*, **14**, 465-472. [280]

MINES, G. R. (1913) 'On functional analysis by the action of electrolytes', *J. Physiol.*, **46**, 188-235. [364]

MITCHELL, G. A. G. (1953) *Anatomy of the autonomic nervous system.* Livingstone. Edinburgh. [4]

MITCHELL, S. W. (1874 a) 'Traumatic neuralgia ; section of the median nerve', *Amer. J. Med. Sci.*, **68**, 1-29. [63]

— (1874 b) 'Post-paralytic chorea', *Amer. J. Med. Sci.*, **68**, 342-352. [395, 424]

MITRINOWICZ, A. (1949) 'Iontophoresis in the treatment of vertigo', *Proc. IVth Int. Cong. Otolaryngol.*, **2**, 916-918. [22]

MONAKOW, C. VON (1926) 'Biologisches und Morphogenetisches über die Microcephalia vera', *Schweitzer Arch. f. Neurol.*, **18**, 3-39. [406]

MONCRIEFF, R. W. (1944) *The chemical senses.* Leonard Hill. London. [209, 213, 406]

MOORE, J. W. (1950) 'Electric current transients through the human body', *J. Appl. Physiol.*, **2**, 355-362. [20]

MORISON, R. S., & DEMPSEY, E. W. (1942) 'A study of thalamo-cortical relations', *Amer. J. Physiol.*, **135**, 281-292. [246]

MORLEY, J. (1931) *Abdominal pain.* Livingstone. Edinburgh. Pp. xvi, 192. [72]

MORUZZI, G. (1950) *Problems in cerebellar physiology.* Thomas. Springfield, Ill. [158, 175, 179, 196]

— & MAGOUN, H. W. (1949) 'Brain stem reticular formation and activation of the E.E.G.', *E.E.G. Clin. Neurophysiol.*, **1**, 455-473. [461]

MOTT, F. W., & SHERRINGTON, C. S. (1895) 'Experiments upon the influence of sensory nerves upon movement and nutrition of the limbs', *Proc. Roy. Soc.*, B, **57**, 481-488. [368]

MOUNTCASTLE, V. B., COVIAN, M. R., & HARRISON, C. R. (1952) 'The central representation of some forms of deep sensibility', *Res. Publ. Ass. nerv. ment. Dis.*, **30**, 339-370. [409]

— & HENNEMAN, E. (1949) 'Pattern of tactile representation in thalamus of cat', *J. Neurophysiol.*, **12**, 85-100. [405]

MOWRER, O. H., RUCH, T. C., & MILLER, N. E. (1936) 'The corneo-retinal potential difference as the basis of the galvanometric method of recording eye movements', *Amer. J. Physiol.*, **114**, 423-428. [309]

MULLER, H. R., & WEED, L. H. (1916) 'Notes on the falling reflex of cats', *Amer. J. Physiol.*, **40**, 373-379. [157]

MÜLLER, J. (1826) *Zur vergleichenden Physiologie des Gesichtssinnes des Menschen und der Thiere nebst einem Versuch über die Bewegungen der Augen und über den menschlichen Blick.* Knobloch. Leipzig. Pp. xxxii, 462. [35]

MURALT, A. VON (1947) 'Signal transmission in nerve', *Harvey Lectures*, **43**, 230-253. [6]

MURCHISON, C. (1929) Editor. *The foundations of experimental psychology.* Clark Univ. Press. [220, 453]

MURPHY, J. P., & BARENNE, J. G. DUSSER DE (1941) 'Thermocoagulation of motor cortex exclusive of its sixth layer', *J. Neurophysiol.*, **4**, 174-152. [247]

MUSKENS, L. J. J. (1914) 'An anatomico-physiological study of the posterior longitudinal bundle in its relation to forced movements', *Brain*, **36**, 352-426. [159]

MUSSEN, A. T. (1931) 'The cerebellum. Comparison of symptoms resulting from lesions of individual lobes with reactions of the same lobes to stimulation: a preliminary report', *Arch. Neurol. Psych.*, **25**, 702-722. [165]

MYERS, R. (1951) 'Dandy's striatal theory of "the centre of consciousness"', *Arch. Neurol. Psych.*, **65**, 659-671. [258]

MYERS, R. E. (1956) 'Function of corpus callosum in interocular transfer', *Brain*, **79**, 358-363. [352]

MYGIND, S. H. (1921) 'Head-nystagmus in human beings', *J. Laryngol. Otol.*, **36**, 72-78. [146]

NACHMANSON, D. (1953) 'Metabolism and function of the nerve cell', *Harvey Lectures*, **49**, 57-99. [6]

NAPIER, J. R. (1952) 'The return of pain sensibility in full thickness skin grafts', *Brain*, **75**, 147-166. [14]

NATHAN, P. W. (1947) 'On the pathenogenesis of causalgia in peripheral nerve injuries', *Brain*, **70**, 145-170. [24]

— (1953) 'Nervous discharge from small painless lesions in skin and muscle', *J. Neurol. Neurosurg. Psychiat.*, **16**, 144-151. [67]

— & SMITH, M. C. (1951) 'The centripetal pathway for the bladder and urethra within the spinal cord', *J. Neurol. Neurosurg. Psychiat.*, **14**, 262, 280. [100, 373]

NATHAN, P. W., & SMITH, M.C. (1955) 'The Babinski response: a review and new observations', *J. Neurol. Neurosurg. Psychiat.*, **18**, 250-259. [373]

— & TURNER, J. W. A. (1942) 'The efferent pathway for pupillary constriction', *Brain*, **65**, 343-351. [298]

NATHANSON, M., BERGMAN, P. S., & BENDER, M. B. (1953) 'Visual disturbances as a result of nystagmus on direct forward gaze', *Arch. Neurol. Psych.*, **69**, 427-435. [360]

NAUTA, W. H. J. (1946) 'Hypothalamic regulation of sleep in rats: an experimental study', *J. Neurophysiol.*, **9**, 285-316. [459]

NELSON, J. H. (1938) 'Anomalous trichromatism and its relation to normal trichromatism', *Proc. Physical Soc.*, **50**, 661-702. [306]

NETSKY, M. G. (1953) 'Syringomyelia', *Arch. Neurol. Psych.*, **70**, 741-777. [56]

NEWMAN, H. W., DOUPE, J., & WILKINS, R. W. (1939) 'Some observations on the nature of vibratory sensibility', *Brain*, **62**, 31-40. [55]

NIELSEN, J. M. (1946) *Agnosia, apraxia, aphasia: their value in cerebral localisation.* Hoeber. London. [440]

— (1947) 'The cortical motor pattern apraxias', *Res. Publ. Ass. nerv. ment. Dis.*, **27**, 565-581. [433]

— & THOMPSON, G. N. (1947) *The engrammes of psychiatry.* Blackwell. Oxford. [257]

NIKIFOROWSKY, P. M. (1912) 'Der Abluss der akustichen Energie aus dem Kopfe, wenn ein Schall durch die Stimme oder durch den Diapason-Vertex zugeleitet wird', *Z. f. Psychol.*, Abt. 2. Sinnesphysiol., **46**, 179-197. [265]

NOELL, W. K. (1952) 'Azide-sensitive potential difference across the eye bulb', *Amer. J. Physiol.*, **170**, 217-238. [309]

NORMAN, R. M. (1940) 'Primary degeneration of the granular layer of the cerebellum: an unusual form of familial cerebellar atrophy occurring in early life', *Brain*, **63**, 365-379. [184]

NORRIS, F. H., & GASTEIGER, E. L. (1955) 'Action potentials of single motor units in normal muscle', *E.E.G. Clin. Neurophysiol.*, **7**, 115-126. [18]

NYLÉN, C. O. (1931) 'A clinical study on positional nystagmus in cases of brain tumour', *Acta Otolaryngol.*, Suppl. 15. [141]

OBRADOR, S., & LORRAMENDI, M. H. (1950) 'Some observations on the brain rhythms after surgical removal of a cerebral hemisphere', *E.E.G. Clin. Neurophysiol.*, **2**, 143-146. [238]

O'CONNOR, J. M., & McCARTHY, B. F. (1952) 'The origins of sensations of heat and cold', *Brain*, **75**, 325-342. [46]

O'DONNELL, M. C. (1953) 'Hemi-facial spasm: an affection of the facial nerve', *Ann. Otol. Rhinol. Laryngol.*, **62**, 969-978. [225]

OGLE, K. N. (1950) *Binocular vision.* Saunders. Philadelphia. [339, 340]

— (1951) 'Optics and visual physiology'. Review of literature for 1949 and 1950. *A.M.A. Arch. Ophth.*, **45**, 684-703. [290, 345]

— (1952) 'Optics and visual physiology', *A.M.A. Arch. Ophth.*, **47**, 801-830. [345]

OLDFIELD, R. C., & ZANGWILL, O. L. (1942) 'Head's concept of the schema and its application in contemporary British psychology', *Brit. J. Psychol.*, **32**, 267-286. [430]

O'LEARY, J. L. (1941) 'Structure of the area striata of the cat', *J. Comp. Neurol.*, **75**, 131-164. [204]

OTTOSON, D., & SVAETICHIN, G. (1953) 'The electrical activity of the retinal receptor layer', *Acta Physiol. Scand.*, **29**, 31-39. [307]

OYER, H. J. (1955) 'Relative intelligibility of speech recorded simultaneously at the ear and mouth', *J. Acoust. Soc. Amer.*, **27**, 1207-1212. [265]

PACELLA, B. L., & BARRERA, S. E. (1940) 'Postural reflexes and grasp phenomena in infants', *J. Neurophysiol.*, **3**, 213-218. [152]

PALLIS, C. A. (1955) 'Impaired identification of faces and places with agnosia for colours', *J. Neurol. Neurosurg. Psychiat.*, **18**, 218-224. [441]

PANTIN, C. F. A. (1952) 'The elementary nervous system', *Proc. Roy. Soc.*, B, **140**, 147-168. [81]

PAPEZ, J. W. (1937) 'A proposed mechanism of emotion', *Arch. Neurol. Psych.*, **38**, 725-743. [284, 465]

PARKINS, W. M., JENSEN, J. M., & VARS, H. M. (1954) 'Brain cooling in the prevention of brain damage during periods of circulatory occlusion in dogs', *Ann. Surg.*, **140**, 284-289. [228]

PATERSON, A., & ZANGWILL, O. L. (1944) 'Disorders of visual space perception associated with lesions of the right cerebral hemisphere', *Brain*, **67**, 331-358. [357, 359]

PATON, W. D. M. (1951) 'The paralysis of autonomic ganglia, with special reference to the therapeutic effects of ganglion-blocking drugs', *Brit. med. J.*, **1**, 773-778. [106]

PATTON, H. D., RUCH, T. C., & WALKER, A. E. (1944) 'Experimental hypogeusia from Horsley-Clarke lesions of the thalamus in *Macaca mulatta*', *J. Neurophysiol.*, **7**, 171-184. [407]

PAVLOV, I. P. (1927) *Conditioned reflexes.* Translated by G. V. Anrep. Oxford Univ. Press. [386]

PEELE, T. L. (1944) 'Acute and chronic parietal lobe ablations in monkeys', *J. Neurophysiol.*, **7**, 269-286. [423]

PENDLETON, C. R. (1928) 'The cold receptor', *Amer. J. Psychol.*, **40**, 353-371. [40]

PENFIELD, W. (1952) 'Memory mechanisms', *Arch. Neurol. Psych.*, **67**, 178-198. [258, 427]

— (1954) 'Mechanisms of voluntary movement', *Brain*, **77**, 1-17. [389]

— & EVANS, J. (1935) 'The frontal lobe in man : a clinical study of maximum removals', *Brain*, **58**, 115-133. [475]

— & RASMUSSEN, T. (1950) *The cerebral cortex of man.* Macmillan. New York. [285, 351, 353, 378, 379, 384, 408, 416, 439]

— & ROBERTSON, J. S. M. (1943) 'Growth asymmetry due to lesions of the post-central cerebral cortex', *Arch. Neurol. Psych.*, **50**, 405-430. [423]

— & WELCH, K. (1951) 'The supplementary motor area of the cerebral cortex', *Arch. Neurol. Psych.*, **66**, 289-317. [384, 385]

2 M

PETERSON, E. W., MAGOUN, H. W., McCULLOCH, W. S., & LINDSLEY, D. B. (1949) 'Production of postural tremor', *J. Neurophysiol.*, **12**, 371-384. [394]

PFAFFMAN, C. (1941) 'Gustatory afferent impulses', *J. cell. comp. Physiol.*, **17**, 243-258. [405]

PHILLIPS, D. G. (1945) 'Investigation of vestibular function after head injury', *J. Neurol. Neurosurg. Psych.*, **8**, 79-100. [141]

PIÉRON, H. (1952) *The sensations, their functions, processes and mechanisms.* Translated by M. A. Pirenne and B. C. Abbott. Muller. London. [326, 410]

PINELLI, P., & BUCHTHAL, F. (1953) 'Muscle action potentials in experimental peripheral nerves paresis', *E.E.G. Clin. Neurophysiol.*, **5**, 589-593. [18]

PIKE, F. H. (1913) 'The general condition of the spinal vaso-motor paths in spinal shock', *Quart. J. Exp. Physiol.*, **7**, 1-29. [86]

PINKSTON, J., BARD, P., RIOCH, D. McK. (1934) 'The responses to changes in environmental temperature after removal of parts of the forebrain', *Amer. J. Physiol.*, **109**, 515-531. [449]

PIRENNE, M. H. (1948) *Vision and the eye.* Pilot Press. London. [293]

PITTS, R. F. (1946) 'Organisation of the respiratory center', *Physiol. Rev.*, **26**, 609-630. [84]

—— & BRONK, D. W. (1941) 'Excitability cycle of the hypothalamus-sympathetic neurone system', *Amer. J. Physiol.*, **135**, 504-522. [448]

PITTS, W., & McCULLOCH, W. S. (1947) 'How we know universals. The perception of auditory and visual forms', *Bull. Math. Biophysics*, **9**, 127-147. [236, 334, 355]

PLANCK, M. (1936) *The philosophy of physics.* Allen & Unwin. London. [111, 112]

POCHIN, E. E. (1938) 'Delay of pain perception in Tabes Dorsalis', *Clin. Sci.*, **3**, 191-196. [65]

POLLOCK, L. J. (1919) 'Supplementary muscle movements in peripheral nerve lesions', *Arch. Neurol. Psych.*, **2**, 518-531. [230]

—— & DAVIS, L. (1927) 'The influence of the cerebellum upon the reflex activities of the decerebrate animal', *Brain*, **50**, 277-312. [178]

—— —— (1930 *a*) 'The reflex activities of a decerebrate animal', *J. Comp. Neurol.*, **50**, 377-411. [126]

—— —— (1930 *b*) 'Muscle tone in Parkinson states', *Arch. Neurol. Psych.*, **23**, 303-319. [17, 154, 394]

—— —— (1932) 'Relation of modifications of muscle tone to interruption of certain anatomic pathways', *Arch. Neurol. Psych.*, **28**, 586-602. [111]

POLYAK, S. L. (1941) *The retina.* Chicago Univ. Press. [295, 311]

POOL, J. L. (1949) 'Topectomy—the treatment of mental illness by frontal gyrectomy or bilateral subtotal ablation of frontal cortex', *Lancet*, II, 776-781. [473]

PORTER, T. C. (1902) 'Contributions to the study of flicker. Paper 2', *Proc. Roy. Soc.*, **70**, 313-329. [317]

PRIBRAM, K. H., & FULTON, J. F. (1954) 'An experimental critique of the effects of anterior cingulate ablation in monkey', *Brain,* **77,** 34-44. [466]

PRICE, F. W. (1946) Editor. *A textbook of the practice of medicine.* 7th Ed. Oxford Univ. Press. [474]

PRITCHARD, E. A. B. (1929) 'The significance of some variations in the knee jerk in diseases of the central nervous system', *Brain,* **52,** 359-423. [123]

— (1929) 'Electromyographic studies of voluntary movements in paralysis agitans', *Brain,* **52,** 510-528. [428]

PROSSER, C. L. (1950) Editor. *Comparative animal physiology.* Saunders. London. [309]

PUMPHREY, R. J. (1950) 'Hearing', *S.E.B. Symposium,* **4,** 1-18. [135]

PURDY, D. M. (1934) 'Tactual space perception in translocated tissue', *J. Gen. Psychol.,* **10,** 227-229. [223]

PURVES-STEWART, J. (1945) *The diagnosis of nervous diseases.* 9th Ed. Arnold. London. [20, 21, 370, 447, 449]

PUTNAM, T. J. (1940) 'Treatment of unilateral paralysis agitans by section of the lateral pyramidal tract', *Arch. Neurol. Psych.,* **44,** 950-976. [392]

QUINAN, C. (1930) 'The principal sinistral types', *Arch. Neurol. Psych.,* **24,** 35-47. [343]

QUIX, F. H. (1925) 'The function of the vestibular organ and the clinical examination of the otolith apparatus', *J. Laryngol. Otol.,* **40,** 425-443. [138, 139, 140]

RADEMAKER, G. G. J. (1935) *Réactions labyrinthiques et équilibre. L'ataxie labyrinthique.* Masson. Paris. [151]

— (1947) 'On the lengthening and shortening reactions and their occurrence in man', *Brain,* **70,** 109-126. [124]

— & TER BRAAK, J. W. G. (1936) 'Das Umdrehen der fallenden Katze in der Luft', *Acta Oto-laryngol.,* **23,** 313-343. [157]

— — (1948) 'On the central mechanism of some optic reactions', *Brain,* **71,** 48-76. [331, 332]

RÅDMARK, K. (1944) 'Tipping reactions in cases of vertigo after head injury', *Acta Oto-laryngol.,* Suppl. **52.** [141]

RANSON, S. W. (1939) 'Somnolence caused by hypothalamic lesions in the monkey', *Arch. Neurol. Psych.,* **41,** 1-23. [459]

— & CLARK, S. L. (1953) *The anatomy of the nervous system. Its development and function.* 9th Ed. Saunders. London. [172, 184, 408]

RASMUSSEN, G. L. (1946) 'The olivary peduncle and other fibre projections of the superior olivary complex', *J. Comp. Neurol.,* **84,** 141-220. [276]

RATCLIFF, F. (1952) 'The rôle of physiological nystagmus in monocular acuity', *J. Exp. Psychol.,* **43,** 163-172. [322]

RAYLEIGH, LORD (1926) *Theory of sound.* 2nd Ed. Vol. 2, 432. Macmillan. London. [260]

REDLICH, F. C., CALLAHAN, A., & MENDELSON, R. H. (1946) 'Electro-encephalographic changes after eye opening and visual stimulation', *Yale J. Biol. Med.,* **18,** 367-376. [236]

REESE, W. G., DOSS, R., & GANTT, W. H. (1953) 'Autonomic responses in differential diagnosis of organic and psychogenic psychoses', *Arch. Neurol. Psych.*, **70**, 778-793. [222]

RENARD, G., & MASSONNET-NAUX, MME (1951) 'La Synergie pupillaire à la convergence', *Arch. d'Ophtalmol.*, N.S., **11**, 137-145. [297]

RENSHAW, B., FORBES, A., & MORISON, B. R. (1940) 'Activity of iso-cortex and hippocampus : electrical studies with micro-electrodes', *J. Neurophysiol.*, **3**, 74-105. [245]

RICHTER, C. P. (1929) 'Nervous control of the electrical resistance of the skin', *Johns Hopk. Hosp. Bull.*, **45**, 56-74. [481]

— (1943) 'Total self-regulatory functions in animals and human beings', *Harvey Lectures*, **38**, 63-103. [452, 457]

— & BARTEMEIER, L. H. (1926) 'Decerebrate rigidity in the sloth', *Brain*, **49**, 207-225. [126]

— & WOODRUFF, B. G. (1942) 'Facial patterns of electrical skin resistance. Their relation to sleep, external temperature, hair distribution, sensory dermatomes and skin disease', *Johns Hopk. Hosp. Bull.*, **70**, 442-459. [405]

— — (1945) 'Lumbar sympathetic dermatomes in man determined by the electrical skin resistance method', *J. Neurophysiol.*, **8**, 323-338. [96]

— — & EATON, B. C. (1943) 'Hand and foot patterns of low electrical skin resistance : their anatomical and neurological significance', *J. Neurophysiol.*, **6**, 417-424. [481]

RIDDOCH, G. (1917 a) 'Dissociation of visual perceptions due to occipital injuries, with especial reference to appreciation of movement', *Brain*, **40**, 15-57. [360]

— (1917 b) 'The reflex functions of the completely divided spinal cord in man compared with that associated with less severe lesions', *Brain*, **40**, 264-402. [374]

— (1941) 'Phantom limbs and body shape', *Brain*, **64**, 197-222. [425]

— & BUZZARD, E. F. (1921) 'Reflex movements and postural reactions in quadriplegia and hemiplegia, with especial reference to those of the upper limb', *Brain*, **44**, 397-489. [98, 390]

RIESEN, A. H. (1947) 'The development of visual perception in man and chimpanzee', *Science*, **106**, 107-108. [332, 355]

RIOCH, D. McK., & BRENNER, C. (1938) 'Experiments on the corpus striatum and rhinencephalon', *J. Comp. Neurol.*, **68**, 491-507. [454]

ROBERTS, F. (1916) 'Degeneration of muscle following injury', *Brain*, **39**, 297-347. [20]

ROBINSON, V. (1946) *Victory over pain. A history of anesthesia.* Schuman. New York. [257]

ROGER, A., ROSSI, G. F., & ZIRONDOLI, A. (1956) 'Le Rôle des afférences des nerfs crâniens dans le maintien de l'état vigile de la préparation "encéphale isolé"', *E.E.G. Clin. Neurophysiol.*, **8**, 1-13. [253]

ROHRACHER, H. (1935) 'Ueber subjective Lichterscheinungen bei Reizung mit Wechselströmen', *Z. Sinnesphysiol.*, **66**, 164-181. [351]

ROMANES, G. J. (1953) In *The spinal cord*. Ciba Symposium. Churchill. London. [91]

ROSE, J. E. (1952) 'Cortical connections of the reticular complex of the thalamus', *Res. Publ. Ass. nerv. ment. Dis.*, **30**, 454-479. [246]

—— & WOOLSEY, C. N. (1943) 'A study of thalamo-cortical relations in the rabbit', *Johns Hopk. Hosp. Bull.*, **73**, 65-128. [245]

ROSETT, J. (1924) 'The experimental production of rigidity, of abnormal involuntary movements and of abnormal states of consciousness in man', *Brain*, **47**, 293-335. [26]

ROSS, D. A. (1936) 'Electrical studies on the frog's labyrinth', *J. Physiol.*, **86**, 117-146. [138, 143]

ROSS, J. (1888) 'On the segmental distribution of sensory disorders', *Brain*, **10**, 333-361. [70]

ROTHMAN, S. (1954) *Physiology and biochemistry of the skin*. Univ. Chicago Press. [20]

RUCH, T. C., FULTON, J. F., GERMAN, W. J. (1938) 'Sensory discrimination in monkey, chimpanzee and man after lesions of the parietal lobe', *Arch. Neurol. Psych.*, **39**, 919-938. [424]

—— & SHENKIN, H. A. (1943) 'The relation of area 13 on orbital surface of frontal lobes to hyperactivity and hyperphagia in monkey', *J. Neurophysiol.*, **6**, 349-360. [480]

RUSHTON, W. A. H. (1951) 'A theory of the effects of fibre size in medullated nerve', *J. Physiol.*, **115**, 101-122. [16]

RUSSEL, C. K. (1931) 'The syndrome of the brachium conjunctivum and the tractus spinothalamicus', *Arch. Neurol. Psych.*, **25**, 1003-1010. [195]

RUSSELL, J. S. R. (1894) 'Experimental researches into the functions of the cerebellum', *Phil. Trans.*, B, **185**, part 2, 819-861. [165, 167, 196]

—— (1897) 'Phenomena resulting from interruption of afferent and efferent tracts of the cerebellum', *Phil. Trans.*, B, **188**, 103-133. [168]

RUSSELL, W. R. (1945) 'Transient disturbances following gun-shot wounds of the head', *Brain*, **68**, 79-97. [411]

RYLANDER, G. (1939) *Personality changes after operations on the frontal lobes.* Munksgaard. Copenhagen. [475]

SALOMONSON, J. K. A. (1920) 'Tonus and the reflexes', *Brain*, **43**, 369-389. [123]

SANDERS, F. K., & WHITTERIDGE, D. (1946) 'Conduction velocity and myelin thickness in regenerating nerve fibres', *J. Physiol.*, **105**, 152-174. [16]

SANDIFER, P. H. (1946) 'Anosognosia and disorders of body scheme', *Brain*, **69**, 122-137. [429]

SAPIRSTEIN, M. R., HERMAN, R. C., & WECHSLER, I. S. (1938) 'Mechanisms of after contraction', *Arch. Neurol. Psych.*, **40**, 300-312. [423]

SARGENT, F. (1950) 'Value of electromyography in clinical neurology', *Lancet*, I, 937-943. [18, 31]

SARNOFF, S. J., & ARROWOOD, J. G. (1947) 'Differential spinal block. III. The block of cutaneous and stretch reflexes in the presence of un-impaired position sense', *J. Neurophysiol.*, **10**, 205-210. [99]

— SARNOFF, L. C., & WHITTENBERGER, J. L. (1951) 'Electrophrenic respiration. VII. The motor point of the phrenic nerve in relation to external stimulation', *Surg. Gyn. Obst.*, **93**, 190-196. [21]

SCHÄFER, E. P. (1886) 'On the rhythm of muscular response to volitional impulse in man', *J. Physiol.*, **7**, 111-117. [365]

SCHALTENBRAND, G., & COBB, S. (1930) 'Clinical and anatomical studies on two cats without neocortex', *Brain*, **53**, 449-488. [277]

SCHARRER, B., & SHARRER, E. (1944) 'Neurosecretion. VI : A comparison between the intercerebralis-cardiacum-allatum system of the insects and the hypothalamo-hypophyseal system of the vertebrates', *Biol. Bull. Woods Hole*, **87**, 242-251. [451]

SCHILLER, F. (1947) 'Aphasia studied in patients with missile wounds', *J. Neurol. Neurosurg. Psychiat.*, **10**, 183-197. [440]

— (1952) 'Consciousness reconsidered', *Arch. Neurol. Psych.*, **67**, 199-227. [98, 256]

SCHLOSBERG, H. (1928) 'A study of the conditioned patella reflex', *J. Exp. Psychol.*, **11**, 468-498. [222]

SCHMIDT, F. O., & BEAR, R. S. (1939) 'The ultra structure of the nerve axon sheath', *Biol. Rev.*, **14**, 27-50. [10]

SCHOUTEN, J. F., & ORNSTEIN, L. S. (1939) 'Measurements on direct and indirect adaptation by means of a binocular method', *J. Opt. Soc. Amer.*, **29**, 168-182. [296]

SCHREINER, L., & KLING, A. (1953) 'Behavioural changes following rhinen-cephalic injury in cat', *J. Neurophysiol.*, **16**, 643-659. [466]

SCHULTZER, P., & LEBEL, H. (1939) 'Spontaneous hyperventilation tetany', *Acta Med. Scand.*, **101**, 303-314. [26]

SCHWARTZ, H. G. (1937) 'Effect of experimental lesions of the cortex on the "psychogalvanic reflex" in the cat', *Arch. Neurol. Psych.*, **38**, 308-320. [482]

— & WEDDELL, G. (1938) 'Observations on the pathways transmitting the sensations of taste', *Brain*, **61**, 99-115. [407]

SCOTT, M., & LENNON, H. C. (1940) 'Decerebrate tonic extensor convulsions as a sign of occlusion of the basilar artery', *Arch. Neurol. Psych.*, **44**, 1102-1108. [128]

SCRIPTURE, E. W. (1916) 'Records of speech in disseminated sclerosis', *Brain*, **39**, 455-477. [442]

— (1925) 'Cases of epilepsy, general paralysis and disseminated sclerosis, to illustrate speech defects', *Brain*, **48**, 130-131. [442]

SEARLE, L. V., & TAYLOR, F. V. (1948) 'Studies of tracking behaviour. I : Rate and time characteristics of simple corrective movements', *J. Exp. Psychol.*, **38**, 615-631. [190]

SEASHORE, C. E. (1908) *Elementary experiments in psychology.* Holt. New York. [418]

SELLING, L. S. (1939) 'Abnormalities of the eye and their significance in traffic court cases', *J.A.M.A.*, **113**, 994-997. [294]

SENDERS, V. L. (1948) 'The physiological basis of visual acuity', *Psychol. Bull.*, **45**, 465-490. [320]

SHARIFF, G. A. (1953) 'Cell counts in the primate cerebral cortex', *J. Comp. Neurol.*, **98**, 381-400. [201]

SHARRARD, W. J. W. (1955) 'The distribution of permanent paralysis in the lower limb in poliomyelitis', *J. Bone and Joint Surg.*, **37**, B, 540-558. [90]

SHERRINGTON, C. S. (1898 a) 'Experiments in examination of the peripheral distribution of the fibres of the posterior roots of some spinal nerves', *Phil. Trans.*, B, **190**, 45-186. [57]

— (1898 b) 'Decerebrate rigidity and reflex co-ordination of movements', *J. Physiol.*, **22**, 319-332. [127, 128]

— (1900) in *Schafer's textbook of physiology*, Vol. 2. [34, 421]

— (1906) *The integrative action of the nervous system.* Constable. London. [319, 346, 377, 378, 399]

— (1909) 'On plastic tonus and proprioceptive reflexes', *Quart. J. Exp. Physiol.*, **2**, 109-156. [123]

— (1913) 'Reflex inhibition in the co-ordination of movements and postures', *Quart. J. Exp. Physiol.*, **6**, 251-310. [178]

— (1918) 'Observations on the sensual rôle of the proprioceptive nerve supply of the extrinsic ocular muscles', *Brain*, **41**, 332-343. [324]

— (1931) 'Quantitative management of contraction in lowest level co-ordination', *Brain*, **54**, 1-28. [88]

— (1939) *Selected writings.* Edited by Denny-Brown. Hamish Hamilton. London. [91]

— (1951) *Man on his nature.* The Gifford Lectures. Cambridge Univ. Press. Second edition reprinted in Penguin Books 1955. [12, 104, 111, 333]

SHORE, L. E. (1892) 'A contribution to our knowledge of taste sensations', *J. Physiol.*, **13**, 191-217. [406]

SHURRAGER, P. S., & CULLER, E. (1940) 'Conditioning in the spinal dog', *J. Exp. Psychol.*, **26**, 133-159. [229]

SIMONSEN, E., & BROZEK, J. (1952) 'Flicker fusion frequency. Background and applications', *Physiol. Rev.*, **32**, 349-378. [319]

SINCLAIR, A. H. H. (1948) 'Developmental aphasia : also known as con-genital word blindness and sometimes referred to as alexia or dyslexia', *Brit. J. Ophthalmol.*, **32**, 522-531. [359]

SINCLAIR, D. C. (1949) 'The remote reference of pain aroused in the skin', *Brain*, **72**, 364-372. [74]

— & HINSHAW, J. R. (1951) 'Sensory phenomena in experimental nerve block', *Quart. J. Exper. Psychol.*, **3**, 49-72. [65]

— WEDDELL, G., & ZANDER, E. (1952) 'The relationship of cutaneous sensibility to neurohistology in the human pinna', *J. Anat.*, **86**, 402-411. [40]

SISSON, E. D. (1938) 'Voluntary control of accommodation', *J. Gen. Psychol.*, **18**, 195-198. [336]

SITTIG, O. (1925) 'A clinical study of sensory Jacksonian fits', *Brain*, **48**, 233-254. [416]

SJÖQUIST, O., & WEINSTEIN, E. A. (1942) 'The effect of section of the medial lemniscus on proprioceptive functions in chimpanzees and monkeys', *J. Neurophysiol.*, **5**, 69-74. [193, 424]

SKOLNICK, A. (1940) 'The rôle of eye movements in the autokinetic phenomenon', *J. Exp. Psychol.*, **26**, 373-393. [325]

SLINGER, R. T., & HORSLEY, SIR V. (1906) 'Upon the orientation of points in space by the muscular, arthropodial, and tactile senses of the upper limbs in normal individuals and in blind persons', *Brain*, **29**, 1-27. [409, 410]

SLOANE, P., PERSKY, A., & SALTZMAN, M. (1943) 'Midbrain deafness', *Arch. Neurol. Psych.*, **49**, 237-243. [276]

SMITH, C. P. (1952) 'The analysis and automatic recognition of speech sounds', *Electronic Engineering*, **24**, 368-372. [435]

SMITH, K. U., & AKELAITIS, A. J. (1942) 'Studies on the corpus callosum, (1) Laterality in behaviour and bilateral motor organisation in man before and after section of the corpus callosum', *Arch. Neurol. Psych.*, **47**, 519-543. [388]

— & BRIDGMAN, M. (1943) 'The neural mechanisms of movement, vision and optic nystagmus', *J. Exp. Psychol.*, **33**, 165-187. [331]

SMITH, W. K. (1938) 'The representation of respiratory movements in the cerebral cortex', *J. Neurophysiol.*, **1**, 54-68. [480]

— (1945) 'The functional significance of the rostral cingular cortex as revealed by its response to electrical excitation', *J. Neurophysiol.*, **8**, 241-255. [465, 466]

SMYTH, G. E., & STERN, K. (1938) 'Tumours of the thalamus—a clinico-pathological study', *Brain*, **61**, 339-374. [412]

SNIDER, R. S. (1950) 'Recent contributions to the anatomy and physiology of the cerebellum', *Arch. Neurol. Psych.*, **64**, 196-219. [193, 194]

— (1952) 'Interrelations of cerebellum and brain stem', *Res. Pub. Ass. nerv. ment. Dis.*, **30**, 267-281. [175, 181]

— & ELDRED, E. (1951) 'Electro-anatomical studies on cerebro-cerebellar connections in the cat', *J. Comp. Neurol.*, **95**, 1-16. [182]

— & STOWELL, A. (1944) 'Receiving areas of the tactile, auditory and visual system in the cerebellum', *J. Neurophysiol.*, **7**, 331-357. [180]

SOLANDT, D. Y., & MAGLADERY, J. W. (1940) 'Relation of atrophy to fibrillation in denervated muscle', *Brain*, **63**, 255-263. [21]

SOUTHALL, J. P. C. (1937) *Introduction to physiological optics.* Oxford Univ. Press. [291, 295, 337]

SPALDING, D. (1954) 'Instinct with original observations on young animals', *Brit. J. Anim. Behav.*, **2**, 2-11. [329]

SPALDING, J. M. K. (1952 a) 'Wounds of the visual pathway. I : The visual radiation', *J. Neurol. Neurosurg. Psychiat.*, **15**, 99-109. [301, 302]

SPALDING, J. M. K. (1952 b) 'Wounds of the visual pathway. II : The striate cortex', *J. Neurol. Neurosurg. Psychiat.*, **15**, 169-183. [346]

SPENCER, H. (1900) *First principles*. 6th Ed. Reprinted 1937. Thinker's Library. Watts. London. [78, 310]

SPERRY, R. W. (1945) 'The problem of central nervous reorganisation after nerve regeneration and muscle transposition', *Quart. Rev. Biol.*, **20**, 311-369. [223, 225, 227]

— (1947 a) 'Effect of crossing nerves to antagonistic limb muscles in the monkey', *Arch. Neurol. Psych.*, **58**, 452-473. [224]

— (1947 b) 'Cerebral regulation of motor co-ordination in monkeys following multiple transections of sensori-motor cortex', *J. Neurophysiol.*, **10**, 275-294. [386, 387]

SPIEGEL, E. A., & FREED, H. (1951) 'Evaluation of the results of thalamotomy and other surgical procedures for the relief of psychoses', *Surg. Gyn. Obst.*, **92**, 615-617. [473]

— MILLER, H. R., & OPPENHEIMER, M. J. (1940) 'Forebrain and rage reactions', *J. Neurophysiol.*, **3**, 538-548. [466]

— & SCALA, N. P. (1942) 'Positional nystagmus in cerebellar lesions', *J. Neurophysiol.*, **5**, 247-260. [173]

— & WYCIS, H. T. (1954) 'Ansotomy in paralysis agitans', *Arch. Neurol. Psych.*, **71**, 598-614. [392]

SPILLANE, J. D. (1938) 'Olfactory alloaesthesia', *Brain*, **61**, 393-401. [213]

— (1939) 'Clinical investigation of olfactory function in brain tumour patients', *Brain*, **62**, 213-221. [213]

SPILLER, W. G. (1924) 'Ophthalmoplegia internuclearis anterior : a case with necropsy', *Brain*, **47**, 345-357. [159]

SPRAGUE, J. M. (1953) 'Spinal "border cells" and their rôle in postural mechanism (Schiff-Sherrington phenomenon)', *J. Neurophysiol.*, **16**, 464-474. [158]

— & CHAMBERS, W. W. (1953) 'Regulation of posture in intact and decerebrate cat. I : Cerebellum, reticular formation, vestibular nuclei', *J. Neurophysiol.*, **16**, 451-463. [128, 129, 175]

SPURWAY, H., & HALDANE, J. B. S. (1953) 'The comparative ethology of vertebrate breathing. I : Breathing in newts, with a general survey', *Behaviour*, **6**, 8-34. [469]

STÄMPFLI, R. (1954) 'Saltatory conduction in nerve', *Physiol. Revs.*, **34**, 101-112. [10]

STARLING, E. H. (1941) *Principles of human physiology*. Edited and revised by C. Lovatt Evans. 8th Ed. Churchill. London. [343]

STARR, I. (1946) 'The ballistocardiograph—an instrument for clinical research and routine clinical diagnosis', *Harvey Lectures*, **42**, 194-220. [138]

STARZL, T. E., & MAGOUN, H. W. (1951) 'Organisation of the diffuse thalamic projection system', *J. Neurophysiol.*, **14**, 133-146. [249]

— TAYLOR, C. W., & MAGOUN, H. W. (1951) 'Collateral afferent excitation of reticular formation of brain stem', *J. Neurophysiol.*, **14**, 479-496. [252, 400]

STAVRAKY, G. W. (1943) 'Some aspects of the effects of intravenous injections of acetylcholine on the central nervous system', *Trans. Roy. Soc. Canad.*, Section V, 127-140. [87]

STEER, C. M. (1954) 'The electrical activity of the human uterus in normal and abnormal labor', *Amer. J. Obst. Gyn.*, **68**, 867-890. [103]

STEIN, L. (1942) *Speech and voice.* Methuen. London. [442]

STERN, K. (1934) 'Note on the nucleus magnocellularis and its efferent pathway in man', *Brain*, **61**, 284-289. [160]

STEVENS, S. S. (1951) Editor. *Handbook of experimental psychology.* Wiley. New York. Chapman & Hall. London. [185, 194, 261, 268, 269, 274, 281, 328, 391, 407, 436, 437]

—   & DAVIS, H. (1938) *Hearing.* Chapman & Hall. London. [260, 272]

—   & NEWMAN, E. B. (1934) 'The localisation of pure tones', *Proc. Nat. Acad. Sci.*, **20**, 593-596. [273]

STEWART, T. G., & HOLMES, G. (1904) 'Symptomatology of cerebellar tumours : a study of forty cases', *Brain*, **27**, 522-591. [168]

STILES, W. S. (1939) 'The directional sensitivity of the retina and the spectral sensitivity of the rods and cones', *Proc. Roy. Soc.*, B, **127**, 64-105. [300]

STONES, L. S. (1953) 'Normal and reversed vision in transplanted eyes', *A.M.A. Arch. Ophth.*, **49**, 28-35. [342]

STRATTON, G. M. (1903) *Experimental psychology and its bearing upon culture.* Macmillan. London. [327, 328, 354]

STRAUSS, E. W. (1952) 'The upright posture', *Psychiatric Quarterly*, **26**, 529-561. [162]

STRONG, O. S. (1926) 'Unsolved problems suggested by cerebellar connections and cerebellar histology', *Res. Publ. Ass. nerv. ment. Dis.*, **6**, 3-36. [180]

STROUD, J. (1950) *Cybernetics*, edited by H. von Foerster. Macy Foundation. New York. [320, 331]

SUNDERLAND, S. (1940) 'The projection of the cerebral cortex on the pons and cerebellum in the macaque monkey', *J. Anat.*, **74**, 201-226. [181]

—   (1950) 'Capacity of re-innervated muscles to function efficiently after prolonged denervation', *Arch. Neurol. Psych.*, **64**, 755-771. [22]

SUGAR, O., & BUCY, P. C. (1951) 'Post-herpetic trigeminal neuralgia', *Arch. Neurol. Psych.*, **65**, 131-145. [412]

SYMONDS, SIR C. (1953) 'Aphasia', *J. Neurol. Neurosurg. Psychiat.*, **16**, 1-6. [436]

SZENTAGATHAI, J. (1950) 'The elementary vestibulo-ocular reflex arc', *J. Neurophysiol.*, **13**, 395-407. [159]

TAIT, J. (1926) 'Ablation experiments on the labyrinth of frogs', *Arch. Otolaryngol.*, **4**, 281-295. [150]

—   (1932) 'Is all hearing cochlea ?', *Ann. Otol. Rhinol. Laryngol.*, **41**, 681-705. [260]

—   & McNALLY, W. J. (1925) 'Rotation and acceleration experiments, mainly on frogs', *Amer. J. Physiol.*, **75**, 140-154. [137]

TAIT, J., & MCNALLY, W. J. (1934) 'Some features of the action of the utricular maculae (and of the associated action of the semi-circular canals) of the frog', *Phil. Trans.*, B, **224**, 241-286. [139]

TARCHANOFF, I. (1895) 'Experiments on normal sleep', summarised in leading article (unsigned), *Lancet*, I, 1069-1070. [459]

TASAKI, I. (1953) *Nervous transmission.* Thomas. Springfield, Ill. [9]

— (1954) 'Nerve impulses in individual auditory nerve fibres of guinea-pig', *J. Neurophysiol.*, **17**, 97-122. [272, 275]

— & FERNÁNDEZ, C. (1952) 'Modification of cochlear microphonics and action potentials by KCl solution and by direct currents', *J. Neurophysiol.*, **15**, 497-513. [271]

TAYLOR, F. V., & BIRMINGHAM, H. P. (1948) 'Studies of tracking behaviour, (2) The acceleration pattern of quick manual corrective responses', *J. Exp. Psychol.*, **38**, 783-795. [362]

TEASDALL, R. D., & STAVRAKY, G. W. (1953) 'Responses of deafferented spinal neurones to corticospinal impulses', *J. Neurophysiol.*, **16**, 367-375. [88]

TEUBER, H.-L., & BENDER, M. B. (1951) 'Neuro-ophthalmology: the oculo-motor system', *Progress in Neurol. & Psychiat.*, **6**, 148-178. [335]

THEOBALD, G. W. (1949) 'The rôle of the cerebral cortex in the apper-ception of pain', *Lancet*, II, 41-47. [92]

THERMAN, P. O. (1938) 'The neurophysiology of the retina in the light of chemical methods of modifying its excitability', *Acta Soc. Sci.*, Fenn. Nova Series, B, Tom II, No. 1, 1-74. [307]

THIBAULT, C. (1949) 'Action de la lumière blanche et monochromatique sur la posture des poissons téléostéens. Utilisations de cette action pour l'étude de la vision', *Arch. de Sci. Physiol.*, **3**, 101-124. [157]

THOMAS, J. M. (1932) 'Post-hemiplegic athetosis', *Arch. Neurol. Psych.*, **28**, 1091-1103. [395]

THOMASEN, E. (1948) *Myotonia.* Universitetsforlaget i Aarhus. [31]

THOMPSON, A. P. D. (1951) 'Relation of retinal stimulation to oestrus in the ferret', *J. Physiol.*, **113**, 425-433. [307]

THOMPSON, J. M., WOOLSEY, C. N., & TALBOT, S. A. (1950) 'Visual areas I and II of cerebral cortex of rabbit', *J. Neurophysiol.*, **13**, 277-288. [353]

THOMSON, L. C. (1953) 'The localisation of function in the rabbit retina', *J. Physiol.*, **119**, 191-209. [313]

THORBURN, W. (1887) 'Cases of injury to the cervical region of the spinal cord', *Brain*, **9**, 510-543. [90]

THULIN, C. (1953) 'Motor effects from stimulation of the vestibular nuclei of the reticular formation', *Acta Physiol. Scand.*, **28**, Suppl. 103. [158]

TILNEY, F. (1929) 'A comparative sensory analysis of Helen Keller and Laura Bridgman. II: Its bearing on the further development of the human brain', *Arch. Neurol. Psych.*, **21**, 1237-1269. [208, 417]

— & PIKE, F. H. (1925) 'Muscular co-ordination experimentally studied in its relation to the cerebellum', *Arch. Neurol. Psych.*, **13**, 289-334. [231]

TINBERGEN, N. (1953) *Social behaviour in animals.* Methuen. London. [433, 479]

TOMAN, J. (1941) 'Flicker potentials and the alpha rhythm in man', *J. Neurophysiol.*, 4, 51-61. [320]

TOMAN, J. E. P., & OSTER, R. H. (1942) 'Muscle potentials accompanying a single volitional twitch', *Amer. J. Physiol.*, 136, 743-745. [365]

TOMITA, T., & FUNAISHI, A. (1952) 'Intraretinal action potentials with low resistance micro-electrodes', *J. Neurophysiol.*, 15, 75-84. [307]

TOW, P. M., & ARMSTRONG, R. W. (1954) 'Anterior cingulectomy in schizophrenia and other psychotic disorders : clinical results', *J. Ment. Sci.*, 100, 46-61. [466]

TOWBIN, E. J. (1949) 'Gastric distension as a factor in the satiation of thirst in esophagostomised dogs', *Amer. J. Physiol.*, 159, 533-541. [452]

TOWER, S. S. (1940) 'Pyramidal lesion in the monkey', *Brain*, 63, 36-90. [373, 375]

— BODIAN, D., & HOWE, H. (1941) 'Isolation of intrinsic and motor mechanisms of the monkey's spinal cord', *J. Neurophysiol.*, 4, 388-397. [86]

TRAQUAIR, H. M. (1927) *An introduction to clinical perimetry.* Kimpton. London. [292]

TRAVIS, A. M. (1955) 'Neurological deficiencies after ablation of the pre-central motor area in *Macaca mulatta*' and 'Neurological deficiencies following supplementary motor area lesions in *Macaca mullata*', *Brain*, 78, 155-173 and 174-198. [385]

TUMARKIN, I. A. (1936) 'Some observations on the function of the laby-rinth', *Proc. Roy. Soc. Med.*, 30, 599-610. [134, 147]

TUNTURI, A. R. (1950) 'Physiological determination of the arrangement of the afferent connections to the middle ectosylvian area in the dog', *Amer. J. Physiol.*, 162, 489-502. [282]

TURNER, R. S., & GERMAN, W. J. (1941) 'Functional anatomy of the brachium pontis', *J. Neurophysiol.*, 4, 196-206. [168, 187]

TURNER, W. A., & CRITCHLEY, M. (1925) 'Respiratory disorders in epidemic encephalitis', *Brain*, 48, 72-104. [84]

TUSTIN, A. (1950) 'Automatic control systems', *Nature*, 166, 845-846. [112]

TYLER, D. B., & BARD, P. (1949) 'Motion sickness', *Physiol. Rev.*, 29, 311-369. [131]

UPRUS, V., GAYLOR, J. B., & CARMICHAEL, A. E. (1934) 'Localised abnormal flushing and sweating on eating', *Brain*, 57, 443-453. [407]

— — — (1935) 'Shivering : a clinical study with especial reference to the afferent and efferent pathways', *Brain*, 58, 220-232. [449]

UTTLEY, A. M. (1954) 'The classification of signals in the nervous system', *E.E.G. Clin. Neurophysiol.*, 6, 479-494. [231]

VERNEY, E. B. (1947) 'The anti-diuretic hormone and the factors which determine its release', *Proc. Roy. Soc.*, B, 135, 25-106. [450]

VERNON, M. D. (1930) 'The movements of the eyes in reading', *M.R.C. Special Report*, No. 148. [356]

VERZEANO, M., & CALMA, I. (1954) 'Unit activity in spindle bursts', *J. Neurophysiol.*, **17**, 417-428. [246]

VIETS, H. (1920) 'Relation of the form of the knee-jerk and patellar clonus to muscle tonus', *Brain*, **43**, 269-289. [123]

VILSTRUP, G., & VILSTRUP, T. (1952) 'Does the utricular otolith membrane move on postural changes of the head ?', *Ann. Otol. Rhinol. Laryngol.*, **61**, 189-197. [138]

VILSTRUP, T. (1950) 'Studies on the completed structure and mechanism of the cupula', *Ann. Otol. Rhinol. Laryngol.*, **59**, 46-71. [142]

VINCE, M. A. (1948) 'Corrective movements in a pursuit task', *Quart. J. Exp. Psychol.*, **1**, 85-103. [366]

VORIS, H. C., & ADSON, A. W. (1935) 'Tumours of the corpus callosum', *Arch. Neurol. Psych.*, **34**, 965-972. [466]

— & LANDES, H. E. (1940) 'Cystometric studies in cases of neurologic disease', *Arch. Neurol. Psych.*, **44**, 118-139. [102]

WAGMAN, I. H. (1954) 'Reflex time during growth considered in relation to internodal length and conduction velocity', *J. Neurophysiol.*, **17**, 66-71. [222]

— & GULLBERG, J. E. (1942) 'The relationship between monochromatic light and pupil diameter. The low intensity visibility curve as measured by pupillary measurements', *Amer. J. Physiol.*, **137**, 769-778. [296]

WALKER, A. E. (1937) 'The projection of the medial geniculate body to the cerebral cortex in the macaque monkey', *J. Anat.*, **71**, 319-331. [282]

— (1938 *a*) *The primate thalamus*. Univ. Chicago Press. [246, 283, 401]

— (1938 *b*) 'An oscillographic study of the cerebello-cerebral relationships', *J. Neurophysiol.*, **1**, 16-23. [192]

— (1940) 'A cytoarchitectural study of the prefrontal areas of the macaque monkey', *J. Comp. Neurol.*, **73**, 59-86. [479]

— (1946) 'The somatic functions of the central nervous system', *Ann. Rev. Physiol.*, **8**, 421-446. [382]

— (1949) *Post-traumatic epilepsy*. Blackwell. Oxford. [233]

— & BOTTERELL, E. H. (1937) 'The syndrome of the superior cerebellar peduncle in the monkey', *Brain*, **60**, 329-353. [194, 195]

— & JOHNSON, H. C. (1948) 'Normal and pathological after-discharge from the frontal cortex', *Res. Publ. Ass. nerv. ment. Dis.*, **27**, 460-475. [232, 233]

— KOLLROSS, J. J., & CASE, T. J. (1944) 'The physiological basis of concussion', *J. Neurosurg.*, **1**, 103-115. [258]

WALL, P. D., REMOND, A. G., & DOBSON, R. L. (1953) 'Studies on the mechanism of the action of visual afferents on motor cortex excitability', *E.E.G. Clin. Neurophysiol.*, **5**, 385-393. [353]

WALLER, A. D. (1903) *The signs of life*. Murray. London. [2]

WALLER, W. H. (1940) 'Progression movements elicited by subthalamic stimulation', *J. Neurophysiol.*, **3**, 300-307. [393]

WALLS, G. L. (1942) *The vertebrate eye and its adaptive radiation.* Cranbrook Institute of Science. [289, 300, 301]
— (1951 *a*) 'The problem of visual direction', *Amer. J. Optom.*, **28**, 55-83, 115-146, 173-212. [322, 345, 355]
— (1951 *b*) 'A theory of ocular dominance', *A.M.A. Arch. Ophthal.*, **45**, 387-412. [343]
— (1953) *The lateral geniculate nucleus and visual histophysiology.* Univ. of California Press. [346]
WALSH, E. G. (1952) 'Visual reaction time and the alpha rhythm : an investigation of a scanning hypothesis', *J. Physiol.*, **118**, 400-508. [236, 316, 352]
— (1953) '"Visual attention" and the α rhythm', *J. Physiol.*, **120**, 155-159. [236]
— (1954) '"Closed chain" bipolar recording : phase reversals demonstrable only by extensions of bipolar chains on to face or neck', *E.E.G. Clin. Neurophysiol.*, **6**, 346. [240]
— (1957) 'An investigation of sound localisation in patients with neurological abnormalities', *Brain* (in press). [272]
WALSH, J. (1773) 'Of the electric property of the torpedo', *Phil. Trans.*, **63**, 461-480. [2]
WALSHE, F. M. R. (1921) 'On disorders of movement resulting from loss of postural tone with special reference to cerebellar ataxy', *Brain*, **44**, 539-556. [177]
— (1923 *a*) 'On variations in the form of reflex movements notably the Babinski plantar response, under different degrees of spasticity and under the influence of Magnus and de Kleijn's tonic neck reflex', *Brain*, **46**, 281-300. [154]
— (1923 *b*) 'A case of complete decerebrate rigidity in man', *Lancet*, II, 644-647. [127, 154]
— (1927) 'The significance of the voluntary element in the genesis of cerebellar ataxy', *Brain*, **50**, 377-388. [178, 192]
— (1929 *a*) 'Oliver-Sharpey Lectures on the physiological analysis of some clinically observed disorders of movement', *Lancet*, I, 963-968. [122]
— (1929 *b*) 'Oliver-Sharpey Lectures on the physiological analysis of some clinically observed disorders of movement. (2) : The tremor-rigidity symptom complex', *Lancet*, I, 1024-1029. [393]
— (1942 *a*) 'The anatomy and physiology of cutaneous sensibility : a critical review', *Brain*, **65**, 48-112. [97]
— (1942 *b*) 'The giant cells of Betz, the motor cortex, and the pyramidal tract : a critical review', *Brain*, **65**, 409-461. [371, 383]
— (1944) *Diseases of the nervous system.* 3rd Ed. Livingstone. Edinburgh. [376]
— (1947) 'On the rôle of the pyramidal system in willed movements', *Brain*, **70**, 329-354. [376]
— & HUNT, J. H. (1936) 'Further observations upon grasping movements and reflex tonic grasping', *Brain*, **59**, 315-323. [382]

WALSHE, F. M. R., & ROBERTSON, E. G. (1933) 'Observations upon the form and nature of the "grasping" movements and "tonic" innervation seen in certain cases of lesion of the frontal lobes', *Brain*, **56**, 40-70. [382]

— & ROSS, J. (1936) 'The clinical picture of minor cord lesions in association with injuries of the cervical spine : with special reference to the diagnostic and localising value of the tendon reflexes of the arm (inversion of the radial reflex)', *Brain*, **59**, 277-290. [89]

WALTER, W. G. (1950) 'The functions of the electrical rhythms in the brain', *J. ment. Sci.*, **96**, 1-31. [236]

— & SHIPTON, H. W. (1951) 'A new toposcopic display system', *E.E.G. Clin. Neurophysiol.*, **3**, 281-292. [241]

WANG, G.-H., & LU, T.-W. (1941) 'Development of swimming and righting reflexes in frog (*Rana guentheri*) : effects thereon of transection of central nervous system before hatching', *J. Neurophysiol.*, **4**, 135-146. [139]

WAPNER, S., & WITKIN, H. A. (1950) 'The rôle of visual factors in the maintenance of body balance', *Amer. J. Psychol.*, **63**, 385-408. [140]

WARD, A. A. (1947) 'Decerebrate rigidity', *J. Neurophysiol.*, **10**, 89-101. [126]

— (1948) 'The anterior cingulate gyrus and personality', *Res. Publ. Ass. nerv. ment. Dis.*, **27**, 438-445. [202, 466]

— & McCULLOCH, W. S. (1947) 'The projection of the frontal lobe on the hypothalamus', *J. Neurophysiol.*, **10**, 304-314. [468]

WARD, J. W. (1938) 'The influence of posture on responses elicitable from the cortex cerebri of cats', *J. Neurophysiol.*, **1**, 463-475. [381]

WARTENBERG, R. (1945) *The examination of reflexes.* Year Book Publishers. Chicago. [121]

WATTS, J. W., & UHLE, C. A. W. (1935) 'Bladder dysfunction in cases of brain tumor', *J. Urol.*, **34**, 10-30. [102]

WAUGH, G. E., et al. (1914) 'On the resection of the posterior spinal roots (Rhizotomy)', *Brit. J. Surg.*, **2**, 205-247. [116]

WEALE, R. A. (1953 a) 'Spectral sensitivity and wavelength discrimination of the peripheral retina', *J. Physiol.*, **119**, 170-190. [303]

— (1953 b) 'Cone monochromatism', *J. Physiol.*, **121**, 548-569. [305]

— (1953 c) 'Photochemical reactions in the living cat's retina', *J. Physiol.*, **122**, 322-331. [294]

WEBSTER, J. E., & WEINBERGER, L. M. (1940) 'Convulsions associated with tumours of the cerebellum', *Arch. Neurol. Psych.*, **43**, 1163-1184. [185]

WEDDELL, G. (1941 a) 'The pattern of cutaneous innervation in relation to cutaneous sensibility', *J. Anat.*, **75**, 346-367. [38, 40]

— (1941 b) 'The multiple innervation of sensory spots in the skin', *J. Anat.*, **75**, 441-446. [40]

— FEINSTEIN, B., & PATTLE, R. E. (1944) 'The electrical activity of voluntary muscle in man under normal and pathological conditions', *Brain*, **67**, 178-257. [112]

WEDDELL, G., SINCLAIR, D. C., & FEINDEL, W. H. (1948) 'An anatomical basis for alterations in quality of pain sensibility', *J. Neurophysiol.*, **11**, 99-109. [64]

— & ZANDER, E. (1950) 'A critical evaluation of methods used to demonstrate tissue neural elements, illustrated by reference to the cornea', *J. Anat.*, **84**, 168-194. [40]

WEINSTEIN, E. A., & KAHN, R. L. (1950) 'The syndrome of anosognosia', *Arch. Neurol. Psych.*, **64**, 772-791. [426]

WEISENBURG, T. H. (1927) 'Cerebellar localisation and its symptomatology', *Brain*, **50**, 357-377. [170, 171]

WEISS, P. (1950) Editor. *Genetic neurology.* Univ. Chicago Press. [13, 14, 42, 79, 82, 89, 91, 201]

— (1952) 'Patterns of organisation in the central nervous system', *Res. Publ. Ass. nerv. ment. Dis.*, **30**, 3-23. [364]

WEISSCHEDEL, E. (1938) 'Über eine systematische Atrophie der oberen Olive', *Arch. f. Psychiat. und Nervenkrankeiten*, **108**, 219-227. [276]

WEITZ, J. (1939) 'Vibratory sensitivity as affected by local anaesthesia', *J. Exp. Psychol.*, **25**, 48-64. [55]

WELLS, H. G. (1944) 'The illusion of personality', *Nature*, **153**, 395-397. [217]

WENDT, G. R. (1936) 'The form of the vestibular eye-movement response in man', *Psychol. Rev. Monographs*, **47**, 311-328. [143]

WENZEL, B. M. (1948) 'Techniques in olfactometry : a critical review of the last one hundred years', *Psychol. Bull.*, **45**, 231-247. [211]

WEST, R. (1935) 'Studies in the neurological mechanism of parathyroid tetany', *Brain*, **58**, 1-20. [26]

WEVER, E. G., & LAWRENCE, M. (1954) *Physiological acoustics.* Princeton Univ. Press. London : Geoffrey Cumberlege. [262, 264, 265]

WHEATLEY, M. D. (1944) 'The hypothalamus and affective behaviour in cats', *Arch. Neurol. Psych.*, **52**, 296-316. [462]

WHITE, C. S., & BENSON, O. O. (1952) Editors. *Physics and medicine of the upper atmosphere.* Univ. New Mexico Press. Albuquerque. [136, 137]

WHITE, J. C. (1954) 'Conduction of pain in man', *Arch. Neurol. Psych.*, **71**, 1-23. [58]

— & SWEET, W. H. (1955) *Pain: its mechanism and neurosurgical control.* Thomas. Springfield. [4, 58, 67, 74, 92, 415]

WHITESIDE, J. A., & SNIDER, R. S. (1953) 'Relation of cerebellum to upper brain stem', *J. Neurophysiol.*, **16**, 397-413. [180]

WHITTERIDGE, D. (1948) 'The rôle of acetyl choline in synaptic transmission : a critical review', *J. Neurol. Neurosurg. Psychiat.*, **11**, 134-140. [200]

— (1950) 'Multiple embolism of lung and rapid shallow breathing', *Physiol. Rev.*, **30**, 475-486. [84]

WHITTIER, J. R. (1947) 'Ballism and the subthalamic nucleus (nucleus hypothalamicus ; Corpus Luysi)', *Arch. Neurol. Psych.*, **58**, 672-692. [393]

WIENER, N. (1948) *Cybernetics or control and communication in the animal and the machine.* Technology Press. Wiley. New York. [198, 422, 423]

WILKIE, J. S. (1953) *The science of mind and brain.* Hutchinson's University Library. [434]

WILLIAMS, D., & REYNELL, J. (1945) 'Abnormal suppression of cortical frequencies', *Brain,* **68,** 123-161. [238]

WILLIAMS, D. J., & SCOTT, J. W. (1939) 'The functional responses of the sympathetic nervous system of man following hemi-decortication', *J. Neurol. Neurosurg. Psych.,* **2,** 313-322. [215]

WILSKA, A. (1935) 'Eine Methode zur Bestimmung der Horschwellen-amplituden des Trommelfells bei verschiedenen Frequenzen', *Skand. Arch. f. Physiol.,* **72,** 161-165. [260]

— (1954) 'On the vibrational sensitivity in different regions of the body surface', *Acta Physiol. Scand.,* **31,** 285-289. [420]

WILSON, S. A. K. (1908) 'A contribution to the study of apraxia with a review of the literature', *Brain,* **31,** 164-216. [431, 432, 433]

— (1911) 'Progressive lenticular degeneration : a familial nervous disease associated with cirrhosis of the liver', *Brain,* **34,** 295-509. [391]

— (1920 a) 'On decerebrate rigidity in man and the occurrence of tonic fits', *Brain,* **43,** 220-268. [127]

— (1920 b) In 'Discussion on aphasia', *Brain,* **43,** 433-438. [436]

— (1925) 'Disorders of motility and of muscle tone with special reference to the corpus striatum', *Lancet,* II, 215-219. [395]

— (1927) 'Dysaesthesiae and their neural correlates', *Brain,* **50,** 428-462. [398, 413]

WILSON, W. C., & MAGOUN, H. W. (1945) 'The functional significance of the inferior olive in the cat', *J. Comp. Neurol.,* **83,** 69-77. [188]

WINDLE, W. F. (1955) Editor *Regeneration in the central nervous system.* Thomas. Springfield. [89, 229]

WITKIN, H. A. (1949) 'Perception of body position and of the position of the visual field', *Psychol. Mon.,* No. 302, Vol. 3, 1-46. [130, 131]

WOLDRING, S., & DIRKEN, M. N. J. (1951) 'Site and extension of bulbar respiratory centre', *J. Neurophysiol.,* **14,** 227-241. [84]

WOLF, S., & HARDY, J. D. (1941) 'Studies on pain : observations on pain due to local cooling and on factors involved in the "cold pressor" effect', *J. Clin. Invest.,* **20,** 521-533. [69]

— & WOLFF, H. G. (1942) 'Evidence on the genesis of peptic ulceration in man', *J. Amer. Med. Assoc.,* **120,** 670-675. [70]

WOLFF, H. G. (1948) *Headache and other pain.* Oxford Univ. Press. New York. [74]

WOLSTENHOLME, G. E. W. (1953) Editor. *The spinal cord.* Churchill. London. [4]

WOOD, R. W. (1895) 'The "Haunted Swing" Illusion', *Psychol. Rev.,* **2,** 277-278. [130]

WOODS, A. H. (1919) 'Misleading motor symptoms in the diagnosis of nerve wounds', *Arch. Neurol. Psych.,* **2,** 532-538. [230]

WOODWORTH, R. S. (1938) *Experimental psychology*. Methuen. London. [336, 355, 398, 417]

WOOLLARD, H. H., & CARMICHAEL, E. A. (1933) 'The testis and referred pain', *Brain*, **56**, 293-303. [92]

— & HARPMAN, J. A. (1940) 'The connexions of the inferior colliculus and of the dorsal nucleus of the lateral lemniscus', *J. Anat.*, **74**, 441-458. [278]

— WEDDELL, G., & HARPMAN, J. A. (1940) 'Observations on the neuro-histological basis of cutaneous pain', *J. Anat.*, **74**, 413-440. [37, 42, Plate 2]

WOOLSEY, C. N., & CHANG, H. (1948) 'Activation of the cerebral cortex by antidromic volleys in the pyramidal tract', *Res. Publ. Ass. nerv. ment. Dis.*, **27**, 146-161. [371]

— & ERICKSON, T. C. (1950) 'Study of the post-central gyrus of man by the evoked potential technique', *Trans. Amer. Neurol. Ass.*, **75**, 50-52. [404]

— & FAIRMAN, D. (1946) 'Contralateral, ipsilateral and bilateral representation of cutaneous receptors in somatic areas I and II of the cerebral cortex of pig, sheep, and other mammals', *Surgery*, **19**, 684-702. [405]

— MARSHALL, W. H., & BARD, P. (1942) 'Representation of cutaneous tactile sensibility in the cerebral cortex of the monkey as indicated by evoked potentials', *Johns Hopk. Hosp. Bull.*, **70**, 399-441. [403, 417]

— & SETTLAGE, P. H. (1950) in *Progress in Neurol. & Psychiat.*, **5**, 43-61. Edited by E. A. Spiegel. Grune & Stratton. New York. [182, 193]

— — MEYER, D. R., SPENCER, W., HAMUY, T. P., & TRAVIS, A. M. (1952) 'Patterns of localisation in precentral and "supplementary" motor areas and their relation to the concept of a premotor area', *Res. Publ. Ass. nerv. ment. Dis.*, **30**, 238-264. [383]

— & WALZL, E. M. (1942) 'Topical projection of nerve fibres from local regions of the cochlea to the cerebral cortex of the cat', *Johns Hopk. Hosp. Bull.*, **71**, 315-344. [281]

WRIGHT, S. (1945) *Applied physiology*. 8th Ed. Oxford Univ. Press. [32]

— (1952) *Applied physiology*. 9th Ed. Oxford Univ. Press. [201]

WRIGHT, W. D. (1946) *Researches on normal and defective colour vision*. Kimpton. London. [303]

WYATT, R. B. H. (1924) *William Harvey* (1578-1657). Parsons. London. [67]

WYLLIE, J. (1894) *The disorders of speech*. Oliver & Boyd. Edinburgh. [438]

YERKES, R. M. (1905) 'The sense of hearing in frogs', *J. Comp. Neurol.*, **15**, 279-304. [80]

YOUNG, G. (1921) 'The vestibular reactions in deaf mutes', *J. Laryngol. Otol.*, **36**, 524-525. [132]

YOUNG, J. Z. (1951 *a*) 'Growth and plasticity in the nervous system', *Proc. Roy. Soc.*, B, **139**, 18-37. [229]

YOUNG, J. Z. (1951 *b*) *Doubt and certainty in science.* Clarendon Press. [Plates 1, 3 & 4]

ZADOR, J. (1938) *Les Réactions d'équilibre chez l'homme.* Masson. Paris. [119, 155, 161]

ZIEGLER, D. K. (1952) 'Word deafness and Wernicke's aphasia', *Arch. Neurol. Psych.*, **67**, 323-331. [435]

ZIGLER, M. J. (1944) 'Neurophysiology of post-contraction', *Psychol. Rev.*, **51**, 315-325. [422]

ZOLLINGER, R. (1935) 'Removal of left cerebral hemisphere. Report of a case', *Arch. Neurol. Psych.*, **34**, 1055-1064. [438]

ZOTTERMAN, Y. (1939) 'Touch, pain and tickling : an electro-physiological investigation on cutaneous sensory nerves', *J. Physiol.*, **95**, 1-28. [64, 67]

— (1943) 'The microphonic effect of teleost labyrinths and its biological significance', *J. Physiol.*, **102**, 313-318. [143]

— (1953) 'Special senses : thermal receptors', *Ann. Rev. Physiol.*, **15**, 357-372. [45]

ZWORYKIN, V. K., FLORY, L. E., & PIKE, W. S. (1950) *Sensory devices: reading aids for the blind, in 'Medical Physics'.* Edited by O. Glaser. Vol. II, pp. 975-979. Year Book Publishers. Chicago. [434]

INDEX